QUANTUM ELECTRONICS

QUANTUM ELECTRONICS

A SYMPOSIUM

Edited by CHARLES H. TOWNES

New York 1960

COLUMBIA UNIVERSITY PRESS

PREFACE

This volume represents papers and discussion at the Conference on *Quantum Electronics—Resonance Phenomena* held at Shawanga Lodge, High View, New York on September 14-16, 1959. Origins of the Conference are outlined in the following remarks of Dr. Irving Rowe with which it was opened:

"I want to welcome you to the Conference on Quantum Electronics—Resonance Phenomena on behalf of the sponsor, the Office of Naval Research, and would like to indicate briefly how this conference came into being. The idea for calling this meeting originated with members of the Electronics and Physics Branches of the Office of Naval Research, who realized the growing significance of the field of quantum electronics, which is actually producing a revolution in microwave techniques. We hoped that such a conference would consolidate what knowledge we have today and would act as a stepping stone toward further advances. We asked Professor Townes whether he would be willing to act as chairman for this meeting. Professor Townes agreed that the research stemming from the development of the maser and from related resonance phenomena was reaching a degree of maturity where an international scientific meeting would be well justified. He accepted the chairmanship and formed a steering committee to aid him in establishing the policies of the Conference. From that time on, full credit for selecting the speakers and arranging the program goes to Professor Townes and his committee. We want to thank these people for the great efforts which they exerted in spite of the fact that each of them had a heavy workload of his own.

"Those of you who are not familiar with the Office of Naval Research may wonder why the Navy should spend its money on a scientific conference of this type. The reason is that the Navy is fully aware of the importance of basic research in quantum electronics, and indeed has already begun to utilize its applications. For instance, I believe that the first reported results from a maser as an operating device came from the Naval Research Laboratory, which used the ruby maser built at Columbia University, in conjunction with its own 50-foot radio telescope. This was used to study the emissions from the planets Venus and Jupiter, and from several radio stars. Similarly, the Naval Observatory is charged by law with the responsibility of being the custodian of official time for the United States. The Observatory now uses an atomic clock as its most precise time standard.

"Those of you who have had previous contacts with the Office of Naval Research know, however, that its interests are not devoted primarily to immediate practical applications, although we do welcome them whenever possible. Instead, we are interested primarily in encouraging basic scientific research, with the emphasis on providing a better understanding of the fundamental processes of nature. I am sure that this conference, including both the formal papers and the informal discussions to follow, will be a milestone on the way toward that better understanding."

There have been many significant contributions to the Conference which are not directly recorded in this volume. In addition to the very important services of Dr. Rowe, the ONR through him, Dr. Arnold Shostak, and Frank Isakson gave the initial impetus for this conference and both financial and administrative support. Other Governmental agencies, such as the U. S. Army Signal Research and Development Laboratory, the Air Force Office of Scientific Research, the Bureau of Ships, the Office of Ordnance Research, and the Air Research and Development Command, while not acting as sponsors of the Conference itself, have assisted various parts of the work reported here.

The policies and program of the Conference were planned by the Steering Committee, consisting of:

Dr. G. Birnbaum, Hughes Research and Development Laboratories

Professor N. Bloembergen, Harvard University

Professor R. H. Dicke, Princeton University

Professor Charles Kittel, University of California

Dr. R. Kompfner, Bell Telephone Laboratories

Dr. B. Lax, Lincoln Laboratories, Massachusetts Institute of Technology

Dr. I. Rowe, Office of Naval Research

Professor A. E. Siegman, Stanford University

Dr. G. J. Stanley, California Institute of Technology

Professor M. W. P. Strandberg, Massachusetts Institute of Technology

Professor C. H. Townes, Columbia University, Chairman

Success of the Conference is due in considerable measure to the effort, thought, and support of members of this committee. The Bell Telephone Laboratories provided, through the help of Dr. J. P. Gordon and Miss Muriel Morrow, more than its normal share of assistance.

The Conference is much indebted to the staff of the Columbia University Physics Department: to Ann Hart Rappaport for administrative work in the early stages of the Conference and particularly to Mr. R. W. Siegel and Barbara Turlington Gersfeld for devoted and efficient management of the large burden of administrative details as well as untiring assistance throughout the course of the conference. They and a number of graduate students, including P. Thaddeus, H. Lecar, J. A. Giordmaine, W. Rose, F. R. Nash, I. Abella, and H. Cummins, are also responsible for much of the planning and editing of this volume.

The reader will find that the following pages begin with brief general remarks on the subject matter to be discussed. Principal topics are then introduced by summarizing papers, the majority of which are followed by a number of related specialized topics. Much of the discussion which followed each paper is also recorded and in some cases includes new material as well as clarifying comments.

CHARLES H. TOWNES
Columbia University

INTRODUCTION

The subject matter of this symposium lies near the interface between two highly developed disciplines—the field of electronics and that of spectroscopy. We are grateful to Dr. Rowe and the Office of Naval Research for recognizing the rapidly expanding interactions at this interface and for initiating and supporting the present conference. The wide variety of interests represented here provides an opportunity for clarifying and unifying basic ideas which are common or may become common to both disciplines, for discussing recent developments, and possibly for preliminary examination of areas where important research developments may be expected in the future.

Electronic techniques have been used for what might be called spectroscopy over a long period of time, if we recognize as spectroscopy the study of dielectric constants and losses in the radiofrequency region. However, we are concerned here primarily with resonance spectroscopy and resonant interactions examined by approximately coherent electromagnetic waves. The resonances of interest are of course not those which are primarily dependent on macroscopic properties such as mass or size of a piece of material—that is, those which are dependent on the number of molecules—but the resonances which are primarily determined by characteristics of individual atoms or molecules. There were, of course, important developments in examining the resonant interactions between molecules and radiofrequency or microwaves before the war with the experiments of Cleeton and Williams, and those of Rabi and his associates. However, much more intensive activity in this area has occurred during the last fifteen years.

Immediately following the war, there were many physicists who had of necessity become quite familiar with electronics and who rapidly applied the techniques and apparatus of this field to spectroscopy. More recently, there has been a diffusion of information and techniques back again from spectroscopy and physics across the interface into regions clearly recognizable as engineering, and the area of interaction between the two fields has considerably widened. We now have from resonant spectroscopy a wide variety of practical devices such as non-reciprocal circuits, nonlinear elements, detectors, coherent amplifiers, and oscillators. In fact, the spectroscopist can probably produce from atomic and molecular resonances almost any type of circuit element or phenomenon to which the electronics engineer is normally accustomed.

It is quite natural that electronic use of ferromagnetic resonance, cyclotron resonance, and orbital resonances of electrons have been among the first to be developed, since these involve very large matrix elements and hence strong interactions with the electromagnetic field. The large matrix elements also imply large angular momenta and hence an essentially classical situation. Although electron orbital motions and ferromagnets are included in the symposium to some degree, primary emphasis will be placed on situations where quantum effects more characteristically appear, and which are perhaps not yet so familiar to the field of electronics. In many cases, the physical ideas and phenomena involved are still not well understood, and are the subject of very active research efforts and discussion among those who feel no great concern about electronics itself.

As one progresses towards higher frequencies, interactions between electromagnetic waves and molecules or atoms become increasingly prominent; furthermore, classical electronic techniques become more difficult and quanta larger. It is hence natural that spectroscopic techniques or ideas and quantum phenomena will become increasingly important in the high-frequency region, providing perhaps the principal means for affecting and controlling electromagnetic waves having wavelengths shorter than one millimeter. Thus the electronics engineer, as clearly as the physicist, needs to become acquainted with quantum physics to be able to utilize the most sophisticated electronics.

Both electronics and spectroscopy are, in fact, more techniques and tools than fields of knowledge in themselves. They are, furthermore, characterized by great precision and delicacy and provide techniques for a wide variety of beautiful experiments in physics and for a great deal of technology. Thus this symposium leads in a number of directions and includes discussions of problems in such fields as fundamental physics, radioastronomy, and communications.

C. H. T.

CONTENTS

QUANTUM ELECTRONICS

MOLECULAR BEAM MASERS

J. P. GORDON

Bell Telephone Laboratories, Murray Hill, New Jersey

IN THE early 1950's, microwave spectroscopy of gases had reached a level where most of the more straightforward experiments had been done, and experimenters were looking for new directions in which to go. Several groups were attempting to achieve exceptionally high resolution through utilization of restricted velocity classes of molecules, thus partly eliminating doppler broadening of the spectral lines. Some of the experiments I might mention are those of Newell and Dicke (1951),[1] Johnson and Strandberg (1952)[2] (I believe this was the first detection of a molecular beam by microwave methods), Strandberg and Dreicer (1954),[3] and Romer and Dicke (1955).[4] All of these experiments were concerned with the intense inversion spectrum of ammonia. At the same time, others were concerned with the possibility of microwave amplification and generation on the maser principle,[5] although to be sure the word maser had not yet been coined. Gordon, Zeiger, and Townes began work on what was to be the first ammonia beam maser. Weber[6] suggested that maser amplification was possible, and gave figures for the gain which might follow an extremely rapid Stark field reversal in a waveguide filled with ammonia. Bassov and Prokhorov,[7] in 1954, published some conjectures about the use of beams for spectroscopy. They observed that since beams could be deflected by nonuniform fields, and since in this way one could separate an upper state from a lower state, it might be possible to construct a molecular oscillator. For the particular example they took, that of CsF, they calculated that oscillation could be obtained if a cavity Q of 7×10^6 could be achieved. In 1954 came publication of the first successful molecular beam

Fig. 1

Resonant cavity, upper state selector, and beam source of an ammonia beam maser. The cavity resonates in the TM_{010} mode
(longitudinally uniform electric microwave field) at the transition
frequency. The state selector has twelve poles, giving an elec-
tric potential of the form $\varphi \approx \varphi_0 r^6 \cos 6\theta$. The beam source is
of the multi-channel type.

oscillator by Gordon, Zeiger, and Townes,[8] who utilized an
electric quadrupole deflection field [similar to the magnetic one
of Freidburg and Paul (1951)[9]] and a long (compared to a wavelength) cavity which gave very narrow spectral lines. Fig. 1
shows a later model built at Bell Telephone Laboratories by
Gordon and White.[12]

The success of the beam maser provided impetus in three
directions — high resolution spectroscopy, molecular clocks,
and low noise amplifiers. In the inversion spectrum of ammonia,
the beam maser turned up some previously unresolved magnetic
hyperfine structure, caused by reorientation of the spins of the
three hydrogen nuclei in the molecular magnetic field. Resolution of about seven kilocycles was obtained for this spectrum,
representing an order of magnitude improvement over the doppler
width of ammonia lines in the standard waveguide cell spectrometer. At the same time, the action of the state selector, or focuser, considerably improved sensitivity over what had been
done with the other types of spectrometers which had achieved
the same sort of resolution. It was therefore conjectured that the

beam maser might have considerable usefulness in the field of spectroscopy.

Secondly, the oscillation of the beam maser was tested for spectral purity and frequency stability, and it was found to be pure to better than a few parts in 10^{12}, and stable for 15 minutes or so to about one part in 10^{10}. Hope was raised that here was an extremely useful "molecular clock." The random effects of thermal noise were found both experimentally and theoretically to be quite small, and Shot noise virtually nonexistent. The various pulling effects, in particular that caused by thermal expansions and contractions of the resonant cavity, were found to be the practical limit on the usefulness of the maser oscillator as a time standard.

Finally there was the low noise amplifier aspect, but for this purpose the narrow bandwidth, low power, and limited tunability of the beam maser made it fairly unattractive. Nevertheless, the beam maser was, in 1957, the first to substantiate experimentally the low noise predictions made for maser amplifiers in general.[10],[11],[12]

SPECTROSCOPY

After the ammonia spectrum had been thoroughly examined,[13],[14],[15] no further spectroscopy was done with beam masers, although several unsuccessful attempts were made to observe other molecules. Very recently, however, there has been a quite successful renewal of effort in the field of beam spectroscopy, which will be discussed in a later paper. This is an important aspect of beam masers, and I should like to present here a rough sensitivity comparison of beam maser versus waveguide absorption cell.

The signal-to-noise ratio in these two different spectrometers is approximately proportional to the product of sample susceptibility and the square root of the saturation power level; thus

$$S/N \approx \chi'' P_o^{\frac{1}{2}}. \tag{1}$$

To have a good comparison, we must make the reasonable assumptions that metal of the same conductivity is used to make up the walls of the absorption or emission cells, and that the cross-sectional areas of the cells are reasonably similar. The peak susceptibility of a material is given, apart from a numerical factor near unity which depends on the exact line shape, by

$$\chi''_{max} = \frac{(n_1 - n_2)\mu_{12}^2}{h \Delta \nu} \qquad (2)$$

where n_1 and n_2 are the population densities of the two energy levels involved, μ_{12} is the matrix element for the transition, h is Planck's constant, and $\Delta \nu$ is the half-width of the resonance line at half maximum. The saturation power level, assuming that we have optimized the length of the waveguide and optimized the coupling of the cavity, satisfies the approximate relation

$$P_o \overset{\propto}{\sim} V (\Delta \nu)^2 / \mu_{12}^2 \qquad (3)$$

where V is the volume of the absorption or emission cell. In deriving this last equation, we have also assumed that the line is homogeneously broadened by collisions or some similar lifetime effect. Combining these three equations, we find that the signal-to-noise ratio satisfies the relation

$$S/N \overset{\propto}{\sim} (n_1 - n_2)\mu_{12}\sqrt{V}. \qquad (4)$$

In the light of this equation, let us compare the waveguide cell and the beam maser. Table 1 gives the results. The dipole moment matrix element μ_{12} is, of course, the same for both. If

Table 1

	WAVEGUIDE CELL	MASER CAVITY
Volume	1	Q^{-1}
$n_1 - n_2$	$n_1 \dfrac{h\nu}{kT}$	$-n_2' \dfrac{\Delta W}{2kT}$

we arbitrarily take the optimized volume of the waveguide cell to be unity, then the cavity has a volume about equal to $1/Q$. In the row for density, we find for the waveguide simply the number of molecules in the lower state, n_1, times the Boltzmann factor

$h\nu/kT$. The number for the maser will take a little more explanation. ΔW is the potential barrier presented to the upper state molecules by the state selector, and one can show that $\Delta W/2kT$ is the effective solid angle of upper state molecules collected by a selector of cylindrical geometry such as is generally used (see Fig. 1). Then if we neglect losses of molecules by collisions in the beam, etc., n_2' is an effective density of upper state molecules in the beam source. Now the crux of our argument is that the two densities n_1 and n_2' are approximately equal. The waveguide cell is limited for reasons of resolution to pressures of the order of 10^{-2} mm Hg, while the maser beam source is limited by considerations of mean free path in the collimator channels to an effective pressure not very much larger.

Assuming then that $n_1 \approx n_2'$, we arrive at a simple approximate sensitivity comparison

$$\frac{(S/N)_{\text{maser}}}{(S/N)_{\text{waveguide}}} \approx \frac{\Delta W}{2h\nu} \, Q^{-\frac{1}{2}} . \tag{5}$$

For electric dipole transitions in the centimeter frequency range, $\Delta W/2h\nu$ is in many cases not much smaller than unity. Cavity quality factors are in the range of 10^4; thus one might expect that a maser spectrometer would have a sensitivity just about one hundred times less than that of a standard waveguide cell. This is just about what is observed for the ammonia spectrum, and would indicate that electric dipole transitions whose absorption coefficients are greater than about 10^{-7} cm^{-1}, and for which the state selection can be done reasonably well, should be observable in a maser type spectrometer. Magnetically focused beams are relatively harder to detect, since ΔW for this case is about one hundred times smaller. A. Javan spent some time attempting to observe the hyperfine transition in a magnetically focused beam of thallium atoms. He was unsuccessful, but nevertheless feels that with care the experiment should succeed, and moreover that some very interesting spectroscopy could be done on magnetic dipole transitions by beam maser techniques. In particular, atoms whose ground states are P states are not susceptible to optical pumping buffer gas techniques, but might be observed with high resolution by maser methods.[16]

MICROWAVE GENERATION

The second area of considerable importance for beam masers is that of frequency standards and microwave generators. The narrow resonance lines $\left(\dfrac{\Delta \nu}{\nu} \sim 10^{-7} \text{ for a good ammonia maser}\right)$ combined with a large signal-to-noise ratio $(P_o/kT\,2\Delta\nu \sim 10^5)$ and a reasonable freedom from effects of small external electric and magnetic fields makes the beam maser a contender among atomic and molecular frequency standards. Moreover, the beam maser is run by pressure in the gas bottle; thus one is freed from the three-level maser's necessity of a high-frequency energy supply, and one is tempted to look for generators at extremely high frequencies.

Some reasonably well-known equations which are important to this area are the following:

1. The starting condition for oscillation

$$4\pi\chi'' + \frac{1}{Q_L} = 0 \; *\tag{6}$$

where χ'' is the susceptibility of the maser material, and Q_L is the loaded quality factor of the resonant cavity. When written in terms of the densities n_2 and n_1 of particles in the upper and lower states respectively, this equation becomes

$$n_2 - n_1 = \frac{h\,\Delta\nu}{4\pi\mu_{12}^2 Q_L} \cdot\tag{6a}$$

2. The power output, P_o, of the maser oscillator (approximately)

$$P_o \simeq \left(\frac{n_2 - n_1}{2}\right)(Av)\,h\nu\tag{7}$$

*We assume the sample fills the cavity. When it does not, this equation must be replaced by $4\pi\eta\chi'' + 1/Q_L = 0$, where η is the filling factor, a number less than unity defined by

$$\eta = \frac{\displaystyle\int_{\text{SAMPLE}} F^2\,dv}{\displaystyle\int_{\text{CAVITY}} F^2\,dv}$$

F represents the r-f field strength.

where A is the cross-sectional area of the beam, and v is the beam velocity. This equation simply assumes that the transition $2 \rightarrow 1$ is completely saturated as the beam traverses the cavity, so that at the beam output $n_2 \approx n_1$.

3. The frequency pulling equation

$$\nu - \nu_B = \left(\frac{\Delta \nu_B}{\Delta \nu_C} \right) (\nu_C - \nu_B) \tag{8}$$

where ν_B and $\Delta \nu_B$ are the center frequency and half-width of the beam resonance, while ν_C and $\Delta \nu_C$ are the same for the cavity resonance, and ν is the actual oscillation frequency. This equation gives the pulling caused by a simple nondegenerate cavity resonance. More complicated coupled cavity modes have been used to reduce considerably this particular source of frequency drift in a maser oscillator.[17]

Considerable work has been done with oscillators using the intense $J = K = 3$ line of the ammonia spectrum. Short-term ($\simeq 1$ minute) stabilities approaching a few parts in 10^{12} have been achieved by several workers, and measurements to this accuracy were utilized in the very interesting ether drift experiment of Cedarholm, Bland, Havens, and Townes.[18] Somewhat longer-term ($\simeq 1$ hour) stabilities of about ± 1 part in 10^{10} have been reported by Mockler and Barnes.[19] Bonanomi has compared a maser with a cesium beam atomic standard over several years, and finds relative drifts approaching one part in 10^{10}. He will tell us more about these results later in the conference.

The 3-3 line, while it is the most intense line of the ammonia inversion spectrum, has the serious disadvantage that even its strong central $\Delta F = \Delta F_1 = 0$ component is split by quadrupole hyperfine structure into three unresolved components separated by about 1 kc.[14] This small splitting is undoubtedly responsible in part for many of the frequency instabilities, such as variation with residual gas pressure, with focuser voltage, etc. Recent measurements of oscillations on the 3-2 line (at 22,834 Mc/sec), which has no quadrupole splitting, showed considerable improvement in several of these factors. Use of the isotope N^{15} has also been suggested, since N^{15} has a spin of $\frac{1}{2}$ and therefore no quadrupole moment. With this isotope in a closed-off system the strong 3-3 line could be used.

With a spectral line as wide as 5 kc, such as occurs in the ammonia maser, it seems hard to believe that its center could be located absolutely to much better than one or two cycles, so that an absolute accuracy for the standard ammonia maser of much better than one part in 10^{10} is probably not to be expected. Narrower lines (the use of lower velocity molecules would be helpful here) are probably needed for this. One possibility for using slow ammonia molecules would be to use an inhomogenous Stark field to produce large angular deflections.[20] (See Fig. 2.) Since the field can only reflect molecules whose energies are less than about $0.05\,kT$, this procedure would create a beam of slow, upper-state molecules, which would spend more time in the resonant cavity and thus give rise to a sharper line. We might obtain a tenfold or more factor of improvement in line width this way, but the decrease in beam intensity — after all, we are utilizing only the slow tail of the Maxwell distribution — would probably prevent such a maser from oscillating.

There are many factors which limit the stability and accuracy of a beam maser oscillator. Probably the most important practical consideration is the pulling effect due to changes in cavity frequency. Bonanomi has shown that cavity and beam geometries

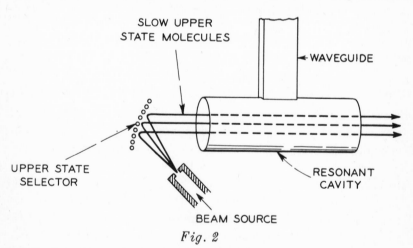

Fig. 2

Use of a state selector which deflects molecules through large angles would result in a beam of *slow* upper state molecules. Considerably sharpened resonance lines would result from such a device.

affect the 3-3 line oscillation frequency by as much as one part in 10^8, but it is not yet certain how much of these effects result from the quadrupole splittings. Another important consideration is the residual doppler shift, caused by the unavoidable propagation of energy along the length of the cavity. Even though the cavity is excited in a mode which, if pure, would not cause any doppler shifts, still there is a running wave carrying of the order of $1/Q$ of the total cavity energy, which must be present to compensate for nonuniform generation and absorption of energy. This running wave gives rise to a small doppler shift in the oscillation frequency, which changes as the beam strength is increased. I do not believe that this particular frequency shift has as yet been experimentally isolated from the others, but it has been shown theoretically to be of considerable importance.[15]

One fundamental limit on the short term frequency stability is thermal noise, and I would like to present here an argument for the effects of thermal noise, which, while its rigor may be challenged, gives a result in good agreement with the more sophisticated analysis of Shimoda, Wang, and Townes. It is a statistical argument which I first heard from C. H. Townes a long time ago and has now been published.[21]

The beam, having a resonance of bandwidth $2\Delta\nu$, has a memory, or ringing time, of about $\tau = (2\pi\Delta\nu)^{-1}$. Thermal noise power in the cavity can therefore produce random phase changes in the oscillation signal, so long as the frequencies of the noise components do not depart from the oscillation frequency by more than $\Delta\nu$. The mean-square value of the phase shifts so introduced is simply

$$<\delta\theta>^2 \equiv \overline{(\delta\theta)^2} = \frac{1}{2}\ \frac{\text{NOISE POWER}}{\text{OSCILLATION POWER}}$$

or

$$<\delta\theta>^2 \simeq kT\Delta\nu/P_o. \tag{9}$$

The phase of these noise components with respect to the signal can take on a new value uncorrelated with its previous value only after a time τ. Signal and noise voltage components are illus-

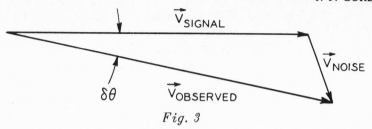

Fig. 3

Addition of signal and noise voltage vectors to give the observed
oscillation signal. The noise voltage can assume a new arbitrary phase with relation to the signal voltage once each time τ.
Molecules entering the cavity amplify the observed oscillation
signal, thus each elementary phase shift $\delta\varphi$ is permanently retained by the oscillation.

trated in Fig. 3. Noise components outside the beam bandwidth
$2\Delta\nu$ are simply ignored by the molecules, and produce no permanent phase shifts in the oscillation signal. Our approximation
now assumes random phase shifts of amount $<\delta\theta>$ separated in
time by τ. If we add up these random-walk type shifts over a
longer time t, the mean-square value of the total phase shift in
time t is just

$$<\Delta\theta>^2 \,=\, <\delta\theta>^2 \, t/\tau$$

or

$$<\Delta\theta>^2 \,=\, 2\pi kT\,(\Delta\nu)^2\,t/P_o\,.$$

The fractional phase error introduced by thermal noise in time t
can then be written as

$$\frac{<\Delta\theta>}{\theta} \,=\, \frac{<\Delta\theta>}{2\pi\nu t} \,=\, \left(\frac{kT}{2\pi P_o}\right)^{\frac{1}{2}} \left(\frac{\Delta\nu}{\nu}\right) t^{-\frac{1}{2}}\,.$$

As usual for random processes, the fractional error goes down as
the square root of the time of observation. If we put in some
typical values for a beam maser oscillator

$$P_o \,=\, 10^{-10}\ \text{watts}$$
$$\Delta\nu \,=\, 2.5 \times 10^3\ \text{cps}$$
$$\nu \,=\, 2.4 \times 10^{10}\ \text{cps}$$
$$kT \,=\, 4 \times 10^{-21}\ \text{joules}$$

then

$$\frac{<\Delta\theta>}{\theta} = 2 \times 10^{-13} t^{-\frac{1}{2}}$$

Actual observations of short term noise in ammonia masers have come to within a factor of ten of this limit; however, thermal noise has not yet become important in a practical sense. Similar fluctuations occur due to spontaneous emission from molecules in the beam, but these may be considered as arising from zero point fluctuations in the cavity field; and since kT is usually much larger than $h\nu$, spontaneous emission can usually be neglected.

Finally there is the question of millimeter and submillimeter wave generators to be considered. No such beam maser has yet been constructed, as far as I know, but the possibility still exists. From Equation (6a) for the starting condition for molecular beam density, we may compare possibilities for millimeter wave generators with, say, the 3-3 line ammonia maser. Quite important, I think, is the line half-width $\Delta\nu$. If one simply scales a low-mode resonant cavity down to shorter wavelengths, then the molecular time of flight is inversely proportional to frequency, thus $\Delta\nu \propto \nu$. The same is true for doppler broadening. If we keep a divergent beam, as is the case with the usual beam masers, then the normal doppler breadth, $\Delta\nu_{\text{DOPPLER}} \simeq \left(\frac{v}{c}\right) \nu$, which is proportional to frequency, can be reduced only by a factor which is equal to the beam spread half-angle expressed in radians. As a possible example, a maser which might try to work on the 4-3 to 3-3 rotational transition of ammonia at 0.125 mm, and which has a beam spread half-angle of about 0.05 radians, or 3 degrees, could not have lines narrower than about 300 kc/sec, due to doppler broadening, no matter what the geometry of the cavity. This means that if we had a cavity whose Q was 10^4, the starting beam density for such a short wavelength maser would be about 50 times larger than for the 3-3 inversion line. One might think to alter the geometry of the focuser to obtain greater collimation in the beam, but this can be done only at a sacrifice of density of molecules, and the basic conclusion remains the same. For the particular case of ammonia, a further unpleasant factor of about 2 appears because the quadrupole hyperfine structure for this transition would split the line into two major resolved components.

Dicke has proposed use of an interferometer as a resonant cavity for these short wavelengths, with multiple beams feeding the interferometer from all sides.[22] Townes and Schawlow[23] have also proposed interferometers as resonant structures for masers operating up to optical frequencies. With such a geometry, it appears that a millimeter or submillimeter beam maser is quite feasible. Similar conclusions have also been drawn by Prokhorov[24] and Barnes.[25]

In conclusion, it would seem that the potentialities of the beam maser in spectroscopy are still considerable, that a beam maser oscillator utilizing either the 3-2 inversion line of $N^{14}H_3$ or the 3-3 line of $N^{15}H_3$ will have a good place among "atomic clocks," and that millimeter and submillimeter wave generators using beam techniques are within reach.

REFERENCES

1. G. Newell and R. H. Dicke, Phys. Rev. *81*, 297 (1951); Phys. Rev. *83*, 1064 (1951).
2. H. R. Johnson and W. M. P. Strandberg, Phys. Rev. *85*, 503 (1952).
3. W. M. P. Strandberg and H. Dreicer, Phys. Rev. *94*, 1393 (1954).
4. R. H. Romer and R. H. Dicke, Phys. Rev. *99*, 532 (1955).
5. For a review of early developments in the maser field see the footnote in reference (11).
6. J. Weber, Trans. IRE Prof. Group on Electron Devices *3*, 1 (1953).
7. N. G. Basov and A. M. Prokhorov, JETP (USSR) *27*, 431 (1954).
8. J. P. Gordon, H. J. Zeiger, and C. H. Townes, Phys. Rev. *95*, 282 (1954).
9. H. Friedberg and W. Paul, Naturwiss. *38*, 159 (1951).
10. J. C. Helmer, Phys. Rev. *107*, 902 (1957).
11. L. E. Alsop, J. A. Giordmaine, C. H. Townes, and T. C. Wang, Phys. Rev. *107*, 1450 (1957).
12. J. P. Gordon and L. D. White, Phys. Rev. *107*, 1728 (1957).
13. J. P. Gordon, H. J. Zeiger, and C. H. Townes, Phys. Rev. *99*, 1264 (1955).
14. J. P. Gordon, Phys. Rev. *99*, 1253 (1955).
15. K. Shimoda, T. C. Wang, and C. H. Townes, Phys. Rev. *102*, 1308 (1956).
16. A. Javan, private communication.

17. J. Bonanomi, J. Herrmann, J. De Prins, and P. Kartaschoff, Rev. Sci. Instr. *28*, 879 (1957).
18. J. P. Cedarholm, G. F. Bland, B. L. Havens, and C. H. Townes, Phys. Rev. Lett. *1*, 342 (1958).
19. R. C. Mockler and J. A. Barnes, talk presented at the 13th Annual Symposium on Frequency Control, sponsored by U. S. Army Signal Engineering Laboratories, Fort Monmouth, N. J. (May, 1959).
20. A. Ashkin, J. P. Gordon, and L. D. White (to be published).
21. C. H. Townes, Suppl. del Nuovo Cimento, V, Serie X, No. 1 (1957).
22. R. H. Dicke, U. S. Patent #2851652 (1958).
23. A. L. Schawlow and C. H. Townes, Phys. Rev. *112*, 1940 (1958).
24. A. M. Prokhorov, JETP (USSR) *34*, 1658 (1958).
25. F. S. Barnes, Colorado Research Corp. Engineering Memoranda, CEM-006, CEM-007 (1959).

DISCUSSION

M. L. STITCH: I think that the calculation of fluctuation due to thermal noise was in fact published by Townes in a very nice article in a supplement to Nuovo Cimento of 1956.

Y. BEERS: It is my impression that the sizes of sample which are practical to employ in beam maser techniques are limited. With conventional absorption techniques, no severe limitation of size exists. Therefore, it is not entirely significant to compare the signal-to-noise ratio of a maser to that obtained with an absorption cell of the same size as the maser cavity or with a conventional waveguide. By using large absorption cells it should by possible to build a K-band absorption spectrometer with signal-to-noise ratios some 40 or 50 db better than obtained with standard waveguide spectrometers of "optimum" length.

J. P. GORDON: The purpose of the calculation was to compare maser sensitivity to that of the more familiar standard waveguide cell. It was intended more to show what a maser can do than what a special purpose waveguide cell can do.

P. THADDEUS: Detailed calculations on the Stark focusing properties of a number of molecules indicate that the signal-to-noise ratio just given of a maser to an ordinary gas cell spectrometer is generally correct. No transitions with an absorption coefficient α less than 10^{-7}, even with favorable Stark effects of the upper and lower states, seem observable at the present time using a beam maser spectrometer and reasonable sweep rates of the klystron oscillator.

A LOW TEMPERATURE ATOMIC BEAM OSCILLATOR*

C. V. HEER†

Department of Physics, Ohio State University

IN ORDER to obtain an oscillator with a spectral purity greater than that obtainable with the ammonia beam maser oscillator[1] the design of a system using the very sharp transitions between the hyperfine states of atoms is reconsidered. The natural extension to a microwave spectrometer, narrow-band amplifier, and very narrow lines in optical pumping is readily apparent in the following considerations. The importance of narrow spectral lines for the evaluation of structure and recoil corrections in atomic hydrogen have been emphasized by Wittke and Dicke.[2]

Causes of line breadth in terms of their traditional classification are first discussed. The natural line breadth or lifetime for a hyperfine transition is of the order of 10^5–10^7 years. This lifetime is reduced by confinement in an enclosure or cavity by a factor of 10^2–10^3, i.e., the spontaneous transition probability

$$W_{b \to a} =$$

$$\{(1/\hbar c)(\mu_0/\varepsilon_0)^{\frac{1}{2}}\} \{Q_c/V_c\} \{\tfrac{1}{3} \, | \, (a| \vec{M} | b) | \,^2 \} \sim 10^{-18} Q_c/V_c \quad (1)$$

where $\vec{M}$ is the magnetic moment of the atom, Q_c the cavity "Q," and V_c the volume (m.k.s. units are used throughout.). Since the atoms are excited coherently by the radiation field and reradiate coherently, the transition probability is increased by the population difference, $N_b - N_a$, in the cavity. Since lifetimes of the order of 1 second are considered, the number of the atoms

*Project supported by the National Science Foundation
†Consultant at the Space Technology Laboratories

in the cavity will range between 10^9 and 10^{11}, depending on the wavelength of the radiation.

The normal Doppler effect is replaced by the time of inter-action with the radiation field in the cavity. Dicke[3] has shown the line breadth can be reduced by a buffer gas; and in terms of the wavelength λ and the diffusion coefficient D, the linewidth is

$$'\Delta\omega_{\frac{1}{2}} = 4\pi^2 \, D/\lambda \, . \tag{2}$$

At $1°$ Kelvin and at a pressure of 0.1 mm Hg, $\Delta\omega_{\frac{1}{2}} \sim 10^{-1}$ for Rb and Cs and $\sim 10^{-3}$ for H. This data is based on the collision cross sections summarized by Ramsey,[4] and effects which might be introduced by the larger de Broglie wavelengths have not been considered.

Since the time between collisions for like atoms is of the order of 10–100 seconds, the line broadening due to collisions between like atoms should be small. The effects due to collisions with the buffer gas are more difficult to estimate. A pressure of 0.1 mm Hg at $1°$ K corresponds to a density of 3 cm Hg at room tem-perature for the helium buffer gas, and shifts of the order of 30 cps for H[2] and 30,000 cps for Cs[5] might be expected. Wall collisions terminate the existence of a hyperfine state. Since this lifetime depends on the diffusion rate, it will be consid-ered later.

One of the first experimental problems which must be under-taken is the production of the atom with the hyperfine splitting in the helium buffer gas at temperatures of the order of $1°$ K. Since collision with the cold walls is expected to result in ab-sorption, the diffusion rate is of interest. In regard to wall ab-sorption, the effect of the thick layer of absorbed helium on the container wall will be of considerable interest and may produce some beneficial effects. For cylindrical tubes, the distribution of h.f. atoms very quickly takes on a distribution given by the Bessel function $J_o \, (\pi\beta_1 r/a)$, where "a" is the radius of the con-tainer. The drift velocity near the container walls is then given by

$$\vec{v}_D = - D \text{ grad } n \approx + 1.25 \, (D/a) \, \vec{r}_o \tag{3}$$

and the reduction in number as a function of time

$$N/N_o \sim \exp\left[-(\pi\beta_1)^2 (D/a^2) t\right] \qquad (4)$$

where $(\pi\beta_1) = 2.44$.

For Cs and Rb

$$D \simeq 10^{-2} \, T^{\frac{3}{2}}/P_{mm} \ (\text{cm}^2/\text{sec}) \qquad (5a)$$

and for H

$$D \simeq 10^{-1} \, T^{\frac{3}{2}}/P_{mm} \ (\text{cm}^2/\text{sec}) \qquad (5b)$$

where P_{mm} is the pressure in millimeters of Hg. At temperatures of the order of $1°$K and diameters the order of a few centimeters, lifetimes of the order of seconds are expected. For alkali metals, two methods for the introduction of the h.f. atoms into the cold buffer gas are being tried. The first method proposes a mixture of the h.f. atom and helium at say $400°$ K and at an over-pressure and lets the mixture flow via a hot capillary tube into an enclosure of cold helium gas where further moderation occurs. The second method places a small amount of alkali metal on a heater and immerses the unit in the cold helium gas. Since the number of atoms required is extremely small, either method should yield a sufficient number, but the problem of heat influx is an important experimental problem. For hydrogen, a microwave or discharge method for the production of atomic hydrogen in helium may be feasible, and the problems of moderation should be less troublesome.

Although the above discussion indicates the possibilities for an absorption measurement or for an optical pumping experiment, the primary purpose of this study was an oscillator using the hyperfine states of atoms. At these very low temperatures, a modified Stern-Gerlach separator is practical. The drift velocity of the h.f. atoms in a magnetic field gradient is

$$\vec{v}_d = (D/kT) \, \mu_{eff} \, \text{grad} \, |B| \qquad (6)$$

where $\vec{F} = -\,\text{grad}\,W = -\,\partial W/\partial B \,\, \text{grad} \, |B| = \mu_{eff} \, \text{grad} \, |B|$ serves as a definition for the effective magnetic moment. Ramsey[4] gives an expression for μ_{eff} and curves for μ_{eff} as a function of magnetic field (see pages 104 and 105). For $I = \frac{1}{2}$ and $I = \frac{3}{2}$, the field-insensitive transition $(F = I + \frac{1}{2}, \; m_F = 0) \leftrightarrow (F = I - \frac{1}{2},$ $m_F = 0)$ is of primary interest. μ_{eff} is negative for the upper state and positive for the lower. A six-pole[6] magnet provides a magnetic field $|B| = B_m (r^2/b^2)$ and yields a drift velocity

$$\vec{v}_d = D(\mu_{eff} B_m/kT)(2r/b^2)\vec{r}_o. \tag{7}$$

Thus for the magnetic fields B_m greater than 1 weber/m^2, the drift velocity due to the magnetic field gradient is comparable with the diffusion velocity and may either aid or oppose the diffusion velocity. Although Equations (3) and (7) for the drift velocity indicate ample separation of states, i.e., that the upper hyperfine state drifts toward the center of the tube and that the lower state is absorbed by the wall, an exponential time dependence for the beam intensity will persist and the intensity as a function of time is approximately given by

$$N/N_o \sim \exp \{(-(\pi\beta_1)^2 \pm \alpha^2) \, Dt/a^2\}$$

where

$$\alpha^2 = \left| 4\mu_{eff} \, B_m/kT \; a^2/b^2 \right|.$$

The h.f. atoms drift through a very inhomogeneous magnetic field, but the process is nearly adiabatic and transitions between hyperfine levels are small.

A schematic diagram of the proposed low temperature atomic beam oscillator is shown in Fig. 1. The principles of operation are essentially the same as for the ammonia beam maser oscillator.[1] The essential difference is the use of a cold buffer gas

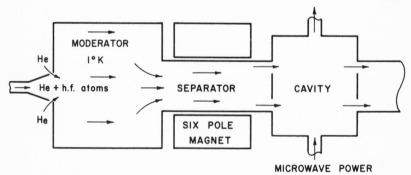

Fig. 1. Schematic of proposed low-temperature atomic beam oscillator

to reduce the linewidth.[2] H.f. atoms are introduced into the moderator and cooled to $1°$ K. The gas mixture flows through the separator where the magnetic field gradient separates the hyperfine states.

Since the atoms in the lower state are absorbed at the wall, the mixture flowing into the cavity is composed largely of atoms in the upper state. As in the ammonia maser, stimulated emission is then induced. The power emitted by the beam is $P_B = N \hbar \omega_{b \to a}$. From first order perturbation theory,

$$W_{b \to a} = (2\pi/\hbar^2) \; |(a|\vec{M}|b)|^2 B_m^2 \; g(\omega - \omega_o).$$

For a Lorentz line shape, the ratio of the beam power to the power loss $P_L = \omega W/Q$ is approximately

$$P_B/P_L \simeq (N/2V) \, (\mu_o \mu_B^2/\hbar) \, T_2 \, Q \sim 10^{-18} \, NT_2 Q/V.$$

If the beam power is defined as $P_B = \omega \chi'' W$, as for the ammonia maser, then

$$\chi'' = N(2\pi/\hbar) \; |(a|\vec{M}|b)|^2 B_M^2 \, g \, (\omega - \omega_o) \times$$
$$[(B_{av}^2/2\mu_o)V_c]^{-1} \simeq 10^{-18} \, NT_2 Q/V$$

where N is the number of atoms in the cavity, $\Delta\omega_{\frac{1}{2}} = 1/T_2$, Q is the loaded "Q" of the cavity, and V is the cavity volume. Oscillations occur for $P_B/P_L \simeq 1$ or $\chi'' \simeq 1/Q$. The preceding development has discussed the production of linewidths of a cycle per second or $T_2 \sim 1$. At liquid-helium temperatures, cavity Q's of the order of 10^5 to 10^6 are quite easily obtained for frequencies between 1000 and 10,000 megacycles. The cavity length is one-half wave length and the cavity volume is limited by the choice of mode. Reasonable design estimates indicate that for N between 10^{+8} to 10^{+10} atoms, oscillations should occur. The power output is of the order of 10^{-14} watts.

Following the analysis of the ammonia beam maser oscillator,[1] the line width of the low temperature atomic beam oscillator is

$$2\delta\nu_{\frac{1}{2}} = (8\pi kT/P_B) \, (\Delta\nu_B)^2 = (2kT/P_B \pi T_2^2)$$

and a spectral purity a few orders of magnitude greater than that suggested for the ammonia oscillator appears possible. Further speculation regarding the merits of the oscillator must await a working model.

Although this paper is primarily devoted to the reduction in line breadth via a buffer gas and low temperatures, a novel method for the production of slow atomic beams or a "bottle" for magnetic dipoles is briefly discussed. The equation of motion of a magnetic dipole in the magnetic field formed in the interior of a doughnut-shaped toroid by six current-carrying conductors hexagonally spaced on the surface of the toroid indicates that slow particles can be confined in the toroid. As indicated in Equation (7), the force on the upper hyperfine state is towards the center of the doughnut. Figure 2 shows a sketch of the configuration. Methods for slowing down the confined particles and and for avoiding the source are being investigated.

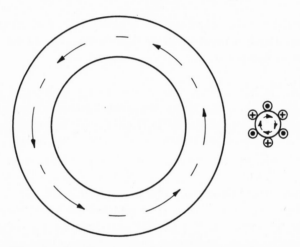

Fig. 2. Configuration for separation of states

The author wishes to acknowledge discussions with Dr. Farmer regarding optical pumping experiments at these low temperatures and to express gratitude to the Space Technology Laboratory for their hospitality during a part of this work.

REFERENCES

1. J. P. Gordon, H. J. Zeiger, and C. H. Townes, Phys. Rev. *99,* 1264 (1955).
2. J. P. Wittke and R. H. Dicke, Phys. Rev. *103,* 620 (1956).

3. R. H. Dicke, Phys. Rev. *89*, 472 (1953).
4. N. F. Ramsey, *Molecular Beams*, Oxford University Press (1956).
5. E. C. Beaty, P. L. Bender, A. R. Chi, Phys. Rev. *112*, 450 (1958).
6. H. Friedburg, Zeits. fur Physik *130*, 493 (1951).

DISCUSSION

P. L. BENDER: It appears quite possible that narrower lines will not be obtained by using a buffer gas at low temperatures. Optical pumping results indicate that the statistical spread in phase shifts for the alkali wave functions rather than the Doppler width, is the limitation. Although the collision rate can be reduced, the phase shift per collision should increase because of larger collision times.

C. V. HEER: Your comment is a source of considerable concern, and experimental data on line widths at these low temperatures is needed.

W. FRANZEN: It seems that moderation necessarily implies a loss of direction. The beam character of the molecules will be destroyed by the process of collision with helium atoms. The molecules will therefore diffuse out of the moderating cell, instead of streaming in the form of a beam. The probability that molecules will diffuse out without having condensed on the walls is very small, leading to a large loss of intensity.

C. V. HEER: The beam for this system is a gas composed of upper state atoms and the motion through the system is via gas flow. The diffusion rate is sufficiently slow so that lifetimes of a few seconds are possible.

C. O. ALLEY: Have you considered the use of optical pumping to prepare the desired quantum states?

C. V. HEER: I have discussed this experiment with Dr. Farmer of Space Technology Laboratory and this may be an excellent method for initiating the experimental investigation of the low temperature line widths.

P. L. BENDER: If alkali atoms can be thermalized by non-sticking collisions with a wall coating such as eicosane at low temperature, this would provide a useful source for an atomic beam apparatus. Do you think this can happen with appreciable probability?

C. V. HEER: The probability of sticking at these low temperatures is probably near unity. Thermalization by non-sticking collisions would be very useful and the effect of the thick helium film on sticking is of considerable interest.

MASER RESEARCH IN JAPAN

K. SHIMODA

Department of Physics, University of Tokyo

A DIRECT transition between l-type doublet levels of OCS at 12.78 Mc/sec was observed either as emission or absorption by using the three-level maser action with the pumping radiation at the frequency corresponding to the transition $J = 2 \leftarrow 1$. Generally the low-frequency transition of molecules is shown to be detectable, if the corresponding microwave transition has an absorption coefficient larger than 10^{-8} cm^{-1}. The linewidth can possibly be reduced to several kc/sec to allow high resolution spectroscopy.

The magnetic hyperfine structure of the formaldehyde molecule was studied using a beam maser. Since formaldehyde has a large electric dipole moment and closely spaced pairs of levels despite its fairly small moment of inertia, the focusing is quite efficient. Experimental studies on the $J = 3$, $K_{-1} = 1$ line and preliminary work on a four-level beam maser as a generator of millimeter and submillimeter waves are given.

The ammonia maser on the 3, 2 line has been observed to be about 100 times more accurate than that on the 3, 3 line, because the 3, 2 line lacks quadrupole hyperfine structure due to N^{14}. The frequency shift as a function of cavity tuning, focuser voltage, and other parameters has been measured. The frequency shift due to a traveling wave component was measured and calculated in some detail. The oscillation frequency agrees to within 1×10^{-10} for two masers tuned independently.

RADIOFREQUENCY SPECTROSCOPY
USING THREE-LEVEL MASER ACTION

Theoretical Considerations. Although a variety of molecules are known to have low-frequency transitions, low-frequency lines

are too weak to be observed by conventional methods of microwave spectroscopy. The application of three-level maser action
can increase the population difference between the involved
levels and make it possible to observe low-frequency transitions
of molecules.[1]

Consider a three-level system as shown in Fig. 1. The
power absorption coefficient at the frequency $\nu = \nu_o$ is written as

$$\alpha = (n_2 - n_3) \, \frac{8\pi^2 \nu_o}{3 \, hc} \, \frac{|\mu_o|^2}{\Delta \nu} \tag{1}$$

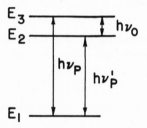

Fig. 1. A three-level system

where n_2 and n_3 are the number of molecules in the energy levels
E_2 and E_3 respectively, μ_o the dipole matrix element between
states E_2 and E_3, and $\Delta \nu$ the half-half-width of the line which
is assumed to be mostly due to pressure broadening. In thermal
equilibrium at temperature T, the absorption coefficient is

$$\alpha_0 = \frac{8\pi^2 \nu_o^2 n_2}{3 \, ckT} \, \frac{|\mu_o|^2}{\Delta \nu}. \tag{2}$$

Therefore the absorption coefficient is proportional to the square
of the frequency, assuming that other factors are constant.

If the transition between states E_1 and E_3 is allowed, pumping power at the frequency $\nu_p = (E_3 - E_1)/h$ is used to saturate
the transition, so that induced emission at the frequency ν_o can
be observed. On the other hand, if the transition between states
E_1 and E_2 is allowed, the pumping power at the frequency $\nu_p' = (E_2 - E_1)/h$ will enhance the induced absorption at the frequency
ν_o. In either case, for complete saturation one obtains the ab-

sorption coefficient or the coefficient of induced emission in the form

$$\alpha_{o,\,\mathrm{pump}} = \frac{4\,\pi^2\,\nu_o\,\nu_p\,n_2}{3\,ckT}\ \frac{|\mu_o|^2}{\Delta\nu} \tag{3}$$

which is $\nu_p/2\nu_o$ times larger than α_o.

If the radiofrequency spectral lines were as broad as those in the microwave range, direct observation of low-frequency transitions would be less worthy of study. The resolution of a microwave spectrometer is, however, largely limited by Doppler broadening, which becomes very small in the low-frequency range. The broadening by collisions of molecules with the cell walls or electrodes can be reduced by using a large cell. As an example, take $d = 2$ cm. $M = 60$, for which broadening by wall collision is $\Delta\nu_w = 1.45$ kc/sec.

The broadening by collisions of molecules with each other is known to be proportional to the gas pressure. In order to reduce it to 1 kc/sec, for example, the gas pressure must be of the order of 10^{-4} mm Hg.

Saturation effects will be appreciable when the field intensity at the frequency ν_o is larger than the critical value E_c which is approximately given by

$$E_c^2 = 3\,h^2\,\frac{(\Delta\nu_o)^2}{|\mu_o|^2} \tag{4}$$

where $\Delta\nu_o$ is the total linewidth. Therefore, the field intensity must be very weak in order to obtain high resolution. For example, when $\Delta\nu_o = 3$ kc/sec and $\mu_o = 1$ Debye, the field intensity must be less than 10 mV/cm.

The theoretical sensitivity of the r.f. resonator type spectrometer is then calculated as

$$\alpha_{\mathrm{min}} = \frac{4\,\pi}{\lambda_o\,KV_o}\ \sqrt{\frac{FkT\,\Delta f}{2\,\pi\nu_o\,CQ_o}}$$

where K is the filling factor, V_o the resonator voltage, C the capacitance, and Q_o the quality factor of the resonator cell.

Experimental Results.   A three-level radiofrequency spectrometer has been constructed and tested to observe direct l-type doubling transitions of ICN and OCS. The spectrometer was first operated on ICN.

The rotational transition of ICN at 13,094 Mc/sec or 13,083 Mc/sec, corresponding to $J = 2 \leftarrow 1$, $F = \frac{9}{2} \leftarrow \frac{7}{2}$, and $v_2 = 1$, was employed to increase the intensity of the direct l-type doubling transition at 5.4 Mc/sec, for $J = 1$. The experiment was unsuccessful, because the pumping radiation supplied by a crystal doubler was not sufficiently strong to achieve appreciable saturation.

Then the three-level spectrometer was tested with carbonyl sulfide. The energy level diagram of OCS for $J = 1$ and $J = 2$ is

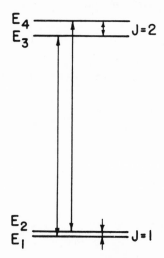

Fig. 2. Energy level diagram of OCS in the first bending vibrational mode

shown in Fig. 2. The transition frequencies and absorption coefficients at thermal equilibrium between these levels are:

$$\nu_{12} = 12.78 \text{ Mc/sec}, \qquad \alpha = 4.0 \times 10^{-13} \text{ cm}^{-1}$$
$$\nu_{34} = 38.35 \text{ Mc/sec}, \qquad \alpha = 1.4 \times 10^{-12} \text{ cm}^{-1}$$
$$\nu_{13} = 24{,}355.50 \text{ Mc/sec}, \qquad \alpha = 4.4 \times 10^{-6} \text{ cm}^{-1}$$
$$\nu_{24} = 24{,}381.07 \text{ Mc/sec}, \qquad \alpha = 4.4 \times 10^{-6} \text{ cm}^{-1}.$$

To achieve high resolution as well as high sensitivity, the separation of the r.f. electrodes must be large, but then large pumping power is required. The optimum pumping power of a plane polarized wave can be approximately expressed as

$$P_{opt} = \frac{3\,ch^2}{4\,\pi}\,\frac{(\Delta\nu_p)^2}{|\mu_p|^2}\,S\,,\qquad(5)$$

where the relaxation time is taken as $\tau = \frac{1}{2}\,\pi\,\Delta\nu_p$. Taking the following values, $|\mu_p|^2 = \frac{1}{2}\,(0.709)^2$, $\Delta\nu_p = 70$ kc/sec, and $S = 23$ cm^2, the optimum pumping power is calculated as

$$P_{opt} = 14\,mW.$$

Microwave power of this order of magnitude at 24 Kmc was supplied by a 2K33 klystron.

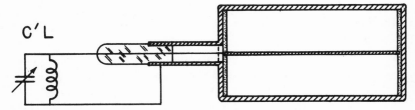

Fig. 3. Cross section of the waveguide cell

The absorption cell is made of 3,000 Mc band waveguide of 2 meters length, whose cross section is shown in Fig. 3. The r.f. voltage is applied to the center electrode which is connected to an external inductance L and a small variable capacitor to tune the resonant frequency.

The r.f. oscillator and detector employed is of a modified Pound-Knight circuit[2] for use at a low r.f. amplitude. The pumping radiation is frequency modulated at a frequency of 175 cycles/sec, and the r.f. amplifier and detector is followed by a tuned 175 cycles/sec amplifier and phase-sensitive detector.

By sweeping the pumping frequency through ν_{13}, the direct l-type doubling transition was observed and recorded as shown in Fig. 4 using a filter time constant of 0.25 seconds. The observed intensity of the line agrees fairly well with the calculated value of the signal-to-noise ratio of 39. Saturation by the r.f.

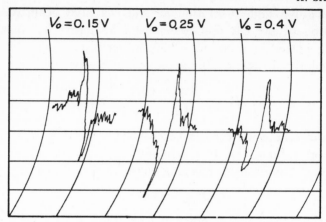

Fig. 4. Traces of records of the l-type doubling transition of OCS

field was observed when the r.f. amplitude was increased above 0.1 volt.

The spectrum could also be recorded by sweeping the r.f. frequency. However, the recorded trace was disturbed and blotted by interferences from other laboratories. The observed line-width at a pressure of about 10^{-3} mm Hg with an r.f. amplitude of about 0.25 volts was nearly 40 kc/sec. It can be supposed that a much higher sensitivity with a slower sweep as well as a smaller r.f. amplitude must be used in order to reduce the line-width below 10 kc/sec and still observe the line with a good signal to noise ratio.

Applications. Most of the low-frequency transitions of simple molecules might be studied by the three-level technique described above. They are: (a) direct transitions between K-type doublets, (b) direct hyperfine transitions, (c) transitions between Stark or Zeeman components under a d.c. external field and (d) other low-frequency transitions due to l-type doubling, inversion, or internal rotation.

Another interesting application of the three-level gas maser is the detection of ultramicrowaves, which was proposed by the author.[3] Now the frequencies in Fig. 1 are higher. Absorption of ultra-microwaves at the frequency ν_p or ν'_p changes the population of levels and results in the increase or decrease of microwave absorption at the frequency ν_o. The increase of population of the level E_2 is given by

$$\Delta n_2 = \frac{\tau}{V h \nu_p} \Delta P$$

where ΔP is the absorbed ultra-microwave power, and V the volume of the gas. The change of α_o when the ultra-microwave power is absorbed by ΔP is

$$\Delta \alpha_o = \Delta n_2 \frac{8 \pi^2 \nu_o}{3 hc} \frac{|\mu_o|^2}{\Delta \nu_o} = \frac{\Delta P}{V} \frac{8 \pi^2 \nu_o \tau}{3 h^2 c} \frac{|\mu_o|^2}{\Delta \nu_o}. \qquad (6)$$

Then the absorbed ultra-microwave power is expressed as

$$\Delta P = \frac{3 h^2 c}{4 \pi} \frac{\nu_p}{\nu_o} \frac{\Delta \nu_o \Delta \nu_p}{|\mu_o|^2} V \Delta \alpha_o. \qquad (7)$$

Taking values as $\Delta \nu_o = \Delta \nu_p = 100$ kc/sec, $|\mu_o|^2 = 3 D^2$, Eq. (7) becomes

$$\Delta P = 10^{-4} V \frac{\nu_p}{\nu_o} \Delta \alpha_o \text{ watts.}$$

A typical microwave spectrometer can observe the change of absorption as small as 10^{-8} cm^{-1}. Thus the minimum detectable power at $\lambda_p = \dfrac{c}{\nu_p} = 0.4$ mm is

$$\frac{\Delta P}{V} = 3 \times 10^{-11} \ W/cm^3 .$$

BEAM MASER INVESTIGATION OF FORMALDEHYDE

Among those molecules* which may be used in beam masers, formaldehyde is the most favorable next to ammonia. Since the moment of inertia of this molecule is small, the population of a given rotational level is fairly large, being 0.65 percent for each $J = 3$, $K_{-1} = 1$ level of a K-type doublet and 0.48 percent for $J = 3$, $K_{-1} = 3$. These values are compared with the population

---

*Some of these are: NH_3, CH_2O, C_2H_2O, CH_3OH, $HCOOH$, HCN, XCN, CH_3X and their deuterated compounds, as well as HDO, HDS, etc.

of ammonia, 3.2 percent for each $J = K = 3$ level and 1.5 percent
for $J = 3$, $K = 2$. The populations for other molecules are generally less than 0.1 percent. Because the dipole moment of formaldehyde is large, the electrostatic focusing is effective as
shown in Fig. 5.

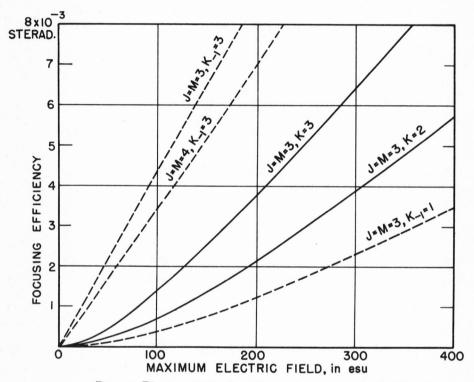

*Fig. 5. Electrostatic focusing of ammonia (solid line)
and formaldehyde (broken line)*

Hence the calculated intensities of the Q branch transitions
in the microwave range are close to that required for a self-
sustained oscillation under typical conditions. However, the
$J = 3$, $K_{-1} = 1$ line at 28,975 Mc/sec was investigated for spectroscopic purposes rather than as an oscillator transition.

The Magnetic Hyperfine Structure of Formaldehyde.[4] The
magnetic interaction of this $^1\Sigma$ molecule with C_{2v} symmetry can

be separated into two parts, the $\vec{I} \cdot \vec{J}$ interaction part and the spin-spin interaction part.

For a two-proton system, the rotational level with odd symmetry has the total nuclear spin $I = 1$, which produces the magnetic hyperfine structure. The magnetic energy is written in the first approximation as

$$
W_1 = \sum_g A_g \frac{\vec{I} \cdot \vec{J}}{I(I+1)J(J+1)} <J_g^2>
$$
$$
- \frac{3\mu_N^2 g_H^2}{r^3} \cdot \frac{3(\vec{I} \cdot \vec{J})[2\vec{I} \cdot \vec{J} - 1 - 2I(I+1)J(J+1)]}{2J(J+1)(2J-1)(2J+3)} \times
$$
$$
\sum_g \frac{r_g^2}{r^2} <J_g^2> - \frac{J(J+1)}{3} \qquad (8)
$$

The first term in Eq. (8) is the $\vec{I} \cdot \vec{J}$ interaction energy, and the latter is the spin-spin interaction. From the above equation, the hyperfine frequency shift $\Delta\nu_{F\to F'}$ for the $\Delta J = 0$, $\Delta F = 0, \pm 1$ transitions can be calculated.

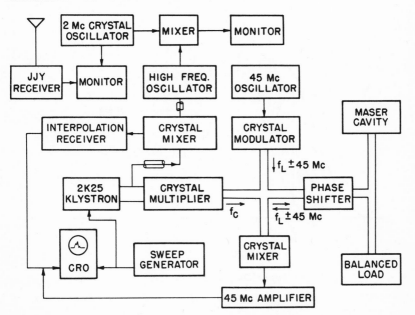

Fig. 6. Block diagram of the beam maser spectrometer

The experimental work on the formaldehyde maser was first performed with the $J = 3$, $K_{-1} = 1$ line at 28,975 Mc/sec. The block diagram of the maser spectrometer is shown in Fig. 6.

The maser tank, beam source, and focuser are the same ones as formerly used for the ammonia 3.3 line maser.[5] The cylindrical TM_{010} mode cavity of 12 cm length is closely coupled to the waveguide, the loaded Q being about 4000. The formaldehyde gas was prepared by heating the powdered paraformaldehyde.

The emission spectrum was observed as a triplet. The observed signal-to-noise ratio on the oscilloscope screen was about 10 at a focuser voltage of 20 kV, the effective amplifier bandwidth being 1.5 kc/sec. The sensitivity of a one-klystron system as in Fig. 5 is limited by the difficulty of balancing the signal at two frequencies $\nu_L \pm \nu_{if}$.

The observed triplet is assumed to be the $\Delta F = 0$ transitions, since the $\Delta F = \pm 1$ transitions are weaker. The splittings were measured as

$$\Delta \nu_2 - \Delta \nu_4 = 23.0 \pm 1.5 \text{ kc/sec}$$
$$\Delta \nu_4 - \Delta \nu_3 = 10.4 \pm 0.7 \text{ kc/sec}.$$

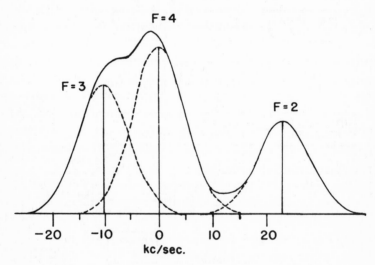

Fig. 7. Hyperfine structure ($\Delta F = 0$) of the $3_{12} \rightarrow 3_{13}$ line of H_2CO

From Equation (8) these values give

$$(\mu_N^2 \, g_H^2 \, r^{-3})_{exp.} = 19.9 \pm 1.3 \text{ kc/sec.}$$

On the other hand, assuming $r = 1.87A$ as the H-H distance in formaldehyde, one obtains

$$(\mu_N^2 \, g_H^2 \, r^{-3})_{calc.} = 18.2 \text{ kc/sec}$$

which is in good agreement with the value obtained from the above splittings. Concerning the $\vec{I} \cdot \vec{J}$ coupling constant,

$$A_y - A_x = 9.1 \pm 0.6 \text{ kc/sec}$$

was determined. Further knowledge will be obtained by the observation of the $\Delta F = \pm 1$ components.

Radiofrequency and Ultramicrowave Masers. Electrostatic focusing of molecules in the upper K-type doubling levels is more effective for larger values of K. The Q-branch transition for $J = 3$, $K_{-1} = 3$ is being studied at the frequency near 650 kc/sec. The frequency is so low that parallel electrodes are used to detect the emission from focused molecules.

Since the transition is easily saturated at an r.f. field of about 1 mV/cm, a superheterodyne system is being used rather than a autodyne system. The theoretical estimate of the signal-to-noise ratio when using a time constant of 1 sec is of the order of 10^3. A preliminary test was unsuccessful because of the stray electrostatic field around the parallel electrodes.

High-resolution spectroscopy which might be attained with such a low-frequency beam maser would make it possible to observe detailed hyperfine structure of the $J = 3$, $K_{-1} = 3$ line of formaldehyde, and would result in a more detailed knowledge of the magnetic hyperfine coupling.

Another reason why we are working on such a transition is its possible use in millimeter and submillimeter work.

Consider a four-level system consisting of two pairs of levels, $J = 3$, $K_{-1} = 3$, and $J = 4$, $K_{-1} = 3$, for example (see Fig. 2). R-branch transitions are allowed between either upper or lower levels of the K-type doublets. The frequency of $J = 4 \longleftrightarrow 3$ transition is about 290 Kmc in the one-millimeter range. Molecules in the states E_2 and E_4 are focused while those in E_1 and E_3 are almost completely removed from the beam.

Since the transition from E_4 to E_1 is not allowed, appreciable emission corresponding to the $J = 4 \rightarrow 3$ transition cannot be delivered from the focused beam. However, by applying an r.f. field to the beam between the focuser and the cavity resonator, the focused molecules in the state E_2 can be transferred to state E_1 before entering the cavity. Then one may get strong emission due to the transition from E_4 to E_2. The r.f. field may also be at the frequency to make transition from E_4 to E_3. In this case, emission from E_3 to E_1 is expected.

The ultramicrowave oscillation might be detected either by directly detecting the ultramicrowave power, or by observing the intensity change of the Q-branch transition of the molecules passed through the cavity. The latter method of detection is the same in principle as that previously proposed. [3]

CHARACTERISTICS OF THE AMMONIA 3,2 LINE MASER AS A FREQUENCY STANDARD

The effect of unresolved hyperfine structure on the frequency of a maser using the 3,3 line of $N^{14}H_3$ has been studied both theoretically[6] and experimentally.[5] It was found that the line center of such a maser cannot be determined with consistency within $\pm 1 \times 10^{-8}$, in agreement with the results of Helmer,[7] although some other masers such as the maser of the Radio Research Laboratories show a smaller effect.

Among the inversion lines of $N^{14}H_3$, the 3,2 line alone has no hyperfine structure due to the quadrupole moment of N^{14}. Two masers on the 3,2 line of ammonia were constructed and tested.

The design of the apparatus is similar to that reported before[5] but the focuser is cooled by liquid air filled in a trap rather than by a flow through a pipe as in the previous model. A cross-sectional view of this maser is shown in Fig. 8. The eight-pole focuser is made of steel rods of 3 mm diameter and 40 cm length, the diameter of the focusing field being 10 mm. The beam source is made of a bunch of holes of 1 mm diameter. The resonator is a TM_{010} mode cavity of 12 cm length, and is slotted

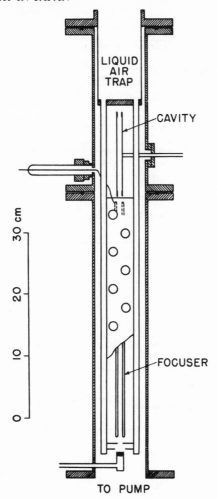

Fig. 8. Cross-sectional view of the 3,2 line maser

lengthwise to allow thermal tuning through a wolfram wire as shown in Fig. 9. The coupling hole is about 2.1 mm in diameter so as to increase the value of the loaded Q which was measured as nearly 9000. The inlet and outlet holes for the beam are 8 mm in diameter and 10 mm in length.

Experimental Results. The 3.2 maser starts oscillation with a threshold focuser voltage of about 5.6 kV after a run of 2 or 3

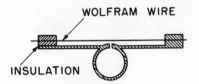

Fig. 9. Thermal tuning of the cavity

hours. The threshold focuser voltage at first decreases with the
elapse of time after the ammonia beam is put in, and then increases after several hours of operation.

The frequency shift of the 3,2 line maser was measured by
beating it with another similar maser. The result is shown in
Fig. 10 where each curve corresponds to a different cavity tun-

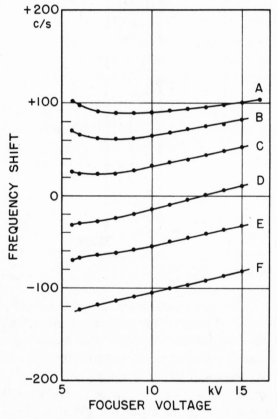

Fig. 10. Frequency shift vs. focuser voltage

ing.   Comparing with Fig. 11 in reference (5) for the 3,3 line,
one finds that the 3,2 line allows a more accurate setting of the
line center.   However, it seems difficult to find the line center
within an accuracy of better than $\pm 1 \times 10^{-9}$ from this result.

The frequency shift caused by the increase of tank pressure
was measured in the pressure range between 3×10^{-7} mm Hg and
1×10^{-5} mm Hg.   The frequency shift was found to be proportional to the amount of frequency pulling by the cavity $(f - f_o)$.
An empirical equation for the frequency shift caused by a tank
pressure of p mm Hg was obtained in the form

$$\Delta f_p = 2 \times 10^4 (f - f_o) p \qquad (9)$$

in cycles per second.   This type of frequency shift can be explained by the decrease of the amplitude of oscillation due to a
reduction of the beam flux by scattering.

The above equation is not entirely accurate, since the observed tank pressure may be in error, and also since it could not
be kept constant while the frequency shift was measured under a
deteriorated vacuum.   But the order of magnitude of the frequency
shift can well be evaluated from Eq. (9).   When the cavity is
roughly tuned so that $|f - f_o| < 30$ c/s, the typical operating
tank pressure of 5×10^{-7} mm Hg causes a frequency shift of less
than 0.3 cycles/sec.   This type of pressure shift is therefore
negligible.

Another type of frequency shift is caused by the Stark effect
of stray electric field inside the cavity.   The Stark shift is estimated to be much smaller than the traveling wave effect, but it
was experimentally measured by using a dummy focuser placed
at a distance of 3 mm from the cavity.

The observed frequency shift with the focuser voltage is shown
in Fig. (11).   This shift is proportional to the square of the voltage, as expected.   Since the beam focuser was actually about
7 mm away from the cavity, the Stark shift at a focuser voltage
of 15 kV was estimated as $+ 3$ c/s.   This Stark shift will be
made smaller, if the alternate electrode potentials of the focuser
are $+ \dfrac{V}{2}$ and $- \dfrac{V}{2}$, or if a shielding diaphragm is put between the
cavity and the focuser.

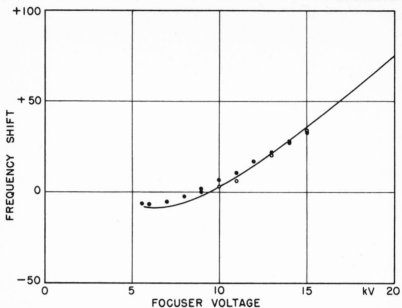

Fig. 11. Frequency shift due to the fringing field of the focuser

Traveling Wave Effect. The frequency pulling due to cavity tuning must be symmetrical with respect to the center frequency, hence the increase of oscillation frequency with focuser voltage should be explained by the traveling wave effect.[5],[8]

In reference (7), the traveling wave effect was calculated for the cavity with an output wave-guide at its end. Now the wave-guide is coupled at the middle of the length of the cavity. The frequency shift for this case is calculated as follows.

The stored energy in the cavity is proportional to

$$\frac{Q}{\omega} \int_{o}^{L} \sin \frac{2\theta z}{L} \, dz$$

where $\theta = [(\omega - \omega_o)^2 + (E\mu/\hbar)^2]^{\frac{1}{2}} L/2v$, Q the quality factor, and L the length of the cavity. The power emitted between $z = 0$ and $\frac{L}{2}$ flows toward the $+z$ direction while that emitted between $z = \frac{L}{2}$ and L flows in the reverse direction. Hence the net power flow towards the $+ z$ direction is approximately proportional to

$$\int_o^{L/2} \sin \frac{2\theta z}{L} \, dz - \int_{L/2}^L \sin \frac{2\theta z}{L} \, dz .$$

Then the effective value of Q corresponding to the traveling wave component can be expressed as

$$Q_{t,\text{eff}} = \frac{4 Q \int_o^L \sin \dfrac{2\theta z}{L} \, dz}{\displaystyle\int_o^{L/2} \sin \frac{2\theta z}{L} \, dz - \int_{L/2}^L \sin \frac{2\theta z}{L} \, dz} =$$

$$-4 Q (1 + \sec \theta), \qquad (10)$$

where a factor of 4 comes in, since the average path length of the traveling wave component is $L/4$.

Equations of the traveling wave effect given in reference (8) should be somewhat modified, if the velocity distribution of molecules is taken into consideration. By using the effective average velocity of the molecules,[6] $< v >$, the amplitude of oscillation, θ, is given by

$$\frac{n_o}{n} \frac{< v >^2}{< v_o >^2} = \frac{\sin^2 \theta}{\theta^2} \qquad (11)$$

where n_o is the starting flux of the beam and $< v_o >$ the effective average velocity at the threshold.

The factor in the right-hand side of Equation (51) in reference (8) should be modified to

$$- \frac{2 i n < v_o >^2}{\bar{\mu} n_o < v >^2 L^2} .$$

Putting our Equation (11) into this term, one finds that Equations (55) and (57) are unchanged. Then, from Equation (55) in reference (8) and Equation (11), the frequency shift is expressed in the form

$$\frac{\omega - \omega_o}{\omega_o} = \frac{\pi}{2 Q Q_l} \frac{L^2}{\lambda^2} \left[1 - \frac{\theta \sin^2 \theta}{2 \theta - \sin 2 \theta} \right] \frac{\cos \theta}{1 + \cos \theta} \qquad (12)$$

where the Q of the line is taken as $Q_l = \dfrac{\omega}{2 \pi} \dfrac{L}{v}$. The factor in the bracket does not change sign depending on the valve of θ, but the last factor does.

Since θ can be calculated from Eq. (3.10) in ref. (6) as a function of the focuser voltage, the above equation enables one to evaluate the frequency shift. Take $Q_l = 5 \times 10^6$, $Q = 9000$, $L = 12$ cm, and $\lambda = 1.3$ cm, corresponding to the 3,2 line, then the frequency shift is calculated as shown in the curve in Fig. 12.

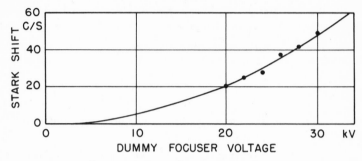

Fig. 12. Traveling wave effect

In this calculation, the starting voltage is assumed to be 5.6 kV. The observed frequency shift with focuser voltage can be obtained from curves C and D in Fig. 10, where the zero point is determined by the method described in the next section. The observed values shown by black dots in Fig. 12 are in excellent agreement with the theoretical values.

Determination of the Center Frequency. The use of a magnetic field perturbation to tune the cavity was first proposed by Shimoda, Wang, and Townes, but it could not well be applied to the 3,3 line maser.[7] However, tuning by the magnetic perturbation method can successfully be applied to the 3,2 line maser, because of its freedom from quadrupole hyperfine structure. Two similar masers on the 3,2 line could be reproducibly tuned to within $\pm 2 \sim 3$ cycles/sec for the same focuser voltage. The reproducibility of tuning of either maser is found to be within a fraction of one cycle per second, if sufficient care is taken. This is probably the best result so far obtained concerning the resettability of any type of frequency standard.

The observed center frequencies obtained by tuning the cavity individually for different focuser voltages with the magnetic perturbation method are shown by blank circles in Fig. 11. In this case, the absolute frequency shifts are obtained with respect to the other maser tuned to the magnetic perturbation line center and operated at a focuser voltage of about 9.5 kV, corresponding to $\theta = \dfrac{\pi}{2}$.

Because the observed frequency shift of the line center with the focuser voltage is in good agreement with the calculated traveling wave effect, the frequency shift given by Eq. (12) may be used as a correction to obtain the true line center. Then the line center can be determined within $\pm 1 \sim 2 \times 10^{-10}$ for different operating conditions. This is better than that on the 3,3 line by a factor of 100.

A schematic diagram for the proposed automatic cavity tuning is shown in Fig. 13. This automatic tuning system will be in-

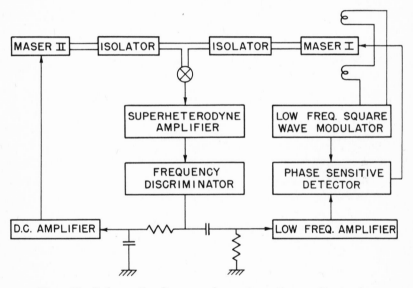

Fig. 13. Schematic diagram for automatic cavity tuning

vestigated in the near future. It is hoped to obtain higher accuracy and easier operation. Preliminary tests of magnetic perturbation were carried out with an inhomogeneous magnetic field; detailed study with a large Helmholtz coil is under way. A more precise setting of the cavity would then be possible.

These results are to be reported in the Journal of the Physical Society of Japan.

REFERENCES

1. K. Shimoda, J. Phys. Soc. Japan *14*, 954 (1959)
2. R. V. Pound and W. D. Knight, Rev. Sci. Instr. *21*, 219 (1950)
3. K. Shimoda, J. Phys. Soc. Japan *14*, 966 (1959)
4. H. Takuma, T. Shimizu, and K. Shimoda, J. Phys. Soc. Japan *14*, 1595 (1959).
5. K. Shimoda, J. Phys. Soc. Japan *13*, 939 (1958).
6. K. Shimoda, J. Phys. Soc. Japan *12*, 1006 (1957)
7. J. C. Helmer, J. Appl. Phys. *28*, 212 (1957)
8. K. Shimoda, T. C. Wang, and C. H. Townes, Phys. Rev. *102*, 1308 (1956)

USE OF PARALLEL PLATE RESONATORS

A. I. BARCHUKOV AND A. M. PROKHOROV
Lebedev Physical Institute, Moscow

WE ARE going to use parallel plate resonators at millimeter and submillimeter region wavelengths for maser purposes. We tested such resonators at $\lambda = 12$, 8, and 2.5 mm wave lengths. If the diameter is equal to 15 λ, the Q is rather high: $5 \times 10^3 - 7 \times 10^3$. The Q is highly dependent upon the parallelism of the plates and the cleanness of the surface of the plates, as in ordinary resonators. If we increase the diameter, the higher modes will be excited. If we want to excite a definite polarization, we can use a wire parallel to the plates. Using plate resonators, it is easy to use Stark modulation, and we can measure dipole moments with great precision, as the high-frequency field has a low intensity at the edge of the plates. We are going to observe the rotational inversion transitions of ND_3 and NH_3.

DISCUSSION

C. H. TOWNES: Have you examined the threshhold conditions for oscillation in this case allowing, of course, for the rather small fraction of molecules which are reflected and focused?

N. G. BASOV: The condition is of the same order as that for a beam type maser with ND_3 if the velocity is reduced ten times.

G. GOULD: In answer to Professor Townes's comment that Dr. Basov's spherical electrical "mirror" will reflect only a small fraction of the NH_3 molecules into a parallel beam and that it may therefore be more difficult to achieve oscillation, the reflected fraction of NH_3 is a slow fraction and therefore more effective.

What dimensions did you use in your parallel plate cavities?

A. M. PROKHOROV: $D \sim 15 \lambda$.

G. GOULD: Did you use any special means for suppressing modes with propagation vectors at considerable angles to the mirror normal?

A. M. PROKHOROV: No. The "walkoff" effect lowers the Q.

USE OF SOME NEW MOLECULES IN A BEAM TYPE MASER FOR SPECTROSCOPY AND FREQUENCY STANDARDS*

P. THADDEUS, J. LOUBSER,[†] A. JAVAN,[††]
L. KRISHER,[†††] AND H. LECAR
Columbia Radiation Laboratory, Physics Department, Columbia University

THE FIRST application of the beam maser was as a high resolution spectrometer to resolve the magnetic hyperfine structure due to the three protons in the ammonia inversion spectrum.[1] The narrowness of the emission lines observed, of the order of 5 kc/sec, or about 1/10 of the width of the sharpest lines produced by a conventional absorption cell spectrometer, made it seem likely that in the future the beam maser would be useful in high resolution spectroscopy of gases, since it was known that a variety of molecular states between which there existed an electric dipole moment matrix element possessed a Stark effect favorable to the electrostatic focusing used in the ammonia maser. In particular, for linear and symmetric top molecules, the $J = 1$ rotational level is focused relative to the $J = 0$ level, and to a lesser degree the $J = 2$ level is focused relative to the $J = 1$ level. The efficiency of the focusing depends of course on the

*Work supported jointly by the U.S. Army Signal Corps, the Office of Naval Research, and the Air Force Office of Scientific Research.

[†]Appointment supported by the International Cooperation Administration under the Visiting Scientist Program administered by the National Academy of Sciences of the United States of America. Permanent address: Physics Dept., University of the Orange Free State, Bloemfontein, South Africa.

[††]Present address: Bell Telephone Laboratories, Murray Hill, New Jersey.

[†††]National Science Foundation Postdoctoral Fellow.

molecular parameters, particularly on the dipole moment of the
molecule, and the rotation constant B_o.

For linear molecules with values of B_o of the order of 5 to 10
kilomegacycles/sec, the second-order term in the Stark effect
is dominant up to fields of about 12,000 volts/cm, above which
fourth-order terms are important.   Hughes[2] has given the high-
field Stark effect for the lower rotational levels of a linear molecule.   From Fig. 1 it is seen that the $J = 0$ and $J = 1$, $M = \pm 1$
levels experience a depression of energy in an electric field,
but that the $J = 1$, $M = 0$ level rises in energy to a maximum
value of about $\frac{2}{3} B_o$ at a field strength such that $\mu E / \hbar B_o \approx 5$,
corresponding to about 25,000 volts/cm when $B_o = 5$ kmc, $\mu = 2$
debye—well below the breakdown field for ordinary maser focusers.   This maximum value of $\frac{2}{3} B_o$ for the increase in energy in turn corresponds to the radial kinetic energy which a
molecule possesses at room temperature when it is moving at an
angle of about $2°$ to the focuser axis, so that we expect all molecules in the $J = 1$, $M = 0$ state traveling at an angle less than
this to be focused.

Symmetric top levels for which $K = 0$ have a Stark effect identical to that found in linear molecules; levels for which $K \neq 0$
have a first-order contribution to the Stark energy, but it is negligible compared to the higher terms at the high fields considered.

Especially favorable from the point of view of focusing are
adjacent levels in light asymmetric rotors (such as HDO) which
are remote from other rotational states.   In this case, the Stark
energy is given by the expression

$$W = \frac{W_1^o + W_2^o}{2} \pm \left[\left(\frac{W_1^o - W_2^o}{2} \right)^2 + E^2 \mu_{12}^2 \right]^{\frac{1}{2}}.$$

When $\mu_{12}, = 1$ debye, $\Delta W \approx 40$ kmc at field strengths of about
80,000 volts/cm, the greatest which most focusers will support.
This corresponds to a focusing angle of about $6°$.

If it happens that the molecule in question contains a nucleus
with a quadrupole coupling constant greater than a few megacycles, states with a given value of F and M_F may pass adia-
batically through the focuser, and some F states may not be
focused at all, irrespective of the value of M_F, so that certain

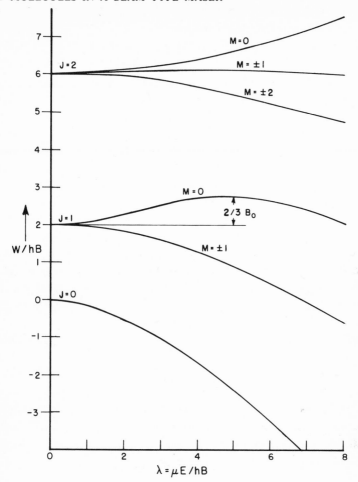

Fig. 1. Stark effect for a linear molecule

hyperfine transitions will be absent from the emission spectrum. An effect of this kind is responsible for the observed weakening of the low frequency quadrupole satellites of the ammonia inversion lines in a beam maser. The nitrogen quadrupole coupling constant is only -4.1 Mc/sec in ammonia; for molecules such as BrCN or ICN, where the halogen coupling constant is of the order of hundreds or thousands of Mc/sec, the adiabatic condition will be much more closely satisfied, and the absence of certain states is expected to be complete.

For molecules with transitions in the microwave region which are associated with low values of J, it is therefore usually possible to find at least one transition with a Stark effect suitable for electrostatic focusing. Even for transitions which are focused, however, the beam maser is about two orders of magnitude less sensitive than a Stark modulated absorption spectrometer, so that only the stronger microwave transitions can be examined —in general those in the usual language which have an absorption coefficient greater than about 10^{-7} cm^{-1}. The two types of molecules which are the most easily accessible to beam maser techniques are therefore: 1. strongly polar linear and symmetric top molecules such as ClCN, ICN, CH_3CN, and CH_3Cl, whose rotation constants lie in the microwave region, and 2. light asymmetric rotors such as HDO and CH_2O whose rotation constants may lie considerably higher, but which posses relatively close-lying pairs of levels in the microwave region. One hopes that in the first case, the strong dipole moment, and in the second case, the favorable partition function associated with the large rotation constants, will overcome the low sensitivity of the maser.

Usually only transitions with hyperfine structure unresolvable in a conventional spectrometer are of interest. Particular interest centers on structure due to purely magnetic interactions, as in the molecules CH_2O and C_2H_2O, or deuteron quadrupole coupling, which are typically of the order of tens and hundreds of kilocycles respectively. In most cases, a measurement of the relative hyperfine splitting of one rotational transition allows a determination of the relevant hyperfine coupling constants, which in turn together with a knowledge of the bond lengths and angles of the molecule, usually available from previous analysis, and nuclear magnetic and quadrupole moments, permits a calculation of those intrinsic molecular parameters such as the electric field gradient tensor at a given nucleus which are the most relevant to the theory of molecular structure.

Work to date at Columbia University has been primarily directed towards the second category of molecules mentioned above—light asymmetric tops—with rotational transitions in the X and Ku band regions. Initial investigation,[3] using one of the original ammonia masers, of the $J = 2 \longrightarrow 1$ transition of the linear molecule ClCN, which falls around 23,885 Mc, was somewhat

disappointing. This was so because of the marginal focusing
properties of this transition, and the complexity of the hyperfine
structure produced by the double quadrupole interaction of the
Cl and N nuclei. Of the more than thirty hyperfine components,
only four could be detected, a number insufficient to determine
the various hyperfine coupling constants. We expect to examine
in the near future, using the present spectrometer, the more favorable $J = 1 \longrightarrow 0$ transition of this molecule which falls just
below 12 kmc.

The maser proper of this spectrometer does not differ in its
essentials from the ammonia maser. It uses an effuser source of
the corrugated foil type, made by feeding a thin ribbon 1 mil
thick and about 6 mm wide of stainless steel or nickel foil between two meshed gears which have rectangular teeth one to two
mils deep. The corrugated foil is then paired with an uncor-
rugated one, and the two rolled up tightly on a small spindle to
give a highly transparent source with, in the present case, a
diameter of about one centimeter. The octupole focuser is made
of kovar rods, 0.080 inches in diameter and 10 inches long,
bonded together at both ends by glass rings into a cylinder of
0.35 inches inside diameter. It will support a potential of about
22 kilovolts during operation of the maser. Resonant reflection
cavities made of oxygen-free copper, about 5 inches in length
and operating in the TM_{010} mode, gave a quality factor of about
10,000 in the frequency range in question. They were coupled
about 70 percent to the waveguide line to give a maximum signal-
to-noise ratio for the emission lines. Rather than attempting to
tune these cavities over a large frequency interval, to insure the
highest Q's possible a separate cavity was machined for each
rotational transition to a frequency about 6 Mc higher than the
transition itself and thermally tuned over the line, using a small
filament heater strapped to the body of the cavity.

The low saturation level of the maser emission lines, typically
of the order of 10^{-10} watts, requires very sensitive detection
techniques. The superheterodyne system shown in Fig. 2 has
the advantage of using only one klystron. A part of the klystron
output is mixed at a crystal with 30 Mc from a crystal-stabilized
oscillator to give sidebands of the original frequency. The maser
cavity is monitored using one of these sidebands, which on re-

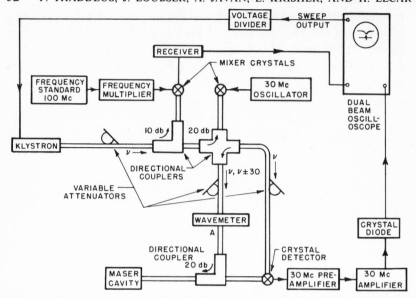

Fig. 2. Detection and Frequency Measurement System

flection from the cavity is combined at the detector crystal with the direct output of the klystron to give a 30 Mc intermediate frequency. The cavity response is too narrow to admit the other sideband 60 Mc away; it too, however, is reflected back to the crystal detector, where it contributes to the noise level. If desired, it could be removed by using a transmission filter in arm A of the circuit.

The hyperfine structure of the $2_{20} \rightarrow 2_{21}$ transitions for HDO and HDS are shown in Figs. 3 and 4. These transitions lie at about 10,280 and 11,283 Mc respectively. The line widths are approximately 5 Kc/sec, in agreement with the uncertainty relation $\Delta \nu \, \Delta t \approx 1$, where in this case Δt is the time of flight of the molecules through the cavity. The four interactions responsible for the hyperfine structure shown are, in descending order of magnitude, the deuteron quadrupole coupling, the $\vec{I} \cdot \vec{J}$ coupling of the proton, the proton-deuteron spin-spin interaction, and the $\vec{I} \cdot \vec{J}$ term for the deuteron. The signal strength for HDS was weaker than expected, and may be due to impurity of the gas sample, or an unequal proportion of deuterium to hydrogen.

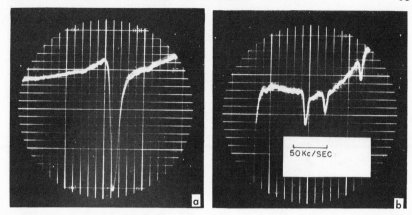

Fig. 3. Hyperfine structure of the $2_{20} \longrightarrow 2_{21}$ *transition in* HDO
The main $\Delta F = \Delta F_1 = 0$ transition is shown in (a), the high frequency
hyperfine components in (b).

The $2_{11} \longrightarrow 2_{12}$ transitions of CH_2O and CHDO, which lie
near 14,489 and 16,038 Mc respectively, are shown in Fig. 5.
The hyperfine interactions for CHDO are as before; for CH_2O
they are abbreviated to $\vec{I} \cdot \vec{J}$ and spin-spin terms for the two
equivalent protons. The relative splittings of the principal lines
of these spectra have been measured to within a probable error
of 0.3 kc/sec, and theoretically fit to within that figure. In

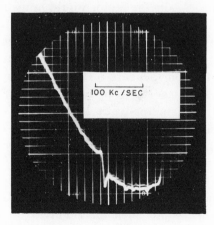

Fig. 4. Hyperfine structure of the $2_{20} \longrightarrow 2_{21}$ *transition in* HDS

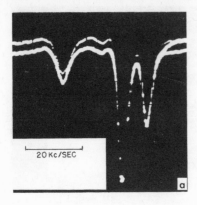 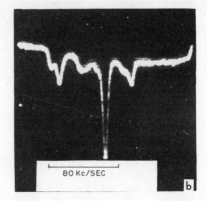

Fig. 5. Hyperfine structure of $2_{11} \longrightarrow 2_{12}$ *transition in* (a) CH_2O *and* (b) CHDO

either case the source of the formaldehyde gas was the polymer paraformaldehyde, which when heated to about 100 °C was found to give off the monomer with a vapor pressure of the order of 1 mm. It was found possible to cool the effuser to dry ice temperatures to increase the line strength without serious condensation of the monomer.

For HDO it was calculated from the observed strength of the main emission line that an increase of the flux of excited state molecules into the cavity by a factor of about four would give maser oscillation. A similar factor would probably be sufficient for the two formaldehydes. A factor of two or greater in the actual flux could probably be obtained in the present case by carefully engineering the maser components, particularly by designing more sophisticated focusers as suggested by Helmer in his paper at the present meeting. In addition, the flux requirement could be eased by a factor of at least two by using a higher-radial-mode silver-plated cavity with a Q of the order of 50,000. Such a cavity in addition could be made several times longer than the ones we have used, decreasing the emission line width, without increasing the probability of wall collisions.

At lower frequencies, the $1_{10} \longrightarrow 1_{11}$ transition of formaldehyde near 4.8 kmc would seem in the light of the above to be favorable for oscillation, although the focuser and cavity would necessarily be inconveniently large. Slightly higher in frequency, near 6.9 kmc, the $F = \frac{3}{2} \longrightarrow \frac{5}{2}$ component of the $J = 1 \longrightarrow 0$ transition of ICN might also be made to oscillate. The quadrupole coupling of the nitrogen is here large enough so that at the high resolution obtained there is no unresolved structure to any of the transitions. Further, the heavy weight of this molecule assures an average thermal velocity about three times smaller than for ammonia, and a consequent narrowing of the emission lines. At room temperature ICN is a solid with a convenient vapor pressure of a few millimeters.

The lines shown in Figs. 3–5 were obtained using a Varian X-12 or X-13 klystron which was mechanically and thermally, but not electrically, stabilized. It was found that at sweep frequencies substantially below 20 kc/sec^2 tube instabilities seriously distorted the line shape, and so limited the receiver band width which could be used. Stabilization of the klystron against a cavity or frequency standard should allow the use of a very narrow bandwidth phase-sensitive detector, and sweep speeds as low as 100 cycles/sec^2. This theoretically allows an increase of the signal-to-noise ratio of the order of 14. Pertinent to this type of detection, we have shown that the emission lines can be conveniently modulated at 130 cycles/sec by using a high voltage transformer on the Stark focuser driven at 65 cycles/sec.

Some other molecules of spectroscopic interest which appear to be accessible to the present techniques are NH_2D, HDSe, ClCN, BrCN, ICN, CH_3CN, CH_3Cl, CH_3Br, CH_3I, and C_2H_2O. Certain transitions in molecules with internal hindered rotation, such as methyl alcohol and hydrogen peroxide, may also be quite favorable. Special interest is of course attached to deuterated species, where possible, of all the above.

REFERENCES

1. Gordon, Zeiger, and Townes, Phys. Rev. *95*, 282 (1954)
   Gordon, Zeiger, and Townes, Phys. Rev. *99*, 1264 (1955)
2. H. K. Hughes, Phys. Rev. *72*, 614 (1947)
3. Thaddeus, Javan, and Okaya, Bull. Am. Phys. Soc. *3*, 28 (1958)

DISCUSSION

J. C. HELMER: How do the strengths of the rotational transitions in HDO compare with the strengths of the rotational transitions in NH_3?

P. THADDEUS: Calculations indicate, and our experiments more or less confirm, that the main $2_{20} \rightarrow 2_{21}$ HDO transition is 30 to 50 times weaker than the NH_3 3,3 line.

V. HUGHES: Have you seen any evidence of $\vec{I}_1 \cdot \vec{I}_2$ interactions of the type observed in HD in any of the molecules you studied? What are the estimated magnitudes of these interactions for the molecules you studied?

P. THADDEUS: In these heavier molecules, the $\vec{I}_1 \cdot \vec{I}_2$ term is expected to be only of the order of cycles/sec, or at best tens of cycles/sec. No terms of this order have been included in our Hamiltonian.

Y. BEERS: In some special cases, it is theoretically possible to obtain with conventional absorption methods resolutions comparable to those reported in the last paper by observing transitions which occur at low frequencies. There is no systematic decrease of the hyperfine splitting with frequency while the Doppler width decreases in proportion to the frequency. Experiments employing large samples and using absorption techniques on other lines of HDO at 825 Mc and 487 Mc are in progress at New York University. With these, total line widths at half power at 10 kc and 3 kc respectively are expected.

P. THADDEUS: At these lower frequencies, conventional spectrometers are in any case more feasible than beam masers, which do not seem practical at all below, say, 2 kmc. I would be surprised, however, if the hyperfine constants could be measured to the same accuracy at these lower frequencies as they can with a beam maser in the centimeter region. A direct comparison of the HDO results would be useful in this respect.

THE FEASIBILITY OF BUILDING BEAM TYPE MASERS IN THE MILLIMETER AND SUBMILLIMETER WAVE RANGE

F. S. BARNES
University of Colorado, Denver, Colorado

THE RECENT interest in extending the useful spectrum to the millimeter and submillimeter waves makes it worthwhile to consider the feasibility of extending the techniques developed for the ammonia beam maser at 24 KMC to millimeter and submillimeter wave regions. In extending these techniques, it is hoped that it will be possible to obtain a very stable maser oscillator which is capable of generating as much as a tenth of a milliwatt and which is capable of being used as a high-precision frequency standard. Additionally, masers of this type may be useful as narrow-band low-noise amplifiers.

In deciding whether a given molecular beam system can be made to operate as a maser oscillator, it is necessary to determine whether the power radiated by induced emission can be made greater than the power losses in the resonant structure and the detecting system. This problem of deciding the usefulness of a given molecular transition as a source of power for a maser oscillation may be divided into two parts. The first of these is the determination of the number of high state molecules in excess of thermal equilibrium required to obtain a power input greater than the losses in the RF structure. The second is the determination of whether or not it is possible to obtain this population difference with a reasonable beam source and focusing structure.

*This study was financed by the Colorado Research Corporation, Broomfield, Colorado

DETERMINATION OF THE MINIMUM NUMBER OF HIGH
STATE MOLECULES REQUIRED TO START OSCILLATION

The basic equation for obtaining the balance between the power in and the power lost may be written in the following form:

$$P_n \hbar \omega N = W_l \tag{1}$$

where $\hbar$ is Planck's constant over 2π; N is the effective beam current, which is defined as the difference between the number of high and low energy molecules in the energy states of interest entering the cavity per second; ω is the angular transition frequency; and P_n is the transition probability. W_l equals the power lost in the resonant structure and detecting system. If it is assumed that the first order perturbation theory applies to the situation, the transition probability is approximately given by[13]

$$P_n = \frac{|\mu_{ij}|^2 E^2 T_o^2}{4\hbar} \tag{2}$$

where μ_{ij} is the dipole matrix element of a molecular transition, E is the electric field strength, and T_o is the effective flight time of the molecule through the resonant structure.

The power lost, $W_l = \dfrac{\omega W_s}{Q}$, where W_s is the energy stored in the resonant structure and Q the loaded Q of the cavity or interferometer.

The choice of a resonant structure is extremely important, as both the noise properties and the minimum starting current are determined by the Q, the dimensions, and the number of modes which the structure will support. At microwave frequencies, where the size and dimensional tolerances are reasonable, the minimum starting current, N, is obtained with the TM_{010} cavity.[12] However, in the millimeter and submillimeter wave range, cavities supporting a single or only a few modes of oscillation become impractically small and the use of some type of multimode structure becomes necessary.

The mode density for cavities large enough to be useful in the region around one millimeter is sufficiently great so that the electric field E can be assumed to be constant throughout the structure. Thus, the energy stored, W_s, is equal to $\dfrac{\varepsilon_o E^2 V}{2}$ where

ε_o is the dielectric constant of the medium in MKS units.

Substituting these results into Equation (1), one obtains the expression for the minimum current N which is given by

$$N = \frac{2\ \varepsilon_o \hbar V}{\lceil \mu_{ij} \rceil^2 Q T_o^2}. \tag{3}$$

In a multimode cavity, each mode which is coupled to the beam provides a means for spontaneous emission. Thus, in order to obtain useful coherent power from each of these modes, N must be sufficiently large so that Equation (3) applies to each mode individually. For a cavity with dimensions which are large compared to a wave length, the mode density in a given frequency range, $p(\nu)d\nu$, is approximately given by

$$p(\nu)d\nu = \frac{8\pi V}{\lambda^3}\ \frac{d\nu}{\nu} \tag{4}$$

where ν is the frequency, λ is the wavelength, and V is the volume of the cavity. In order to reduce the minimum starting current, N, it is desirable to suppress as many of the extra modes as possible.

A structure which seems to be very promising in this respect is the Fabry-Perot Interferometer developed by W. Culshaw.[3] This structure, neglecting diffraction effects, has the useful property of supporting only two plane wave modes. Additionally, the dimensional tolerances for the construction of the reflector plates are quite reasonable even for wave lengths down to one millimeter.

The effective Q of this interferometer is given by

$$Q = \frac{n}{2}\ Q_l$$

where n is the number of wave lengths separating the reflector plates and Q_l is a constant of the structure which is determined by the reflectivity of the end plates and diffraction effects. Experimentally, W. Culshaw has obtained a Q_l of 2,000 at 6.2 mm using perforated plate reflectors. This resulted in effective Q's of 50,000 to 80,000 for 12-inch plates separated by about 18 inches.

The constants Q, V, and T may be written in terms of the dimensions of the resonant structure and the properties of the molecule. If the beam moves at right angles to the direction of propagation of the plane waves in a Fabry-Perot Interferometer as indicated in Fig. 1, then

$$V = l^2 \left(\frac{n\lambda}{2} \right)$$

$$Q = Q_l \frac{n}{2} \tag{5}$$

$$T_o = \frac{l}{V} = l \sqrt{\frac{m}{3kT}}$$

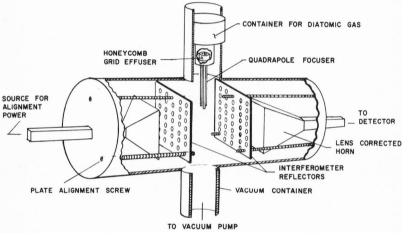

Fig. 1. Sketch of proposed beam maser system for millimeter and sub-millimeter waves

where l is the length of a side of the interferometer reflector plates, V is the root mean square velocity of the molecules, m is the molecular mass, k is Boltzman's Constant, and T is the absolute temperature of the source. Substituting these values into Equation (3) yields the following expression for the minimum starting current:

$$N = \frac{3 \, \varepsilon_o \, h \, k \, T}{\pi \, |\mu_{ij}|^2 \, Q_l m} \tag{6}$$

This expression for N assumes only a single excited mode in the interferometer and a parallel univelocity beam. In practice, it would be expected that the second plane wave mode and the diffraction effects would increase N by a factor of slightly more than two. Additionally, the number of useful molecules is reduced by the divergence of the beam. The component of the molecular velocity in the direction of the propagation of the electromagnetic waves effectively shifts the natural frequency of radiation or broadens the line width of the molecular radiation and thus reduces the number of molecules which will supply power to an oscillator at the line center to those which enter the interferometer with an angle less than $\theta \approx \tan^{-1} \dfrac{\lambda}{l}$.

The matrix element μ_{ij} is given by the product of μ, the effective dipole moment for the molecule, and a constant which depends on the structure and energy states of the molecule of interest. In the case of a linear polyatomic molecule subjected to polarized radiation, the matrix element is given by[14]

$$(\mu_{ij})^2 = \mu^2 \frac{(J + 1)^2 - M^2}{(2J + 1)(2J + 3)} \tag{7}$$

where J is the quantum number describing the total angular momentum and M is the magnetic quantum number.

SOURCE AND FOCUSER REQUIREMENTS

The population difference N arriving at the resonant structure depends on the fraction of the molecules at the source in the quantum states of interest and the focusing efficiency.

In general, the number of molecules in a given energy state will be given by

$$N_i = \frac{N_T g_i \, e^{\frac{-E_i}{kT}}}{\sum\limits_{j=0}^{\infty} g_j \, e^{\frac{-E_j}{kT}}} \tag{8}$$

where N_T is the total number of molecules and g_i is a statistical weight factor to account for the degeneracy of states, with an energy E_i. Equation (8) is frequently somewhat difficult to use and the approximations which are appropriate to each type of transition must be examined individually. For a diatomic molecule, the fraction of molecules in a given rotational state is approximately given by[14]

$$f_J = (2J + 1) \frac{\hbar B}{kT} e^{\frac{-\nu h w_e}{kT}} \left(1 - e^{\frac{-h w_e}{kT}}\right) e^{\frac{-\hbar B J(J+1)}{kT}} \tag{9}$$

where B is the rotational constant, ν is the vibration quantum number, and w_e is the vibrational frequency.* Typical values for population densities are shown in Table 1. However, it should be noted that the useful fraction of these population densities may be further reduced by a hyperfine splitting or l type doubling. In the case of LiBr where both particles have nuclear spins the hyperfine splitting reduces the useful population by a factor of approximately 16.

The force which can be applied to a molecule by a high inhomogeneous electric field is computed by differentiating the second order Stark energies. For linear molecules in a field small compared to $\dfrac{\hbar B}{\mu}$, the radial focusing force is approximately given by[14],[10]

$$f_r = \frac{-\mu^2 \, [J(J + 1) - 3 \, M^2]}{\hbar B \, J(J + 1) \, (2J - 1) \, (2J + 3)} E \frac{\partial E}{\partial r} = CE \frac{\partial E}{\partial r}. \tag{10}$$

It is a lot of work to compute an exact focusing efficiency by integrating the trajectories of the molecules from a distributed source over a Maxwell velocity distribution. A simpler approximate method for estimating the focusing efficiency is to compare the force constant C with the force constant for the $J = 3$, $K = 3$, inversion transition in ammonia and to assume the focusing efficiencies are related in the same manner. This approximation should be good as long as the ratio of the force constants are not too large. For ammonia, the number of focused molecules has been found to be proportional to the focusing force over the usual range of maser operation.[2] Table 1 contains values of C as computed for a number of molecules which look promising for use in a high frequency maser.

*For tables of molecular constants, see references 8, 9, 14.

Table 1. Population and focusing constants for possible maser molecules

Molecule	Quantum state			Population density[a] (percent)	Focusing force constant C in Farad meters^2
NH_3	$J = 3$	$K = 3$	$M = 2$	6	5.6×10^{-37}
	$J = 2$	$K = 1$	$M = 1$	4	3.9×10^{-37}
	$J = 1$	$K = 1$	$M = 1$	2.8	5.7×10^{-37}
	$J = 1$	$K = 0$	$M = 1$	2	$-.09 \times 10^{-37}$
	$J = 3$	$K = 2$	$M = 2$	4.2	2.64×10^{-37}
	$J = 4$	$K = 3$	$M = 3$		4.6×10^{-37}
HCN	$J = 1$	$M = 0$		1	6.9×10^{-37}
	$J = 0$	$M = 0$		.7	-11.3×10^{-37}
	$J = 1$	$M = 1$		1	-3.5×10^{-37}
$L_1{}^7Br^{79}$	$J = 1$	$M = 0$		.4	6.7×10^{-36}
	$J = 0$	$M = 0$		.3	-11×10^{-36}
	$J = 1$	$M = 1$		.4	-3.4×10^{-36}
$L_1{}^7H$	$J = 1$	$M = 0$		1.3	6.5×10^{-37}
	$J = 0$	$M = 0$		.93	-11×10^{-37}
	$J = 1$	$M = 1$		1.3	-3.2×10^{-37}

[a]The population densities for NH_3 represent the percentage of molecules in a given J and K state. In the case of HCN the population in each M state was assumed to be approximately the same.

A rough estimate of difficulty of obtaining maser oscillation can be obtained by comparing the product of initial population density, the focusing force constants, and the reciprocal of the minimum starting current, N, with the figures for the $J = 3$, $K = 3$

Table 2. Wave lengths for possible masers

Molecule	Transition	Wave length (in mm)	Relative difficulty	Est. Min. starting current (mol./sec)
NH_3	$J = 3$ $K = 3$ inversion	$\lambda = 12.5$	1	5×10^{12}
NH_3	$J = 3$ $K = 2$ inversion		≈ 8	1.13×10^{13}
Li^7Br^{79}	$J = 1 \to 0$	$\lambda \approx 9$	6	4.8×10^{12}
Li^6Br^{79}	$J = 1 \to 0$	$\lambda = 7.9$	50	4.8×10^{12}
LiF	$J = 1 \to 0$	$\lambda \approx 3.94$		
HCN	$J = 1 \to 0$	$\lambda = 3.4$	≈ 1.6	3.3×10^{12}
LiH	$J = 1 \to 0$	$\lambda = .68$	10	2.4×10^{13}
NH_3	$J = 1 \to 0$	$\lambda = .503$	500	2.7×10^{13}
NH_3	$J = 2 \to 1$	$\lambda = .252$	7	1.51×10^{13}
NH_3	$J = 4 \to 3$	$\lambda = .126$	≈ 6	1.17×10^{13}

inversion transition in ammonia. This figure of merit is shown in Table 2 with the wave length at which the transition takes place. Since it is relatively easy to get an ammonia beam maser to oscillate on the $J = 3$, $K = 3$ inversion transition, one would expect to get maser oscillation on $J = 1 \longrightarrow 0$ transition with HCN and to have a good chance of obtaining oscillation on transitions with a figure of merit less than 20. The figures of merit shown in Table 2 are somewhat more favorable than that computed by others[6],[7] primarily because of the advantages obtained by using a Fabry-Perot Interferometer. However, they are also subject to additional corrections resulting from beam divergence and spontaneous radiation into non-plane wave modes.

If the maser is operated at a beam current below that needed to start maser oscillation, it behaves like a narrow band regenerative amplifier. The effective noise temperature due to spontaneous emission from a cavity is reported by Townes to be approximately given by[14]

$$T_e = \frac{h\nu}{k}. \tag{11}$$

For wave lengths down to half a millimeter, this temperature is less than $28°$ K. Thus, the beam type maser provides a very promising approach to obtaining a very low noise narrow band amplifier for wave lengths down to at least a few tenths of a millimeter.

The most probable use of a high frequency beam maser is in establishing a frequency reference or standard. If, as in the case of the ammonia beam maser, the most important source of frequency fluctuations is in changes in the dimensions of the resonant structure, then it should be possible to build a high frequency maser with stabilities of a few parts in 10^{11} or better. Calculated coefficients for changes in frequency with changes in the critical dimensions are shown as follows:

$$\text{(a)} \ \Delta\nu \approx 3 \times 10^6 \ \Delta a$$

$$\text{(b)} \ \Delta\nu \approx 1.3 \times 10^7 \ \Delta d$$

where Δa is the change in the radius in centimeters of a TM_{010} cavity used with an ammonia beam maser at 1.25 cm and Δd is

the change in the plate separation in centimeters for an interferometer to be used with an HCN maser at 3.4 mm.

In conclusion, it may be said that there is a high probability
that several beam type masers can be made to work in the millimeter and submillimeter wave region. Additionally, these masers
should be usable either as stable oscillators or narrow band low
noise amplifiers.

The author wishes to express his appreciation for several helpful discussions with R. Mockler and W. Culshaw of the National
Bureau of Standards, and to Colorado Research Corporation for
supporting this study.

REFERENCES

1. B. Bak, *Elementary Introduction to Molecular Spectra,* Interscience,
New York (1954).
2. F. S. Barnes, "Experimental Study of an Ammonia Beam Maser,"
Stanford University Microwave Laboratory Report No. 486 (Feb-
ruary, 1958).
3. W. Culshaw, "Reflectors for a Microwave Fabry-Perot Interferometer," NBS Report No. 5527 (October, 1957).
4. W. Culshaw, "Diffraction Corrections in Microwave Optics," NBS
Report No. 5578.
5. W. Culshaw, "Reflectors for a Microwave Fabry-Perot Interferometer," IRE Trans., Vol. MTT-7 (April, 1959), p. 221.
6. Hellworth, "Atomic and Molecular Resonance for Millimeter Wave
Generation," Hughes Aircraft Company, Second Quarterly Progress
Report (October–December, 1956).
7. J. Helmer, "Research on Molecular and Atomic Resonance Devices," Varian Associates, Quarterly Report No. 4 (April–June,
1958).
8. G. Herzberg, *Spectra of Diatomic Molecules,* D. Van Nostrand, New
York (1950).
9. G. Herzberg, *Infra-red and Raman Spectra,* D. Van Nostrand, New
York (1945).
10. M. Peter, M. W. P. Strandberg, "Theoretical and Experimental
Study of Molecular-Beam Microwave Spectroscopy," MIT Research
Lab of Electronics, Technical Report 336 (August 26, 1957).
11. Prokhorov, "Molecular Amplifiers and Generators for Submillimeter
Waves," JETP (USSR) (April 1, 1958).
12. K. Shimoda, "Characteristics of Beam Type Maser II," J. Phys.
Soc. Japan *12* (1957).

13. K. Shimoda, T. C. Wang, and C. H. Townes, "Further Aspects of the Theory of the Maser," Phys. Rev. *102*, 1308 (1956).
14. C. H. Townes and A. L. Schawlow, *Microwave Spectroscopy*, Mc-Graw-Hill, New York (1955).
15. C. H. Townes and A. L. Schawlow, "Infrared and Optical Masers," Bell Telephone Labs (1958).

DISCUSSION

C. H. TOWNES: Is any group actively constructing a gaseous submillimeter maser oscillator?

J. J. GALLAGHER: We are at present constructing a submillimeter maser to operate at 618 KMC using the $J = 1 \longrightarrow 2$, $K = 1$ transition of ND_3.

J. M. MINKOWSKI: Concerning Dr. Townes's question as to who is constructing submillimeter and millimeter masers, the Radiation Laboratory at Johns Hopkins University is in the process of constructing a gas beam maser operating at 150 KMC with methyl fluoride.

M. W. P. STRANDBERG: It seems worthwhile to point out that studies on mode control in high mode cavities have been reported some years ago by Peter and Strandberg in the MIT Research Laboratory of Electronics report number 336.* We were interested in studying the cavity mode control problem for mm and sub-mm masers and a scaled study was carried out at 1.24 cm. The cavities were approximately 12λ by 12λ by 70λ, and indicated that reduction of mode density by a factor of several thousand was indeed achievable by the method used at that time.

*August 26, 1957.

MOLECULAR BEAM FORMATION BY LONG PARALLEL TUBES*

J. A. GIORDMAINE AND T. C. WANG[†]
Columbia University

IN RECENT years, several types of molecular beam devices have been constructed in which beams of intensity of the order of 10^{19} molecules per steradian per second are required. In order to reduce pumping requirements in such systems, arrays of long parallel tubes[1] have been used as sources of collimated beams. With the use of this technique, the peak beam intensity has been increased in some systems by a factor of about 20 compared to a cosine law source, for the same total flow. In this paper, the results of a theoretical study of beam formation are summarized and compared with observations of beams from several types of sources. A more complete account of this work is being published elsewhere.

At pressures sufficiently low that collisions within the tube are negligible, the peak beam intensity is

$$I(0) = \frac{n_o \bar{c} a^2}{4} \tag{1}$$

and the angle θ at which $I(\theta) = I(0)/2$ is

$$\theta_{\frac{1}{2}} \approx \frac{a}{L} . \tag{2}$$

In Equations (1) and (2), $I(\theta)$ is the beam intensity (molecules steradian^{-1} second^{-1}) at the angle θ measured with respect to the tube axis, n_o is the gas density (molecules cm^{-3}) at the high

*Work supported jointly by the U.S. Army Signal Corps, the Office of Naval Research, and the Air Force Office of Scientific Research.
†Present address: Arthur D. Little, Inc., Cambridge, Mass.

pressure end of the tube, a is the tube radius (cm), L is the tube length (cm), and $\bar{c}$ is the average molecular velocity.

At higher source pressures, collisions within the tube begin to play a major role, and the peak beam intensity is no longer proportional to the source pressure. For the same reason, the beam width becomes dependent on the source pressure. In devices such as the ammonia maser[2] the beam source is always operated in this region of high pressure.

The calculation of beam intensity is made on the basis of the following model of the pressure distribution in the source. It is assumed that, at least near the low pressure end of the tube, the mean free path λ is much larger than the tube radius. This Knudsen type of flow is assumed to occur for a distance from the end which is large compared to the tube radius. It is further assumed that the molecular density distribution in the tube is given by Equation (3)

$$n = rz \tag{3}$$

where $n(z)$ is the molecular density (molecules cm^{-3}), z is the distance into the tube measured from the low pressure end, and r is a constant. Although Equation (3) may be expected to be valid for $z \gg a$, it ignores the appreciable pressure in the region near $z = 0$ and in the region outside the tube. However, it appears that almost all the molecules which contribute to the peak intensity at the detector suffer their last collisions within the tube, and in a region where Equation (3) is a good approximation.

The peak intensity is calculated as follows. The number of collisions per second occurring in the volume element $\pi a^2 dz$ at z is $\dfrac{\pi^2 r^2 \sigma^2 \bar{c} a^2 z^2 dz}{\sqrt{2}}$. From these collisions arise $\dfrac{\pi r^2 \sigma^2 \bar{c} a^2 z^2 dz d\omega}{2\sqrt{2}}$ molecules traveling within the solid angle $d\omega$ in the direction of the tube axis toward the detector. Of these molecules, only a fraction exp $\left[\dfrac{-\pi \sigma^2 r z^2}{\sqrt{2}} \right]$ leave the source without a further collision. By integrating the contributions from volume elements throughout the tube, and by taking account of molecules which pass through the entire length of the tube without a collision, the peak beam intensity is found to be

$$I(0)d\omega = \frac{a^2 r^{\frac{1}{2}}\overline{c}d\omega}{2^{\frac{7}{4}}\pi^{\frac{1}{2}}\sigma} \int_0^{L'} e^{-y^2} \, dy \qquad (4)$$

where σ is the molecular collision diameter, and L', the reduced length, is equal to $\dfrac{\pi^{\frac{1}{2}}\sigma \, r^{\frac{1}{2}}L}{2^{\frac{1}{4}}}$.

Equation (4) can be written in terms of the total flow rate with the use of the Knudsen equation in the form of Equation (5).

$$r = \frac{3N}{2\pi\overline{c}a^3} \qquad (5)$$

where N is the flow rate (molecules sec^{-1}). Then Equation (4) becomes

$$I(0)d\omega = \frac{3^{\frac{1}{2}}\overline{c}^{\frac{1}{2}} a^{\frac{1}{2}} N^{\frac{1}{2}}}{4 \, 2^{\frac{1}{4}}\pi\sigma} \int_0^{L'} e^{-y^2} dy \qquad (6)$$

where $L' = \dfrac{3^{\frac{1}{2}}\sigma \, L\sqrt{N}}{2^{\frac{3}{4}}\overline{c}^{\frac{1}{2}} a^{\frac{3}{2}}}$.

Equation (6) gives the peak intensity at all flow rates at which useful directivity can be obtained. At sufficiently low flow rates, $L' \ll 1$, Equation (6) approaches Equation (1). At large flow rates such that $L' \gg 1$, Equation (6) approaches

$$I(0)d\omega = \frac{3^{\frac{1}{2}}\overline{c}^{\frac{1}{2}} a^{\frac{1}{2}}}{8 \, 2^{\frac{1}{4}}\pi^{\frac{1}{2}}\sigma} \sqrt{N} \, d\omega \, . \qquad (7)$$

Equation (7) is valid for the experimental conditions in most applications of these sources, and in the experimental work to be described in this report. Physically, the condition for validity of Equation (7) is that the source be "opaque," that is, that all molecules leaving the tube undergo their last collision within the tube, and no molecules pass through the tube without a collision.

The angular distribution can be calculated under the same assumptions as those used in calculating peak beam intensity. The additional assumption is made that molecules, after collision with the tube walls, leave the walls with a cosine distribution. It is also assumed that the tubes have a circular cross section. When the effect of collisions in the source is neglected, the angular distribution is found to be

$$I(\theta)/I(0) = \frac{8}{3\pi} \frac{a}{L} \frac{\cos^2\theta}{\sin\theta} \qquad \frac{\pi}{2} > \theta \geqslant \arctan\left(\frac{2a}{L}\right) \qquad (8a)$$

$$I(\theta)/I(0) = \frac{2}{\pi}\cos\theta \left\{ \cos^{-1}y - y\sqrt{1-y^2} + \frac{2}{3}y\left[1 - (1-y^2)^{\frac{3}{2}}\right] \right\}$$

$$\arctan\left(\frac{2a}{L}\right) > \theta > 0 \qquad (8b)$$

where $y = \dfrac{L\tan\theta}{2a}$.

From Equations (8), $\theta_{\frac{1}{2}}$ is found to be $\dfrac{1.68a}{L}$. In the opposite extreme of an opaque source, it can be shown that to a good approximation,

$$I(\theta)/I(0) \approx \frac{8}{\pi^{\frac{3}{2}}} \cos^{\frac{3}{2}}\theta \int_0^1 (1-z^2)^{\frac{1}{2}} \int_0^{2kz} e^{-y^2}\,dy dz \qquad (9)$$

where $k = \dfrac{2a}{\tan\theta}\left(\dfrac{\pi\sigma^2 r}{\sqrt{2}\cos\theta}\right)^{\frac{1}{2}}$.

From Equation (9) it follows that the angle at which $I(\theta) = I(0)/2$ is given by

$$\theta_{\frac{1}{2}} = \frac{2^{\frac{7}{4}} 3^{\frac{1}{2}} \sigma\sqrt{N}}{1.78\, a^{\frac{1}{2}} c^{\frac{1}{2}}} \qquad (10)$$

The angular distribution of beam intensity predicted by Equation (9) is shown in Fig. 1 for choices of the parameters leading to beam half widths of $5°$, $10°$, and $20°$.

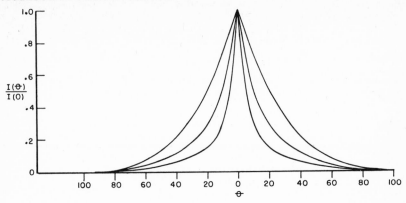

Fig. 1. $I(\theta)/I(0)$ *as a function of* θ, *calculated from Eq.* (9) *showing the beam shapes corresponding to half-widths at half intensity of* 5°, 10°, *and* 20°

Experimental observations on sources were made with the use of the apparatus shown in Fig. 2. The detector was a Pirani gauge with chambers milled in a pair of lapped stainless steel blocks.[3] The gauge was mounted 40 cm from the source po-

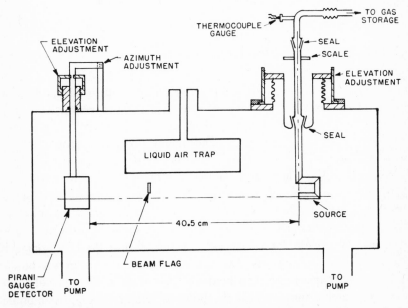

Fig. 2. Experimental apparatus, showing the mounting and relative positions of the source and detector

sition. The detector fluctuation level was of the order of 5×10^{12} molecules $cm^{-2}sec^{-1}$. The pressure in the apparatus with a source operating was in the range 1 to 6×10^{-5} mm.

The Pirani gauge was calibrated by comparing the integrated intensity measured by the gauge with the absolute flow rate as measured by the rate of change of pressure in a bulb of known volume connected to one of the sources.

The over-all accuracy of the flow rate and peak intensity measurements is estimated as about ± 20 percent. Ratios of peak intensity to flow rate are known to about ± 5 percent. The measured quantities are corrected for beam attenuation in the can and for the dependence of the effective Pirani gauge sensitivity on overall source size. All of the work reported was done with the use of CO_2.

Table 1 shows the characteristics of the three sources studied.

Table 1. Characteristics of long tube sources

Source	Tube length cm	Effective radius of single tube cm	No. of tubes	Overall source diam. cm	Approximate shape of tube cross section
A	0.66	1.65×10^{-2}	224	0.51	hexagonal
B	0.31	2.35×10^{-3}	1.28×10^4	1.3	circular
C	0.95	2.69×10^{-3}	1.80×10^4	1.1	triangular

Source A was an extended klystron grid structure with a honeycomb cross section. Source B was an aligned stack of metal foils with photographically etched circular holes.[4] Source C was a crinkly foil source.[5] The effective radius quoted is defined as the perimeter of the tube cross section divided by 2π.

Typical beam shapes produced by the sources are shown in Fig. 3. The beam shapes are shown normalized to the same peak intensity. These illustrations are reproduced to indicate the changing character of the beam shape with source pressure that was observed for all three sources, rather than to compare the effectiveness of the various sources. For a given beam width at half intensity, the beam shapes were approximately the same for each source. The similarity between the observed beam shapes and those of Fig. 1 is apparent.

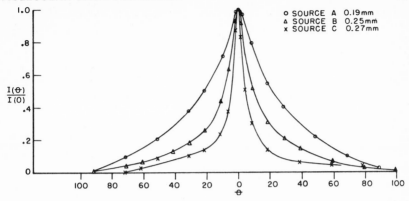

Fig. 3. Some representative measurements of $\dfrac{I(\theta)}{I(0)}$ *as a function of* θ *for various sources and source pressures, showing the characteristic dependence of beam shape on half-width*

The experimental data are collected in Table 2. The peak intensity and the beam width varied approximately as the square root of the total flow rate for all the observations. The dependence on $\sqrt{N}$ is shown in Figs. 4 and 5. The intensities and flow

Table 2. Beam formation by long tube sources

Source	Pressure behind source mm.	Peak intensity molecules sec^{-1} steradian^{-1}	Total flow molecules sec^{-1}	Half-width of beam at half intensity degrees
A	.024	1.42×10^{17}	8.91×10^{16}	5.0
	.060	3.19	1.87×10^{17}	8.3
	.110	5.70	5.26	15.0
	.190	9.66	1.21×10^{18}	21.1
B	.03	9.16×10^{17}	2.69×10^{17}	3.5
	.075	1.49×10^{18}	4.56	4.3
	.15	2.80	1.25×10^{18}	6.0
	.25	3.73	2.28	9.1
	.44	5.01	4.61	15.7
C	.035	3.05×10^{17}	5.42×10^{16}	2.5
	.13	7.87	1.81×10^{17}	3.3
	.265	1.30×10^{18}	3.88	4.5
	.61	2.29	1.03×10^{18}	5.7
	1.28	3.74	2.18	7.8
	1.90	4.79	3.58	11.3

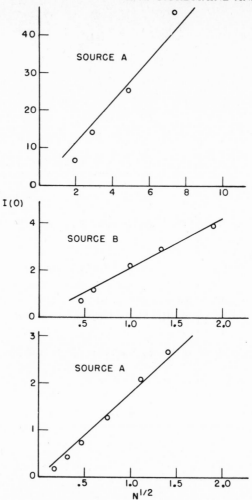

Fig. 4. Peak intensity per tube as a function of the square root of the total flow rate per tube

The units of $N^{\frac{1}{2}}$ are (molecules per second)$^{\frac{1}{2}} \times 10^7$, and of $I(0)$ (molecules per steradian per second) $\times 10^{14}$

rates plotted are those per single tube, i.e., the observed quantities divided by the number of tubes.

In Tables 3 and 4, the observed and predicted values of $I(0)/\sqrt{N}$ and $\theta_{\frac{1}{2}}/\sqrt{N}$ are compared. The observed values are those obtained from the slopes of the straight lines in Figs. 4 and 5.

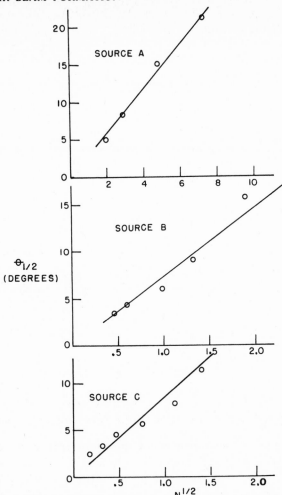

*Fig. 5. Half-width of beam at half intensity as a function
of the square root of the total flow rate per tube*

The units of $\theta_{\frac{1}{2}}$ are degrees, and of $N^{\frac{1}{2}}$ (molecules per second)$^{\frac{1}{2}} \times 10^{7}$

The agreement between the observed values and those predicted
by Equations (7) and (10) is seen to be satisfactory.

The predicted values of beam width for sources A and C were
calculated from Equation (10) using for A the effective radius of
the tube, which had a non-circular cross section. It should be

noted, however, that the theory is strictly applicable only for tubes of circular cross section.

Table 3. Comparison of predicted and observed peak intensities

$$\frac{I(0)}{\sqrt{N}} \text{ molecules per steradian per}$$

second (molecules per sec)$^{-\frac{1}{2}}$

Source	Observed	Calculated from Equation (7)
A	5.6×10^7	5.5×10^7
B	2.1×10^7	2.1×10^7
C	1.8×10^7	2.2×10^7

Table 4. Comparison of predicted and observed beam widths

$$\theta_{\frac{1}{2}}/\sqrt{N} \text{ degrees (molecules sec}^{-1})^{-\frac{1}{2}}$$

Source	Observed	Calculated from Equation (10)
A	2.9×10^{-7}	3.6×10^{-7}
B	7.3×10^{-7}	9.2×10^{-7}
C	8.4×10^{-7}	8.6×10^{-7}

It follows from this work that for an array of tubes of given overall area, the peak intensity for a fixed flow rate varies as $a^{-\frac{1}{2}}$, where a is the radius of a single tube, while the beam width varies as $a^{+\frac{1}{2}}$. The collimation therefore increases as the diameter of the individual tubes is reduced. The optimum tube diameter is probably of the order of 10^{-3} inches, since at this diameter the tube walls usually begin to occupy a large fraction of the source cross section.

For a given peak intensity $I(0)$ from a multiple tube source, it can be shown by the methods used in deriving Equation (7) that increasing the length of the source beyond a critical length

$$\Lambda \approx \frac{2.5 \; 2^{\frac{1}{4}} \; \bar{c} a^2}{8 \; \pi^{\frac{1}{2}} \; \sigma^2 \; I(0)}$$

does not improve the collimation. The quantity Λ represents an approximate minimum source length for a given gas, tube radius, and peak intensity.

REFERENCES

1. This technique was first used by J. R. Zacharias, *vid.* N. F. Ramsey, *Molecular Beams*, Oxford University Press (1956), p. 363.
2. J. P. Gordon, H. J. Zeiger, and C. H. Townes, Phys. Rev. *99,* 1264 (1955).
3. R. S. Julian, Ph.D. thesis, MIT (1947). This type of gauge is described by N. F. Ramsey, *loc. cit.,* p. 392.
4. This source was kindly loaned by J. P. Cedarholm.
5. J. R. Zacharias and R. D. Haun, Jr., MIT Research Laboratory of Electronics, Quarterly Progress Report 34 (October, 1954), unpublished.

DISCUSSION

W. A. NIERENBERG: Could one of the authors present a specific result of the calculation?

J. A. GIORDMAINE: The principal results of the calculation are given by Equation (7) and Equation (10), which show the dependence of peak intensity and beam width on the total flow rate. It is noted that both quantities are proportional to the square root of the total flow rate under normal operating conditions.

FOCUSING MOLECULAR BEAMS OF NH_3*

J. C. HELMER AND F. B. JACOBUS
Varian Associates, Palo Alto, California
AND
P. A. STURROCK
W. W. Hansen Laboratories of Physics, Stanford, California

THE PROBLEM of forming molecular beams for use in ammonia masers is examined. It is shown theoretically and experimentally that through the use of a new parabolic focuser with a "point source" effuser, the molecular flow may either be reduced by a factor of 8, for the same power output, or the power output may be increased by a factor of 2 for the same molecular flow. A theory of beam formation in a multitube effuser is described. This shows that the most intense molecular beam is formed by an effuser of small overall diameter. Design considerations are discussed for parabolic upper-state focusers, and for coaxial lower-state focusers. The operation of a system is described, using a lower-state focuser and an ionization detector, in which lower-state molecules produced by maser oscillation may be detected. Measurements with this system suggest the presence of infrared oscillation.

The device we have constructed is shown in Fig. 1. This is the electric analog of the well-known atomic beam machine. The cylindrical symmetry of the focusing structure provides a very intense beam, so that detection by a nonselective ionizer is easily possible in spite of the unavoidable background count. The device has been tested with the 3,3 inversion transition of ammonia, which oscillates spontaneously in the cavity shown.

*Supported by the U. S. Army Signal Corps under Contract No. DA-36-039 sc-73266.

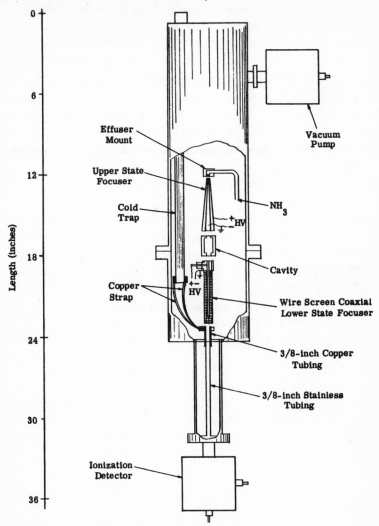

Fig. 1. Lower state beam detector

The resulting lower state molecules are focused into the ionization detector, producing an increase in detector current of about 5 percent over background.

We wish to use this detector for the study of rotational transitions in the ammonia beam at $\lambda = 125$ microns. By proper cavity design, maser oscillation may be obtained at this wavelength.

The linewidth is due entirely to the Doppler effects of beam divergence, which for ammonia becomes about 1/10th of the full Doppler bandwidth, or 300,000 cps. For oscillation, this requires a cavity Q near 100,000. Optical type cavities, by virtue of their large size relative to the wavelength, in principle have Q's of this order, and therefore there is hope of obtaining coherent, infrared radiation. In this application, smooth, cylindrical cavities with $D/\lambda = 100$ may be quite superior to the parallel plate, Fabry-Perot type, since diffraction loss from the side opening is eliminated. Then it is possible to obtain a good filling factor with a single beam and to reduce end diffraction losses by making the cavity long.

This work was initiated by the observation of anomalous saturation effects in the 3,3 inversion oscillation. These could have been due to the interference of rotational transitions which terminate on the lower inversion states of the molecule. Such effects are possible since the usual microwave cavity is also a pretty good infrared cavity, as pointed out above. However, the hypothesis regarding the cause of anomalous saturation effects remains to be proved or disproved.

OPTICAL PUMPING AND RELATED EFFECTS

J. BROSSEL

University of Paris

THE STARTING point of all research in optical detection of magnetic resonance was a paper by F. Bitter[1] in 1949. This was quickly followed by a description of the so-called "double resonance" method,[2] and a few months later, A. Kastler[3] proposed the scheme known as "optical pumping." Different ways of achieving the same end have been used since that time and the words "optical pumping" have come to cover many different things.

I plan to describe very briefly the principles involved. I will mention the main applications and say a few words on the problems which seem to be of interest and which the above techniques might help to solve.

Let us consider a set of closely spaced energy levels belonging to an isolated atom or to an atom or an ion in interaction with a lattice. These levels might be, for instance, a set of hyperfine Zeeman sublevels of an atomic state. Several techniques can be used to study the transitions between these levels, and even though this is *not* in principle necessary, nearly all methods used to detect a resonance between two states, (a) and (b), *give signals which are proportional to the difference of populations of the levels involved.*

In most cases, one makes use of the Boltzmann distribution which is favorable at very low temperatures only. "Optical pumping" is a way to obtain, in a steady state condition, large population differences at any temperature.

The levels we consider have a radiation lifetime T, which is very long for the ground state, but may be as short as 10^{-9} sec

for some excited states. Whenever the atom is in interaction
with a lattice, the sublevels have among themselves a thermal
relaxation time T_1. The relative values of these two times determine the methods which can be used to study the transition
$a \rightarrow b$.

I. $T \ll T_1$

The atom escapes from this set of levels before it has the
time to thermalize.

This is the case of an isolated atom in an excited state, and
in order to have a steady state population there must be a continuous flow of atoms in the set of levels under consideration.

This is achieved through some kind of excitation, followed by
a decay to the ground state. The atoms are set moving in a
pumping cycle as shown in Fig. 1.

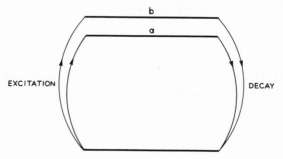

Fig. 1. Pumping cycle

If one wants to achieve $n_a \neq n_b$, two ways are open:

1. (a) and (b) are produced at the same rate but they decay at
   different rates (they have different lifetimes). This scheme is
   being tried in some optical maser experiments.[4] It has already been used in the Lamb Shift[5] measurements of level
   $n = 2$ of hydrogen.

2. Levels (a) and (b) have the same lifetime, but they are produced at different rates. Several processes have been used
   to that end.

   (i) Optical excitation with polarized light. This is the so-
   called "double resonance"[6] technique, which has been
   used with great success to study the structure of "optical resonance" levels in a few atoms.

(ii) Electron bombardment[7] with a beam of unidirectional slow electrons (around 30 volts) traveling in the direction of the steady field.

(iii) Quite often this last type of excitation followed by an optical decay to levels (a) and (b) will give large population differences between (a) and (b). This cascade effect is very efficient in mercury (Pebay-Peyroula, reference 7).

Now, detection of magnetic resonance rests on the following property: two nondegenerate atomic levels (a) and (b) usually *do not have the same emission (or absorption) diagram*. They radiate (or absorb) different proportions of π and σ radiation. When transition $a \rightarrow b$ takes place, the π/σ ratio and the amount of polarized absorbed light is changed. Detection takes place during the decay or during absorption leading to a higher set of levels.

The experiment is done in the following way: the atoms are enclosed in a glass or quartz cell at a low vapor pressure. They are illuminated with polarized resonance radiation (or bombarded with slow electrons). The light reemitted is polarized. A set of rf coils outside the cell produces the oscillating field inducing the transition. This appears as a change in the degree of polarization of the light emitted, or in the amount of (polarized) light absorbed as in Dehmelt experiment[7] on the 6^3P_2 (meta-

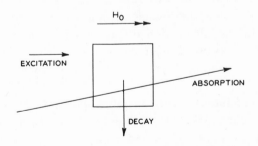

Fig. 2. Schematic of experiment

stable) level of mercury. Of course, if one can measure directly n_a and n_b (as in Lamb's[5] experiment) this can be used for detection. A characteristic feature of the case just analyzed ($T \ll T_1$) is that the speed at which atoms circulate in the pumping cycle is unimportant.

II. $T \gg T_1$

The levels thermalize before the atoms radiate. One is left with the Boltzman distribution, which is most unfavorable at room temperatures or when negative temperatures are desired. This situation is always met when one studies ground states, and it is a most serious drawback when one cannot work at low temperatures. But the same kind of thing happens in the study of excited states as well. It is revealed, for instance, by the depolarization of optical resonance radiation in the presence of a foreign gas.

Another example is seen in the fluorescence of solids: It is known that many paramagnetic ions in crystal lattices show very sharp absorption and fluorescence lines.[8] The discrete levels from which the sharp fluorescence lines originate are often fairly long lived (for Cr^{+++} in ruby, for instance, $\sim 10^{-2}$ sec). As a rule, however, one can expect very short relaxation times T_1, in these states, because there are many levels close by and there is usually a residual angular momentum giving a strong coupling to the lattice. So, at liquid helium temperatures, large population differences can be expected between the sublevels of the excited states of these ions.

At liquid-helium temperatures, optical detection of magnetic resonance will use, in this case ($T \gg T_1$), the same techniques as described above. One will look for a change in the degree of polarization of sharp fluorescence lines (to study excited states) or a change in the absorption of polarized light by a sharp absorption line (to study the ground states). Here, however, one has to flip the spin in time T_1, which may require a lot of rf power.

It might be of interest here to point out that optical detection of magnetic resonance might have advantages over paramagnetic absorption in the study of ground states of paramagnetic ions in crystal lattices. For instance, Cr^{+++} can be imbedded in the MgO lattice. There are several types of Cr^{+++} sites in which the crystal field is different. The ordinary site is Cr^{+++} in the pure cubic MgO field. But there are sites where Cr^{+++} is near an Mg^{++} vacancy or near another Cr^{+++}, etc.[9] One may reasonably expect that the different sites have different fluorescence or absorption lines. Accordingly, optical detection of magnetic resonance offers a convenient way to study the different sites separately.

At room temperature, one can obtain a very great increase of signal strength if one upsets the Boltzmann distribution. The trick used is to go back to the situation analyzed in part I; that is, to make T shorter than T_1. *One will allow the atoms to stay in states (a) and (b) only for a time which is short compared to* T_1.

In the study of ground and metastable states, several methods have been used.

The "optical pumping" scheme of Kastler[3] is as follows: An atom, initially in state m_F of the ground state, goes into state $m'_F = m_F + 1$ of the excited state when it absorbs circularly right polarized optical resonance radiation. When it falls back to the ground state through spontaneous emission, it will go in states m_F, $m_F + 1$, $m_F + 2$, (Fig. 3) depending on the Zeeman component $(\sigma^+, \pi, \sigma^-)$ used to that end.

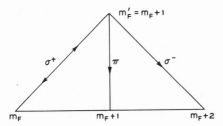

Fig. 3. Kastler's "optical pumping" scheme

On the average, angular momentum is transferred from the light to the atom, and when one repeats the process often enough, all atoms will eventually go in a state of greatest $|m_F|$ value, $(m_F > 0$ with σ^+ light, $m_F < 0$ with σ^- light) provided the relaxation time is long enough in the ground state.

Very large population differences can be built in that way. The pumping cycle is illustrated in Fig. 4a for an $F = \frac{1}{2} \rightarrow F' = \frac{1}{2}$ transition and in Fig. 4b for an $F = \frac{1}{2} \rightarrow F' = \frac{3}{2}$ transition.

There is a one-way passage from (a) to (b). With light sources currently available, pumping times of the order of 10^{-4} sec can be obtained with alkali metals—T_1 must be longer than that. The first experiments using the above scheme were made with

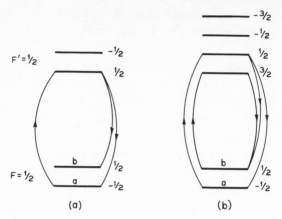

Fig. 4. Pumping cycles for (a) $F = \frac{1}{2} \longrightarrow F' = \frac{1}{2}$ and (b) $F = \frac{1}{2} \longrightarrow F' = \frac{3}{2}$

atomic beams ($T_1 \sim \infty$), then with atoms sealed in a glass vessel a few centimeters in diameter.

At low enough pressures, the mean free path is greater than the dimensions of the bulb. The atom travels in a straight line from wall to wall. During a collision on the wall an atom may retain its orientation, or lose it. For instance, nuclear orientation of a mercury atom is not destroyed after thousands of collisions with a quartz wall.[11] On the other hand, an alkali metal atom does lose its orientation after a single collision with a glass wall. In this last case, T_1 is the time it takes an atom to go from one side of the cell to the other.

In order to get more completely oriented vapors, efforts have been made to lengthen T_1. It has been found that coating the glass[12] wall with long chain paraffin was very efficient in that respect.

The other approach has been to prevent oriented atoms from reaching the wall through the use of a "buffer gas."[13] Besides the alkali metal, the cell contains a gas (H_2, rare gas, N_2, etc.,) at a few millimeters pressure. It is found that, during a collision with a gas molecule, the alkali metal retains its orientation and that its wave function is unaltered[14] but it follows now a very complicated path in the cell instead of going in a straight line from wall to wall. T_1 is increased and the pumping process takes place over a much longer period of time. This results in a greatly increased orientation.

The use of a buffer gas has led to many interesting developments.

It is easily seen that the degree of polarization of optical resonance radiation depends on the relative populations of the Zeeman sublevels of the *ground* state. This has been used to detect ground-state resonance. Using this method, one can plot the observed intensity of a resonance versus the buffer gas pressure. One finds a maximum at a pressure of a few tens of millimeters.[15] At 1 mm, the resonances are barely visible. On the other hand, one may plot the same curve for the same resonance as observed through the change in absorption of polarized light. The pressure dependence is completely different — resonances can be seen at 20 mm buffer gas pressures. This is because in the first method of detection the atom had the time to thermalize with the buffer gas while in the excited state. Whatever the populations in the ground state, resonance radiation is completely depolarized at those pressures — there was some orientation but the method failed to reveal it.

This results in a very different kind of optical pumping, as was pointed out for the first time by Dehmelt.[15] The atoms fall back to all ground state sublevels at the same rate — and one will get a population difference between (a) and (b) if (a) and (b) are pumped at different rates. In the limit of very long T_1, the steady-state populations are inversely proportional to the absorption transition probabilities for the type of polarized light actually used for pumping.

Because of the optical transition sum rules, this kind of pumping is not always operative. For instance, in the case of alkali metals, the pumping light must have different intensities on D_1 and D_2 and, if D_1 (or D_2) alone is used, one will *not* build a population difference between the Zeeman sublevels $m_F = 0$ of the hyperfine states $I - \frac{1}{2}$ and $I + \frac{1}{2}$ if the hyperfine components of D_1 (or D_2) in the pumping light have the same intensity. In fact, however, the $0 \rightarrow 0$ transition is easily observed, because the hyperfine components are absorbed to a different degree in the front part of the cell.

As pointed out before, detection of orientation at high buffer gas pressures rests on absorption of polarized light (in most cases, use is made of the pumping light itself). If one plots the

intensity of a given resonance (or the intensity of the signal obtained in Dehmelt[15] field reversal technique) as a function of
alkali metal vapor pressure, one obtains a curve with a maximum as shown in Fig. 5.

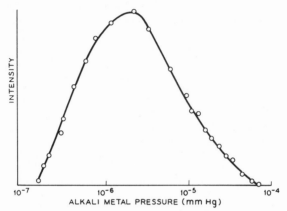

Fig. 5. Dependence of signal intensity on pressure in Dehmelt's technique

At low pressure, there is no absorption (and accordingly no
change in absorption); at high vapor pressures no light reaches
the detector, and there is no signal also. In both cases, the
orientation may be quite large, but the method fails to reveal it.

It is quite clear that the position of this curve on the pressure
axis must depend on the thickness of the cell. Indeed, one
finds the optimum pressure to be around 10^{-6} mm (for Na) in a 5
mm thick cell, whereas it is in the vicinity of 10^{-5} mm for a 7
mm thick cell. So, with thin cells, optical pumping can be studied
at fairly high vapor pressures. In a similar way, two isotopes
may be present in the same cell, but with different abundances.
The curve for the most abundant isotope will have its maximum
at a lower temperature than the less abundant one, and the relative intensities of the resonances of the two isotopes depend on
the oven temperature, etc.

We feel it is very much worth-while to investigate optical
pumping at high vapor pressures in view of the possible applications. For instance, the total number of oriented atoms may increase sufficiently to make an optically pumped maser possible.

It may also prove feasible to create a measurable nuclear orientation in a buffer gas like ^{3}He through collisions with optically oriented alkali atoms.

Another method of orienting atoms is electron exchange.[16] If one takes a mixture of two alkali metals A and B and orients A by optical pumping, one finds that some orientation is transferred to B.

A lot of work has been done using this technique which is very useful when B cannot be pumped directly (because the resonance line does not fall in a convenient region, etc.).

One interesting case is when B is a free electron.[17] The whole process of electron exchange should be investigated in more detail than it has been so far — relaxation times, exchange cross sections, and in general the dynamics of optical pumping should be studied in particular under those circumstances when the pressures of A and B are very different.

When the ground state of the atom is diamagnetic, $m_F = m_I$, optical pumping results in nuclear orientation (or alignment); this has been done successfully[11] with the ^{199}Hg and ^{201}Hg nuclei and there is every reason to believe that radioactive species can be studied in this way. One can safely predict developments in this direction. I will not talk about other applications of optical pumping like gas masers, optical masers, atomic clocks, etc., since they are being discussed in subsequent papers.[18]

On the other hand, a lot of speculation[19] has centered, in late years, on the possibility of extending optical pumping techniques to the study of paramagnetic impurities in crystals at low temperatures. Optical detection of magnetic resonance in ground states and in excited states is perfectly feasible, if one takes advantage of the favorable Boltzmann distribution at liquid helium temperatures. However, upsetting the Boltzmann distribution through optical pumping will be far more difficult.

In all cases where optical pumping has proved effective, the oscillator strength of the lines used was close to 1. This means both that the absorption probability per atom in the cell was very large, and that a large light output (several watts) could be obtained from the pumping light source at the proper wavelength.

At the same time, one had to fight relaxation times which were around 1 sec in the case of Hg (nuclear orientation) or 10^{-4} sec for the alkali metals (without buffer gas).

Our experience is that one cannot afford to lose too much on either count. Thus, it is safe to assume that oscillator strength and relaxation time should not be too far off the above values when one tries the solid state case.

The problem of relaxation times (in the ground state) in solids has been studied in detail and values which are not too short can be found in the iron group, in Gd, Eu, or in F centers. But the oscillator strengths of *sharp* absorption lines of paramagnetic ions are smaller than 1 by orders of magnitude, and proper pumping light sources do not exist (in the very favorable case of ruby it has been possible to have a light output of 0.1 watt on the fluorescence line), so that one is at a great disadvantage on both points.

On the other hand, some broad bands have oscillator strengths which are reasonably large (but still usually much smaller than 1). One must look then at the detail of the optical pumping cycle.

As a rule, one can expect thermalization in the excited state (this is already an unfavorable feature at low temperatures when the ground state relaxation times have a reasonable value). At room temperature, therefore, one can expect the atoms to go back to the Zeeman sublevels of the ground state at the same rate — usually through radiationless processes.

The pumping will then follow a pattern similar to the one analyzed previously in the case of an alkali metal in the presence of a buffer gas at high pressure — *one must pump the ground state sublevels at different rates*. At this point, one finds that very little is known about the following question: when a paramagnetic ion absorbs polarized light in a broad band, do the ground state sublevels absorb differently? In fact the situation is not even satisfactory in the case of the great majority of the sharp absorption or fluorescence lines.

We feel that a considerable amount of work must be done before one can say whether optical pumping can succeed on paramagnetic impurities in crystals. Each case will require a detailed study. A great theoretical effort to understand the spectra and the Zeeman patterns is needed. Transition probabilities should be calculated and measured, and relaxation processes in excited states should be investigated.

REFERENCES

1. F. Bitter, Phys. Rev. *76*, 833 (1949).
2. J. Brossel, A. Kastler, C.R. Acad. Sci. *229*, 1213 (1949).
3. A. Kastler, J. Phys. Rad. *11*, 255 (1950).
4. See A. Schawlow's paper in this volume.
5. W. E. Lamb, Proc. Phys. Soc. *A14*, 19 (1951).
6. J. Brossel and F. Bitter, Phys. Rev. *86*, 308 (1952).
7. H. G. Dehmelt, Phys. Rev. *103*, 1125 (1956).
   J. C. Pebay-Peyroula *et al.*, C.R. Acad. Sci. *244*, 57 (1957) and *245*, 840 (1957).
8. Many additional references can be found in the review article by W. A. Runciman, Reports on Progress in Physics *21*, 30 (1958).
9. J. E. Wertz, P. Auzins, Phys. Rev. *106*, 484 (1957).
   J. E. Griffiths, J. W. Orton, Proc. Phys. Soc. *A22*, 947 (1959).
10. Many references will be found in the following review articles:
    A. Kastler, Proc. Phys. Soc. *A17*, 853 (1954); Suppl. Nuovo cimento *6*, 1148 (1957); J.O.S.A. *47*, 460 (1957).
    R. H. Sands and P. A. Franken, *A Bibliography of Optical Pumping and some Allied Methods,* University of Michigan Press.
11. B. Cagnac, J. Brossel, A. Kastler, C.R. Acad. Sci. *246*, 1827 (1958).
12. See for instance, W. Franzen, Bull. Am. Phys. Soc. II, *4*, 259 (1959), where some references to previous work are given.
13. J. Brossel, J. Margerie, A. Kastler, C.R. Acad. Sci. *241*, 865 (1955).
    P. L. Bender, thesis, Princeton University (1956).
14. C. Cohen-Tannouoji *et al.*, C.R. Acad. Sci. *244*, 1027 (1957). See also the article by P. L. Bender in this volume.
15. H. G. Dehmelt, Phys. Rev. *105*, 1487 (1957).
16. H. G. Dehmelt, J. Phys. Rad. *19*, 797 (1958).
17. H. G. Dehmelt, Phys. Rev. *109*, 381 (1958).
18. See the corresponding articles in this volume.
19. Some experimental work also, see G. Series and M. J. Taylor, J. Phys. Rad. *19*, 901 (1958).

DISCUSSION

R. H. DICKE: Dr. Brossel has given a nice description of the optical pumping techniques which produce a population difference. It is also possible to obtain strong resonance phenomena by producing not a population difference but phase relations between states, the phase relation being destroyed by a microwave transition. Mr. C. Alley of Princeton has detected such strong transitions in rubidium vapor.

A HONIG: A scheme which employs optical transitions to produce *phase incoherence* resulting in detection of the optical transitions is being tried by us. An electron in a ground S state is fast passaged. The maintenance of coherence in the transverse plane is evidenced by the reversed magnetization. If, however, an optical transition to a p state is excited within a time of the order of (or less than) the fast passaging time, the transverse magnetization will be dephased because of the different hyperfine field to which the electron is subjected in the p state, provided the lifetime of the p state exceeds $1/\gamma \, \delta H$, where δH is the difference in hyperfine fields in the s and p states. In phosphorus-doped silicon, which is one of the substances we are trying, this lifetime must exceed 10^{-9} second. The optical transitions are in the infrared.

OPTICAL EFFECTS ON F-CENTER SPIN RESONANCE AT LOW TEMPERATURES*

J. LAMBE AND J. BAKER

Willow Run Laboratories, University of Michigan

THE SUBJECT of the interaction of light with spin systems has been of considerable interest from the point of view of possible maser applications. Effects which come under the general heading of "optical pumping" may permit one to use light sources as the pump in maser systems. Such effects have been extensively studied in gases, but the work in solids is much less extensive.

In this paper we shall discuss measurements made on a system consisting of F-centers in KCl. Such centers have well established spin-resonance and optical properties. Of special interest is the fact that the F-center has very strong optical absorption and a long spin lattice relaxation time at $4\,°K$. A value of 15 seconds has been reported.[1]

Basically, what we wish to do is to alter the spin temperature of the F-centers by irradiation with F-band light. This is a crude but simple way to see if optical pumping will occur. It should be noted that the optical excited states are very broad in energy and one probably would not be able to do the more elegant type of experiments such as are carried out in sodium vapor. Thus it is doubtful that one could optically invert the spin population in the F-center case.

The question of the nature of the excited electronic states of the F-center is of fundamental importance in determining whether spin-flips can occur in the optical excitation process. This is dependent on the mixing of spin states in the excited state.

*This research was supported by Project MICHIGAN (administered by the U. S. Army Signal Corps).

The usual picture is to consider the first excited state as a p state and calculations have been made of the energy of this state. No calculations appear to have been made on the spin orbit coupling in the excited state. For our purposes we assume a situation analogous to an alkali metal atom with broadened energy levels. On this basis, significant spin-optical interaction would exist.

It should be noted that in addition to spin-flipping occurring during optical transitions, we have the problem of what happens to the spin of the F-center due to the local "heating" of the F-center. That is, the F-center absorbs 2.5 ev of energy and emits about 1 ev as light.[2] The rest of the energy is coupled to the lattice surrounding the F-center. The surrounding atoms vibrate quite strongly and the F-center finally cools off. This process may increase the temperature of the spin system. Little is known about such a process and the present type of measurement may aid in understanding such effects.

EXPERIMENTAL METHOD

The apparatus used consisted of a magnetic resonance spectrometer operating at about 9400 MC and an arc light source with appropriate filters to select a band of radiation in the F-center wavelength region.

The microwave cavity had the dimensions of standard X-band waveguide and was operated in the TE_{012} mode. The cavity was made of a ceramic type of material which was silver coated. A window was cut in the broad face of the cavity to permit illumination of the sample (Fig. 1).

It was necessary to use superhetrodyne detection since small microwave power was used to minimize saturation problems. The power level used was between .05 and .005 microwatt. This was still somewhat excessive, but reasonable data could be taken under the conditions.

Crystals used were of commercially available KCl which were cleaved to about 3 mm thickness and 1 cm on a side. These crystals were x-rayed for about an hour to produce a peak F-band optical density of about 1.2 at room temperature. The crystals were kept in the dark or in red light until immersion in liquid

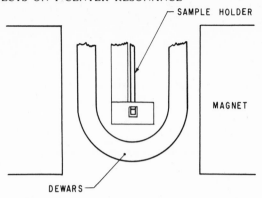

Fig. 1. Apparatus used for optical-spin resonance experiment
Cavity and sample are immersed in liquid helium. Dewar system is
slit silvered to permit sample illumination. The cavity is shown with
the connecting waveguide.

helium.   It is necessary to avoid growth of M- and R-bands
which are known to affect the F-center luminescence.

The crystals were immersed in liquid helium and on into the
cavity.   The spin resonance signal was then observed with light
on and off the crystal.

A Zr arc used together with the optical system give an illumination intensity of about 1 milliwatt/cm^2 at the crystal.   The
light had to pass through the dewar system (the dewars were slit
silvered) and onto the crystal.

Experimental Results
The first runs were made to simply observe the spin resonance of the F-center.   At this point it was noted that numerous
other spin resonance signals were present from the sample.   A
typical spectrum is shown in Fig. 2.   The F-center resonance is
distorted due to saturation effects.   The other lines are present
in the KCl even before X-raying.   These signals were found in
commercially available KCl from 3 different sources.   We do not
know the origin of this spectrum as yet, but these lines serve the
useful purpose of a lattice thermometer for our experiment.   They
have a spin-lattice relaxation time which is much shorter than the
F-center so they can function as a thermometer for the lattice.

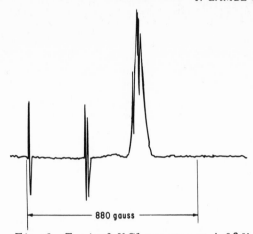

Fig. 2. Typical KCl spectra at 4.2°K
The *F*-center absorption is distorted. The other narrow line spectra is
angular dependent.

The effect of light on the crystal is shown in Fig. 3. Here the
microwave bridge was adjusted to observe dispersion signals.
The *F*-center signal is distorted, but it is still useful as a population measurement. It is seen that the *F*-center resonance
signal decreases by about 50 percent. The "thermometer signal"
is essentially unaffected. From this, we conclude that the spin

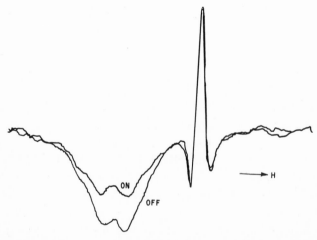

Fig. 3. Dispersion signal obtained with light on and light off
The signal to the high field side of the *F*-center is used as a thermometer.

population of the F-center system has been altered. The effect is equivalent to a $4\,^{\circ}$K increase in temperature.

After the light was turned off, the F-center resonance returned to its original form. This required about 1 minute to remove all trace of the light effect. This is what one should expect on the basis of the long spin lattice relaxation time of the F-center.

CONCLUSION

As seen in the foregoing sections, an effect is observed on the F-center spin resonance signal. It is of interest to see what a crude calculation would predict as to the expected magnitude of the effect.

We are dealing with a system containing about 10^{16} F-centers which is absorbing 1 milliwatt of green light. This means about 2×10^{15} quanta per second are being absorbed. The situation can be analyzed as follows:

Let n_1 = number of spins in lower state

n_2 = number of spins in upper state

F = rate of spin flipping by light per center

then

$$\frac{dn_1}{dt} = -Fn_1 + Fn_2 - w_{12}n_1 + w_{21}n_2$$

$$\frac{dn_2}{dt} = -Fn_2 + Fn_1 + w_{12}n_1 - w_{21}n_2$$

Let $\Delta n = n_1 - n_2$ and,

τ = spin lattice relaxation time (15 sec)

then we have

$$\frac{d\,\Delta n}{dt} = -2F\Delta n - \frac{1}{\tau}(\Delta n - \Delta n_0)$$

An estimate of F is given by

$$F = \frac{2 \times 10^{15}\ \text{photons/sec}}{10^{16}\ \text{centers}} \times \tfrac{1}{2}$$

the factor of $\tfrac{1}{2}$ is a statement of the assumption that the optically excited center has equal probability of going back to either spin state. Then we have

$$\frac{d\Delta n}{dt} = -\frac{1}{5}\Delta n - \frac{1}{15}(\Delta n - \Delta n_0)$$

at equilibrium $\dfrac{d\Delta n}{dt} = 0$, so that

$$\Delta n = \frac{1}{4}\Delta n_0$$

Thus the observed effect is of the proper order of magnitude. The data is not good enough to provide a severe test of the assumed model.

The local heating effect may also be contributing to the observed spin temperature effect. An interesting experiment would be to see if the nuclear spin temperature is affected by the fact that nuclei are set in rapid motion in the neighborhood of the paramagnetic center. In this way, more information might be obtained on local heating around the F-center.

It should be pointed out that one has little hope of optically inverting the F-center spin system. Even so, the fact that one can heat a spin system optically has an important implication for optical pumping in solids. A very interesting system could be achieved by placing such a heated spin system in contact with a three-level maser system. By matching levels 1 and 3 to the hot two-level system, cross relaxation effects could tend to saturate the transition between levels 1 and 3. Maser action could then be achieved between levels 2 and 3. This would be of special interest in cases where the separation between 1 and 3 is very large since in this case, optical "spin heating" becomes more feasible. Thus optical "spin heating" may be used where the usual optical pumping inversion techniques are not applicable.

REFERENCES

1. G. A. Noble, Bull. Am. Phys. Soc. II *4*, 326 (1959).
2. Botden, van Doorn, and Haven, Philips Research Reports *9*, 469 (1954).

E. Z. HAHN: Have you considered the effect of the optical pumping on the T_1 of the F center system?

J. LAMBE: The effect can be observed when light is removed if the observation is done immediately. Then light per se need not be present when the EPR is observed. Thus the effect is not due to a light effect on T_1. Such an effect may exist, however.

H. H. THEISSING: Since unpolarized light was used there could not have been any redistribution of the sublevel populations as intended by genuine optical pumping.

J. LAMBE: It would be better to call it optical spin heating, since the detailed mechanisms whereby spin inversion could be produced may not be possible in this case.

PARAMAGNETIC RESONANCE DETECTION OF THE OPTICAL EXCITATION OF AN INFRARED STIMULABLE PHOSPHOR

R. S. TITLE

Research Laboratory, International Business Machines Corporation, Poughkeepsie, New York

OPTICAL EXCITATION of a phosphor containing paramagnetic activators may cause a change in the paramagnetic resonance absorption of the phosphors. Hershberger,[1] Low,[2] and Prokhorov[3] have attempted to observe such changes in inorganic phosphors without success. In this talk, the observation of the optical excitation of the infrared stimulable phosphor SrS : Eu, Sm, using paramagnetic resonance techniques, will be described.

The physical properties of this phosphor have been investigated, the most extensive investigations being those of Keller *et al.*[4] The property that is of concern to us in this talk is the ability of this phosphor to store energy when irradiated with ultraviolet or blue light. The stored energy may subsequently be released by irradiation with infrared or orange wavelengths. The lifetime of the phosphor while storing energy is long, being in the order of years.

A simplified band-theory model was proposed by Keller[4] to explain the storage and other observed properties of this phosphor. This is illustrated in Fig. 1. Europium is normally present in the SrS lattice as Eu^{2+} and samarium as Sm^{3+}. Excitation with ultraviolet radiation corresponds to SrS base absorption. An electron hole pair is formed, the electron being trapped at the Sm^{3+} site which becomes as designated in the figure $(Sm^{3+}) \cdot e^{-}$. The hole is trapped at the europium site which becomes as a result Eu^{3+}. Excitation with blue radiation ionizes

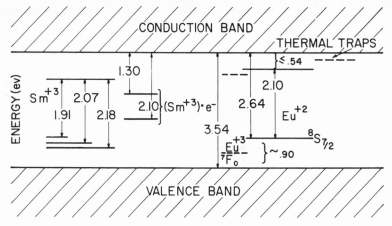

Fig. 1. The energy levels of SrS : Eu, Sm

the Eu^{2+} directly to Eu^{3+} and the electron is subsequently trapped at the Sm^{3+} site. In the case of either ultraviolet or blue excitation, the net effect has been to convert Eu^{2+} to Eu^{3+} and Sm^{3+} to Sm^{2+}. The Eu^{2+} has a $(4f)^7$ configuration and a $^8S_{7/2}$ ground state. The Eu^{3+} ground state is ^7F_o which is non-magnetic. Excitation with ultraviolet or blue radiation should therefore result in a diminution of the Eu^{2+} paramagnetic spectrum.

Release of the stored energy is accomplished by ionizing the $(Sm^{3+}) \cdot e^-$ site. Ionization of this site is possible in two ways and hence there are two wavelengths, 970 $m\mu$ and 590 $m\mu$, that may be used to exhaust the stored energy of the phosphor.

A diminution in the magnitude of the Eu^{2+} paramagnetic spectrum when optically excited has been observed for a SrS : Eu, Sm phosphor containing equal amounts of europium and samarium (0.02 molar percent).

The sample in the form of a powder was placed on a 0.9 by 0.4 inch teflon button. This button was placed along the median plane (the region of maximum H_1 field) of a rectangular cavity operating in a TE_{102} mode. Irradiation of the sample was through the end of the cavity which instead of the usual solid end plate, had a 96 × 96 mesh screen. An Asram Xenon arc lamp XBO 1001 combined with a Bausch and Lomb 33-86-40 grating monochromotor were used to irradiate the sample. Measurements were carried out at room temperature with a Varian Associates 4500 EPR spectrometer.

A plot of the relative stored energy of the phosphor against exciting wavelength is given in Fig. 2. The curve was obtained in the following way. The paramagnetic spectrum of Eu^{2+} in the exhausted phosphor was plotted. The phosphor was brought to the exhausted state by irradiation with 970 mμ light for four minutes. To determine the relative stored energy for a particular exciting wavelength, the phosphor was first irradiated with that wavelength for four minutes. The light was shut off and the Eu^{2+} paramagnetic resonance spectrum replotted, the diminution in its intensity being proportional to the stored energy in the phosphor. Before determining the relative stored energy at a second exciting wavelength, the phosphor was once again exhausted with 980 mμ light.

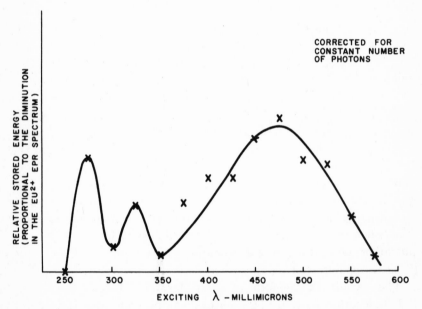

Fig. 2. Relative stored energy as measured by the diminution in the Eu^{2+} *paramagnetic spectrum plotted against exciting wavelength*

The heights in Fig. 2 have been corrected for constant number of exciting photons. The results obtained using the paramagnetic resonance absorption agree favorable with those found by Keller, Mapes, and Cheroff,[4] who used as a measure of the stored energy the intensity of emitted light during exhaustion of the phosphor by 970 mμ radiation.

As a measure of the efficiency of optical excitation, it may be noted that at the peak in Fig. 2 at 475 mμ, the Eu^{2+} paramagnetic spectrum decreased by 13 percent. It is planned to measure the variation of efficiency with varying europium and samarium concentrations and with variation of light intensity incident on the sample. Experiments will also be carried out at liquid helium temperatures in order to observe the change in the Sm paramagnetic spectrum.

It was found, as had been observed optically,[4] that 590 mμ light was equally effective as 970 mμ light in exhausting the phosphor.

In conclusion, the use of paramagnetic resonance absorption to detect the optical excitation provides an independent verification of the simplified band-theory model proposed by Keller[4] to explain the physical properties of the phosphor.

The author wishes to acknowledge the encouragement and interest of Dr. S. P. Keller and Dr. W. V. Smith and wishes to thank Mr. J. Kucza for material preparation.

REFERENCES

1. W. D. Hershberger, J. Chem. Phys. *24*, 168 (1956).
   W. D. Hershberger and H. N. Liefer, Phys. Rev. *88*, 714 (1952).
2. B. Bleaney and W. Low, Proc. Phys. Soc. *A68*, 55 (1955).
   W. Low, Phys. Rev. *98*, 426 (1955).
3. A. A. Manenkov, A. M. Prokhorov, Trapeznikova, and M. V. Fok, Optika i Spectroskopia (USSR) *2*, 470 (1957).
4. S. P. Keller, J. E. Mapes, and G. Cheroff, Phys. Rev. *108*, 663 (1957).
   S. P. Keller and G. D. Pettit, Phys. Rev. *111*, 1533 (1958).
   S. P. Keller, Phys. Rev. *113*, 1415 (1959).

DISCUSSION

L. WILCOX: Have you observed changes in the absorption coefficient as the phosphor reaches a saturated state? Assuming the mechanism is known, would this not be a simpler means of studying the relaxation effects caused by infrared irradiation of the phosphor?

R. S. TITLE: We have plotted the change of paramagnetic resonance absorption against time and noted that it dropped off, achieving its final value in about a minute. The optical work you suggest has been done by Keller. The purpose of our work was to verify his conclusions using paramagnetic resonance techniques.

A. M. PROKHOROV: In the Lebedev Physical Institute, we examined the phosphor SrS : Eu, Sm and observed diminution of about the same amount in the Eu^{2+} paramagnetic spectrum after excitation.

W. LOW: The phosphor SrS: Eu, Sm shows a number of peculiar aspects:

1. The microwave transitions are fairly sharp, 4–6 gauss wide, and symmetrical. This means that the second order corrections of the form $\dfrac{a^2}{g\beta H}$ must be small and, therefore, the initial splitting small. On the other hand, the optical absorption band is very wide. One would have expected the optical transition, if it arose within the f^F configuration, to be very sharp. It is, therefore, likely that this transition is to the conduction band.

2. The paramagnetic resonance spectrum and optical spectrum show different intensities as the Sm to Eu ratio is varied. This should be studied in more detail.

3. If SrS phosphor is irradiated with neutrons as X-rays, new paramagnetic resonance lines are found which are radiation-induced centers.

R. S. TITLE: We intend also to measure the efficiency of ionization as a function of relative europium and samarium concentration.

SOME MICROWAVE-OPTICAL EXPERIMENTS IN RUBY*

I. WIEDER

Westinghouse Research Laboratories, Pittsburgh, Pennsylvania

IN ORDER to extend the technique of optical pumping to solids, it is convenient to employ a solid system with sharp optical lines.[1] One such material is ruby, which consists of Cr^{+++} ions in a host crystal of Al_2O_3. The optical spectrum of ruby has been studied extensively[2],[3],[4],[5],[6] and includes two sharp lines denoted by R_1 and R_2 which appear in both absorption and emission. The Zeeman effect of these lines was also observed and has recently been investigated both theoretically and experimentally in detail.[7],[8] The results of the above mentioned work are shown in the high field transition diagrams of Fig. 1. The expected zero field intensities were obtained by assuming[9] that the optical matrix elements are magnetic field independent and adding the appropriate values for the degenerate levels. It is apparent that many possibilities exist for preferentially depopulating one of the sublevels of the ground state. For example, a mixture of R_1 and R_2 radiation polarized with the electric vector along the optic axis can be expected to preferentially depopulate the $\pm \frac{3}{2}$ level.

The present experiments were performed at about $2°K$ (below the lambda point of liquid helium) to lengthen spin lattice relaxation times and to eliminate bubbles in the optical path. At this temperature, the R absorption widths are about 0.6 cm^{-1} for pink ruby.[8] Although broad spectrum sources emit about 0.01 watt of light energy in this bandwidth at 6900 Å, there is an associated extraneous background light even with narrow-band

*This research was supported by Contract AF 33(616)-5258 with Wright Air Development Center.

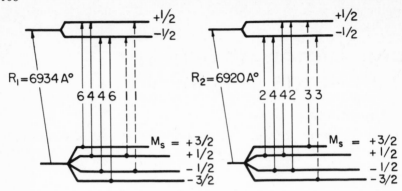

Experimentally verified high field transition
probabilities

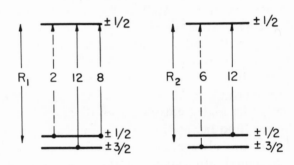

Projected zero field transition probabilities

Fig. 1. Transition probabilities for the R lines in ruby

The dotted and solid lines refer to the cases where the exciting light
has its electric vector parallel and perpendicular, respectively, to the
optic axis.

optical filters. This background light causes undesirable heating of the sample and excludes optical detection methods.

It is apparent that a source of "resonance radiation" can
overcome both of the above difficulties. In the case of ruby, the
R lines appear as fluorescent lines upon absorption of light by
the Cr^{+++} ions in the two broad bands denoted in Fig. 2 by U
and Y. The relaxation from the broad excited states to the
sharp levels denoted[7] by ^2E is radiationless, and the decay to
the ground state has a lifetime of milliseconds.[10] This photo-

luminescent effect was utilized in the design of a solid state
light source which emits a total of about 0.1 watt in each of the
R lines. The details of this source have been described elsewhere.[11]

The experimental arrangement is shown schematically in Fig.
2. Sample I, which is utilized as the source, is irradiated with
light from a tungsten source and undergoes the photoluminescent
cycle mentioned above. The R fluorescence from sample I is
collected, polarized, and focused on sample II, which is in the
cavity of a microwave spectrometer. Due to the temperature dependence of the R frequency,[3],[8] it is necessary to keep sample
I at liquid nitrogen temperature or cooler so that its R emission
frequencies overlap the R absorption frequencies of sample II at
liquid helium temperature. In general, optical pumping disturbs
the equilibrium populations of the sublevels of the ground state
and can be detected by using ordinary paramagnetic resonance

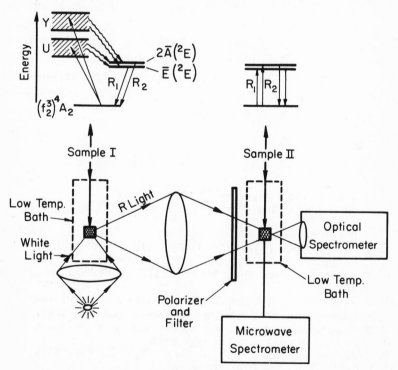

Fig. 2. Microwave-optical experiment in ruby

techniques. In this case, the R light is chopped, and a corresponding time varying microwave absorption signal can be synchronously detected. The expected signal-to-noise ratio using this method is about $\frac{5}{1}$ with the present apparatus, so that the absence of a signal cannot be taken too seriously.

However, in order to verify that the conditions necessary for optical pumping actually exist in solids, another experiment with a considerably larger expected signal-to-noise ratio was attempted. The same physical components are utilized, but in this case amplitude-modulated microwaves (at a frequency less than the reciprocal spin lattice relaxation time) are used to saturate the ground state paramagnetic resonance, and the signal should appear as a modulation on the transmitted R light. For ruby at $2°K$, there is a 13 percent alignment in the ground state, and resonance saturation destroys the alignment. This shifts some of the centers into levels with different optical absorption strengths and should change the total R absorption. For the experimental setup described, along with a monochrometer for singling out the individual R lines, the expected signal would be about 100 times the measured rms noise level at the output of the phase sensitive detector. Nevertheless, no signal was observed. This negative result is not understood as yet and further work is in progress.

REFERENCES

1. A. Kastler, Proc. Phys. Soc. *A 67*, 853 (1954).
2. O. Deutchbein, Ann. Physik (5) *14*, 712, 729 (1932); (5) *20*, 828 (1934).
3. K. S. Gibson, Phys. Rev. *8*, 38 (1916).
4. H. Lehman, Ann. Physik (5) *19*, 99 (1934).
5. J. Becquerel, C. R. Acad. Sci. *151*, 981 (1910).
6. B. V. Thosar, Phys. Rev. *60*, 616 (1941); J. Chem. Phys. *10*, 246 (1942).
7. S. Sugano and Y. Tanabe, J. Phys. Soc. Japan *13*, 880 (1958).
8. S. Sugano and I. Tsujikawa, J. Phys. Soc. Japan *13*, 899 (1958).
9. This assumption is valid only for the case where the external magnetic field is parallel to the optic axis.
10. G. H. Dieke and L. A. Hall, J. Chem. Phys. *27*, 465 (1957).
11. I. Wieder, Rev. Sci. Instr. (in press).

S. FONER: What sort of field dependence would you require for the relaxation time T_1?

I. WIEDER: The field dependence of T_1 does not affect the experiment. A field dependence of the optical transition probabilities would be critical.

N. BLOEMBERGEN: Why is the optical pumping in ruby not carried out in a magnetic field with circularly polarized light?

I. WIEDER: It is not practical to pass large quantities of circularly polarized light through an optically active crystal. This follows from the fact that the only allowed direction is exactly along the optic axis.

W. LOW: If I recall correctly, Tanabe and Sugano have used a perturbation theory for the axial field and spin-orbit contribution to the splitting of the two red levels at 14,200 cm^{-1}. It is possible that, if the complete matrix including spin-orbit coupling and axial field for the d^3 configuration is solved, this might modify the transition probabilities somewhat. It should also be noted that Al_2O_3 has no center of symmetry and therefore other configurations of the type d^2p and d^2f may be admixed.

ATOMIC FREQUENCY STANDARDS AND CLOCKS

P. L. Bender

National Bureau of Standards, Washington, D. C.

THERE HAS recently been a great deal of interest in the high stability and accuracy obtainable with atomic frequency standards and clocks. Scientific interest has been stimulated by the recent ether drag experiments[1] using ammonia beam masers and by the possibility of using an atomic clock in a satellite to check on the gravitational frequency shift predicted by the general theory of relativity.[2] The need for high-precision frequency and time measurements in satellite and missile tracking, in space and terrestrial communication systems, and in navigation has provided impetus for rapid developments in the field.

Three types of atomic standards appear today to be the most promising for the immediate future. They are the cesium beam, the ammonia maser, and the alkali vapor frequency standard. The first two types are discussed at length in other conference papers and their general characteristics will be assumed known. However, a description of one kind of alkali vapor frequency standard* will be given in order to facilitate comparison with the cesium beam and ammonia maser instruments.

RUBIDIUM VAPOR STANDARDS

Rubidium vapor frequency standards are now being constructed at a number of laboratories. They are based on the hyperfine transition at 6835 Mc/s in the ground state of Rb^{87}. A schematic

---

*Alkali vapor frequency standards using optical pumping and Doppler reduction techniques were suggested by R. H. Dicke. The earliest experimental work on them was done with rubidium by T. R. Carver, and the first optical detection of the transitions was achieved by Arditi and Carver with sodium.

diagram of the apparatus used at the National Bureau of Standards and the Naval Research Laboratory[3] to observe this transition is shown in Fig. 1. Light from a rubidium discharge was passed through a Rb^{85} filter bulb and then to the sample. The intensity of the light absorbed and spontaneously reemitted by the Rb^{87} in the sample was observed as a function of the applied microwave frequency.

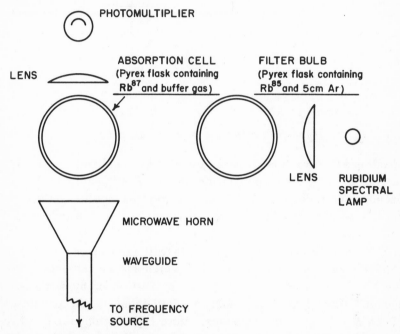

PHOTOMULTIPLIER

LENS

ABSORPTION CELL
(Pyrex flask containing
Rb^{87} and buffer gas)

FILTER BULB
(Pyrex flask containing
Rb^{85} and 5cm Ar)

LENS   RUBIDIUM
SPECTRAL
LAMP

MICROWAVE HORN

WAVEGUIDE

TO FREQUENCY
SOURCE

Fig. 1. Schematic diagram of apparatus for optical detection of the ground state hyperfine transition in Rb^{87} vapor

Fig. 2 shows an idealized picture of the hyperfine components of either of the two main rubidium resonance lines at 7800 and 7947 Å. Excited state hyperfine splittings are neglected. The Rb^{85} absorption lines in the filter, broadened and perhaps somewhat shifted by the presence of another gas, absorb one of the two Rb^{87} hyperfine components more strongly than the other. The light reaching the sample thus consists mainly of component (b). Atoms in the $F = 1$ sublevel are therefore preferentially raised to the excited states. Since the atoms return by

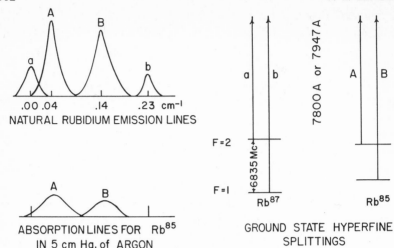

Fig. 2. Hyperfine structure of rubidium resonance lines

spontaneous emission to both ground state sublevels with similar rates, an excess population in the $F = 2$ sublevel is produced. As a result, the optical absorption coefficient for the sample decreases, since fewer atoms are in the state where they can absorb component (b).

The equilibrium level populations will depend on the rate of photon absorption and the rate at which atoms can return from the $F = 2$ to the $F = 1$ sublevel by relaxation or by some other means. When hyperfine transitions are induced, the population of the $F = 1$ sublevel increases. More light is absorbed and reradiated by the sample, and the photomultiplier output increases.

For a compact unit it is desirable to place the sample in a cylindrical TE_{011} mode cavity with holes cut in the ends and to detect changes at resonance in the amount of light absorbed by the sample. The amount of transmitted light can be measured by a silicon solar cell. Satisfactory rubidium light sources have been run on three watts of power and transistorized versions running on one watt or less should be possible. The remainder of the apparatus, exclusive of temperature control, can be run on about one-half watt. This would include, for instance, a quartz crystal oscillator at 4.996 Mc/s, a frequency multiplier to 59.95 Mc/s, a crystal harmonic generator giving the final factor 114 multiplication, and a phase modulation and servo system to lock the oscillator to the center of the hyperfine resonance line.

PRACTICAL LIMITATIONS OF PRESENT ATOMIC STANDARDS

A discussion of the precisions obtainable with passive atomic standards requires some assumptions about how well one can pick out the center of the resonance line. I will assume that with care and a reasonable signal-to-noise ratio one can pick out the center of a symmetrical line to 1 part in 10^3, and that any higher stability requires experimental demonstration.

For the cesium beam frequency standard, the primary limitation comes from transit time broadening of the resonance line. Essen and Parry[4] in England have succeeded in achieving an accuracy of 1 part in 10^{10} using a Ramsey cavity separation of about 50 cm and a line width of 350 cycles. For the National Company Atomichron, a commercially available version of the cesium beam standard, the separation between Ramsey cavities is about 100 cm and the linewidth is 120 cycles. The signal-to-noise ratio is about 100 for a one second time constant. This should permit a stability of 1 part in 10^{11}, but there are some additional difficulties with phase shifts between the cavities, frequency synthesis, stability of the flywheel oscillator, etc. Currently available models have shown an accuracy[5] of about 2 parts in 10^{10} but have frequently given day-to-day stabilities over periods of weeks or more of several parts in 10^{11}.

A new model of the Atomichron which will be available soon is expected to have an accuracy of about 5 parts in 10^{11} and a day-to-day stability of 1 part in 10^{11} or better. In this model, the R.F. structure has been carefully designed to minimize phase shift errors. Direct multiplication from an oscillator at about 5.4 Mc/s is used to avoid frequency synthesis difficulties, with synthesis of an even frequency output being done in a separate frequency translation unit. Longer beam tubes with cavity separations of 3 to 4 meters should be in operation soon at the National Physical Laboratory in England and at the Boulder Laboratories of the National Bureau of Standards. Linewidths of 50 cycles have already been achieved with the NPL apparatus. It thus appears that accuracies of a few parts in 10^{11} may be attainable within the next year or so. Several proposals for still longer apparatuses have also been made. The accuracy of comparison with astronomical time[6] is at present limited mainly by the accuracy of the astronomical measurements, and this will apparently continue to be the case for some time.

For alkali vapor frequency standards, the linewidth limitations are not as well understood as for the cesium beam. In order to reduce disorientation by collision with the wall, one has to have a suitable buffer gas in the sample or a non-disorienting coating on the wall. If the phase of the R.F. field is uniform over the sample or if the diffusion rate of alkali atoms through the buffer gas is low, the Doppler breadth will also be greatly reduced.[7] With a completely non-disorienting buffer gas or wall coating, one could hope to obtain arbitrarily narrow lines. Dehmelt actually showed that one could obtain relaxation times of the order of a few tenths of a second with an inert buffer gas[8] and seconds with an eicosane wall coating. Since then linewidths as low as three cycles have been obtained for Zeeman transitions in rubidium vapor.

Despite the demonstrated long relaxation times, it has not been possible to obtain correspondingly narrow hyperfine transition lines. For cesium, the narrowest lines obtained have been 40 cycles with neon or helium as buffer gas and 120 cycles with argon. For rubidium-87, linewidths of 20 cycles at 6835 Mc/s were obtained with neon or helium as the buffer gas. In all cases the observed relaxation times were much longer than would correspond to the observed linewidths. For rubidium in neon, the linewidth remained about 20 cycles over a range of pressures from 1 cm Hg to 20 cm Hg.

In addition to broadening the lines, collisions with the buffer gas or wall coating can also cause shifts in the frequency at which the transition occurs.[9] The shifts are of the order of 1 part in 10^6 per cm Hg of buffer gas, with the lighter gases giving positive shifts and the heavier gases negative ones. One can make mixtures of buffer gases which will give very small pressure shifts. However, since sealed samples are used in the frequency standards, the important quantity is the change in frequency with temperature. The shifts in frequency with temperature for sealed glass samples were found to be of different signs for different buffer gases, but not proportional to the corresponding pressure changes. Samples containing rubidium-87 in a 50-50 mixture of argon and neon at a pressure of 1 cm Hg were found to have a temperature coefficient of only 3 parts in 10^{11} per degree Centigrade near room temperature, and still smaller temperature coefficients should be possible.

The frequency shifts can be thought of as being caused by successive small relative phase changes in the coefficients of the $M_F = 0$ parts of the alkali wave function. In each collision, the relative phase is changed somewhat by the integrated effect of the shift in hyperfine splitting as a function of distance between the atoms. The shift in angular frequency is given by the average phase shift per collision times the number of collisions per second. The average phase shift per collision is found to be of the order of 10^{-3} radians.

The observed linewidths are at present believed to be due to statistical fluctuations in the phase shifts. If σ is the standard deviation of the phase shift per collision and Σ is the standard deviation in the total accumulated phase shift for an observation time T, then $\Sigma \sim \sigma \cdot (nT)^{\frac{1}{2}}$ where n is the number of collisions per second. The observed linewidth will then be given by $\Delta\nu \sim \Sigma/T \sim \sigma \cdot (n/T)^{\frac{1}{2}}$, or $\Delta\nu \propto \sigma \cdot (p/T)^{\frac{1}{2}}$. In the linewidth measurements mentioned above, the observation time T was evidently limited in some cases by diffusion of the alkali atoms into regions of quite different relative R.F. phase, and T was thus proportional to P. This would then give a roughly pressure-independent linewidth, as observed for rubidium in neon. At high enough pressures one would, of course, expect T to be proportional to $1/P$ because of relaxation, and the linewidth would then be proportional to P.

Although one can obtain lines as narrow as 20 cycles with gas cells, it is probably desirable to allow this width to be about doubled by light intensity and R.F. power broadening in order to improve the signal-to-noise ratio. Under these conditions, a signal-to-noise ratio of about 100 has been obtained for a laboratory apparatus with a time constant of .01 sec. For reasonable periods of time, one would thus expect a stability of somewhat better than 1 part in 10^{11}. However, the possibility of changes in the buffer gas pressure or composition must also be considered. The leakage of 10^{-4} mm Hg of nitrogen into the sample, for instance, would cause a frequency shift of 1 part in 10^{11}. Such a large change in buffer gas composition for a carefully prepared sample seems unlikely except over quite long periods of time. The accuracy with which one can determine the unperturbed transition frequency with a gas cell device will, of course, be limited by the need to extrapolate to zero buffer gas pressure. For this reason, alkali vapor devices will probably be much more useful as secondary standards than as primary standards.

For the ammonia maser frequency standard,[10],[11] the limitations are of quite a different nature than for the other types of frequency standards. The existence of unsymmetrical quadrupole structure in the 3,3 transition has been a problem until recently. However, this difficulty has now been overcome by Bonanomi and by Shimoda by using either nitrogen-15 ammonia or the 3,2 transition in natural ammonia.

The largest remaining difficulty is pulling of the transition frequency when the resonant cavity is detuned. The frequency shift is given by

$$\left(\frac{\Delta \nu}{\nu}\right) \sim \left(\frac{Q_C}{Q_L}\right) \cdot \left(\frac{\Delta \nu_C}{\nu_C}\right),$$

where $\Delta \nu_C$ is the error in cavity setting, Q_C is the quality factor of the cavity, and Q_L is the ratio of the frequency to the width of the resonance line when the device is used as a spectrometer. Under normal conditions $(Q_C/Q_L) \sim 10^{-3}$, and thus the requirements on cavity tuning are quite severe even with careful thermostating and the use of low expansion coefficient materials for the cavity. One method which has been used to meet this problem is to couple two cavities together in such a way that the cavity response is quite flat on top.

Recently Bonanomi has achieved a resettability of 3 parts in 10^{11} by using a magnetic modulation method. If a magnetic field of a few gauss is applied when the cavity is detuned, Q_L will be decreased by broadening of the resonance line and the frequency shift will increase. The cavity is swept slowly through resonance and the emitted frequency is measured with respect to another standard alternately with and without the magnetic field present. When the successive measurements agree, the cavity is on resonance and the pulling is very small.

If the effect of cavity pulling is taken care of, the next problem becomes one of Doppler shifts due to running waves in the cavity.[12] For a parallel beam of molecules and conditions well away from saturation, the stimulated emission will take place mainly in the rear part of the cavity and there will be a net flow of power toward the front of the cavity. The Doppler shift will be negative, since the frequency seen by the moving molecules tends to agree with the molecular resonance frequency. For operation near saturation or for a diverging beam, the shift can be of either sign. Mockler has built a double beam maser at Boulder with beams coming in from each end in order to reduce the Doppler shift. He finds that shifts as high as 2 parts in 10^9 can occur when one beam is turned off.[11] However, this experiment needs to be repeated with nitrogen-15 ammonia and with the two beams symmetrized as much as possible. If this is done at several laboratories, with magnetic modulation to adjust the cavity tuning, it seems quite possible that an accuracy of several parts in 10^{11} can be achieved.

A maser, of course, has the advantage that a quartz crystal oscillator is not needed as a flywheel, and that the very short term stability can thus be quite high. Minute-to-minute stabilities of one or two parts in 10^{12} have been demonstrated for two masers beating against each other. For this reason, Mockler has used an ammonia maser to check on the spectral purity of quartz crystal oscillator and frequency multiplier chain outputs. It has also been suggested that it may be necessary to use masers to drive long cesium tubes in order to obtain sufficient spectral purity for use with very narrow resonance lines.

APPLICATIONS

The types of atomic frequency standards which have been discussed actually complement each other quite well. While the long cesium beam tube appears to be the best hope at present for high accuracy, the ammonia maser is the most suitable for short term stability and the alkali vapor devices are promising as portable secondary standards. Which type of standard is most desirable will depend on the intended application.

Recently there has been a demand for rugged frequency standards for use in missile guidance systems. Here the desired stability is of the order of 1 part in 10^{10} for about .1 second averaging times, but the frequency needs to be uniform only for the several minutes of launching. Two types of short cesium beam tubes are being built for this purpose, as well as rubidium vapor devices and ruggedized ammonia masers. For the passive devices, the philosophy has been to broaden the resonance lines in order to improve the signal-to-noise ratio and to permit the use of a short time constant in the feedback loop.

For the gravitational frequency shift experiment, there has not yet been a choice of which type of device will be used. Precision, reliability, and power requirements will be the most crucial factors here, although weight and size will also be important. It has been suggested recently that the experiment could also be done by using a quartz crystal oscillator in a satellite with a highly elliptical orbit.[13] A transponder with provision for frequency subtraction in the satellite could be used to cancel out the first order Doppler shift. The expected shifts should then show up as periodic differences between the frequencies near apogee and near perigee. Accuracies of a few percent in checking the gravitational frequency shift seem possible in the near future with several of the proposed methods.

REFERENCES

1. J. P. Cedarholm, G. F. Bland, B. L. Havens, and C. H. Townes, Phys. Rev. Lett. *1*, 342 (1958).
2. V. L. Ginzburg, JETP (USSR) *30*, 213 (1956); JETP *3*, 136 (1956).
   S. F. Singer, Phys. Rev. *104*, 11 (1956).
   C. Moller, Suppl. Nuovo cimento *6*, 381 (1957).
3. P. L. Bender, E. C. Beaty, and A. R. Chi, Phys. Rev. Lett. *1*, 311 (1958).
4. L. Essen and J. V. L. Parry, Nature *176*, 280 (1955).
   L. Essen and J. V. L. Parry, Phil. Trans. Roy. Soc. A *250*, 45 (1957).

5. L. Essen, J. V. L. Parry, J. H. Holloway, W. A. Mainberger, F. H. Reder, and G. M. R. Winkler, Nature *182*, 41 (1958).
   J. Holloway, W. Mainberger, F. H. Reder, G. M. R. Winkler, L. Essen, and J. V. L. Parry, Proc. IRE *47*, 1730 (1959).
6. W. Markowitz, R. G. Hall, L. Essen, and J. V. L. Parry, Phys. Rev. Lett. *1*, 105 (1958).
7. R. H. Dicke, Phys. Rev. *89*, 472 (1953).
8. H. G. Dehmelt, Phys. Rev. *105*, 1487 (1957).
9. M. Arditi and T. R. Carver, Phys. Rev. *109*, 1012 (1958).
   M. Arditi and T. R. Carver, Phys. Rev. *112*, 449 (1958).
   E. C. Beaty, P. L. Bender, and A. R. Chi, Phys. Rev. *112*, 450 (1958).
   P. L. Bender, E. C. Beaty, and A. R. Chi, Phys. Rev. Lett. *1*, 311 (1958).
10. J. P. Gordon, H. J. Zeiger, and C. H. Townes, Phys. Rev. *99*, 1264 (1955).
    J. Bonanomi and J. Herrmann, Helv. Phys. Acta *29*, 451 (1956).
11. R. C. Mockler, J. Barnes, R. Beehler, H. Salazar, and L. Fey, IRE Trans. Inst. *I-7*, 201 (1958).
12. K. Shimoda, T. C. Wang, and C. H. Townes, Phys. Rev. *102*, 1308 (1956).
13. R. S. Badessa, R. L. Kent, and J. C. Nowell, Phys. Rev. Lett. *3*, 79 (1959).

DISCUSSION

S. HOPFER: It has been mentioned in the paper read that the effect of the existing traveling waves in the maser cavity upon the frequency of oscillation may be sharply reduced by employing a balanced dual beam of molecules traversing the cavity in opposite directions.

Experience shows, however, that a balanced beam is difficult to realize and results in a rather bulky system. It seems possible to reduce greatly the Doppler effect by employing a dual cavity system coupled not at a single point as shown by Bonanomi but over the entire length of the cavity. Practically, this is accomplished by a series of small irises along the cavity. In this way, the real part of the Poynting vector at any point in the cavity should be primarily normal to the axis of the cylindrical cavity and should thus produce no Doppler effect if the molecular velocity vector is primarily axial.

F. H. REDER: Higher accuracy of an atomic beam frequency standard may preferably be obtained through using slower atoms rather than a longer beam.

Extension of the beam length makes it increasingly difficult to maintain phase coherence in the two Ramsey cavities, magnetic field homogeneity in the C region, and the proper high vacuum along the beam axis. Also the beam intensity seen by the detector will decrease somewhat with length.

Consequently, the use of slower atoms in beam tubes of the present length seems to be a solution worth investigation. It would certainly be more convenient to use in practical applications. It should be noted that the National Company has obtained a 60 cps bandwidth by selection of slow atoms in a 6-foot beam tube. (Normal bandwidth: 120 cps.)

J. BONANOMI: This comment is on the resetability of atomic clocks over long periods of time as achieved in practice. DePrins and I have determined since March 1957 through August 1959 an atomic time scale, which we called TA_1, by means of ammonia masers. Markowitz at the Naval Observatory defined another time scale, A_1 based on the frequency of one Atomichron. We have compared these two time scales by comparing the reception times of WWV time signals in terms of TA_1 and A_1: this was done regularly twice a month. During the stated period of 2.5 years, the difference $TA_1 - A_1$ remained constant within $a \pm 2.5$ msec, indicating that any systematic drift of NH_3-frequency at our laboratory from Cs-frequency at Washington has been smaller than 10^{-10} during this period.

EXPERIMENTAL INVESTIGATION OF ATOMIC BEAM RESONANCE TECHNIQUE AS APPLIED TO CESIUM CLOCK

S. N. KALRA AND R. BAILEY

Division of Applied Physics, National Research Council, Ottawa, Canada

AN ATOMIC beam apparatus using $F = 4$, $m_F = 0 \longleftrightarrow F = 3$, $m_F = 0$ transition has been working as a frequency resonator[1],[2] in this laboratory since July 1958. In the early days of its operation, it was discovered that the frequency of resonance transition as measured here was about 15 cps higher than the same frequency as measured by a similar apparatus[3] at the National Physical Laboratory of England (NPL). We now believe that this was due to an effect discovered last April where the frequency depends on the acceptance angle of the beam. This effect will now be described in detail.

Figure 1 shows the schematic diagram of the beam apparatus. There is a set of slits between the oven and the "A" magnet (Slits "A") and a similar set of slits between the "B" magnet and the detector (Slits "B"). Slits "A" and "B" were originally put in to reduce the scatter and to isolate the center chamber of the apparatus. In the early days of the use of this equipment, these slits were set at convenient openings and their settings were frequently changed. On some odd occasions large shifts in frequency were observed, but they were always cleared up by realignment of the beam, or so we then thought. Last April a shift in frequency was again observed and we were able to correlate it to the setting of the "A" slits. It is interesting to note that "B" slits have no effect on the frequency.

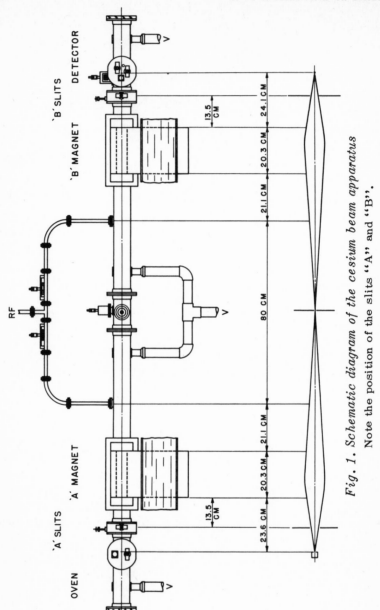

Fig. 1. Schematic diagram of the cesium beam apparatus
Note the position of the slits "A" and "B".

When the aperture of "A" slits is changed, it changes the angle at which atoms can enter the "A" magnet. Since the magnitude of H and grad H are fixed, this results in a change of the velocity spectrum of the atoms in the beam. For large apertures the ratio of slow atoms in the beam will increase. We have, therefore, attempted to think of this effect in terms of change of velocity spectrum. It is fairly obvious from the analysis of Professor Ramsey[4] that under ideal conditions a change of velocity spectrum will not result in any shift of the observed frequency of resonance. But, under nonideal conditions, such an effect could be expected. This effect was experimentally studied by deliberately departing from ideal conditions and measuring the shift in the observed frequency of resonance.

First, we will consider the effect on nonequality of phase in the two RF cavities. It was observed that a change of phase of 10° shifts the frequency by 12 cps and the 0° phase setting is symmetrically placed between the ± 10° settings. This is additional confirmation that there is no gross error in our method of zero adjustment for phase between the two RF cavities. Changing the aperture of slits "A" from 7.62 mm to 0.76 mm shifted the frequency by about 4 cps. This shift was independent of the magnitude of phase difference between the two cavities. The effect of sliding screw tuners was similarly investigated and the magnitude of the screw penetration did not influence the frequency shift due to aperture size. From this, we draw the conclusion that there are no gross errors in setting the phase equality in the two cavities and the aperture effect or velocity spectrum effect was not due to a phase error.

Position of the beam with respect to "A" and "B" magnets was varied by ± 0.5 mm and it made no difference to the observed frequency or the aperture effect. The beam was then misaligned with respect to the magnets by moving the oven by ± 0.5 mm and the detector by ± 0.5 mm leaving the center slit fixed in position. There was no shift in frequency and no change in the "aperture effect." Next, the beam was misaligned by moving the position of the oven only and there was no change in "aperture effect" and no shift in observed frequency.

The shift in observed frequency and the "aperture effect" were investigated as a function of the magnitude of the "C" field and for varying amount of inhomogeneity of the "C" field; and as a function of input RF power which was varied over a 10 db range (approximately 300 to 30 microwatts). No shift was observed in the frequency of resonance. "Aperture effect" was observed in each and every case.

The resonant frequency for $F = 3$, $m_F = 0 \longrightarrow F = 4$, $m_F = 0$ transition only has also been measured. A difference of frequency of 3 cps was measured between this condition and when transitions both ways were allowed. Since the standard deviation of a set of measurements varies between 1 and 2 cps, a difference of 3 cps is not conclusive. There was no difference between the frequency measured using $F = 4$, $m_F = 0 \longrightarrow F = 3$, $m_F = 0$ transition and the frequency when transitions both ways were allowed.

To date we have not been able to find any cause for the shift in frequency due to change in the velocity spectrum. On different days the magnitude of this effect seems to vary from about 4 to 12 cps. We have not been able to correlate it to any of the ambient conditions. The effect of side bands in the RF feed has not yet been investigated in detail. However, investigations have shown that the side bands present in the RF feed are not influencing the observed frequency of resonance.

The effect of the magnitude of "C" field on the observed frequency of resonance has been investigated in detail. Fitting the observations to the equation $f_o - f_r = \alpha H^2$ gives $\alpha = 463$ cps/Oe^2, where f_o is the observed frequency of resonance and f_r is the frequency for zero field transition. Essen and Parry[3] report a value $\alpha = 422$ cps/Oe^2. Since normally a "C" field of less than 0.1 Oe is being used by all the observers, this difference in α does not contribute any significant error.

It was mentioned earlier that there used to be a difference between the frequencies as measured by NPL and by this laboratory (NRC). Since the discovery of the "aperture effect" we have been careful to use the apparatus with slits "A" full open. For the period April to July, 1959 (both inclusive), the average fractional difference of frequency between NPL and NRC standards was 0.75×10^{-10} and between the NRC standard and U.S.

Naval Observatory system of Al it was 1.75×10^{-10}. These differences are obtained from the frequency of station WWV as measured by the three laboratories.

Only one effect which is yet unexplained has been discussed in this paper in the short time available. In other respects we are quite satisfied with the operation of this apparatus. We are confident that this technique can be used for the purpose of the definition of a standard of frequency. Further investigations of the "aperture effect" or "velocity spectrum effect" are continuing.

REFERENCES

1. S. N. Kalra, R. Bailey and H. Daams, Canad. J. Phys. *34*, 1442 (1958).
2. S. N. Kalra, R. Bailey, and H. Daams, Nature *183*, 575 (1959).
3. L. Essen, and J. V. L. Parry, Phil. Trans. Roy. Soc. *A 250*, 45 (1957).
4. N. F. Ramsey, *Molecular Beams*, Oxford University Press (1956).

DISCUSSION

F. H. REDER: There are three possible explanations for the observed frequency shift as a function of slit opening:

1. If, for some reason, there is a running wave in the cavity system in a direction perpendicular to the beam axis, then the admission of atoms going through the cavities under an angle $\neq 0$ with the axis will cause a Doppler shift.

2. The presence of "unbalanced" side bands in the driving signal will affect the slow atoms introduced by the slit opening more than the "normal" atoms. The fact that no side band effect was found with narrow slits is no proof against this explanation, because weak side bands act more strongly on slow atoms, whose number alone is increased by the slit opening.

3. The opening of the slit increases the flux into the interaction region which will give rise to atomic interaction in the beam and, if impurities are present in the beam source, also to the background pressure. In both cases, frequency shifts must be expected.

S. N. KALRA: Dr. Reder's comments are possible in a general way, but these effects do not seem to be present in our particular case. More specifically, if the first effect were present, then there would have been a change in the "aperture effect" when the beam was misaligned by moving the oven by ± 0.5 mm and the detector by ± 0.5 mm, leaving the center slit fixed. No change was observed. The microwave circuit effects have yet to be investigated in detail.

If the second effect were present, it would have been detected when the position of the oven was changed by large amounts, leaving the center slits and the detector fixed in position. When the sideband structure was changed there was no shift in the resonant frequency. For this investigation the slits "A" were full open.

As regards the third comment, pressure variation from 2×10^{-7} mm to 1×10^{-6} mm of Hg are not enough to give a measurable change in frequency. Besides, no such correlation was observed.

R. C. MOCKLER: The effect you describe might be expected if the two oscillating fields are not in phase. That is, for a nonsymmetrical Ramsey pattern the frequency of the central peak will change somewhat with a change in the velocity distribution.

S. N. KALRA: The accuracy to which the phase in the two Ramsey cavities can be set to equality is determined by the signal-to-noise ratio of the resonance signal. The phase uncertainty in our case is definitely less than $10°$. When the phase is further changed by + and $- 10°$, the phase error cannot possibly be the same at the three settings of $+ 10°$, $0°$, and $- 10°$. At each setting the aperture effect was investigated and found to be independent of phase error.

AN EVALUATION OF A CESIUM
BEAM FREQUENCY STANDARD

R. C. MOCKLER, R. E. BEEHLER, AND J. A. BARNES

National Bureau of Standards, Boulder, Colorado

A CESIUM atomic beam frequency standard constructed at the National Bureau of Standards has been tested for reproducibility and accuracy. The estimated standard deviation of the frequency measurements is 8.5 parts in 10^{11}. Measurements and control of the various parameters affecting the measured frequency indicate that the accuracy of the machine falls within the precision, i.e., within 8.5×10^{-11}.

Comparisons with other cesium standards have been made. Agreement is satisfactory in view of the uncertainties incurred by the method and circumstances of comparison. Relative frequency excursions of several parts in 10^{10} between Atomichrons introduce uncertainties in these comparisons.

An unsymmetrical power spectrum of the radiation exciting the cesium transition would, in general, give a different frequency measurement for a spectral line than would monochromatic radiation. Power spectra of the multiplied frequencies of several crystal oscillators were observed. In some cases the power spectrum displayed large asymmetries. Furthermore, the spectral asymmetry was observed to change in time for one particular oscillator. It seems essential—for a reliable standard—that the exciting radiation be without frequency modulation, or—if frequency modulation is needed for servo purposes—the modulating signal should be introduced into an otherwise clean spectrum. Multiple frequency modulating signals introduce asymmetrical character to the power spectrum.

THE EXPERIMENTAL APPARATUS

The NBS cesium beam frequency standard (hereafter referred to as NBS-1) employs Ramsey type excitation, has a spectral line width of 300 cps (at 9192.631 Mc), and provides a signal-to-noise ratio in the range 100 to 400. The atomic beam is produced by heating pure cesium metal to 150°C and allowing it to effuse from the oven through a channel 0.038 inch long with a cross section of 0.003×0.100 inch^2. The beam is detected by a surface ionization detector. The hot wire is made of a platinum-iridium alloy (80 percent Pt; 20 percent Ir). The ion current is measured with an electrometer. Typical values of the undeflected beam current fall in the range 1 to 3×10^{-11} amperes.

The beam excitation is derived from a quartz crystal oscillator (10.317...Mc). The output of this oscillator is multiplied in frequency up to the cesium transition by the scheme shown schematically in Fig. 1. The exciting radiation is swept in frequency over the width of the spectral line by tuning the 10.317...Mc crystal oscillator by means of voltage sensitive capacitors in the crystal circuit. The detected beam signal is applied to the y-axis and the analog output of a frequency counter is applied to the x-axis of a x-y plotter. A Ramsey line shape plotted in this manner is shown in Fig. 2. The frequency scale on the x-axis is linear. This allows the position of the peak of the line to be determined by taking the average of the frequency of two points on opposite sides of the central peak, both points having the same value of y. Several averages of this sort are made for each line trace. The line is swept in both directions and a linear interpolation is made. This compensates for delays that occur in the detecting circuit.

The Ramsey excitation structure consists of a long electroformed resonant cavity of rectangular cross section bent into the shape of a U. The Q of this cavity is about 6000. It is symmetric about the coupling iris and operates in the TE$_{1, 0, 60}$ mode. The beam passes through the two ends of the cavity—which are separated by 56 cm—and just grazes the end surfaces. Frequency shifts incurred through frequency "pulling" of the cavity are given approximately by

$$\Delta \nu_R = \left(\frac{Q_{\text{cavity}}}{Q_{\text{line}}} \right)^2 \Delta \nu_c$$

where $\Delta \nu_R$ is the shift in the peak of the atomic resonance re-

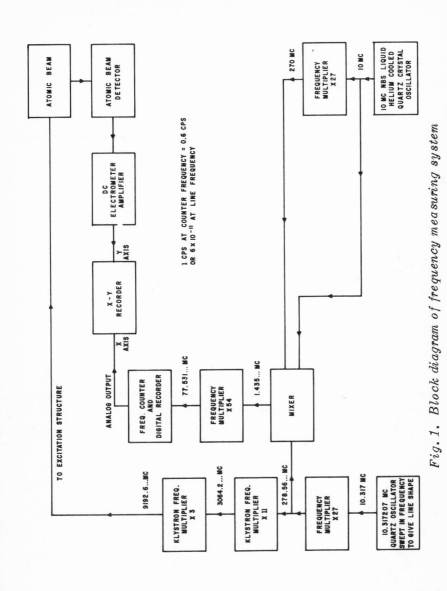

Fig. 1. Block diagram of frequency measuring system

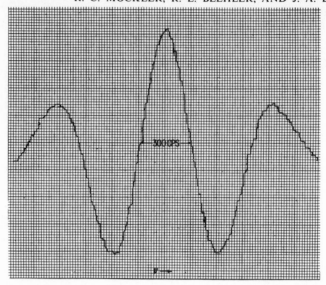

Fig. 2. Ramsey line shape of the (F = 4, M_F = 0) ↔ (F = 3, M_F = 0) *transition*

The trace was made on an *x-y* plotter. The *x*-axis sweep is derived from the analog output of a frequency counter. The step variations in the curve occur because of the step behavior of the counter output.

sponse, and $\Delta\nu_c$ is the difference in frequency between the peak of the cavity response and the peak of the atomic response. Q_{line} is the Q of the atomic response. $\Delta\nu_R$ is negligible for this machine for reasonable values of $\Delta\nu_c$. Consequently, temperature variations which shift the cavity resonance only tend to vary the intensity of the exciting radiation. No measurable shift is observable for variations in radiation intensity.

The "C" field is ordinarily adjusted to .080 oersted and is produced by a brass strip parallel to the atomic beam through which a current is passed. The uniformity of the field is determined by measuring the low frequency transitions in the beam (~ 28 kc) induced by small coils placed at different positions along the "C" field. The measured uniformity is within ± .003 oersted. The "C" field region is magnetically shielded from external fields by a mu-metal shield.

ACCURACY

The accuracy of the machine depends upon the precision to which certain parameters can be controlled (and/or measured).

The uncertainty in the measured magnitude of the "C" field is ± 0.003 oersted. This corresponds to an uncertainty in the microwave frequency measurements of 2×10^{-11}—well within the precision.

There is an uncertainty introduced in the measured frequency if the phase relation between the two oscillating fields of the Ramsey exciting structure is not precisely known. In the machine described here, a single resonant cavity is used. Consequently, the phases are precisely the same at the two cavity ends. The beam passes through these two regions of identical phase. As further evidence of phase identity, the cavity can be rotated 180° (except for the shorted ends) and the two measured transition frequencies compared. A lack of phase identity in the two oscillating field regions can also be detected by observing the symmetry of the line shape. The absence of perfect line symmetry implies unequal phases in the two regions. The degree to which the inaccuracy can be determined by this kind of observation is limited by the signal-to-noise ratio to a greater extent than by comparing the frequencies for one orientation of the waveguide structure and the inverted orientation. However, if the line breadth is 300 cps and the signal-to-noise ratio is 400, this method permits the inaccuracy in the frequency to be specified within about 1.4×10^{-10}. No asymmetry is observable in the line traces.

Any frequency shift caused by electric fields has been shown by Haum and Zacharias[1] to be negligible for magnitudes of the electric field intensity that would be expected in the "C" field region. They have found that the frequency shift in the cesium line is

$$\Delta \nu_o = 1.89 \times 10^{-6} E^2 \text{ cps,}$$

where E is the electric field intensity in volts/cm.

The microwave frequency magnetic field is polarized parallel to the static "C" field. Under these circumstances, the most important selection rule is $\Delta M_F = 0$. There are seven transitions in cesium for which this selection rule applies. It can be shown that these are sufficiently well resolved at .080 oersted so that the resonant peak of interest is not shifted beyond the present uncertainties in measurement by the overlapping of neighboring lines.

Uncertainties can be introduced by the exciting radiation. If this radiation consists of more than one signal and if these signals are not symmetrical in frequency and amplitude about a frequency that is an integer multiple of the primary crystal oscillator driving the multiplier chain, then erroneous line frequencies will obtain.[2] It is not unusual to find unsymmetric power spectra of this sort from frequency multiplier chains and large errors could result. The square root of the power spectrum of an oscillator identical to that used in NBS-1 is shown in Fig. 3. Notice that the spectrum has no sidebands and any asymmetry of the central peak will be of no consequence

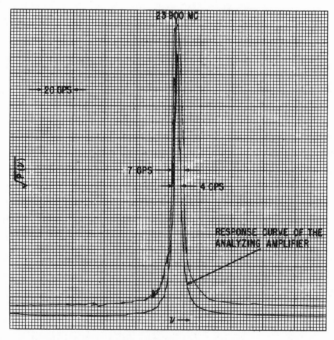

Fig. 3. $\sqrt{p(\nu)}$ *versus frequency for a 9.835 Mc crystal oscillator multiplied in frequency 2430 times*

since this peak is much narrower than the spectral line breadth. Other tests were made on the NBS-1 oscillator to show that its spectrum was similar to that of its twin (Fig. 3)—in particular, no low-frequency sidebands were detected in the multiplier chain output. This spectral character will provide accurate frequency comparisons. The usual assumption that the median frequency of a frequency multiplier is an exact integer multiple of the primary oscillator is an accurate assumption for the sort of spectrum displayed in Fig. 3.

Considering the various sources of inaccuracy and the results of their study, we believe—with some confidence—that the accuracy of the machine falls within the precision or $\pm 8.5 \times 10^{-11}$.

THE MEASUREMENTS

The reproducibility of the cesium standard (NBS-1) was determined by comparison with a 10 Mc quartz crystal oscillator in which the quartz crystal and associated crystal circuit are immersed in liquid helium. The stability of this oscillator over periods of several days is 3 to 5×10^{-11}*—a figure determined from a continuous comparison with an Atomichron (106) during periods of good behavior. This Atomichron, even though large excursions in frequency occur in short time intervals (Fig. 4b), has excellent stability when averaged over time intervals of 1 minute or more. Periods during which the helium-cooled oscillator and Atomichron (106) showed no significant variations relative to each other were considered best to determine a reproducibility figure (precision) for NBS-1.

The helium oscillator has also been demonstrated to be stable to $2\text{-}4 \times 10^{-11}$ over periods of $\frac{1}{2}$ sec to 6 hours by comparison with a maser stabilized frequency multiplier chain (Fig. 4a).

In handling the data, the mean of a single day's measurements is considered one piece of data. An estimate of the standard deviation was obtained from successive differences. Let

$$\delta^2 = \sum_{i=1}^{n-1} \frac{(x_i - x_{i+1})^2}{n}$$

*The aging rate of the helium-cooled oscillator appears to be less than 1×10^{-11} per day.

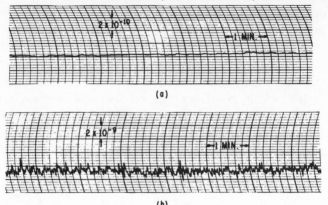

$$\textit{Fig. 4.}$$

(a) Maser stabilized chain compared with 10 Mc helium-cooled crystal oscillator. The recorder plots the analog output of a frequency counter versus time. The counting period is 1 sec and the display time is 1 sec.

(b) Maser stabilized chain compared with 5 Mc Atomichron crystal oscillator. In this trace, the difference signal is measured with a frequency meter and not with a counter. The time constant for the meter is about $\frac{1}{2}$ sec. Note the change in frequency scale between (a) and (b).

where x_i is the frequency measurement for the ith day and x_{i+1} is the frequency measurement for the $(i + 1)$ day; n is the total number of data points (or days). The estimate of the standard deviation by successive differences is given by

$$\sigma\,(\delta) = \sqrt{\frac{\delta^2}{2}}^{\;*}$$

For our set of data $\delta = 1.1$ cps and $\sigma(\delta) = 0.77$ cps which is 8.5×10^{-11} of the cesium frequency. Successive differences are likely to be random even though certain systematic changes may occur. These systematic changes are small when data is taken on succeeding days but nevertheless still exist. It is impossible to attribute these variations to the Atomichron, the helium-cooled oscillator, or NBS-1, or to a combination when the variations are small. Actually the standard deviation estimated from suc-

---

*R. H. Kent and J. VonNeumann have shown that $\sigma^2(\delta) = (\sigma')^2$ where σ' is the true standard deviation.

cessive differences is almost the same as that estimated in the usual way. In fact, this standard deviation,

$$\sigma = \sqrt{\sum_{i=1}^{n} \frac{(\bar{x} - x_i)^2}{n}},$$

is .5 cps or 8×10^{-11}.

The data show Atomichron (106) to be lower than NBS-1 by 3.6 cps for the week of August 30. The mean of all the data taken over the months of July and August show about the same difference. Data of one day was deleted from the average because the Atomichron (106) made a large excursion, 8×10^{-10}, just prior to a general retuning. The excursion was verified by NBS-1, the helium-cooled oscillator, the masers, and Cruft Laboratory data.

In addition to the tests carried on at the Boulder Laboratories to determine precision and accuracy, frequency comparisons were made between NBS-1 and other cesium standards in the United States and England. The comparisons were made through propagated signals between the different locations.

In the discussion that follows, the following designations will be used to identify the various cesium standards:

Designation	Location
NBS-1	Cesium resonator, NBS, Boulder, Colo.
106	Atomichron, NBS, Boulder, Colo.
109	Atomichron, Station WWV, Beltsville, Md.
110	Atomichron, Naval Research Laboratories, Washington, D. C.
112	Atomichron, Cruft Laboratory, Cambridge, Mass.
M4	The mean of 106, 109, 110, 112
NPL	British cesium resonator, Teddington, England

Table 1. ($1 \ unit = 1 \times 10^{-10}$)

1. (NBS-1) − 106 = + 3.9*,   mean over July and August, 1959
2. M4 − 106 = + 4.2,   6-month mean for the period
3. M4 − (NBS-1) = + 0.3   Sept. 1958 to March 1, 1959
4. NPL-M4 = + 1.5,   6-month mean for the period
5. NPL-(NBS-1) = + 1.8   Sept. 1958 to March 1, 1959

*A positive sign means that the first standard is higher in frequency than the second.

It should be emphasized that this comparison assumed that 106 had the same mean frequency during July and August 1959 as it had during the 6-month period September, 1958, to March, 1959. The accumulated data over the past two years indicate that the Atomichrons tend to wander in frequency. In fact, Atomichrons 112, 106, 110 were in rather good agreement during March 1959— differing by probably less than 2×10^{-10}. This comparison was made by a single Atomichron transported by air to each of the locations to provide a more direct comparison between the different units.* The relative frequencies of Atomichrons 112, 106, 110, 109 have changed considerably between March and July according to the propagation data of July. During the month of July, 1959, 112 differed from 106 by about 1×10^{-9} and it differed from 110 by several parts in 10^{10}. Other variations of this nature are evident from the various data including the direct comparison data made at Boulder between 106, NBS-1, and the helium-cooled oscillator.

Table 2. $(1 \ unit = 1 \times 10^{-10})$

Date	(NBS-1) − 106	112 − 106	112 − 109	112 − 110	(NBS-1) − M4
July 8	+ 4.5	+ 8.6	+ 4	+ 7.6	+ 0.9
July 9	+ 2.5	+ 9.3	+ 5	+ 8.4	− 1.1

The link between Boulder and Cruft Laboratory is through the 60 kc transmission of station KK2XEI at Boulder. This transmission is reported to be very weak, and comparison with it difficult. Recently, new alternatives for comparison through radio signals have come into being. The Navy VLF stations in San Diego and Hawaii are now transmitting signals of high power and of suitable stability measurements. These strong signals measured at Boulder and at Cruft are expected to provide a more satisfactory comparison between standards at the Boulder Laboratories and the east coast.

THE POWER SPECTRUM OF THE EXCITATION RADIATION— ITS EFFECT ON THE MEASURED FREQUENCY

For the purpose of understanding the detailed nature of extremely precise microwave frequency measurements, it is neces-

*The experiment was performed under the auspices of the U.S. Signal Corps by Dr. J. H. Holloway from the National Company.

sary to investigate the power spectra of the radiation from frequency multiplier chains used in such measurements. This is especially important in atomic frequency standards where a quartz oscillator is compared with an atomic resonance through a frequency multiplication process. The multiplier chain measured output frequency would be some sort of average—depending upon the method of measurement. If the power spectrum were unsymmetric, this average would not be an exact integral multiple of the primary crystal oscillator frequency.

In the method of observing the power spectrum used here, the output signal of the multiplier chain to be investigated is mixed with an essentially monochromatic signal. This relatively pure signal is obtained from an ammonia maser stabilized chain (Fig. 11). In this fashion the power spectrum is shifted to low frequencies—in fact, audio frequencies—where it can be conveniently examined with a variable frequency narrow band filter

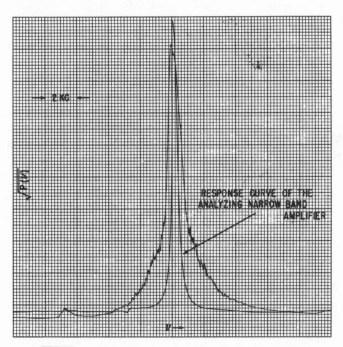

Fig. 5. $\sqrt{p\,(\nu)}$ versus frequency for a 10 Mc helium-cooled crystal oscillator multiplied in frequency 1458 times

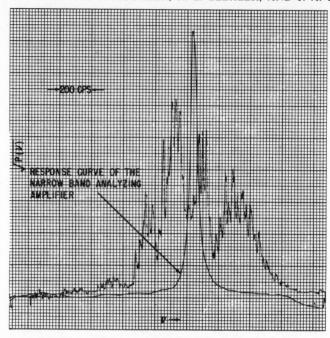

Fig. 6. $\sqrt{p\,(\nu)}$ versus frequency for a 10 Mc helium-cooled crystal oscillator multiplied in frequency 1458 times

(amplifier). In the experiments, 100 kc, 10 Mc, and 5 Mc crystal oscillators—and chains—were investigated (Figs. 3, 5, 6, 7, 8, 9, 10). The frequency multiplication factors used were 1458 for the 10 Mc oscillators, 2916 for the 5 Mc oscillators, and 145,800 for the 100 kc oscillators. Direct multiplication of these oscillators by these factors would give the frequency 14,580 Mc. The most prominent features of the observed power spectra are the 60 cps (the commercial power frequency) and the harmonics of 60 cps sidebands. These sidebands are enhanced very significantly by the multiplication process—in fact, by a factor of roughly the frequency multiplication. These sidebands are apparently introduced through frequency modulation in the crystal oscillator, buffer amplifiers, and the first stages of frequency multiplication. The existence of limiters in the frequency multipliers removes practically all of the amplitude modulation. One would expect the 60 cps (and harmonics of 60 cps) sidebands of an amplitude-modulated signal to be symmetric in their amplitude about the central peak. This is not necessarily true of frequency-modulated signals—provided that the primary signal is modulated with two or more modulating signals. Thus unsymmetric power spectra are expected—under certain circumstances—when frequency modulation occurs in frequency multipliers. Suppose that the output frequency of such a frequency-modulated chain were measured. Suppose this is done by beating it with a known and relatively monochromatic signal, and the beat note is measured with a counter. The counter would measure the center of gravity of the power spectrum and this frequency will not be an integer multiple of the basic quartz oscillator (unless the power spectrum is symmetric). Furthermore, if this radiation were used to excite the atomic transition in an atomic beam frequency standard, the measured frequency of the spectral line would be different than that measured if the multiplier chain output were monochromatic. In general, the frequency measured by the spectral line will be different than that measured by the counter under

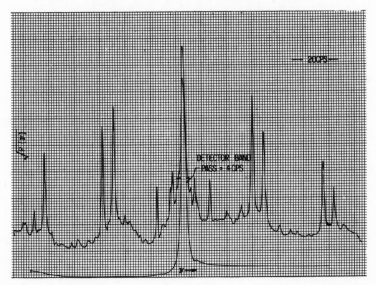

Fig. 7. 5 Mc helium-cooled crystal oscillator power spectrum

Multiplication factor = 2916.
The detector band pass ~ 4 cps.
The individual peaks in the spectrum have a width less than 1 cps.

the unfavorable—but not unusual—conditions discussed above. Elimination of the sidebands and the reduction in the frequency multiplying factor is the best cure—and also a possible cure for these difficulties.* If the power spectrum is symmetric, regardless of whether the frequency is measured by a spectral line or a counter, the measured frequencies will be the same so long as the receiver amplifier is not extremely narrow banded.

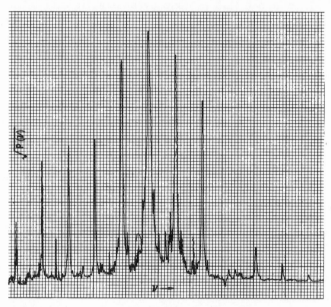

Fig. 8. The power spectrum of a 5 Mc helium-cooled quartz crystal oscillator multiplied in frequency 2916 times

The prominent sidebands are due to frequency modulation of 60. cps and harmonics of 60 cps. Note that the spectrum is unsymmetric. The center of gravity of the spectrum has been shifted 41 cps in the multiplication process from the values it would have had, had there been no sidebands.

In the investigations described here, power spectra for the 5 Mc helium-cooled quartz crystal oscillator, taken at different times, showed large changes in appearance and symmetry for no known reason. See Figs. 7 and 8—notice that one of the sidebands is missing in Fig. 8. This particular oscillator has been shown to

*See Fig. 3.

have a maximum deviation in frequency of about 2×10^{-11} over a six-hour interval (by comparison with the maser stabilized chain) during periods of a fixed power spectrum. Variations of this sort in the power spectrum would undoubtedly produce a corresponding change in the "fixed" frequency of an atomic frequency standard.

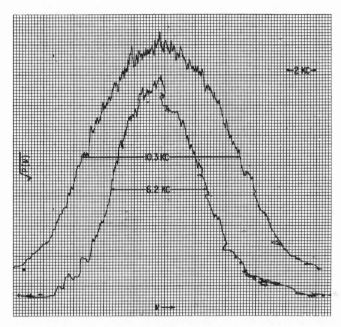

Fig. 9. 100 kc GT crystal oscillator

Multiplication factor = 145,800. The two traces differ in that the upper trace was obtained 1 hour after the multiplier chain was switched on, and the lower trace was obtained 6 hours after the chain was switched on.

The extremely sharp spectrum (1 cps or less at 14,580 Mc) shown by the 5 Mc crystal oscillator—disregarding the 60 cps sidebands—suggests that the high stability feature of quartz crystal oscillators has not been completely exploited. The width of the peaks in the spectrum of the 5 Mc helium-cooled oscillators is not perceptible with the dispersion used in our experiments. However, the width is observable in the square root of the power spectrum of the 9.835 Mc oscillator shown in

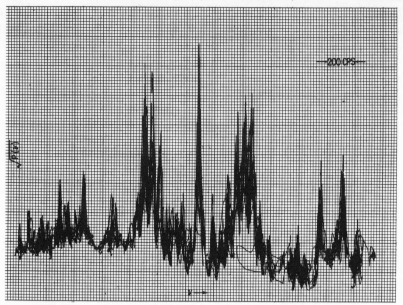

Fig. 10. Power spectrum of the 5 Mc crystal oscillator of an Atomichron (multiplied by 2916)

Fig. 3 in which the crystal circuit is maintained at 46°C. Perhaps this suggests that this width is due to fundamental noise in the quartz crystal and crystal circuit. The extremely narrow spectrum of a helium-cooled oscillator (< 1 cps) implies that crystal oscillators could be used in atomic beam frequency standards for line widths less than 10 cps. Evidently, when the breadth of a spectral line is less than the breadth of the power spectrum of the exciting radiation, a plotted resonance curve will have a width determined primarily by the breadth of the radiation spectrum. Fig. 9 shows the square root of the power spectrum for a 100 kc oscillator and multipler chain. If this spectrum were used to excite the transition in NBS-1) (line breadth = 300 cps), the Ramsey pattern would be completely obliterated leaving only the broad Rabi line shape. This has actually been observed to occur.[3] It is for this reason that higher frequency oscillators are used in atomic standards. As a matter of interest, this 100 kc oscillator has a frequency stability of $1-2 \times 10^{-10}$ per day. Figs. 5 and 6 display the square root of the power spectrum of the 10 Mc

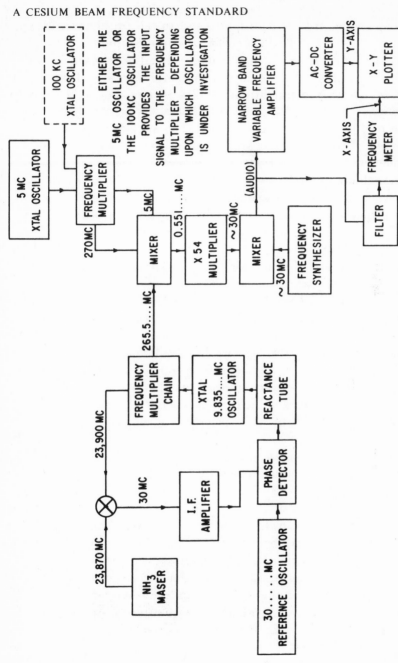

Fig. 11. Diagram of the scheme used to plot power spectra

helium-cooled crystal oscillator used in the frequency comparison with NBS-1. The spectrum is quite complex and is also unsymmetric. It provides a superb signal for frequency comparisons (Fig. 4a) but would not be useful as a signal source to induce the atomic transition.[4] The square root of the power spectrum of the 5 Mc oscillator belonging to the NBS Atomichron (106) is shown in Fig. 10. The spectrum is symmetric. In spite of its complex character it provides a uniform averaged frequency over long periods of time.

In establishing the performance of an atomic standard it is important to know the spectral character of the excitation. A clean spectrum is likely to give the most reliable behavior.

CONCLUSION

The agreement between the NBS cesium atomic standard frequency and a mean frequency of four Atomichrons (M4) is rather good—within $\pm 1 \times 10^{-10}$. This agreement may be fortuitous, however, because there is considerable disagreement among the Atomichrons used in determining the mean frequency M-4. The comparison between the NBS atomic standard and that of England [NPL-(NBS-1) = + 1.8] may be more meaningful.

The variations between atomic standards seem to be quite real and remain unexplained. The source of disagreement can only be determined by test experiments on the individual machines.

At the present time a new cesium resonator is being put into operation at the Boulder Laboratories. This machine will have a line breadth of 90–100 cps.

The authors acknowledge with gratitude a large amount of work on the cesium beam by Mr. Lowell Fey during the initial stages of the experiment. Mr. Henry Salazar constructed most of the electronic apparatus. Mr. John Carlson and Mr. Donald Harriman constructed the cesium beam and maser apparatus. We further recognize the invaluable cooperation of Messrs. A. H. Morgan, J. Shoaf, V. E. Heaton, and especially, P. Simpson of the Radio Broadcast Service Section to whom belong the helium-cooled oscillators and Atomichron 106 used in the experiments.

REFERENCES

1. R. D. Haun, Jr., and J. R. Zacharias, Phys. Rev. *107*, 107 (1957).
2. N. F. Ramsey, Phys. Rev. *100*, 1191 (1955).
3. R. C. Mockler, R. E. Beehler, and J. A. Barnes, "A Practical Limitation to the Length of an Atomic Beam Machine," to be published.
4. A more detailed report on the power spectra is in preparation by two of the authors of this paper.

COHERENT PULSE TECHNIQUES IN THE OPTICAL DETECTION OF THE 0↔0 GROUND STATE HYPERFINE RESONANCE IN RUBIDIUM 87*

C. O. ALLEY

Palmer Physical Laboratory, Princeton University

A METHOD of optical detection of the $0 \longleftrightarrow 0$ magnetic hyperfine transition in the ground state of an alkali atom has been devised and demonstrated for rubidium 87. This method relies on the destruction of phase relations between the 0-states and their partner Zeeman states in the coherent superposition state describing free precession rather than on a shift of populations between the states as is usual in magnetic resonance experiments.

An atomic frequency standard using this $0 \longleftrightarrow 0$ transition in alkali atoms confined in a small glass bulb is made possible by the technique of Doppler reduction through collisions with atoms of an inert buffer gas.[1],[2] It is convenient to alter the Boltzmann distribution of population in the ground state by optical pumping in order to enhance the strength of the resonance.[3] Observation of the resonance can be accomplished by microwave techniques[3] or by the change in absorption or scattering of optical resonance radiation.[4] Straightforward optical detection of the $0 \longleftrightarrow 0$ transition is possible only if the peak intensities of the corresponding hyperfine components are different, since the absorptive cross section is the same for each hyperfine state if the peak intensities are equal. This equality is the usual case in the resonance radiation obtained from electrical dis-

*This research has been supported by the U. S. Army Signal Research and Development Laboratory under Contract No. DA-36-039 SC-70147.

charges in alkali vapor. However, it is possible to achieve selective hyperfine filtering in the gas cell itself or in a preceding gas cell filter (containing Rb^{85} for the Rb^{87} resonance)[5] and such techniques have been tried with success.[6],[7],[8],[9]

It is desirable to have an even more sensitive means of detection than that just described, in order to sacrifice some of the signal-to-noise ratio in favor of narrowing the line width beyond that normally associated with the relaxation time. It is expected that such line narrowing can be accomplished by exciting the hyperfine resonance with two phase-coherent microwave pulses separated in time to select long-lived atoms.[10] The phase-destructive method is a way of detecting the $0 \longleftrightarrow 0$ hyperfine resonance to yield very large optical detection signals on the order of those obtainable from complete reorientation experiments.[4]

THEORY OF THE METHOD

Figure 1 shows the energy level diagram for rubidium 87 ($I = \frac{3}{2}$) with the angular momentum substates displayed. The numbers associated with the ground substates are proportional to the absorptive cross section for circularly polarized (σ^+) optical resonance radiation, those above referring to D_1 and those below referring to D_2. It is convenient to describe the optical absorption for a nonuniform ground state population distribution in terms of an *effective oscillator strength*, f_{eff}, associated with the optical transition. If the spectral width of the incident light is large compared to the thermal Doppler width $(\Delta \nu)_D$ of the absorbing atoms, the absorptive cross section is given by

$$\sigma_\nu = \frac{2}{(\Delta \nu)_D} \sqrt{\frac{\ln 2}{\pi}} \, f_{eff} \, \pi \, c \, r_o \, e^{-\omega^2} \tag{1}$$

where c = velocity of light

r_o = classical radius of the electron

$$\omega = \frac{2\sqrt{\ln 2}}{(\Delta \nu)_D} (\nu - \nu_1)$$

and

$$\int_o^\infty \sigma_\nu \, d\nu = \pi \, c \, r_o \, f_{eff}. \tag{2}$$

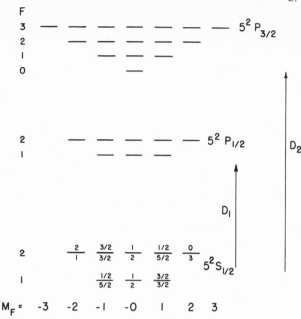

Fig. 1. Energy level diagram for ground state and first two excited states of rubidium 87.

One may express f_{eff} as

$$f_{eff} = \tfrac{1}{6} Tr(\rho\, \mathbf{A}) \tag{3}$$

where ρ is the density matrix describing the system and $\mathbf{A}$ is an absorption operator characteristic of the transition, polarization, and direction $\vec{n}$ of the absorbed light beam. It may be expressed in terms of the angular momentum of the ground state.[11] For example,

$$\mathbf{A}_{D_1}^{\sigma^{\pm}} = \left(\Pi \mp \frac{(-1)^F}{2\hbar} \vec{\mathbf{F}} \cdot \vec{n} \right)$$

$$\mathbf{A}_{D_2}^{\sigma^{\pm}} = 2 \left(\Pi \pm \frac{(-1)^F}{4\hbar} \vec{\mathbf{F}} \cdot \vec{n} \right) . \tag{4}$$

Intense optical pumping with σ^{+} light can be used to polarize the Rb^{87} atoms along the direction of the pumping light. In a weak magnetic field in this same direction, free precession in the plane perpendicular to the magnetic field can be induced by applying a 90° r-f pulse at the Zeeman splitting frequency. In the absence of relaxation or other disturbing effects, a – 90° pulse (i.e. phase inverted but coherent with the first pulse) would yield the original state of polarization. The optical absorption would be the same after as before the pulse sequence. During the free precession, each atom is in a coherent superposition state which may be calculated by transforming to successive rotating coordinate frames and using the known rotation operators. For simplicity of discussion, consider an atom initially in the state 2,2. After the 90° rotation its wave function is

$$U_{90°} \, \psi_{2,2} = \sum_{m=-2}^{2} \, <2,m| \exp\frac{i}{\hbar}\frac{\pi}{2} F_y \Big| 2,2> \psi_{2,m} =$$

$$\frac{1}{4}\,\psi_{2,-2} + \frac{1}{2}\,\psi_{2,-1} + \frac{\sqrt{3}}{2\sqrt{2}}\,\psi_{2,0} + \frac{1}{2}\,\psi_{2,1} + \frac{1}{4}\,\psi_{2,2}. \quad (5)$$

The coefficient of the 2,0 state is large so that if the 1,0 state is coupled in by a microwave field of the right frequency, the wave function will be considerably altered. The state after the application of the – 90° pulse will now no longer be the original pure state but a different one of superposition for which the optical absorption is greatly different. Calculations using the density matrix show that after the pulse sequence the effective oscillator strengths are as given in Fig. 2 for an initial 2,2 state. The quantity α is given by

$$\alpha = \frac{-\frac{1}{2}(g_J \mu_o - g_I \mu_N) B_{\mu w} \Delta t}{2\hbar} \quad (6)$$

where
g_J = electron g factor
g_I = nuclear g factor
μ_o = Bohr magneton
μ_N = Nuclear magneton
$B_{\mu w}$ = Amplitude of microwave field
Δt = time between 90° pulses.

The maximum effect occurs for $\alpha = \pi$. The changes in absorption for D_1 and D_2 are equal and opposite, indicating the possibility of balancing out light source fluctuations.

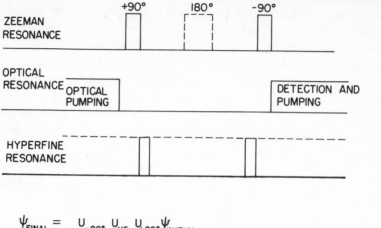

$$\psi_{FINAL} = \quad U_{-90°} \ U_{HF} \ U_{+90°} \psi_{INITIAL}$$

$$f_{D_1}^{\sigma+} = 1/6 \ \text{Tr} \ (\rho \ A_{D_1}^{\sigma+}) \ = 1/8 \left[1 - \cos \alpha \right]$$

$$f_{D_2}^{\sigma+} = 1/6 \ \text{Tr} \ (\rho \ A_{D_1}^{\sigma+}) \ = 3/8 \left[1 + 1/3 \cos \alpha \right]$$

Fig. 2. Triple resonance pulse sequence

The microwave radiation connecting the 2,0 and 1,0 states can be applied in two coherently phased pulses at the beginning and end of the interval between 90° pulses to select just those states which have not undergone dephasing collisions during the interval. One expects line widths on the order of the reciprocal of this time interval. By sacrificing some of the strong signal by lengthening the interval and thus increasing the relaxation, it should be possible to obtain very narrow lines, of 10 cps and less for Rb^{87} ($\nu = 6834.6826$ Mc/s), for it is known that longitudinal relaxation terms approaching one second are possible in buffered and wall-coated cells,[12] and the transverse relaxation times should be of the same order.

The best way of measuring transverse relaxation times for both the Zeeman and hyperfine transitions is probably by pulse techniques of the sort described here. Although the $0 \longleftrightarrow 0$ transition is insensitive to field inhomogeneities, the same is unfortunately not true for the Zeeman transitions. The dephasing effect of these inhomogeneities can be countered by inserting a

$180°$ pulse between the $90°$ pulses as shown in Fig. 2. It is
not completely effective since the Rb atoms are not stationary
but are diffusing among the buffer gas atoms. A sequence of
$180°$ pulses to preserve phase memory as the atoms diffuse is
more effective.

SOME EXPERIMENTAL RESULTS

The observation of lines narrower than expected from T_2 relaxation times has not yet been accomplished. However, the
method of optical detection using pulsed Zeeman resonances
works well and yields large signals and the interpolation of $180°$
pulses serves to preserve phase memory. The difficulties which
have been encountered are of a familiar kind in physics laboratories: large field inhomogeneities and large time-varying fields.
These can be eliminated, however, at the cost of some trouble.

The field homogeneity has been considerably improved over
that of a 14-inch radius Helmholtz pair configuration by shielding a 1200 turn solenoid 1 meter long and 25 cm in diameter with
seven concentric layers of 4-inch by 4-mil permalloy tape. The
60 cycle and harmonic fields are only reduced by a factor of three
in the longitudinal direction, however. Even more serious is a
10^{-2} gauss 20 cycle field having ten times the magnitude of the
60 cycle field which is produced by a prototype section of a
proton synchrotron magnet being tested in a neighboring room.
Work is in progress to compensate these fields by using a feedback control system but this is not yet operating.

A block diagram of the experimental arrangement is shown in
Fig. 3. The light source consists of the inner section of an
Osram lamp immersed in a bath of silicone oil which can be
water cooled. The discharge is excited by direct current from a
generator and the useful light output seems to increase linearly
as the current is raised to 2 amperes (the maximum current used),
provided the temperature of the bath is kept at $\sim 140°$C. A large
(10 henry, 1 ohm) inductance in series with the lamp acts as a
constant current source and serves to stabilize the discharge.
The lamp can be turned on and off very cleanly by using a power
transistor as a switch in parallel with it. The timer is a sequence of transistorized shift registers acting as decade coun-

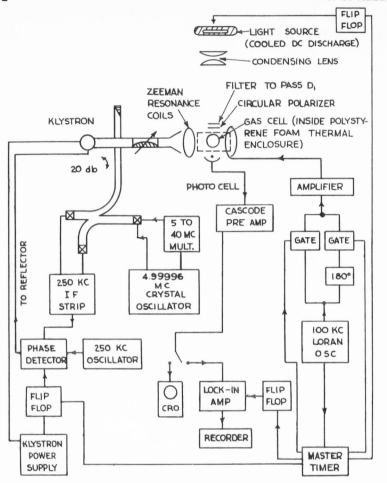

Fig. 3. Block diagram of apparatus

ters, the timing pulses being obtained from coincidence circuits. The 90° pulses are 10 cycles of 100 kc/s and are identical in phase from one sequence to the next. The klystron stabilization circuit is essentially the type developed by C. L. Searle and D. D. McRae at MIT.[13]

Typical transmission signals are shown in Figs. 4 and 5. These were obtained for $D_1 \sigma^+$ pumping and detection for a 2-inch diameter pyrex bulb containing Rb^{87} vapor and 5 cm Hg of neon at 45 °C. The very inhomogeneous unshielded Helmholtz

pair field (140 milligauss) was used. The time between 90°
pulses is 2 msec. Without the 180° pulse, phase memory was
lost. The multiple trace following the −90° pulse is caused by
60 cycle fields detuning the Zeeman resonance and causing the
last pulse to appear sometimes as −90° and sometimes as +90°.
When the $0 \longleftrightarrow 0$ resonance, is excited, the mixing of the 1,0
and 2,0 states destroys the phase coherence and the 60 cycle
jitter caused by the detuning disappears. It is apparent that
signals comparable to those obtainable from reversal of the spin

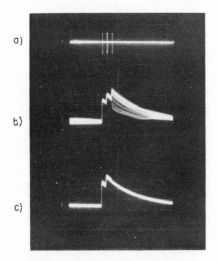

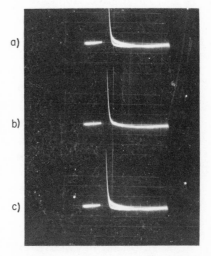

*Fig. 4. Optical detection
signal*

(a) pulse sequence: 90°, 180°,
    −90°
(b) light absorption, no
    microwaves
(c) light absorption, with
    microwaves

*Fig. 5. Pumping light off
during pulse sequence*

(a) and (c) no microwaves
(b) with microwaves

direction can be obtained. What appears as noise in the traces
is a slight oscillation in the light source which can be removed.

The change in light transmission following the 180° pulse is
caused by the reversal of those atoms that have absorbed and
reradiated optical photons, after the first 90° pulse. This illustrates the desirability of eliminating this optical relaxation.

The signal is increased by a factor of 3 or 4 by cutting off the pumping radiation during the interval between 90° pulses as is shown in Fig. 5 (gain less by 10 than in Fig. 4).

When four additional 180° pulses were used with a 2 msec interval between them, time intervals of 10 msec between 90° pulses could be obtained with preservation of phase memory.

For the 2 msec interval, the hyperfine resonance (for c-w radiation) as observed at the output of the phase detector (its action is hampered by the averaging effect of the 60 cycle jitter) is a broad plateau about 10 kc/s wide on which resonances about 500–1000 cycles wide are superposed. This is to be expected for the 100 μs 90° pulses separated by 2 msec.

The shielded solenoid has made possible intervals of at least 22 msec with only one 180° pulse interposed. It seems probable that phase memory can be preserved for times in excess of 100 msec using multiple pulses. It is hoped that soon the substantial reduction of the time-varying magnetic field will enable the proper use of synchronous detection and the observation of the narrow hyperfine lines using the method described.

REFERENCES

1. R. H. Dicke, Phys. Rev. *89*, 472 (1953).
2. J. P. Wittke and R. H. Dicke, Phys. Rev. *103*, 620 (1956).
3. R. H. Dicke, T. R. Carver, C. O. Alley, and N. S. Vander Ven, U. S. Army Signal Research and Development Laboratory, Quarterly Report No. 8 (Final Report on Microwave Detection Phase), Contract No. DA-36-039 SC-70147.
4. H. G. Dehmelt, Phys. Rev. *105*, 1487 (1957).
5. C. O. Alley, Quarterly Reports No. 9 and 10 under the contract cited in Reference 3.
6. M. Arditi and T. R. Carver, Phys. Rev. *109*, 1012 (1958).
7. W. E. Bell and A. L. Bloom, Phys. Rev. *109*, 219 (1958).
8. P. L. Bender, E. C. Beaty and A. R. Chi, Phys. Rev. Lett. *1*, 311 (1958).
9. J. M. Andres, D. J. Farmer, and G. T. Inoye, 13th Annual Frequency Control Symposium (May, 1959).
10. R. H. Dicke, unpublished.
11. H. G. Dehmelt, Phys. Rev. *105*, 1924 (1957), gives the operator for $D_1\sigma^+$ light for a hypothetical sodium atom of angular momentum $\frac{1}{2}$. W. E. Bell and A. L. Bloom, Phys. Rev. *107*, 1559 (1957), point

out the existence of such operators in general but give no actual examples.

12. W. Franzen, 13th Annual Frequency Control Symposium (May, 1959).
13. C. L. Searle and D. D. McRae, MIT Research Laboratory of Electronics, Quarterly Report (April 15, 1956).

MOLECULAR BEAM ELECTRIC RESONANCE METHOD WITH SEPARATED OSCILLATING FIELDS*

J. C. ZORN, G. E. CHAMBERLAIN, AND V. W. HUGHES

Gibbs Laboratory, Yale University

THE USE of a rotational state transition as observed by the molecular beam electric resonance method with separated oscillating fields is being considered as a possible frequency standard, particularly in the millimeter wavelength range. A promising example is the 100 KMc/sec transition between the $J = 0$ and $J = 1$ rotational states of $Li^6 F^{19}$. The relative insensitivity of the transition frequency to external electric and magnetic fields and the low microwave power requirements appear favorable; the small fraction of the molecular beam that is in a single rotational state is a limiting factor. A fuller discussion of design considerations is given in a recent article in the Review of Scientific Instruments.[1]

Construction of a long molecular beam electric resonance apparatus with provision for separated oscillating fields in the radiofrequency range has just been completed. Figure 1 shows a schematic diagram of the apparatus. The separated fields are spaced 109 cm apart. Electric quadrupole transitions in RbF in the radiofrequency range have been observed with a single oscillating field; as yet the separated oscillating fields pattern has not been observed. High precision studies of internal nuclear-molecular interactions are planned, including a search for nuclear polarizability in molecular electric fields.[2]

*This work has been supported by the National Aeronautics and Space Administration.

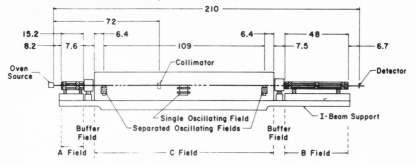

Fig. 1. Field arrangement of molecular beam electric resonance apparatus

REFERENCES

1. V. W. Hughes, Rev. Sci. Instr. *30*, 689 (1959).
2. Gunther-Mohr, Geschwind, and Townes, Phys. Rev. *81*, 289 (1951).

DISCUSSION

G. BIRNBAUM: Could you comment on the potential of the electric as compared with the magnetic beam resonance method for use as a frequency standard?

V. W. HUGHES: The primary advantage of the molecular beam electric resonance method is the number of opportunities it offers for choosing millimeter wavelength rotational state transitions in molecules having permanent electric dipole moments. Also, electric dipole transitions are used so that microwave power even in the millimeter wavelength range is not a serious problem. Electric rather than magnetic deflecting fields are used. The principal disadvantage of the molecular beam electric resonance method is that only a single rotational state in the beam can be used and hence for molecules requiring a high temperature source there is a considerable loss in useful beam intensity.

F. H. REDER: There does not seem to be any advantage for achieving higher accuracy in an atomic frequency standard by going from Cs atoms to LiF molecules.

1. The bandwidth will most likely be larger because of the higher oven temperature.

2. The signal-to-noise ratio will be considerably lower because of the unfavorable partition function and the decreased detector efficiency.

Even with constant bandwidth, the signal-to-noise ratio would have to be less than 10 times worse than in the case of Cs to yield any advantage caused by the 10 times higher Q (because of 10 times higher frequency).

It is felt that any small advantage in precision achieved by using LiF could also be achieved with present Cs devices by selection of slower atoms.

V. W. HUGHES: In answer to Dr. Reder's remarks, I might say that the principal point of our work at present is to investigate a new approach to a molecular frequency standard. It is well known that frequencies of hfs transitions in atoms do not exist in the millimeter wavelength range and it is generally agreed that a useful approach to higher precision frequency standards it to try to use higher frequency transitions. The molecular beam electric resonance method,* whose possibilities for frequency standard applications we are studying, has the primary advantage of allowing a wide choice of molecular rotational state transitions in the millimeter, as well as other, wavelength ranges. In principle, a frequency standard based on the molecular beam electric resonance method will be similar to the Cs atomic beam standard except that electric deflecting fields and electric dipole transitions rather than magnetic deflecting fields and magnetic dipole transitions will be employed. The electric resonance method will allow the use of any molecule with an adequately large permanent electric dipole moment.

Our present interest in Li^6F^{19} is largely due to the fact that it appears to be the most favorable of the alkali halide mole-

*P. Kusch and V. W. Hughes, "Atomic and Molecular Beam Spectroscopy," Handbuch der Physik, Vol. XXXVII/1 (1959).

cules, which are easily detectable by the hot wire surface ionization detector. It is true that the high temperature source required for LiF would imply that only a small fraction of the molecules in the beam are in the $J = 0$ rotational state we propose to use. Indeed, this is the principal disadvantage to the use of alkali halide molecules. I might mention that I understand that at MIT studies are in progress of the possibility of the use of CO by the molecular beam electric resonance method. A low temperature source can be used, thus avoiding the intensity loss. For CO, however, a universal detector must be used.

As to Dr. Reder's detailed comments, the bandwidth will depend on the source temperature and C-field length, of course, and could be the same as for Cs. The detection efficiency for Li need not necessarily be less than for Cs if an oxygenated detector wire is used. For a given bandwidth, the signal-to-noise may be less for LiF than Cs, as you say. In my recent article in the Review of Scientific Instruments,* I give a more quantitative discussion of these considerations.

In general, however, as regards a frequency standard, the principal point I wish to make is that the molecular beam electric resonance method appears to offer interesting possibilities and extends greatly the molecules which may be used. I feel that it is too early for us to make detailed engineering comparisons with the well-developed Cs standard.

Finally, I must admit to our ulterior interest in doing very high precision molecular spectroscopy (~ several hundred cycle per second linewidth) by the molecular beam electric resonance method with separated oscillating fields.

M. STITCH: What would you use for a source to get your 100 KMc for excitation?

V. W. HUGHES: Since very low power is required, we can use harmonic multiplication. Actually only about 1 microwatt is needed.

*V. W. Hughes, Rev. of Sci. Instr. *30*, 689 (1959).

THE ZERO-FIELD SOLID STATE MASER AS A POSSIBLE TIME STANDARD

N. BLOEMBERGEN

Harvard University

THE USEFULNESS of the ammonia beam maser as an atomic clock[1] and of the three-level solid state maser[2] as a low-noise microwave amplifier have been well established. The traveling wave[3] and zero-field[4] modifications are also well known. It is the purpose of this note to point out that the zero-field version of a solid state maser may have superior qualities as a frequency standard.

The width of the resonance line used in a clock should be narrow, but should be rather broad in an amplifier. In ruby and $K_3Co(CN)_6$ with low Cr^{+++} concentration ($N < 3 \times 10^{18}$ Cr^{+++} ions/cm^3), the line width is determined by internal magnetic fields from the Al and N nuclear moments respectively, and is of the order of 2 Mc/sec. At higher concentrations, e.g. ruby with 2 percent Cr ($N = 2.35 \times 10^{19}$ ions/cm^3), the line width is determined by dipole-dipole interactions between the Cr^{+++} ions and is more than 30 Mc/sec. These line widths are orders of magnitude larger than the line width of 4 kc/sec in the ammonia beam maser.

Consider, however, the line width in zero field of ions with integral spin in a crystalline field with rhombic or lower symmetry. Examples are Ni^{++} in a number of sulphates with $S = 1$, and Cr^{++} in $CrSO_4 \cdot 5H_2O$ with $S = 2$.

Many other Ni^{++} and Cr^{++} compounds, of which the microwave spectrum has not yet been investigated, should also satisfy this criterion. The $2S + 1$ levels are nondegenerate. There is no Kramers degeneracy left. As a consequence, the magnetic moment operator has no diagonal matrix elements. In first order an external magnetic field H_0 produces no shift in the energy levels. The internal magnetic fields from nuclear spins and impurity magnetic ions of other species produce no broadening in first approximation. Interactions between ions of the same kind, however, contribute in first order to the width because of the simultaneous flip-flop of two ions between the same pair of energy levels.[5]

Other ions with integral S and no nuclear spin I may be found among the rare earth elements. Ions which have both half-integral values of S and I will have integral F values in zero field. If the hyperfine coupling is sufficiently anisotropic, the states will again be nondegenerate. The same is true in principle for integral nuclear spins (B^{10} with $I = 3$, N^{14} with $I = 1$) in electric field gradients of non-axial symmetry. In these cases, the splittings between levels will fall in the megacycle range and they are not suitable for the present purpose.

Consider as an example a very dilute Tutton salt, $(NH_4)_2Zn(Ni)(SO_4)_2 \cdot 6H_2O$ with $N = 3 \times 10^{16}$ Ni^{++} cm^{-3}. The pump frequency is $\nu_{13} = 75,000$ Mc/sec and the oscillator maser frequency is $\nu_{23} = 29,000$ Mc/sec. The protons produce a second-order broadening of 0.7 kc/sec. Further narrowing by a factor of 10 could be achieved in the deuterated salt. The broadening by other Ni^{++} ions in the very dilute salt may be estimated by the method of Kittel and Abrahams,[6] and amounts to 1.2 kc/sec. The broadening due to the interaction with the lattice vibrations is equal to the inverse spin lattice relaxation time. At 1.5°K, this contribution will be less than 1 kc/sec, since presumably $T_1 > 1.5 \times 10^{-4}$ sec.

Therefore, a line width comparable to the ammonia beam transition of about 4 kc/sec could be obtained in the solid, if the uniformity of the crystalline field splitting could be made better than $1 : 10$.[7]

In practice, the line width will be limited by stress fields around dislocations and impurities. Conversely, the width of the zero-field lines affords a measurement of such imperfections. The concentration of magnetic ions may be chosen so high that the dipolar width becomes comparable to the crystalline field inhomogeneity. The width should be measured in frequency, as the width in oersted will naturally tend to infinity for these field-independent transitions. Extrapolation of observations in finite fields appear to indicate that the crystalline field inhomogeneity will usually be larger than 4 Mc/sec, or about $1 : 10^4$.

It is possible, however, that most of this inhomogeneity is due to mosaic structure, causing a distribution in grain orientation of the order of a few minutes of arc with respect to the externally applied field. Then the true zero-field line would be much narrower. It is also possible that a few crystallites of great perfection may give a sharper, frequency-determining pip on a broad background.

For the purpose of comparison with the ammonia maser, it will be assumed that the line width is 4 Mc/sec and that the concentration of magnetic ions can be chosen so high that the dipolar broadening is comparable to the inhomogeneous broadening of crystal fields. Under these circumstances it is reasonable to assume[4] that a value

$$Q_M = (4 \pi \chi'' \eta)^{-1} = -25$$

can be achieved at 1.5 °K. The filling factor η of a transmission line filled with polycrystalline magnetic salt can be at least 0.5 and χ'' is the powder susceptibility at the maser resonance. The ions of half-integral spin Fe^{+++} and Gd^{+++} may be considered also, when line widths over 1 Mc/sec are assumed. The nuclear spin broadening of Fe^{+++} in TiO_2 is negligible and an external field which would split the Kramers doublets may be kept below 10^{-2} oersted in a superconducting microwave structure. The crystalline field has low symmetry which allows for zero-field maser operation between three Kramers doublets. Peter[7] reports lines of 200 Mc/sec for Fe^{+++} in $MgWO_4$, although not in zero field. Since the Fe^{+++} concentration is low and cannot be increased, this material is not suitable for the present purpose.

Consider a length l of transmission line filled with well annealed magnetic crystals and shorted at one end. The propagation constant in the transmission line is (for $\eta = 1$)

$$\gamma_m = \gamma_o \, \varepsilon^{\frac{1}{2}} [1 + 4 \pi (\chi' - i \chi'')]^{\frac{1}{2}} \approx$$
$$\gamma_o \, \varepsilon^{\frac{1}{2}} (1 + 2 \pi \chi') - 2 \pi i \gamma_o \, \varepsilon^{\frac{1}{2}} \chi'' \quad (1)$$

where $\gamma_o = 2 \pi / \lambda_g$ is the propagation constant in the empty transmission line. The losses in the superconducting walls are neg-
lected but could easily be corrected for by a complex γ_o.

An adjustable discontinuity produces a complex reflection coefficient Γ. The boundary conditions require

$$e^{-2 i \gamma_m l} = \Gamma = |\Gamma| e^{i \varphi} \quad (2)$$

The phase φ or length l is adjusted so that the imaginary part of
this equation is satisfied for $\chi' = 0$. The magnitude of the re-
flection $|\Gamma|$ is then adjusted for marginal oscillation, i.e.
slightly larger than $\exp (+ 8 \pi^2 \varepsilon^{\frac{1}{2}} \chi'' l / \lambda_g)$, where χ'' is the negative unsaturated value at resonance. The condition (2) will
then be satisfied by a partial saturation at the signal frequency,
which determines the power level of the microwave field. With
$Q_M = -25$ and $|\Gamma|$ between one third and two thirds, about
twelve guide wave lengths should produce oscillation. This
leads to the simple experimental arrangement shown in Fig. 1,
which should be practicable for $\nu_{13} > \nu_{12} > 30$ kmc/sec. A random frequency modulation on the pump power assures greater
stability of the oscillator frequency. The entire narrow resonance ν_{13} is pumped in an incoherent manner.

The advantage of the solid clock is that cavity pulling is essentially eliminated. Although the spin resonance may be a
thousand times broader than the ammonia inversion line, the
$Q_o \sim 5,000$ of the cavity is replaced by the wave guide with a
"Q" near unity. Furthermore, the thermal expansion is reduced
by a factor 10^6 compared to its value near room temperature according to Gruneisen's law. The operation at low temperature
should insure extremely good long-range stability, because
chemical and physical changes do not readily occur. The power
output is large and spontaneous emission noise is negligible.

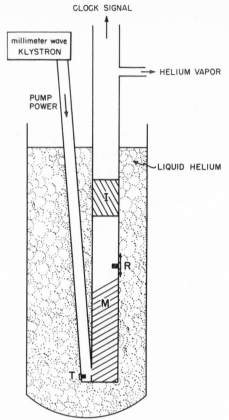

Fig. 1. The solid clock

The millimeter wave pump power has a random frequency modulation, T is a tuner.

The signal wave guide is filled with the magnetic material M with at least three zero-field energy levels. It contains helium vapor at a well-regulated temperature and pressure of about 10^{-3} mm Hg. The precision variable probe R is adjusted for marginal oscillation. The isolator I eliminates load pulling. A rejection filter for pump power may also be added.

The effect of temperature and pressure variations on the resonant frequency of the spins can be kept small. Walsh[8] has shown that the volume effect of a paramagnetic spin resonance may be described by $\Delta \nu / \nu_{12} = \alpha \, \Delta V / V_o$, where the constant α is between 0.5 and 3 for many compounds. If the pressure of the helium vapor necessary to keep the maser salt at a constant temperature is kept low ($\sim 10^{-3}$ cm Hg) and regulated to $\sim 10^{-4}$ cm Hg, frequency variations are limited to $\Delta \nu / \nu_{12} < 1 : 10^{11}$. The temperature variation of a resonant frequency near absolute zero of temperature should also become vanishingly small. Although no experimental data are available below $4\,°$K, it is estimated that the spin frequency variation should be smaller than $1 : 10^{10}$ for a temperature variation from $1.50\,°$K to $1.51\,°$K.

The susceptibility $\chi' - i\,\chi''$ itself obeys Curie's law and would change by 0.7 percent for a temperature variation of $10^{-2}\,°$K near $1.5\,°$K. Exactly at spin resonance χ' will remain zero and χ'' will not change either because the condition (2) remains satisfied by a slight change in the saturation level. The same holds true for variations in pump power. In practice, however, χ' will not be tuned exactly at resonance. Assume that the length l or the phase shift φ can be adjusted to within $1 : 10^{3}$ of a guide wave length or radian. Then it may deduced from (2) that the oscillator frequency may deviate from exact resonance by an amount $10^{-3}\,\Delta\nu$, where $\Delta\nu$ is the width of the spin resonance. If now a temperature variation of 1 percent occurs, a change in saturation levels keeps χ'' constant, but χ' is kept constant by a change in oscillator frequency $10^{-5}\,\Delta\nu$. For $\Delta\nu = 4 \times 10^{6}$ cps this amounts to 60 cps, or a variation of about $1 : 10^{9}$ in the oscillator frequency.

It appears that the crucial factor is how well one can adjust the reflection coefficient to the center of a relatively broad spin resonance. If a suitable magnetic salt with a line width smaller than 1 Mc/sec can be found, the solid clock could well be competitive with atomic beam and vapor clocks. Even for broader, already observed, resonances the solid clock may have some usefulness as a time standard over longer periods. More knowledge about crystalline field imperfections can and should be obtained from zero-field resonances.

REFERENCES

1. Gordon, Zeiger, and Townes, Phys. Rev. *99*, 1264 (1955).
2. N. Bloembergen, Phys. Rev. *104*, 324 (1956).
3. deGrasse, Schulz-du Bois, and Scovil, *BSTJ* 38, 305 (1959).
4. G. S. Bogle and H. R. Symmons, Austr. J. of Phys. *12*, 1 (1959).

5. A. Abragam and K. Kambe, Phys. Rev. *91*, 894 (1953). The specific case of interest, integral spin in non-axial field, has not yet been analysed, although the procedure is straightforward.
6. C. Kittel and E. Abrahams, Phys. Rev. *90*, 238 (1953).
7. M. Peter, Phys. Rev. *113*, 801 (1959).
8. W. M. Walsh, Phys. Rev. (to be published), thesis, Harvard University (1958).

DISCUSSION

W. LOW: There are in general several mechanisms giving rise to inhomogeneous broadening in spin resonance. One of these is a random distribution of the parameters in the spin Hamiltonian, i.e., variations in the initial splitting. The other is misorientation of various crystallites. This gives rise to a broadening if an external magnetic field is applied. One can discriminate between these two by measuring so-called forbidden transitions which, to first order, are independent of the crystal field parameters. In many cases the linewidth corresponding to these transitions is narrower than the usual $\Delta M = \pm 1$ transition. The residual linewidth may be caused in part by the misorientation of crystallites. Experiments along these lines are under way in our laboratory.

POLARIZATION OF NUCLEI AND GENERATION OF RADIOFREQUENCY ENERGY BY NUCLEAR PRECESSION

J. COMBRISSON

Centre d'Études Nucléaires de Saclay, France

WE SHALL describe some work done recently at the "Centre d'Études Nucléaires de Saclay" and we first want to stress it has been achieved by several of Dr. Abragam's collaborators whose names appear in the bibliography of the present article. In studying nuclear polarization, we are concerned with basic studies in magnetic resonance with, as a practical application, the possibility of providing nuclear physicists with polarized targets. Of course every time we get negative nuclear polarization we can theoretically obtain radiofrequency energy. Whether this energy is enough to compensate the losses in the circuit into which the sample is incorporated, is a matter of experimental conditions. In many cases, the energy stored by the spin system is not enough to provide oscillations, in others we actually have oscillations, and in a particular case, which we shall describe in detail, our maser has a practical application (earth's field magnetometer) and can be thoroughly studied quantitatively and qualitatively. That is, we can predict its behavior by combining Bloch's equations and the electric circuit equations.

As we have been dealing with nuclear spins, the frequencies involved extend from 2 kc/s (H_o = 0.5 gauss) to 50 Mc/s (H_o = 12,000 gauss) in the case of protons. The polarization implies an irradiation at an electronic resonance frequency which ranges from a few Mc/s to 32,000 Mc/s. A coil or a cavity is used for this irradiation. The nuclear polarization is checked by a nuclear resonance apparatus, the sensitive part of which is the coil containing the sample. In the cases where spontaneous oscillations occur, a voltage at the Larmor frequency of the polarized nuclei appears at the terminals of this coil.

We shall not describe here the experimental schemes which can be found in the literature.[1],[2],[3],[4],[5] We shall just mention that they can be different one from the other, depending upon the frequency, the temperature, or the relaxation times involved in each case.

BASIC PRINCIPLES OF DYNAMIC POLARIZATION

Let us consider a system of nuclear spins $\vec{I}$ and of electronic spins $\vec{S}$ with their gyromagnetic ratios γ_I, γ_S. Let us suppose I and S are $\frac{1}{2}$ and call N_+, N_- the number of spins $\vec{S}$ in the states $+\frac{1}{2}$ and $-\frac{1}{2}$ and n_+, n_- the number of spins $\vec{I}$ in the states $+\frac{1}{2}$ and $-\frac{1}{2}$. $W(+-) \rightarrow (-+)$ will be a transition probability flipping the nuclear spins from $I_z = +\frac{1}{2}$ to $I_z = -\frac{1}{2}$ and the electronic spins from $S_z = -\frac{1}{2}$ to $S_z = +\frac{1}{2}$.

Overhauser Effect. In the case of scalar coupling $(A\vec{I} \cdot \vec{S})$ between $\vec{I}$ and $\vec{S}$ and assuming the relaxation of the spins, $\vec{I}$ is only due to the coupling with spins $\vec{S}$, which means a spin $\vec{I}$ will flip only if a spin $\vec{S}$ flips at the same time, we can write for the steady state distribution of populations

$$n_+ N_- W(+-) \rightarrow (-+) = n_- N_+ W(-+) \rightarrow (+-). \tag{1}$$

As is well known, the W's are unequal and

$$\frac{W(+-) \rightarrow (-+)}{W(-+) \rightarrow (+-)} = \exp\left(-\hbar \frac{\gamma_S - \gamma_I}{kT} H_o\right). \tag{2}$$

Combining (1) and (2) yields

$$\frac{n_+}{n_-} \exp\left(-\frac{\hbar \gamma_I H_o}{kT}\right) = \frac{N_+}{N_-} \exp\left(-\frac{\hbar \gamma_S H_o}{kT}\right)$$

which can be written

$$<I_z> - I_o = <S_z> - S_o \tag{3}$$

where

$$<I_z> = \frac{n_+ - n_-}{n_+ + n_-} \qquad <S_z> = \frac{N_+ - N_-}{N_+ + N_-}$$

and where the exponentials have been replaced by the first terms in their development. I_o and S_o are the thermal equilibrium polarizations. When the electronic spins are saturated, $< S_z > = 0$ and $< I_z > = - S_o$, since $I_o \ll S_o$. In the case of a dipolar type of coupling between $\vec{I}$ and $\vec{S}$, one must take into account transition probabilities of the type $W(--) \leftrightarrows (++)$, $W(+-) \leftrightarrows (++)$, $W(--) \leftrightarrows (-+)$ as well as $W(+-) \leftrightarrows (-+)$. If there is movement between the spins, one can generalize Equation (3) and write[6][7]

$$< I_z > - I_o = - f \rho [< S_z > - S_o] \qquad (4)$$

where $\rho = + \frac{1}{2}$ (while ρ was -1 in the case of scalar coupling) and where f is a leakage coefficient taking into account spin lattice relaxation of spins $\vec{I}$ not due to the interaction with spins $\vec{S}$.

Solid-State Effect.[8] For nonmetallic solids, the lattice is not able to provide the necessary energy for an Overhauser effect. But $W(+-) \leftrightarrows (-+)$ or $W(++) \leftrightarrows (--)$ can be produced artificially by irradiating the sample with a radiofrequency Ω such that $\Omega = \omega_S \mp \omega_I$, which provides the energy $\hbar (\gamma_S \mp \gamma_I) H_o$.

As a matter of fact, the transitions $(++) \leftrightarrows (--)$ and $(+-) \leftrightarrows (-+)$ are not completely forbidden, a state such as $(--)$ being $(--) + \alpha (-+)$ where α^2 is the order of $\left(\dfrac{H_{SI}}{H_o} \right)^2$. H_{SI} is the static local field produced by spin $\vec{S}$ at spin $\vec{I}$.

When $(1/T_1)_S \gg W \gg (1/T_1)_I$, which can often be achieved, Equation (1) becomes

$$\frac{n_+}{n_-} = \left(\frac{N_+}{N_-} \right)_o \quad \text{or} \quad \frac{n_+}{n_-} = \left(\frac{N_-}{N_+} \right)_o .$$

Or,

$$< I_z > = \mp S_o .$$

This effect gives an enhancement of the nuclear polarization which is $\mp \gamma_S / \gamma_I$. In contradistinction with the Overhauser effect, the polarization time $1/W$ can be much shorter than the spin lattice relaxation time T_1 of the spins I, a fact which may have some practical application.

NEGATIVE POLARIZATION

We get negative polarization under the following conditions:
— scalar coupling (case of a metal or a semiconductor) when the

magnetic moment of the nucleus is negative (Overhauser).
Example: silicon 29 in silicon at room temperature.

— dipolar coupling with motion between $\vec{I}$ and $\vec{S}$ when the magnetic moment of the nucleus is positive (Overhauser).
Example: protons of water containing a free radical.

— dipolar coupling in a nonmetallic solid where the solid-state effect always yields a negative polarization under irradiation at a frequency either $\omega_S + \omega_I$ or $\omega_S - \omega_I$.
Examples: silicon 29 in phosphorus-doped silicon at low temperature; protons in polystyrene where a free radical has been dissolved.

Of course, to get radiofrequency energy and a voltage across a coil wound around the sample, the magnetization per unit volume M_o of this sample and the Q of the coil must be such that[9]

$$Q \geqslant (2\pi\eta T_2 |\gamma M_o|)^{-1} \tag{5}$$

where η is a filling factor and T_2 is the transverse relaxation time of the nuclei.

EXPERIMENTAL RESULTS

We shall list the cases when negative nuclear polarization has actually been obtained in our laboratory:

— Silicon 29 in phosphorus-doped silicon at $2°$K through the Overhauser effect (silicon with 10^{28} P/cm^3) or through the solid-state effect (silicon with $5 \cdot 10^{16}$ P/cm^3).[5] The enhancements obtained for the nuclear signals are about 100 (theoretical gain 3,300) and taking into account the rather small moment and small abundance of Si29, condition (5) cannot be fulfilled.

— Protons in polystyrene where D.P.P.H. is dissolved can be polarized at low temperature through the solid-state effect.[10] A polarization of 3 percent was obtained in a field of 12,500 gauss and though oscillation did occur only with a reaction amplifier, a few experimental arrangements could very well provide a maser operating at the proton Larmor frequency (50 Mc/s).

— Protons in water containing the free radical peroxylamine disulfonate, $(SO_3)_2NOK_2$. This free radical exhibits at high field a triplet hyperfine structure (width of each line $\simeq 1$ gauss). It is possible to saturate one of these lines and consequently enhance the nuclear resonance signals of the protons in the water (or of other nuclei dissolved in it).[2],[3]

Taking into account the triplet structure and the factor $\rho = \frac{1}{2}$, the best obtainable enhancement is $\frac{1}{2} \cdot \frac{1}{3} \cdot \frac{\gamma_c}{\gamma_H} = 100$.

This factor 100 has been obtained and it makes M_o of the protons big enough to satisfy Equation (5) with a Q of the coil equal to 20. The experiment is performed at 3,000 gauss with an irradiation frequency of 9,000 Mc/s and a proton resonance frequency of 12 Mc/s. Figure 1 shows a typical enhancement of a proton signal, and one can note that M_o is negative. The two traces are taken with a ratio 50 in the gains of the amplifier. Figure 2 shows a stimulated emission obtained for three different Larmor frequencies of the protons when sweeping the field H_o and saturating one after the other the three lines of the free radical spectrum. The coil wound around the sample is connected directly to a wide-band amplifier followed by a detection system. Such a maser might be useful as a source of oscillation, the frequency of which is locked to a magnetic field. The most spectacular result is obtained at very low field (earth's

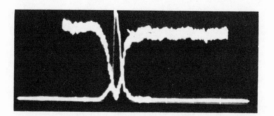

Fig. 1. Proton resonance signals at 9000 Mc/s with and without enhancement

(the gain has been reduced by a factor 50 between the two traces)

field) where the theoretical enhancement is 3,800 (as a consequence of the zero field splitting of the electronic lines) and where a maser can be operated giving directly the Larmor fre-

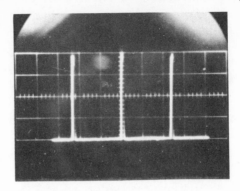

Fig. 2. Oscillations due to the nuclear precession of protons in water containing a free radical

quency of the protons in the earth's magnetic field.   A magnetometer consists of:
— a sample (100 cm^3) of water containing $(SO_3)_2 NOK_2$
— a coil connected to a 55 Mc/s power oscillator
— a coil across the terminals of which appears the proton Larmor frequency (2,000 c/s)
— a low frequency amplifier and a frequency meter.

A SIMPLE THEORY OF THE EARTH'S FIELD MASER

The macroscopic magnetic moment $\vec{M}$ of the protons can be represented in the rotating frame (rotating frequency ω) by Bloch's equations

$$\frac{dM_x}{dt} = (\omega_o - \omega) M_y - \gamma H_y M_z - \frac{M_x}{T_2}$$

$$\frac{dM_y}{dt} = -(\omega_o - \omega) M_x + \gamma H_x M_z - \frac{M_y}{T_2} \qquad (6)$$

$$\frac{dM_z}{dt} = \gamma (H_y M_x - H_x M_y) - \frac{M_z - M_o}{T_1}.$$

In an auto-oscillator, the field H_1 is produced by the induced current due to the nuclear magnetization in the coil.   We now write the differential equation relating the magnetic field $\vec{H}$ in the coil (resonant frequency ω_c, quality factor Q) to the mean magnetization M_H along $\vec{H}$ in the sample.

$$\frac{d^2 H}{dt^2} + \frac{\omega_c}{Q} \frac{dH}{dt} + \omega_c^2 H = -4\pi\eta \frac{d^2 M_H}{dt^2}$$

where η is a filling factor for the sample in the coil. Solution of (6) and (7) gives the behavior of the system.

Steady-State Solution. We look for a solution where M and H_1 are stationary in the rotating frame. We can choose its phase in order to have this steady-state solution in the plane yoz: $M_x = 0$. H can be written

$$H = -2H_1 \sin(\omega t + \delta) \tag{7}$$

(The origin of time has been chosen such that $M_H = M_y \cos \omega t$) with

$$ty\ \delta = Q\ \frac{\omega_c^2 - \omega^2}{\omega\ \omega_c} \tag{8}$$

and

$$H_1 = -2\pi\eta Q \cos \delta\ \frac{\omega}{\omega_c} \cdot M_y. \tag{9}$$

We shall keep only one rotating component of $\vec{H}_1$ stationary in the rotating frame.

$$H_x = H_1 \cos \delta \qquad H_y = H_1 \sin \delta$$

Bloch's equations become

$$\frac{dM_x}{dt} = (\omega_o - \omega)M_y - \gamma H_1 \sin \delta M_z = 0$$

$$\frac{dM_y}{dt} = \gamma H_1 \cos \delta M_z - \frac{M_y}{T_2} = 0 \tag{10}$$

$$\frac{dM_z}{dt} = -\gamma H_1 \cos \delta M_y - \frac{M_z - M_o}{T_1} = 0$$

Frequency pulling. The two first equations in (10) give

$$-T_2(\omega_o - \omega) = ty\ \delta$$

or
$$\omega - \omega_o = \frac{\Delta \omega_o}{\Delta \omega_o - \Delta \omega_c} \cdot (\omega_c - \omega_o)$$

with $\Delta \omega_o = 1/T_2$, width of the proton resonance line, and $\Delta \omega_c = \omega_c/2Q$, width of the circuit resonance.

Condition for oscillations. M_y and M_z can be written

$$\left. \begin{array}{l} M_y^2 = \dfrac{T_2}{T_1} \cdot M_o \cdot \dfrac{\omega_c}{\omega} \dfrac{Q_o}{Q \cos^2 \delta} \left(1 - \dfrac{\omega_c}{\omega} \cdot \dfrac{Q_o}{Q \cos^2 \delta} \right) \\[4mm] M_z = M_o \cdot \dfrac{Q_o}{Q \cos^2 \delta} \end{array} \right\} \qquad (11)$$

where

$$Q_o = (- 2 \pi \eta \gamma T_2 M_o)^{-1}$$

with $\omega = \omega_c = \omega_o$, $\delta = 0$ we get oscillations if $Q \gtrless Q_o$. Now if, Q being fixed, the circuit is detuned ($\omega_c \neq \omega_o$), oscillations still occur for

$$\frac{|\omega_c - \omega_o|}{\omega_o} \leqslant \frac{1}{2} \sqrt{\left(\frac{1}{Q_o} - \frac{1}{Q} \right) \frac{1}{Q}}.$$

The range of oscillations is maximum for $Q = 2Q_o$.

Dynamical Solutions. Equations (6) and (7) would be difficult to solve completely but we can consider the time constant of the electric circuit to be short compared with T_1 and T_2. H_1 follows M instantaneously and we can still use Equations (8) and (9). The system becomes

$$\left. \begin{array}{l} M_x = 0 \\[3mm] \dfrac{dM_y}{dt} = \dfrac{M_y}{T_2} \left[\dfrac{M_z}{M_o} \cdot \dfrac{Q \cos^2 \delta}{Q_o} - 1 \right] \\[4mm] \dfrac{dM_z}{dt} = - \dfrac{1}{T_2} \dfrac{M_y^2}{M_o} \dfrac{Q \cos^2 \delta}{Q_o} - \dfrac{M_z - M_o}{T_1} \end{array} \right\} \qquad (12)$$

We shall write $M_y = \overline{M_y} + m_y$, $M_z = \overline{M_z} + m_z$, where $\overline{M_y}$, $\overline{M_z}$ are the steady-state solutions and where m_y, m_z are small fluctuations around them. Equations (12) become

$$\frac{dm_y}{dt} = \frac{1}{T_2} \frac{\overline{M_y}}{M_o} - \frac{Q \cos^2 \delta}{Q_o} m_z$$

$$\frac{dm_z}{dt} = -\frac{2}{T_2} \frac{\overline{M_y}}{M_o} \frac{Q \cos^2 \delta}{Q_o} m_y - \frac{m_z}{T_1}$$

(13)

with

$$\overline{M_y} = M_o \sqrt{\frac{T_2}{T_1} \left(1 - \frac{Q_o}{Q \cos^2 \delta}\right)} \frac{Q_o}{Q \cos^2 \delta} .$$

Solving (13) gives

$$\frac{Q \cos^2 \delta}{Q_o} \leqslant 1 + \frac{1}{8} \frac{T_2}{T_1} ,$$

i.e. just above the oscillation condition. There is an exponential return to the steady-state solution with the time constant T, such as

$$\frac{1}{T} = \frac{1}{2T_1} \mp \frac{1}{2\sqrt{T_1 T_2}} \cdot \sqrt{\frac{T_2}{T_1} + 8 - \frac{8 Q \cos^2 \delta}{Q_o}} .$$

For

$$\frac{Q \cos^2 \delta}{Q_o} > 1 + \frac{1}{8} \frac{T_2}{T_1} ,$$

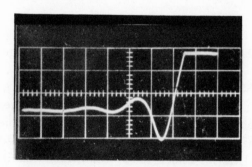

Fig. 3. Oscillations in the output of the maser

there is a damped oscillation with a time constant $2T_1$ and a frequency

$$\Omega = \frac{1}{2\sqrt{T_1 T_2}} \sqrt{\frac{8Q \cos^2 \delta}{Q_o} - 8 - \frac{T_2}{T_1}}.$$

For example, with $T_1 = T_2$ and $\delta = 0$, the critical damping is obtained for $Q = \frac{9}{8} Q_o$. With $Q = 2Q_o$, the oscillation will exist with a frequency $1/2T_1 \cdot \sqrt{7}$. These oscillations are shown in Fig. 3.

Considerations on the noise and more details on the precision measurements of the earth's magnetic field can be found in the reference[9] by I. Solomon. Part of this article is an abstract of that publication.

REFERENCES

1. A. Abragam, J. Combrisson, and I. Solomon, C. R. Acad. Sci. *245*, 157 (1957).
2. A. Landesman, C. R. Acad. Sci. *246*, 1538 (1958).
3. E. Allais, C. R. Acad. Sci. *246*, 2123 (1958).
4. J. Combrisson, J. Phys. Rad. *19*, 840 (1958).
5. J. Combrisson and I. Solomon, J. Phys. Rad. *20*, 683 (1959).
6. A. Abragam, Phys. Rev. *98*, 1729 (1955).
7. I. Solomon, Phys. Rev. *99*, 529 (1955).
8. A. Abragam and W. G. Proctor, C. R. Acad. Sci. *246*, 1538 (1958).
9. I. Solomon, "Théorie de l'auto-oscillateur nucleaire utilisé pour la mesure du champ magnétique terrestre," C.E.A. report, unpublished.
10. M. Borghini and A. Abragam, C. R. Acad. Sci. *248*, 1803 (1959).

DISCUSSION

H. J. GERRITSEN: What was the Q value at the signal frequency?

J. COMBRISSON: Noise considerations which I have not mentioned here show that the best Q for the low frequency circuit is $2Q_o$ (Q_o = critical value for oscillations). A value of Q around $2Q_o$ is obtained by introducing some feedback into the low frequency amplifier. Under these conditions, oscillations occur and are very stable.

SPONTANEOUS RADIATION FROM LIQUID HELIUM 3 FOLLOWING AN ADIABATIC FAST PASSAGE*

H. E. RORSCHACH, Jr., AND F. J. LOW
The Rice Institute, Houston, Texas

WE HAVE RECENTLY observed nuclear maser operation following an adiabatic fast passage in liquid helium 3. Somewhat different observations of radiation damping and nuclear maser operation in benzene have been recently reported by Szöke and Meiboom.[1] Our measurements show several radiation bursts similar to those observed in electron resonance by Feher *et al.*[2] and Chester *et al.*[3] We believe these radiation bursts are due to energy exchange between the nuclear system and the tuned circuit as described by Bloembergen and Pound[4] and Senitzky.[5]

Figure 1 is a schematic of the nuclear resonance apparatus. Two different lengths of transmission line have been used to connect the resonant circuit in the helium dewar with the Rollin-type detector at room temperature. If the resonant circuit is matched to the transmission line, then the detector output is proportional to the absorption mode if the line is one-quarter wavelength long and to the dispersion mode if the line is one-eighth wavelength long. Since an adiabatic fast passage signal is a dispersion signal, it was necessary to tune the signal generator to one side of the resonant frequency of the dewar circuit in order to observe a signal when the quarter wavelength line was used. The detector is then sensitive to both the absorption and the dispersion modes.

Adiabatic fast passage measurements were made to determine the equilibrium magnetization M_0 and the relaxation times T_1

*Supported in part by a grant from the National Science Foundation

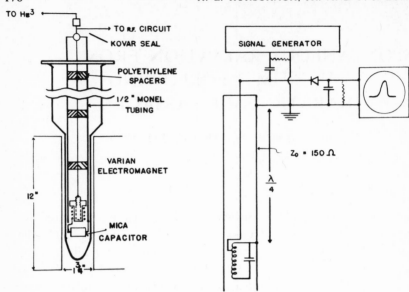

Fig. 1. Schematic of nuclear resonance apparatus

and T_2. The helium-3 sample chambers were $\frac{1}{8}$ inch $\times$ $\frac{3}{4}$ inch
cylinders and were machined in nylon. For H_o = 10 kg, values
of T_1 were obtained ranging from 100 sec to 320 sec. These
variations were presumably due to the varying importance of
wall relaxation for the various chambers. The measured values
of T_2 were limited by the diffusion time to the walls, where dephasing could occur, and varied from 30 sec to greater than 100
sec.

Most of the observed signals were ordinary Lorentzian signals
as predicted by the Bloch equations.[6] However, at the lowest
temperatures, nuclear maser action was observed when the
magnetization exceeded a critical value. Figure 2 shows a
typical fast-passage signal followed by three bursts of radiation. This signal was observed with the quarter wavelength
transmission line. For this sample chamber, T_1 = 320 sec and
T_2 = 30 sec. The temperature was 1.3°K, H_o = 10 kg, and H_1 =
3 g. The bursts have a repetition frequency of about 50 cps,
and the envelope of the decay has a time-constant of about 20
msec. The signal amplitude is 20 mv. For a given value of

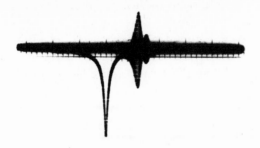

Fig. 2. Typical fast-passage signals followed by bursts of radiation

H_1 and dH_o/dt, there is a critical value of the magnetization below which the radiation does not occur. Smaller values of H_1 and dH_o/dt favor a smaller critical magnetization. An adiabatic fast passage immediately following the radiation bursts shows that the magnitude of M_z is diminished but still inverted.

The observations of Szöke and Meiboom[1] were made under conditions such that the time constant for radiation damping, τ_r, was smaller than the transverse relaxation time, T_2. Under these conditions, the magnetization returns to equilibrium through radiating states. Their results were reported to be consistent with a theory of Bloom[7] which treats this case. The theory of Bloom does not seem to be directly applicable to our results. Although his theory predicts a critical value of M when the induced field is equal to H_1, this condition cannot be satisfied in our case with $H_1 = 3$ gauss. Since the magnetization is still observed to be inverted following the radiation, we also conclude that the system does not return to equilibrium through radiating states, and that therefore τ_r is larger than the inhomogenity-produced T_2. The successive radiation bursts appear to be due to energy exchange between the tuned circuit, which has a Q of about 500, and the nuclear system. This exchange has been described qualitatively by Bloembergen and Pound[4] and by Senitzky,[5] but the appropriate coupled nonlinear equations have not been solved for our case in which M makes a large angle with H_o. The 20 msec decay time of the envelope is primarily due to the inhomogeneity-produced transverse relaxation, although radiation damping and receiver band-pass may have some effect.

Figure 3 shows a signal obtained when an eighth wavelength line was used. A critical value of M is again observed, but the radiation occurs when the transverse component of M is largest,

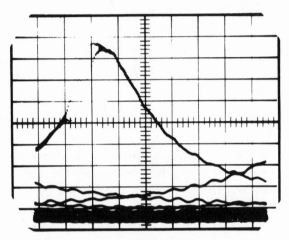

Fig. 3. Signal obtained with use of eighth wavelength line

instead of on the tail of the fast-passage signal. In this case, the signal generator is tuned to the resonant frequency of the dewar circuit, and the dispersion signal only is observed. The energy exchange is very small under these conditions. With the eighth wavelength line, we have not so far observed any signals of the type shown in Fig. 2.

REFERENCES

1. A. Szöke and S. Meiboom, Phys. Rev. *113*, 585 (1959).
2. G. Feher, J. P. Gordon, E. Buehler, E. A. Gere, and C. D. Thurmond, Phys. Rev. *109*, 221 (1958).
3. P. F. Chester, P. E. Wagner, and J. G. Castle, Jr., Phys. Rev. *110*, 281 (1958).
4. N. Bloombergen and R. V. Pound, Phys. Rev. *95*, 9 (1954).
5. I. R. Senitzky, Phys. Rev. Lett. *1*, 167 (1958).
6. F. Bloch, Phys. Rev. *70*, 460 (1946).
7. S. Bloom, J. Applied Phys. *28*, 800 (1957).

N. BLOEMBERGEN: The dependence of the effect on sweep rate dH_o/dt suggests that the magnetization is not completely inverted on passage. The conditions are then similar to those responsible for the occurrence of "wiggles."

H. E. RORSCHACH: We have observed "wiggles" for very rapid passage, but we believe that we have satisfied the adiabatic fast-passage conditions as required by the Bloch equations, for the cases discussed.

LOW TEMPERATURE STUDIES ON SPIN-LATTICE INTERACTION IN SOLIDS*

C. F. SQUIRE, S. M. DAY, A. C. THORSEN, AND T. W. ADAIR

The Rice Institute, Houston, Texas

MAGNETIC COOLING experiments below 1°K have been carried out to explore the state of magnetization after electron spin interaction has set in at very low entropy values. For this work and electron resonance studies, we have built a liquid-nitrogen-cooled solenoid for high fields at low power consumption. We will here describe the equipment for this development. Our main contribution is to point out what we believe to be a new result in nuclear spin lattice relaxation time measurements. The possible influence of electron spins should be kept in mind in discussing our experiments.

We have investigated the exponential growth of nuclear polarization of I^{127} in a single crystal of KI at liquid helium temperatures 1.5°K–4°K and found an interesting new behavior. In Fig. 1, we show the experimental points of the intensity of the nuclear resonance absorption, using for a short time a measuring r-f field too weak to disturb the polarization, plotted against the time in minutes. The temperature is 4.2°K and the external field, H_o, remained steady at 6.3 kilogauss. The solid curves through the two sets of experimental points give the characteristic relaxation time, T_1, which usually describes the approach to thermal equilibrium.

The fact that there are two curves is the point of this communication. The upper curve with the long time constant, $T_1 = 560$ min, is observed by starting at zero time with zero external field and then turning on a field H_o. The single crystal of KI

*Supported by the Robert A. Welch Foundation

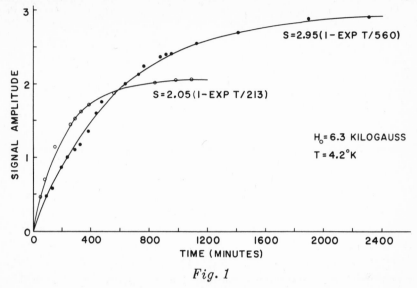

$$S = 2.95(1 - EXP\ T/560)$$

$$S = 2.05(1 - EXP\ T/213)$$

$H_o = 6.3$ KILOGAUSS

$T = 4.2°K$

Fig. 1

had been at 4.2°K and in zero magnetic field for several hours prior to starting the growth curve shown. The lower curve with the shorter time constant, T_1 = 213 min, is observed only after completion of the data for the upper curve. It is started by saturating the nuclear resonance absorption with a strong r-f field and doing this so thoroughly that there is no observable signal. Not only are the relaxation times, T_1, different for the growth from the two different initial conditions but the final signal amplitude, as shown in Fig. 1, remains different by the ratio of three to two. If the smaller signal amplitude finally does go over to the larger one, it is with a relaxation time which is longer than it would seem reasonable for us to carry out an experiment, i.e. greater than 10^4 min.

DISCUSSION

A. HONIG: What are the relaxation times at liquid hydrogen temperatures and what happens as temperature is increased?

C. F. SQUIRE: We found the value of T_1 at liquid H_2 temperatures to be the same value (16 sec), no matter which method was used to study this quantity. The temperature dependence of T_1 follows the Van Kranendonk theory above 14°K.

NUCLEAR SPIN RELAXATION AND POLARIZATION IN AN IONIC CRYSTAL

J. M. WINTER

Centre d'Étudés Nucléaires de Saclay, France

THERE IS strong evidence that in an ionic crystal the nuclear relaxation is caused mainly by paramagnetic impurities. Among the various operations contained in the dipolar coupling between the paramagnetic ion and the nucleus, the operator $A = -\frac{3}{2} \sin \theta \cos \theta \, e^{-i\varphi} S_3 I_+$ induces a nuclear flip requiring the energy $\hbar \omega_I$ (θ and φ define the orientation of the vector SI with respect to the applied field H_o).

The nuclear relaxation time T_1' due to this process is

$$\frac{1}{T_1'} = \frac{3}{2} \frac{\gamma_s^2 \gamma_I^2}{r^6} \hbar^2 \sin^2 \theta \cos^2 \theta \, S(S+1) \frac{2\tau_1}{1 + \omega_I^2 \tau_1^2} = \frac{C}{r^6} \quad (1)$$

(τ_1 is the electronic relaxation time, r the length of SI).

There is a discrepancy with experimental values. The mechanism of spin diffusion suggested by Bloembergen[1] carries the relaxation to remote nuclear spins by the mutual flips between neighboring nuclear spins.

The total nuclear magnetization p obeys a diffusion equation

$$\frac{\partial p}{\partial t} = D \Delta p - C \sum_n \frac{1}{|r - r_n'|^6} (p - p_o) - 2 A p \quad (2)$$

where A is the rate of flip due to a radiofrequency field H_1. $A = \frac{\gamma_I^2 H_1^2}{\Delta H}$, where ΔH is nuclear line width.

T_1 can be defined by $\frac{1}{T_1} = 2 A_{\frac{1}{2}}$, $A_{\frac{1}{2}}$ being the value of A for which the steady value of p is $p_o/2$.

De Gennes has shown[2] that it is possible to obtain for T_1 the simple expression

$$\frac{1}{T_1} = 4\pi N b D \qquad b = 0.7 \left(\frac{C}{D}\right)^{\frac{1}{4}} \tag{3}$$

where N is the number of impurities per cc.

De Gennes also finds that the total magnetization grows exponentially from a value 0 at time $t = 0$ with a unique time constant equal to the previously defined T_1.

The formula (3) can be tested by measuring T_1 at various frequencies, ω_I. T_1 should be proportional to $(1 + \omega_I^2 \tau_I^2)^{\frac{1}{4}}$. The relaxation time of F^{19} in a crystal of LiF has been measured from 4 to 48 Mc/s and we have found very good agreement with the theoretical predictions. These experiments have been carried out at $300°$K and $77°$K (Figs. 1, 2, 3, and 4).

From these curves, the electronic relaxation time τ_1 can be deduced. If D is known, an estimation of N can be deduced.

DYNAMIC POLARIZATION

The polarization of nuclear spins can be greatly enhanced by irradiating a crystal containing paramagnetic impurities by an external radiofrequency, Ω, given by references (3) and (4) as

$$\Omega = \omega_s \mp \omega_I$$

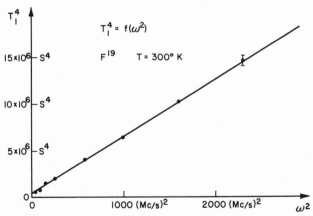

Fig. 1. Plot of T_1^4 against ω^2 for F^{19} at $300°K$

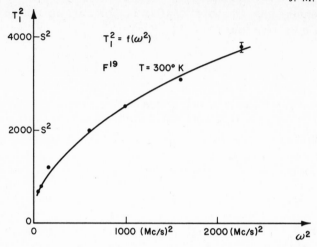

Fig. 2. Plot of T_1^2 *against* ω^2 *for* F^{19} *at* $300°K$

This mechanism uses a forbidden transition, the S_3I+ term of the dipolar coupling mixes slightly the electronic and nuclear levels. The probability w' for this simultaneous flip is

$$w' \sim w_o \left(\frac{H_s}{H_o}\right)^2$$

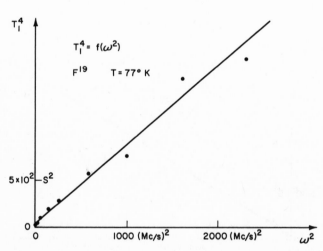

Fig. 3. Plot of T_1^4 *against* ω^2 *for* F^{19} *at* $77°K$

where w_o is the probability for an allowed electronic transition and H_s is the local field produced by the paramagnetic ion. w' is very small except in the neighborhood of the impurity. The spin diffusion mechanism can transfer the polarization as well as the relaxation. The two problems are formally identical.

With $H_s^2 \sim \dfrac{\Gamma}{r^6}$, p obeys the diffusion equation

$$\frac{\partial p}{\partial t} = D \, \Delta \, p + \frac{w_o \Gamma}{H_o^2} \Sigma \frac{1}{|r - r_n|^6} \left\{ p \pm \frac{\gamma_s}{\gamma_I} \, p_o \right\} \qquad (4)$$

(we neglect relaxation terms).

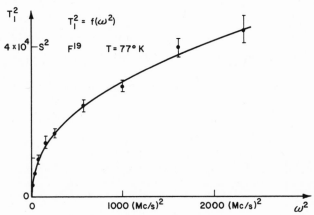

Fig. 4. Plot of T_1^2 against ω^2 for F^{19} at $77°K$

We can compute the dynamic polarization rate

$$w = 0.7 \; 4 \pi N \; \frac{\Gamma^{\frac{1}{4}} \, w_o^{\frac{1}{4}}}{H_o^{\frac{1}{2}}} \; D^{\frac{3}{4}} . \qquad (5)$$

Now w is not proportional to the radiofrequency power P; it varies as $P^{\frac{1}{4}} H_o^{-\frac{1}{2}}$.

REFERENCES

1. N. Bloembergen, Physica *14*, 386 (1949).
2. De Gennes, J. Phys. Chem. Solids 7, 4 (1958).
3. A. Abragam and W. C. Proctor, C. R. Acad. Sci. *246*, 2253 (1958).
4. M. Borghini and A. Abragam, C. R. Acad. Sci. *248*, 1803 (1959).

DISCUSSION

B. BÖLGER: When the diffusion process is the bottleneck for energy transfer from the spin system to the lattice as described by formula (2), then the saturation behavior of the spin system has a form as encountered in the case of an inhomogeneous broadened resonance line. So $\chi'' \propto 1/H_1$, for high H_1. This is due to the fact that spins close to the energy sink relax faster than those further away, and under saturation conditions there exists an inhomogeneous distribution for the spin temperature. It is therefore not right to derive T_1 from the relation $1/T_1 = 2A_{\frac{1}{2}}$, $A_{\frac{1}{2}}$ being the value of A for which the steady value of p is $\frac{1}{2}$.

J. M. WINTER: The definition of T_1 by the relation $1/T_1 = 2A_{\frac{1}{2}}$ is only a formal definition. But De Gennes[2] has shown that this T_1 is also the time constant for the growing of the mean magnetization from 0 to P_0.

NOISE AND ABSORPTION SPECTRA IN THREE-LEVEL MASERS

P. N. BUTCHER

Royal Radar Establishment, Malvern, England

THE WORKING substance in a three-level maser is excited by a large pump field and a small signal field.[1] The large pump field makes the working substance a time-dependent medium and the response to the signal field contains a component at the difference between the pump and signal frequencies. At the pump field strength necessary for saturation, the response at the difference frequency is weaker than the response at the signal frequency by the factor $(T_2/T_1)^{\frac{1}{2}}$ where T_1 and T_2 are the longitudinal and transverse relaxation times respectively. In paramagnetic crystals, $T_2/T_1 \sim 10^{-7}$ and the response at the difference frequency can be neglected. In gases and nonviscous fluids, T_2 may have the same order of magnitude as T_1 and the response at the difference frequency must be taken into account.

Javan[2] and Clogston[3] have discussed the absorption spectrum in the gaseous case. In this paper, we are primarily concerned with the noise spectrum. However, the two spectra are intimately related. We will show that the net absorption spectrum is equal to the difference between the stimulated absorption and the stimulated emission, while the noise temperature is determined by their ratio. The stimulated absorption and emission are then determined separately by solving the equations of motion of the density matrix with appropriate driving terms. Explicit formulas for the net absorption spectrum and the noise temperature are derived and discussed. The absorption effects arising from the excitation of the response at the difference frequency have their counterparts in the behavior of the noise temperature.   Previous discussions of the noise in three-level masers [4],[5],[6],[7],[8],[9],[10] have been largely concerned with the case $T_2 \ll T_1$ and these effects have been ignored.

We consider the idealized maser shown in Fig. 1. The gas molecules are assumed to be electric dipoles. The modifications of the theory necessary when considering magnetic dipoles are obvious. The resonant cavity and waveguide feeds are assumed to be lossless so that all the noise appearing at the signal terminals comes from the gas. Noise arising from the ohmic losses in an actual device can easily be taken into ac-

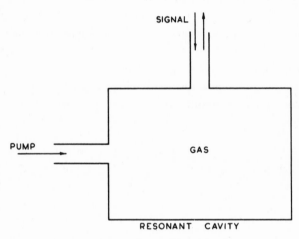

Fig. 1. Idealized maser

count if it is desired to do so. [10] We are concerned with the physical properties of the gas; the particular type of maser chosen is irrelevant; it serves merely as a definite case to contemplate.

THE NOISE SPECTRUM

When the signal generator is switched off, we are left with a noise output from the signal terminals due to the fluctuations of the electric dipole moments of the gas molecules. The fluctuations of the dipole moments of different molecules are usually uncorrelated. We may therefore calculate the total noise power output per unit bandwidth by adding together the contributions from every molecule. The electric polarization density produced by a molecule with position vector $\vec{r}_q$ is

$$\vec{m}_q(t) = \delta(\vec{r} - \vec{r}_q)\,\vec{\mu}(t) \tag{1}$$

where $\delta(\vec{r} - \vec{r}_q)$ is the three-dimensional unit impulse function and $\vec{\mu}(t)$ is the fluctuating dipole moment of the molecule. We ensure that $\vec{\mu}(t)$ has a Fourier transform by truncating it at $t = \pm\,\tau$ where τ is ultimately to approach infinity. Then the Fourier transform of $\vec{m}_q(t)$ at the "signal" frequency ω_s is

$$\vec{M}_q = \delta(\vec{r} - \vec{r}_q)\,\vec{U} \tag{2}$$

where

$$\vec{U} = \int_{-\tau}^{\tau} dt\,\vec{\mu}(t)\,\exp(-i\,\omega_s t) \tag{3}$$

is the Fourier transform of $\vec{\mu}(t)$. It is unnecessary to show explicitly the dependence of the Fourier transforms on ω_s because we are never concerned with Fourier transforms at any other frequency. In what follows "the Fourier transform" will be understood to mean "the Fourier transform at the frequency ω_s."

The Fourier transform I_q of the output noise current produced by the molecule at $\vec{r}_q$ is linearly related to $\vec{M}_q$ through Maxwell's equations. An explicit formula can be derived after the manner described in one of the references.[12] Let $\frac{1}{2}[\vec{E}_s\,\exp(i\,\omega_s t) + \vec{\overline{E}}_s\,\exp(-i\,\omega_s t)]$ be the electric vector of the signal field established in the cavity by maintaining a current $\frac{1}{2}[I_s\,\exp(i\,\omega_s t) + \overline{I}_s\,\exp(-i\,\omega_s t)]$ at the signal terminals (here and subsequently a bar over a symbol indicates its conjugate). Then

$$I_q = \frac{i\,\omega_s}{(Z_o + Z_L)I_s} \int_g dv\,\vec{E}_s \cdot \vec{M}_q \tag{4}$$

where Z_o is the output impedance seen looking into the cavity, Z_L is the load impedance seen looking out of the cavity and the integration is over the volume g of the gas. There is no need to complicate matters by introducing the "transposed" amplifier as was done in a reference.[12] The electromagnetic field vectors in the cavity of our idealized maser are always proportional to the electromagnetic field vectors of the resonant cavity mode; they merely suffer an amplitude change under different conditions of excitation. Equation (4) holds under these conditions. Moreover, the electric field in the cavity is linearly polarized, which allows us to simplify the notation slightly by choosing a Cartesian coordinate system such that $\vec{E}_s$ lies along the x-axis. Then, by substituting Equation (2) into Equation (4), we obtain the simpler result

$$I_q = \frac{i\,\omega_s E_s U_x}{(Z_o + Z_L)I_o} \tag{5}$$

where E_s is the x-component of $\vec{E}_s$ at $\vec{r}_q$.

The energy fed to the load resistance $R_L = \mathrm{Re}(Z_L)$, in the time interval $(-\tau, \tau)$, by the Fourier components of the noise current in one cycle of bandwidth about both $+\omega_s$ and $-\omega_s$ is, by Parseval's theorem,[11]

$$W_q = 2R_L \left| I_q \right|^2 \tag{6}$$

where the factor of 2 takes care of the negative frequencies. The output noise power spectrum is the system average of the noise power output per cycle

$$\begin{aligned}
n_q &= < W_q/2\tau > \\
&= R_L < \left| I_q \right|^2 >/\tau
\end{aligned} \tag{7}$$

where $< >$ denotes a system average.

So far we have proceeded as though $\vec{\mu}(t)$ were a classical vector because the above analysis is easier conceptually when we adopt a classical point of view. However, we are free to interpret $\vec{\mu}(t)$ as the Heisenberg dipole moment operator. Then $\vec{U}$ is the operator defined by Equation (3) and I_q is the operator defined by Equation (5). There is the usual difficulty about the interpretation of $\left| I_q \right|^2$ because $I_q \overline{I}_q$ is not the same operator as $\overline{I}_q I_q$. To preserve the symmetry between positive and negative frequencies, we adopt the symmetrical form

$$\left| I_q \right|^2 = \tfrac{1}{2}(I_q \overline{I}_q + \overline{I}_q I_q) \tag{8}$$

where $\overline{I}_q$ is the Hermitian conjugate of I_q. Hence Equation (7) becomes, on using Equations (5) and (8),

$$n_q = \frac{R_L}{|Z_o + Z_L|^2} \left[\frac{\omega_s^2 |E_s|^2}{2\tau |I_s|^2} < U_x \overline{U}_x + \overline{U}_x U_x > \right] \qquad (9)$$

By inspecting this equation, we see that the output noise power per cycle is equal to that which would be fed to the load by a noise voltage generator placed in series with the output impedance of the maser, and having a spectral density V_q^2 given by the quantity in square brackets. It is convenient to express $|I_s|^2$ in terms of the power fed into the maser by the terminal current $p_s = \frac{1}{2} R_o |I_s|^2$, where $R_o = \text{Re}(Z_o)$ is the output resistance. Then we have

$$V_q^2 = \frac{R_o \omega_s^2 |E_s|^2}{4\tau p_s} \{< U_x \overline{U}_x > + < \overline{U}_x U_x >\} \qquad (10)$$

where the system averages of $U_x \overline{U}_x$ and $\overline{U}_x U_x$ are to be evaluated by multiplying by the Heisenberg density operator ρ^* and forming the trace of the product.

THE ABSORPTION SPECTRUM

When the signal generator is switched on, so as to establish the electric field $\frac{1}{2}[\vec{E}_s \exp(i\omega_s t) + \vec{\overline{E}}_s \exp(-i\omega_s t)]$ in the cavity, the molecule at $\vec{r}_q$ absorbs power. The calculation of the power absorbed may be carried out by adopting the Shrödinger picture and evaluating the Shrödinger density operator ρ in the presence of the signal. The equation of motion of ρ is Liouville's equation

$$\frac{d\rho}{dt} = \frac{1}{i\hbar} [H^o + H^p - \frac{1}{2}\{E_s \exp(i\omega_s t) + \overline{E}_s \exp(-i\omega_s t)\}\mu_x, \rho] \qquad (11)$$

where H^o is the Hamiltonian of the molecule in the absence of the microwave fields, H^p is the perturbation introduced by the pump, and the last term in the total Hamiltonian is the perturbation introduced by the signal. For small signals, we may expand the contribution to the commutator from the signal perturbation and replace ρ in these terms by ρ^p, the Shrödinger density operator in the absence of the signal. Then we have

$$\frac{d\rho}{dt} = \frac{1}{i\hbar} [H^\circ + H^p, \rho] + d_1 + d_2 + \overline{d}_1 + \overline{d}_2 \qquad (12)$$

where

$$d_1 = \frac{E_s}{2i\hbar} \exp (i\omega_s t) \rho^p \mu_x \qquad (13)$$

$$d_2 = - \frac{E_s}{2i\hbar} \exp (i\omega_s t) \mu_x \rho^p. \qquad (14)$$

The quantities d_1 and d_2 and their Hermition conjugates $\overline{d}_1$ and $\overline{d}_2$ are called the "signal driving terms."

All the operators in Equations (11) to (14) are Shrödinger operators. However, the solution of Equation (12) is most easily obtained by transforming away the unperturbed motion in the presence of the pump alone, and is best expressed in terms of the Heisenberg operators derived from ρ^p and μ_x. They are

$$\rho^* = T^{-1}(t)\rho^p T(t) \qquad (15)$$

$$\mu_x(t) = T^{-1}(t)\mu_x T(t) \qquad (16)$$

where $T(t)$ and $T^{-1}(t)$ are the unperturbed time-development operator and its inverse respectively which satisfy the equations

$$\frac{dT(t)}{dt} = \frac{1}{i\hbar}(H^\circ + H^p) T(t) \qquad (17)$$

$$\frac{dT^{-1}(t)}{dt} = - \frac{1}{i\hbar} T^{-1}(t)(H^\circ + H^p) \qquad (18)$$

$$T(-\tau) = T^{-1}(-\tau) = 1. \qquad (19)$$

If the signal field is switched on when $t = -\tau$, the solution of Equation (12) is

$$\rho = \rho^p + \rho_1 + \rho_2 + \overline{\rho}_1 + \overline{\rho}_2 \qquad (20)$$

where

$$\rho_1 = \frac{E_s}{2i\hbar} T(t) \left[\int_{-\tau}^t dt' \exp(i\omega_s t')\rho^* \mu_x(t') \right] T^{-1}(t) \qquad (21)$$

$$\rho_2 = -\frac{E_s}{2i\hbar} T(t) \left[\int_{-\tau}^{t} dt' \exp(i\omega_s t')\mu_x(t')\rho^*\right] T^{-1}(t) \quad (22)$$

are the perturbations produced by the signal driving terms d_1 and d_2 respectively. The validity of this solution can easily be checked by substituting it into Equation (12).

The density operator in the presence of the signal field provides all the information needed to evaluate the absorption spectrum. The system averaged dipole moment in the x-direction is

$$<\mu_x> = Tr(\rho\mu_x) \quad (23)$$

where Tr is short for "the trace of." The system and time average of the power absorbed from the field by the molecule at $\vec{r}_q$ during the time interval $(-\tau, \tau)$ is

$$p_q = \frac{1}{2\tau}\int_{-\tau}^{\tau} dt \frac{d}{dt}<\mu_x>\tfrac{1}{2}[E_s \exp(i\omega_s t) + \overline{E}_s \exp(-i\omega_s t)]$$

$$= \frac{i\omega_s \overline{E}_s}{4\tau}\int_{-\tau}^{\tau} dt <\mu_x> \exp(-i\omega_s t) + \text{c.c.} \quad (24)$$

where we have integrated by parts and remembered that τ is ultimately to approach infinity. The symbol c.c. is short for conjugate complex. By substituting Equation (23) and Equation (24), we obtain the simpler result

$$p_q = \frac{i\omega_s \overline{E}_s}{4\tau} Tr(P\mu_x) + \text{c.c.} \quad (25)$$

where

$$P = \int_{-\tau}^{\tau} dt \, \rho \, \exp(-i\omega_s t) \quad (26)$$

is the Fourier transform of ρ.

There are five contributions to ρ on the right-hand side of Equation (20). The first term, ρ^P, is the density operator in the absence of the signal which contains only noise fluctuations at the signal frequency. The next two terms, ρ_1 and ρ_2, are produced by the signal driving terms d_1 and d_2 which both depend on time through the factor $\exp(i\omega_s t)$. After the initial transients have died down, ρ_1 and ρ_2 contain the contribution to ρ with the time-factor $\exp(i\omega_s t)$, while the last two terms on the right-hand side of Equation (20), $\bar{\rho}_1$ and $\bar{\rho}_2$, contain the contribution to ρ with the time-factor $\exp(-i\omega_s t)$. When τ approaches infinity, the contribution to P from all the terms except ρ_1 and ρ_2 are negligible, hence

$$P = P_1 + P_2 \tag{27}$$

where

$$P_1 = \frac{E_s}{2i\hbar} \int_{-\tau}^{\tau} dt \, \exp(-i\omega_s t) \, T(t) \times$$

$$\left[\int_{-\tau}^{\tau} dt' \, \exp(i\omega_s t') \rho^* \mu_x(t') \right] T^{-1}(t) \tag{28}$$

$$P_2 = \frac{E_s}{2i\hbar} \int_{-\tau}^{\tau} dt \, \exp(-i\omega_s t) \, T(t) \times$$

$$\left[\int_{-\tau}^{\tau} dt' \, \exp(i\omega_s t') \mu_x(t') \rho^* \right] T^{-1}(t) \tag{29}$$

are the Fourier transforms of ρ_1 and ρ_2 respectively.

We may now throw Equation (25) into a more useful form by substituting for P from Equation (27)

$$p_q = A_q - E_q \tag{30}$$

where

$$A_q = \frac{i\omega_s}{4\tau} \bar{E}_s \, Tr(P_1 \mu_x) + \text{c.c.} \tag{31}$$

$$E_q = -\left[\frac{i\omega_s}{4\tau} \bar{E}_s \, Tr(P_2 \mu_x) + \text{c.c.} \right] . \tag{32}$$

We refer to A_q and E_q as the stimulated absorption and emission respectively because, as we shall see, that is what they are in the absence of the pump.

The stimulated absorption and emission can be expressed in terms of the quantities $< U_x \bar{U}_x >$ and $< \bar{U}_x U_x >$, which enter into the noise spectrum, by substituting Equations (28) and (29) into

Equations (31) and (32). The time-development operator $T(t)$ can be moved from the left-hand side of the operator product to the right-hand side so as to replace the Shrödinger operator μ_x by the Heisenberg operator $\mu_x(t)$. Then, by interchanging the variables of integration in the conjugate complex term and combining the two integrals (remembering that ρ^* is independent of time), we obtain

$$A_q = \frac{\omega_s |E_s|^2}{8\hbar\tau} < U_x \bar{U}_x > \tag{33}$$

$$E_q = \frac{\omega_s |E_s|^2}{8\hbar\tau} < \bar{U}_x U_x > . \tag{34}$$

Thus the stimulated absorption and emission are respectively proportional to the quantities $< U_x \bar{U}_x >$ and $< \bar{U}_x U_x >$. It is convenient to work in terms of A_q and E_q in what follows.

THE NOISE TEMPERATURE AND NYQUIST'S EQUATION

The contribution to the spectral density of the output noise voltage generator from the molecule at $\vec{r}_q$ [Equation (10)] can be written as follows, by expressing $< U_x \bar{U}_x >$ and $< \bar{U}_x U_x >$ in terms of A_q and E'_q,

$$V_q^2 = \frac{2R_o \hbar\omega_s}{p_s} (A_q + E_q). \tag{35}$$

This equation can be thrown into a more transparent form by multiplying the right-hand side by p_q and dividing it by $A_q - E_q$. Thus we obtain

$$\begin{aligned} V_q^2 &= \frac{p_q}{p_s} 2R_o \hbar\omega_s \frac{A_q/E_q + 1}{A_q/E_q - 1} \\ &= \frac{p_q}{p_s} 4R_o \left[\frac{\hbar\omega_s}{2} + \frac{\hbar\omega_s}{A_q/E_q - 1} \right] \end{aligned} \tag{36}$$

The noisiness of the gas is best expressed by the noise temperature T_n which is defined by the equation

$$\exp(-\hbar\omega_s/kT_n) = E_q/A_q. \tag{37}$$

Then the expression in square brackets on the right-hand side of Equation (36) is recognized as the mean energy of a Planck oscillator with frequency ω_s at temperature T_n. The subsequent analysis can be simplified, without destroying its physical content, by assuming that A_q and E_q are sufficiently close together to make $|\hbar\omega_s/kT_n| \ll 1$. Then the expression in square brackets reduces to kT_n and Equation (36) becomes

$$V_q^2 = \frac{p_q}{p_s} 4 R_o k T_n .$$ \hfill (38)

Finally, by summing the contributions to the noise output from all the molecules in the gas, and assuming for simplicity that T_n does not vary from molecule to molecule, we obtain a Nyquist-like formula for the total spectral density of the output noise voltage generator

$$V^2 = \sum_q V_q^2 = 4 R_o k T_n .$$ \hfill (39)

The net absorption spectrum can also be usefully expressed in terms of the noise temperature. Thus Equations (30) and (37) give, when $|\hbar\omega_s/kT_n| \ll 1$,

$$p_q = A_q - E_q = A_q \frac{\hbar\omega_s}{kT_n}$$ \hfill (40)

EVALUATION OF THE DENSITY MATRIX

To complete the analysis we have to obtain explicit formulae for the stimulated absorption and emission. We can use Equations (31) and (32) for this purpose once we have evaluated ρ_1 and ρ_2, the perturbations of the Shrödinger density operator excited by the signal driving terms d_1 and d_2 respectively. It would be difficult to evaluate ρ_1 and ρ_2 directly from Equation (12) because the Hamiltonian H^o in the absence of the microwave fields includes the coupling of the molecule to all the other molecules and to the surroundings. To make the problem tractable, we adopt the usual procedure of dropping the coupling terms from the Hamiltonian and taking them into account approximately by adding simple relaxation terms onto the equation of motion.[3],[12] The calculation falls naturally into three parts: first, the specification of the density operator in the absence of the microwave fields; second, the evaluation of the density operator in the presence of the pump alone; third, the evaluation of the perturbations produced by the signal driving terms.

In the absence of the microwave fields, each molecule is described by a time-independent Hamiltonian H^o (with the coupling terms neglected) and a thermal equilibrium density operator

$$\rho^o = \zeta \exp\left(- H^o/kT\right) \tag{41}$$

where ζ is a normalization constant, k is Boltzmann's constant, and T is the absolute temperature. We label the energy levels of the molecule by means of integers and write E_n for the nth energy level. Three of the energy levels play a significant role in the three-level maser. We label them 1, 2, and 3 in order of increasing energy (see Fig. 2). The thermal equilibrium density operator is diagonal in the energy representation and its (n,n)th diagonal element is

$$\rho_n^o \equiv \rho_{nn}^o = \zeta \exp\left(- E_n/kT\right). \tag{42}$$

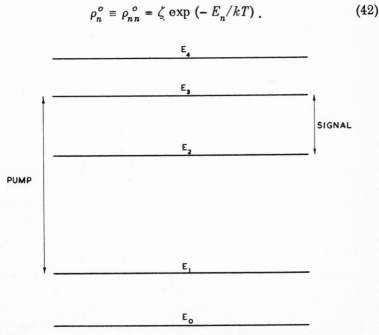

Fig. 2. The energy level diagram

We consider now the situation when the pump is switched on, but not the signal. As is indicated in Fig. 2, the pump field $\frac{1}{2}[\vec{E}_p \exp{(i\omega_p t)} + \vec{\bar{E}}_p \exp{(-i\omega_p t)}]$ has a frequency ω_p which is equal to the resonant frequency of the 1 to 3 transition: $(E_3 - E_1)/\hbar$. It augments the Hamiltonian by the perturbation

$$H^p = -\frac{1}{2}[\vec{E}_p \exp{(i\omega_p t)} + \vec{\bar{E}}_p \exp{(-i\omega_p t)}] \cdot \vec{\mu} \qquad (43)$$

and the density operator changes from ρ^o to ρ^p. The equation of motion of ρ^p is derived from Equation (12) by replacing ρ by ρ^p, dropping the signal driving terms, and adding on the usual relaxation terms. The equations of motion in the unperturbed energy representation fall into two sets: the diagonal equations

$$\frac{d}{dt}\rho_{nn}^p = \frac{1}{i\hbar}\sum_l (H_{nl}^p \rho_{ln}^p - \rho_{nl}^p H_{ln}^p) - \sum_l (\rho_{nn}^p w_{nl} - \rho_{ll}^p w_{ln}) \qquad (44)$$

where w_{ln} is the relaxation transition rate from state l to state n, and the off-diagonal equations

$$\frac{d}{dt}\rho_{nm}^p = \frac{1}{i\hbar}(E_n - E_m)\rho_{nm}^p +$$

$$\frac{1}{i\hbar}\sum_l (H_{nl}^p \rho_{lm}^p - \rho_{nl}^p H_{lm}^p) - \frac{1}{T_2}\rho_{nm} \qquad (45)$$

where T_2 is the relaxation time of the off-diagonal elements of the density matrix, i.e. the transverse relaxation time. It would be more correct to assign a different relaxation time to each off-diagonal element[3],[12] but this would merely increase the number of parameters in the problem without adding anything of physical interest. We ensure that the density operator relaxes back to ρ^o when the pump field is switched off by making the relaxation transition rates satisfy the detailed balancing condition

$$\rho_n^o w_{nl} = \rho_l^o w_{ln}. \qquad (46)$$

By inspecting the equations of motion, we see that the off-diagonal matrix elements ρ_{13}^p and ρ_{31}^p are respectively resonant to plus and minus the pump frequency $\omega_p = (E_3 - E_1)/\hbar$. These matrix elements are therefore driven hard by the pump field, while the other off-diagonal matrix elements, which are not resonant to the pump frequency, are excited with negligible amplitudes. The diagonal matrix elements of ρ^P are resonant to zero frequency and are driven hard by the constant terms on the right-hand side of Equation (44). By keeping on the right-hand sides of Equations (44) and (45) only the terms at the appropriate frequencies we obtain immediately the equations

$$\rho^P_{13} = \overline{\rho^P_{31}} = i(\rho^P_2 - \rho^P_3) D^P T_2 \exp(i \omega_p t) \qquad (47)$$

for the only non-zero off-diagonal matrix elements, and the set of equations

$$
\left.
\begin{array}{l}
\displaystyle\sum_l (\rho^P_3 w_{3l} - \rho^P_l w_{l3}) = 2(\rho^P_1 - \rho^P_3)\,|\,D^P\,|^2\,T_2 \\[3ex]
\displaystyle\sum_l (\rho^P_1 w_{1l} - \rho^P_l w_{l1}) = -2(\rho^P_1 - \rho^P_3)\,|\,D^P\,|^2\,T_2 \\[3ex]
\displaystyle\sum_l (\rho^P_n w_{nl} - \rho^P_l w_{ln}) = 0, \quad n \neq 1,\,3
\end{array}
\right\}
\qquad (48)
$$

for the diagonal matrix elements. In these equations $\rho^P_n = \rho^P_{nn}$ is the (n,n)th matrix element of ρ^P and

$$D^P = -\frac{1}{2\hbar}\,(\vec{E}_p \cdot \vec{\mu})_{13}. \qquad (49)$$

The simplest way to solve Equations (48) for the diagonal matrix elements is to regard the right-hand sides as known for a moment. Then Equations (48) together with the normalization equation $Tr(\rho^P) = 1$ have the obvious solution

$$\rho^P_l = \rho^o_l + \tau_l\,2(\rho^P_1 - \rho^P_3)\,|\,D^P\,|^2\,T_2 \qquad (50)$$

where the τ_l's are determinantal functions of the w_{ln}'s with the dimensions of time. We are actually concerned primarily with the differences $\rho^P_1 - \rho^P_3$ and $\rho^P_2 - \rho^P_3$. Setting $l = 1,\,2$ and 3 in Equation (50) and making the appropriate subtractions, we find that

$$\rho^P_1 - \rho^P_3 = \frac{\rho^o_1 - \rho^o_3}{1 + 4\,|\,D^P\,|^2\,T_1\,T_2} \qquad (51)$$

$$\rho_2^p - \rho_3^p = (\rho_2^o - \rho_3^o) - r_p (\rho_1^o - \rho_3^o) \frac{4|D^p|^2 T_1 T_2}{1 + 4|D^p|^2 T_1 T_2} \quad (52)$$

where

$$\left.\begin{array}{l} T_1 = \frac{1}{2}(\tau_3 - \tau_1) \\[2mm] r_p = \dfrac{\tau_3 - \tau_2}{\tau_3 - \tau_1} \end{array}\right\} \quad (53)$$

are respectively the longitudinal relaxation time and the Over-hauser parameter for the pump transition.[12] Equations (47), (50), (51), and (52) completely specify the density matrix in the presence of the pump.

We are now in a position to evaluate ρ_1 and ρ_2, the perturbations of the Shrödinger density operator excited by the signal drive terms d_1 and d_2 respectively. As is indicated in Fig. 2, the signal frequency ω_s is close to the resonant frequency of the 2 to 3 transition. This means that the frequency $\omega_p - \omega_s$ is close to the resonant frequency of the 1 to 2 transition. Now, from Equations (13) and (14), d_1 and d_2 contain terms at the frequencies ω_s and $\omega_s \pm \omega_p$. Therefore, they strongly excite the nearly resonant off-diagonal matrix elements ρ_{23} and ρ_{21}, and leave the other matrix elements almost unaltered. Thus the only significant matrix elements of ρ^1 and ρ^2 are the 2,3 elements ρ_{23}^1 and ρ_{23}^2 respectively and the 2,1 elements ρ_{21}^1 and ρ_{21}^2 respectively. They can be evaluated by replacing ρ^p in Equation (45) by ρ^1 or ρ^2 and adding on the signal driving term $(d_1)_{nm}$ or $(d_2)_{nm}$. By keeping on the right-hand sides of the equations only the terms at the appropriate frequencies we obtain, after some manipulation,

$$\rho_{23}^1 = \frac{-iE_s T_2 (\mu_x)_{23} \rho_2^p (1 + i\delta)}{2\hbar[(1 + i\delta)^2 + |D^p|^2 T_2^2]} \exp (i\omega_s t) \quad (54)$$

$$\rho_{21}^1 = \frac{E_s T_2 (\mu_x)_{23} \rho_2^p}{2\hbar[(1 + i\delta)^2 + |D^p|^2 T_2^2]} \overline{D^p} T_2 \exp [i(\omega_s - \omega_p)t] \quad (55)$$

$$\rho_{23}^2 = \frac{iE_s T_2 (\mu_x)_{23}[\rho_3^p (1 + i\delta) + (\rho_1^p - \rho_3^p)|D^p|^2 T_2^2]}{2\hbar[(1 + i\delta)^2 + |D^p|^2 T_2^2]} \exp (i\omega_s t) \quad (56)$$

$$\rho_{21}^2 = \frac{-E_s T_2 (\mu_x)_{23}[\rho_3^p - (\rho_1^p - \rho_3^p)(1 + i\delta)]}{2\hbar[(1 + i\delta)^2 + |D^p|^2 T_2^2]} \overline{D^p} T_2 \exp[i(\omega_s -$$

$$\omega_p)t] \quad (57)$$

where

$$\delta = T_2[\omega_s - (E_s - E_2)/\hbar] \quad (58)$$

is the normalized departure of ω_s from resonance.

These expressions deserve some comment. We see that the signal driving terms excite matrix elements with the difference frequency $\omega_s - \omega_p$ as well as those with the signal frequency ω_s. The matrix elements with the difference frequency are down on those with the signal frequency by a factor of the order of $|D^p|T_2$. Now, by referring back to Equation (51), we see that the 1 to 3 transition is 80 percent saturated when $T_1 T_2 |D^p|^2 = 1$. At this pump level $|D^p|T_2 \sim (T_2/T_1)^{\frac{1}{2}}$. In paramagnetic crystals, $T_2/T_1 \sim 10^{-7}$ and the matrix elements with the difference frequency may be neglected. In gases and nonviscous fluids, on the other hand, T_2/T_1 may be of the order of unity and the matrix elements with the difference frequency are comparable with those with the signal frequency. Their presence is reflected in the behavior of the noise temperature and the net absorption spectrum.

DISCUSSION OF THE NOISE TEMPERATURE AND THE NET ABSORPTION SPECTRUM.

The only matrix elements of the Fourier transforms of ρ^1 and ρ^2 which do not vanish are the 2,3 elements P_{23}^1 and P_{23}^2 respectively. They are obtained by replacing $\exp(i\omega_s t)$ by 2τ in the expressions (54) and (56) for ρ_{23}^1 and ρ_{23}^2. Equations (31) and (32) for the stimulated absorption and emission can then be manipulated into the forms

$$A_q = [T_2 \omega_s |E_o(\mu_x)_{23}|^2 \rho_2^p/2\hbar] \left[\frac{1}{2}\left(\frac{1}{1 + (\delta + |D^p|T_2)^2} + \frac{1}{1 + (\delta - |D^p|T_2)^2}\right)\right] \quad (59)$$

$$E_q = A_q \left[\frac{\rho_3^p}{\rho_2^p} + |D^p T_2|^2 \frac{(\rho_1^p - \rho_3^p)(1 + |D^p T_2|^2 - \delta^2)}{\rho_2^p (1 + |D^p T_2|^2 + \delta^2)} \right] \qquad (60)$$

In considering these formulas, we assume for simplicity that the temperature T is high enough to allow the approximation

$$\rho_l^o = \zeta \exp(-E_l/kT)$$

$$\simeq \zeta(1 - E_l/kT), \; l = 1, 2, 3. \qquad (61)$$

Then Equations (50) and (51) show that ρ_2^p is negligibly different from ρ_2^o for all pump fields. The first factor of A_q is, therefore, independent of both the pump field strength and the signal frequency. It is in fact the stimulated absorption at the resonant frequency of the 2 to 3 transition for zero pump field. The second factor of A_q is plotted as a function of δ in Fig. 3 for various values of $|D^p| T_2$. For low pump fields, it is approximately equal to $1/(1 + \delta^2)$ and we find the usual Lorentz line-shape with half-power bandwidth $1/\pi T_2$ cycles. When $|D^p T_2| > 3^{-\frac{1}{2}}$, two symmetrical peaks appear at $\delta = \pm [2|D^p T_2|(1 + |D^p T_2|^2)^{\frac{1}{2}} - (1 + |D^p T_2|^2)]^{\frac{1}{2}}$. Hence, for large pump fields we find two completely separated Lorentz lines centered on the frequencies $\delta = \pm |D^p| T_2$ and both having the half-power bandwidth $1/\pi T_2$ cycles. The pump field strength required to split the stimulated absorption lines in paramagnetic crystals is much greater than that required to saturate the 1 to 3 transition. On the other hand, in gases and nonviscous fluids having $T_2 \sim T_1$, the splitting occurs at the pump field strength necessary for saturation.

By comparing Equations (37) and (60), we see that the coefficient of A_q on the right-hand side of Equation (60) is equal to $\exp(-\hbar \omega_s/kT_n)$ where T_n is the noise temperature. In paramagnetic crystals $T_2 \ll T_1$, and the quantity $|D^p| T_2$ is much less than one for all reasonable pump field strengths. In this case we obtain the familiar result

$$\exp(-\hbar \omega_s/kT_n) = \rho_3^p/\rho_2^p . \qquad (62)$$

The noise temperature is determined by the ratio of the populations established by the pump in levels 3 and 2. Its frequency

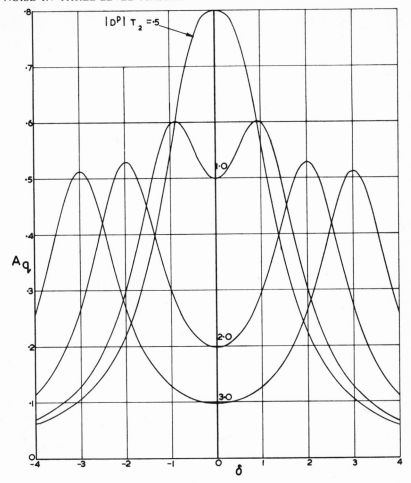

Fig. 3. The stimulated absorption spectrum

A_q is measured in units of the stimulated absorption on resonance for zero pump field.

dependence is negligible in the neighborhood of resonance. On making the high-temperature approximation (61), we find from Equations (52) and (62) that

$$\frac{T}{T_n} = 1 - \frac{4 \, r_p \, \omega_p \, |D^p|^2 \, T_1 T_2}{\omega_s \, (1 + 4 \, |D^p|^2 \, T_1 T_2)}, \quad T_2 \ll T_1. \tag{63}$$

The full line in Fig. 4 is a plot of T/T_n against $|D^p|(T_1T_2)^{\frac{1}{2}}$ when $T_2 \ll T_1$, $\omega_p/\omega_s = 3$, and $r_p = \frac{1}{2}$ (in the Woodward reference,[11] section 4, it is shown that r_p must lie between 0 and 1 at high temperatures). We see that T/T_n becomes negative when $|D^p|(T_1T_2)^{\frac{1}{2}} > 2^{-\frac{1}{2}}$ and approaches -0.5 for large pump fields.

In gases and nonviscous fluids, T_2 may have the same order of magnitude as T_1 so that $|D^p|T_2 \gtrsim 1$ at the pump field strength necessary for saturation. On making the high-temperature ap-

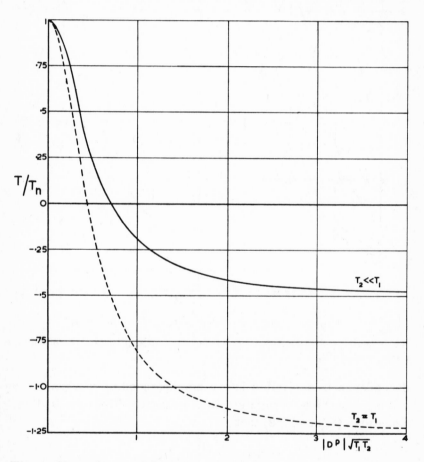

Fig. 4. Dependence of the noise temperature on pump field strength $\omega_p/\omega_s = 3$, $r_p = \frac{1}{2}$; resonance is assumed in the case $T_2 = T_1$.

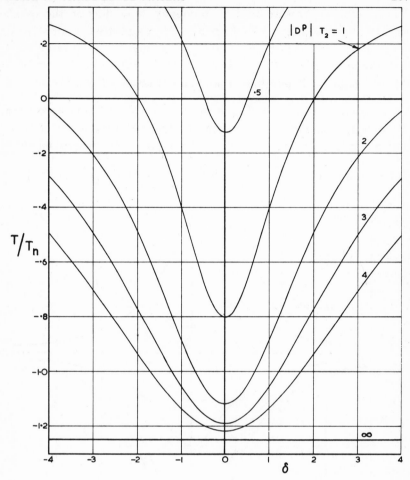

Fig. 5. Frequency dependence of the noise temperature when
$T_2 = T_1$
$\omega_p/\omega_s = 3$, $r_p = \frac{1}{2}$.

proximation (61) again we find, in this case, that

$$\frac{T}{T_n} = 1 - \frac{4 r_p \omega_p |D^p|^2 T_1 T_2}{\omega_s (1 + 4 |D^p|^2 T_1 T_2)} -$$

$$\frac{\omega_p |D^p T_2|^2 [1 + |D^p T_2|^2 - \delta^2]}{\omega_s (1 + 4 |D^p|^2 T_1 T_2)[1 + |D^p T_2|^2 + \delta^2]}. \quad (64)$$

The noise temperature is now frequency dependent in the neighborhood of resonance. In Fig. 5, T/T_n is plotted against δ for various values of $|D^p| T_2$ when $T_1 = T_2$, $\omega_p/\omega_s = 3$, and $r_p = \frac{1}{2}$. For these values of the parameters, T/T_n is always positive far off resonance. It exhibits a minimum when $\delta = 0$ which is negative when $|D^p| T_2 > 5^{-\frac{1}{2}}$ and approaches -1.25 for large pump fields (the dashed curve in Fig. 4 shows the behavior of T/T_n on resonance in this case). The noise temperature becomes infinite and changes sign when $\delta = \pm(5 |D^p T_2|^2 - 1)^{\frac{1}{2}}$; these

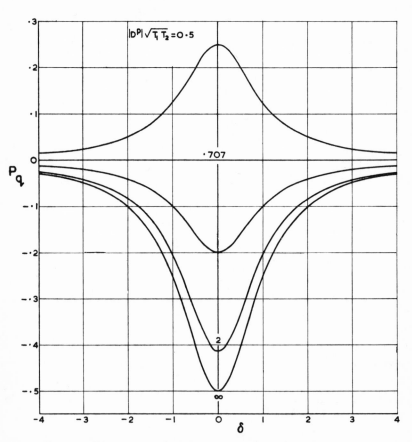

Fig. 6. *The net absorption spectrum when* $T_2 \ll T_1$

p_q is measured in units of the net absorption on resonance for zero pump field; $\omega_p/\omega_s = 3$, $r_p = \frac{1}{2}$.

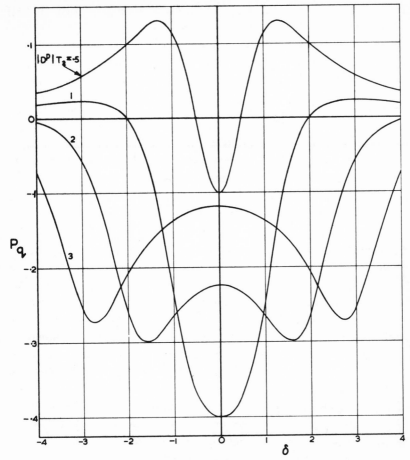

Fig. 7. The net absorption spectrum when $T_2 = T_1$

p_q is measured in units of the net absorption on resonance for zero pump field; $\omega_p/\omega_s = 3$, $r_p = \frac{1}{2}$.

frequencies separate the regions of net emission from those of net absorption.

The net absorption spectrum p_q is the product of A_q and $\hbar\,\omega_s/kT_n$ [see Equation (40)]. Hence, by using Equation (59) and the high-temperature approximation (61), we have

$$p_q = [T_2\,\omega_s\,|E_s\,(\mu_x)_{23}|^2\,(\rho_2^o - \rho_3^o)/2\hbar]$$

$$\times \left[\frac{1}{2}\left(\frac{1}{1+(\delta + |D^p\,T_2|)^2} + \frac{1}{1+(\delta - |D^p\,T_2|)^2}\right)\right]\frac{T}{T_n}. \quad (65)$$

The first factor on the right-hand side is independent of both the pump field strength and the signal frequency. It is in fact the net absorption at the resonant frequency of the 2 to 3 transition for zero pump field. In Fig. 6, the product of the last two factors of the expression for p_q is plotted against δ for various values of $|D^p|(T_1 T_2)^{\frac{1}{2}}$ in the case $T_2 \ll T_1$ (paramagnetic crystals), $\omega_p/\omega_s = 3$, and $r_p = \frac{1}{2}$. The net absorption line shape is Lorentzian at all pump field strengths and the line changes over in its entirety from net absorption to net emission when the noise temperature changes sign. In Fig. 7, the product of the last two factors in the expression for p_q is plotted against δ for various values of $|D^p| T_2$ in the case $T_2 = T_1$, (gases and non-viscous fluids), $\omega_p/\omega_s = 3$, and $r_p = \frac{1}{2}$. The splitting of the stimulated absorption line and the frequency variation of the noise temperature lead to a much more complex behavior of the net absorption spectrum in this case. At low pump field strengths, the line is approximately Lorentzian. Then, even before the two peaks in p_q make their appearance, we find two net absorption peaks in p_q produced by the minimum of T/T_n on resonance. When T_n changes sign on resonance, its frequency variation initially swamps that of A_q and a single emission peak builds up centered at $\delta = 0$. Finally, for large pump fields, the splitting of A_q produces a corresponding splitting of the emission peak. Far off resonance the net absorption spectrum is always positive because the noise temperature remains positive there for the parameter values which we have chosen.

CONCLUSION

The relation between noise and absorption spectra has been discussed. The net absorption spectrum is equal to the difference of the stimulated absorption and the stimulated emission. The noise temperature is determined by their ratio. For maser materials in which the transverse relaxation time is much shorter than the longitudinal relaxation time, the net absorption spectrum has a Lorentz line shape; it changes over in its entirety from absorption to emission at high pump field strengths. The noise temperature is independent of frequency in the neighborhood of resonance and changes sign with the net absorption spectrum. For maser materials in which the transverse and longitudinal relaxation times have the same order of magnitude, the net absorption spectrum has a doublet structure at high pump field strengths; it changes sign at two frequencies symmetrically disposed about the resonant frequency. The noise temperature is frequency dependent; it changes sign with the net absorption spectrum and has a minimum magnitude at the resonant frequency.

We have calculated the noise temperature of a system which is driven away from thermal equilibrium by an auxiliary field— the pump in this case. Auxiliary fields of some sort are present in most electronic devices: tubes and transistors are subjected to a d.c. bias; mixers, converters, and parametric amplifiers are subjected to both a d.c. bias and a high frequency pump. The noise problem in these various devices is very complex, however. It must be related to the absorption problem in much the same way as we have found in the maser. An analysis of the noise in other electronic devices along the lines that we have used here might prove fruitful.

REFERENCES

1. N. Bloembergen, Phys. Rev. *104*, 324 (1956).
2. A. Javan, Phys. Rev. *107*, 1587 (1957).
3. A. M. Clogston, Phys. and Chem. Solids *4*, 271 (1958).
4. M. W. Muller, Phys. Rev. *106*, 8 (1957).
5. R. V. Pound, Annals of Physics *1*, 24 (1957).
6. M. W. P. Strandberg, Phys. Rev. *106*, 617 (1957).
   M. W. P. Strandberg, Phys. Rev. *107*, 1483 (1957).
7. K. Shimoda, H. Takahasi, and C. H. Townes, J. Phys. Soc. Japan *12*, 686 (1957).
8. J. P. Wittke, Proc. IRE *45*, 291 (1957).
9. J. Weber, Phys. Rev. *108*, 537 (1957).
10. P. N. Butcher, Proc. IEE *105*, Part B, Suppl. No. 11, p. 699 (1958).
11. P. M. Woodward, *Probability and Information Theory with Applications to Radar*, Pergamon, p. 31 (1953).
12. P. N. Butcher, Proc. IEE *105*, Part B, Suppl. No. 11, p. 684 (1958).

A THREE-LEVEL SYSTEM AS A RESONANT FREQUENCY CONVERTER—NOISE FROM INCOHERENT PUMPING

I. R. SENITZKY
U. S. Army Signal Corps

AN ANALYSIS is made of the interaction between a three-level quantum-mechanical system (molecule), in which transitions between any two levels are possible, and the electromagnetic field inside a cavity. The cavity is assumed to have three resonant modes coinciding with the three molecular frequencies. The expectation values for the second- and third-order field strengths are calculated for the case where the initial state of the molecule is a (general) superposition of the three energy states.

The third order calculation shows that the molecule acts as a resonant mixer: If two frequencies are driven, then the third frequency mode will be excited. The strength of this excitation depends on the absolute values of the superposition constants, and the phase depends on the phases of the two driving fields. The second order calculation shows that when one frequency is being driven, and the state of the molecule includes two energy states corresponding to a second frequency, then the third frequency of the cavity will be excited. The phase of this excited field depends on the phase of the driving field and on the phases of the superposition constants in the molecular wave function; that is, if ω_1 is driven, and if the molecule is oscillating with ω_2 (among other possible oscillations), then oscillation in the cavity mode of ω_3 will be induced, the phase of the latter oscillation depending on the phases of the driving field and of the molecular oscillation.

If, for a number of molecules, the phases of the molecular oscillations are uncorrelated (as they are expected to be initially), then the effect on the ω_3 mode is insignificant. If, however, the molecular oscillations are correlated, then the effect could be significant. This effect is of interest in regard to an incoherently pumped maser. For the case of an incoherent driving field at ω_1 (pump), and correlated molecular oscillations at ω_2 (idler), some incoherence will be transferred to ω_3 (signal).

The onset of correlation in a number of initially uncorrelated molecules inside a cavity, in which there are modes of the same (or nearby) frequency as the pertinent molecular frequency, is discussed. It is shown that this correlation increases with increasing frequency. The expressions obtained are applied to the case of a high frequency maser.

DISCUSSION

A. E. SIEGMAN: Does this expression

$$\frac{\text{conv. energy}}{\text{Ind. energy}} \sim 10^{-3} \frac{\text{Pump pwr}}{\text{signal pwr}}$$

also apply to a typical solid-state maser, in which the factor on the right is $\gg 1$?

I. SENITZKY: The numerical calculation applies only to the specific case cited; namely, $\lambda \sim 1\mu$, $Q \sim 10^4$. Only at very high frequencies will the correlation of the idler oscillations become important.

H. STATZ: In a solid-state maser the lattice vibration field induces transitions, for example, at the idler frequency. What is the influence of these transitions in your form of theory on the noise at the signal frequency?

I. SENITZKY: Oscillation at the idler frequency can convert power — and noise — from the pump frequency into the signal frequency to any significant extent only when this oscillation is correlated for the various spin systems: that is, only when the various idler oscillations are in phase. It is quite unlikely that oscillations of the various spin systems which are induced by thermal agitation will have substantial correlation.

H. E. RORSCHACH: Have you made your calculation for only a single molecule in a cavity, or have you also considered a statistical ensemble described by a density matrix?

I. SENITZKY: The calculations are first carried out for a single molecule. The results are then used to study the effect of a number of molecules. The initial state of all the molecules is described in sufficiently general terms so as to apply to a statistical ensemble described by a density matrix.

INDUCED AND SPONTANEOUS EMISSION IN A COHERENTLY-DRIVEN CAVITY

I. R. SENITZKY

U.S. Army Signal Corps

THE INTERACTION between a number of atomic systems (referred to as molecules) and the electromagnetic field inside microwave cavity is analyzed for the purpose of studying induced and spontaneous emission. Each molecule is considered to have only two energy levels, and the molecular frequencies are assumed to have a gaussian distribution, the center of which coincides with the frequency of the pertinent cavity mode. Cavity loss is taken into account, and a prescribed coherently-driven field is considered.

A brief outline of the method of introducing cavity loss into a quantum-mechanical formalism for the electromagnetic field is given first. Then, by means of this formalism, expressions are derived, using second-order perturbation theory, for the field strength and field energy in the cavity, and for the power loss by the molecules. The time dependence of these expressions is discussed. It is shown that the two parts of the cavity field energy resulting from induced emission and spontaneous emission, respectively, initially increase as the square of the time, and approach steady-state values after (different, in general) transient periods, each of which is determined by two time constants: cavity relaxation time and inverse molecular line width. The ratio of induced-emission to spontaneous-emission field energy is initially n, and reaches the steady-state value

$$2n \left[e^{r^2} (1 - \operatorname{erf} r) \right]^{-1},$$

where n is the driving field energy in units of the photon energy, r is the ratio of cavity resonance width to molecular frequency width, and

$$\text{erf } r \equiv (2/\sqrt{\pi}) \int_{o}^{r} e^{-x^2} \, dx.$$

It is also shown that both the induced and spontaneous-emission power radiated by the molecules depend on the time, increasing initially linearly with the time, and approaching steady-state values after transient periods. For the induced emission power, the transient period is determined by only one time constant, the inverse molecular line width, while for the spontaneous emission power, it is determined both by the inverse molecular line width and cavity relaxation time. The ratio of induced to spontaneous-emission power is initially n, but approaches the steady-state value

$$n \, [e^{r^2} (1 - \text{erf } r)]^{-1}.$$

The seeming inconsistency of this value with results obtained from the Einstein coefficients is discussed.

GENERATION OF COHERENT RADIATION FROM HEAT

E. O. SCHULZ-DuBOIS

Bell Telephone Laboratories, Murray Hill, New Jersey

IT WAS suggested in a recent letter[1] that there is a fundamental analogy between three-level masers and heat engines. This discussion was carried out mainly to present a different intellectual approach to masers and also to show a novel way of proving the second law of thermodynamics in the classroom. In this talk, it is pointed out that it should be possible experimentally to obtain maser action from heat energy. The principle to be applied is the following: the pump transition should be in good thermal contact with the hot reservoir and the idler transition in good thermal contact with the cold reservoir; the signal transition should have no appreciable contact to any reservoir so that it can invert; signal radiation then can be extracted by an appropriate circuit. Difficulties arise when one tries to select physical processes that provide simultaneously such discriminating interactions. Two schemes will be discussed which could be utilized to obtain maser action from heat in solids. The relevant physical properties of the solid material are evaluated and the present lack of understanding of certain details is pointed out.

REFERENCE

1. H. E. D. Scovil and E. O. Schulz-DuBois, Phys. Rev. Lett. *2*, 262 (1959).

DISCUSSION

L. WILCOX: I think the heat engine concept provides a legitimate model for the analysis of certain aspects of three-level masers. For the experimental conversion of heat into radiation, however, one apparently needs a fairly sophisticated filtering scheme. What particular schemes do you consider in your proposals?

E. O. SCHULZ-DuBOIS: Before answering your question, I should like to mention that interest in this subject arose from a theoretical consideration. It was shown in the reference that the concept of the classical heat engine can be extended to include a quantized working substance such as a three-level system. If generation of radiation from heat can be accomplished experimentally, however, this should have some practical importance. In particular, whereas other maser schemes are more difficult to realize at higher microwave signal frequencies, the excitation by heat should be more effective.

Two filtering systems can be discarded for the present purpose. They are heat contact by black body radiation using conventional frequency filters and by spin diffusion. Both would not provide an efficient thermal contact, the first because of the small number of modes available, the second because of the small distance over which spin-spin interaction takes place.

The first proposed scheme is believed to have a good chance of experimental success. The thermal contacts with the two reservoirs are distinguished in the time domain. In other words, the sample is temperature cycled and maser action is obtained on a transient basis similar to the operation of pulsed two-level masers. It is assumed that the lattice cools in a very short time. It is further assumed that the idler relaxation time, though longer than the lattice time constant, is short compared to the pump and signal relaxation times. During the cooling period, a situation then will arise where the idler transition is already cold while the pump transition is still hot. Thus inversion of the signal transition occurs which can be utilized for generation or amplification of radiation in a coherent fashion. To avoid the difficulty of a phonon bottleneck, particularly at the idler frequency, which would be deleterious for this proposal, it is essential that the original idler spin energy is scattered effectively into phonons of all frequencies via Umklapp or other types of Raman processes.

The second proposed scheme is perhaps more esoteric since it requires the absence of energy exchange between different frequencies both in the spin-phonon and the phonon-phonon interactions. It leads to conversion of heat into radiation in a continuous fashion. The coupling mechanism used is heat conduction. It is reduced for frequency ranges corresponding to the pump, idler, or signal frequencies in different parts of a crystalline sample by the introduction of frequency selective scattering centers. Paramagnetic ions with appropriate transition frequencies, sufficiently high concentration and short relaxation time should act in this fashion. Alternatively, Rayleigh scattering having a steep frequency dependence could be utilized.

M. W. P. STRANDBERG: Measurements by B. Faughnan (MIT Physics Department, Ph.D. thesis, June, 1959) would indicate that in ruby and MgO phonon relaxation times are less than 10^{-6} sec. It appears that quartz may be anomalous in this respect. This puts a stringent limit on the conduction distances available in these devices.

NEW PHENOMENA AND OLD COMMUNICATION PROBLEMS

J. R. PIERCE

Bell Telephone Laboratories, Murray Hill, New Jersey

THERE ARE certain problems of electrical communication which appear and reappear in various contexts. We may well think of these problems as eternal. They include problems concerning noise, including the noise figure or noise temperature of receivers, problems of bandwidth, problems of power, problems of attenuation, and problems of the sort of modulation or encoding to be chosen. These problems are all related in communication theory or information theory, but it is perhaps clearest to introduce them by means of a concrete if unusual example.

The example I have chosen is that of a satellite relaying signals to earth. Let us assume that a satellite at a distance L from the receiver radiates substantially isotropically and that a portion of this radiation is collected by an antenna with a circular aperture of diameter D. At the distance of the antenna, the radiation is uniformly distributed over a sphere of area $4\pi L^2$. The area of the antenna aperture is $\pi D^2/4$. Thus, the ratio of transmitter power P_T to receiver power P_R is

$$P_T/P_R = 16(L/D)^2. \tag{1}$$

Let us assume that the satellite is at a height of 3,000 miles; when it is near the horizon, its distance will be around 6,000 miles or 3×10^7 feet. If we assume an antenna 60 feet in diameter, the ratio of transmitter to receiver power will be approximately

$$P_T/P_R = 16(3 \times 10^7/60)^2 = 4 \times 10^{12}.$$

What receiver power do we need? If the noise temperature of the receiving system, including sky noise, is T, the noise power

N will be

$$N = kTB$$
$$= 1.38 \times 10^{-23} \ TB \text{ watts.} \tag{2}$$

Let us assume a baseband bandwidth of 5×10^6 cps, and a signal-to-noise ratio of 10^4 (40 db); such a channel will be suitable for television transmission. If we wish to economize on bandwidth we can transmit the signal single sideband suppressed carrier; in this case the rf bandwidth and signal-to-noise ratio will be the same as the baseband bandwidth and signal-to-noise ratio. Let us assume a noise temperature of 3,000°K, which isn't bad for a contemporary microwave receiver of the diode mixer type. The receiver power must then be

$$P_R = 1.38 \times 10^{-23} \times 3000 \times 5 \times 10^6 \times 10,000$$
$$= 2 \times 10^{-9} \text{ watts.}$$

Accordingly, the transmitter power must be

$$P_T = 2 \times 10^{-9} \times 4 \times 10^{12} = 8,000 \text{ watts.}$$

This seems very high for a satellite. What can we do to reduce the required power? We can of course use a low-noise maser amplifier in our receiver. However, even if we use a noiseless amplifier, we will still not have a noiseless receiving system, because we will receive noise from the sky. Such noise includes cosmic noise, which is greatest at low frequencies, and noise radiated from the atmosphere, which is neither cold nor, because of oxygen and water vapor absorption, completely transparent. Figure 1 shows both cosmic noise and atmospheric thermal noise as a function of frequency; the atmospheric noise curves were computed by D. C. Hogg and have been checked experimentally at 5,500 Mc.

We see that if we receive from the satellite only when it is more than 5° above the horizon and if we use a frequency lying between 2,000 and 6,000 Mc, we can hope to attain a noise temperature of 30°K. This cuts the required transmitter power by a factor of 100, to

$$P_T = 80 \text{ watts.}$$

Even this seems high. What more can we do?

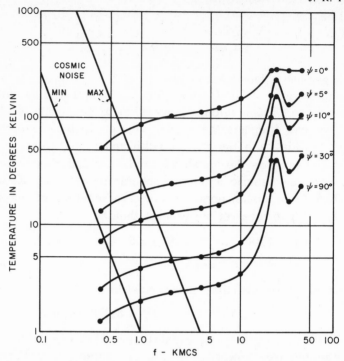

Fig. 1. Temperature due to oxygen absorption seen by an ideal antenna as a function of elevation angle φ and frequency

We know that by using wide-band fm, we can economize on power by increasing the bandwidth. Here I will invoke some approximate relations involving the rf bandwidth B, the baseband bandwidth b, the rf carrier-to-noise ratio C/N, the baseband signal-to-noise ratio S/N, and the modulation index M. These are

$$B = 2b(M + 1) \tag{3}$$

$$S/N = 3(C/N)M^2(M + 1). \tag{4}$$

In order for our fm system to operate satisfactorily, we must have a carrier-to-noise ratio C/N of at least 16 times (12 db). If we assume this value and a signal-to-noise ratio S/N of 10^4 (as before), we see from (4) that

$$10,000 = 3(16)M^2(M + 1)$$
$$M \doteq 6.$$

Thus, from (3) we see that the rf bandwidth B must be

$$B = 2 \times 5 \times 10^6 \times 7 = 7 \times 10^7 \text{ cps}.$$

Using our parameters $T = 30°K$, $C/N = 16$, $B = 7 \times 10^7$, we can calculate the required rf receiver power P by means of (2):

$$P_R = 1.38 \times 10^{-23} \times 30 \times 7 \times 10^7 \times 16 \doteq 5 \times 10^{-13} \text{ watts}.$$

The corresponding transmitter power is

$$P_T = 4.6 \times 10^{-13} \times 4 \times 10^{12} \doteq 2 \text{ watts}.$$

This is a more reasonable power. If we used some other known methods of modulation we would need an even lower transmitter power. However, merely to try one method of modulation after another is a rather unsystematic and unsatisfactory approach in trying to determine how much power we really need.

How much power do we really need? Shannon's paper, "A Mathematical Theory of Communication,"[1] gives us an answer. Shannon defines the channel capacity C as the rate at which a channel can transmit binary digits or *bits* with an error rate smaller than any assigned value. For a signal of average power P and a gaussian noise of power N, the capacity C of a channel of bandwidth B is

$$C = B \log_2 (1 + P/N) \text{ bits/second.} \tag{5}$$

We can find the least power required to transmit C bits per second by assuming Johnson noise according to (2) and letting the bandwidth B become very large. This leads to

$$C = (\log_2 e) (P/kT)$$
$$P = .693 \, kTC. \tag{6}$$

To attain the result of Equations (5) or (6), we must encode our signal in a very complicated and unknown way, so that it resembles a gaussian noise. Nonetheless, in an ideal sense we can regard channels of the same channel capacity as equivalent and say that a signal which is transmitted by means of a particular channel can in principle be reencoded so that it can be transmitted by any other channel of the same capacity.

Let us, then, compute the channel capacity of the baseband television channel, which has a bandwidth of 5 mc and a signal-to-noise ratio or 40 db. From Equation (5) we see that this channel capacity is

$$C = 5 \times 10^7 \log_2 (1 + 10{,}000)$$

$$= 6.7 \times 10^7 \text{bits/second.}$$

If we assume a noise temperature of $30°K$, we see from Equation (6) that ideally the power required for this channel capacity is

$$P_R = (.693) \ (1.38 \times 10^{-23}) \ (30) \ (6.7 \times 10^7)$$

$$\doteq 2 \times 10^{-14} \text{ watts.}$$

The corresponding transmitter power is

$$P_T = 4 \times 10^{-12} \times 2 \times 10^{-14} = .08 \text{ watt.}$$

We see that we have progressed in the following fashion:

Table 1

Condition	Satellite transmitter power
3000°K noise temperature single sideband, 5 mc	8,000 watts
30°K noise temperature single sideband, 5 mc	80 watts
30°K noise temperature fm, 70 mc bandwidth	2 watts
30°K noise temperature information theoretic ideal	.08 watt

This shows the importance of noise, bandwidth, and clever encoding in designing a communication system. It also illustrates the importance of knowing what is ideally attainable, for we are encouraged to seek a practical encoding scheme better than ordinary fm, and indeed, we have found one.[2]

We should note, however, that Equation (5) is a classical expression. It was obtained by representing a continuous band-limited signal and an additive noise by 2B samples per second. The noise was represented by 2B independent numbers with a gaussian distribution of amplitudes and a mean square value N, and the signal samples were chosen, with the restriction that the mean square value be P, so as to maximize the rate of transmission of information.

As we go up in frequency and down in temperature, we encounter quantum effects which are inconsistent with this picture of a continuous signal and an additive noise which can be represented by a set of instantaneous independent samples. In general, we will expect to encounter such effects when hf/kT is not small compared with unity. I have listed some values of this parameter in Table 2, assuming a temperature of $3\,^\circ$K.

Table 2

wavelength, cm	1	.1	.01
frequency, cps	3×10^{10}	3×10^{11}	3×10^{12}
hf/kT	.475	4.75	47.5

From rather elementary considerations, it is possible to conclude that when no thermal photons are added to signal photons it is possible to send an unlimited number of bits per photon if one signals slowly enough. J. P. Gordon has gone somewhat beyond this in an unpublished work, and he has pointed out that it is ideally desirable to use the least energetic photons possible consistent with signaling rate. However, no general exact quantum expression analogous to Equation (5) is available.

I don't think that such an expression can be obtained merely by tinkering with Equation (5); I believe that one has to go back to first principles. The mathematicians who work on information theory haven't done this because they don't understand quantum theory well enough. I don't know why some physicist hasn't solved the problem. I wish that someone would.

REFERENCES

1. C. E. Shannon, "A Mathematical Theory of Communication," Bell System Technical Journal *27,* 379 (1948); 623 (1948).
2. J. R. Pierce and R. Kompfner, "Transoceanic Communication by means of Satellites," Proc. IRE *47,* 372 (1959).

DISCUSSION

H. GAMO: Professor H. Takahasi, University of Tokyo, has derived transition probabilities between the quantized signal transmitted and the received signal by using quantum mechanics.* His purpose is the same as you mentioned. It is, however, not so easy to derive the channel capacity from these quantum mechanical transition probabilities. A limited number of cases can be described by the simple formula. Therefore, it is somewhat doubtful whether the rigorous formulation of channel capacity by quantum mechanics is really useful or not.

J. ROTHSTEIN: Some years ago H. J. Groenewald wrote about "Information in Quantum Measurements" (Konink. Akad. van Wetensch). This work may be useful in considering quantum aspects of communication problems. While his motivation was more that of applying informational ideas to physics than the converse, his work may be of interest for workers in communication theory, as the necessary quantum formalism is developed in considerable detail.

It has perhaps not been sufficiently appreciated that any measuring system is a communication system. The reason is that a measuring system presents a set of alternatives, the set of possible indications, from which a subset is selected, called the result of the measurement. As we have shown [Science *114*, 171 (1951); *Communication, Organization, and Science,* Falcon's Wing Press (1958); and in other papers], this not only leads to a logical isomorphism between measurement and communication, but also makes physical and informational entropies identical in the universe of discourse of physics, rather than fortuitously analogous.

J. R. PIERCE: I am happy to know that some physicists are working on quantum limitations to channel capacity.

While a number of physicists have published concerning communication theory, they have been chiefly concerned with the

*Report of Professional Group on Information Theory, Society of Elect. Comm. Engineers, Japan (1953). See also, Cybernetics, Vol. 2, edited by Kitagawa, Misuzu Publishing Co. (1954), H. Gamo's article.

use of the information measure or entropy of communication theory in connection with the problems of statistical mechanics. This is reminiscent of the detection and prediction theory of Kolmogoroff and Wiener, in which one seeks the best way of detecting or predicting a statistically specified signal in the presence of noise. In communication theory, one seeks to encode a signal from a statistically specified source most suitable for transmission over a noisy channel. The entropy of communication theory is important because it provides the proper measure of source rate from this point of view.

B. LAX: Would you care to comment on the application of the maser in the different regions of the electromagnetic spectrum? We know that at UHF, galactic noise limits its usefulness. Furthermore, in the millimeter region the gain in the noise figure to be obtained over that of the conventional receiver is quite significant.

J. R. PIERCE: From the point of view of making best use of low-noise amplifiers in satellite communication, the most suitable frequency range is from 1,000 to 10,000 mc. At lower frequencies cosmic noise is high and at higher frequencies thermal noise from the atmosphere is high.

GENERAL AMPLIFIER NOISE LIMIT

H. FRIEDBURG

Technische Hochschule Karlsruhe, Germany

IF ONE is going to solve or to optimize a technical problem, one should first try to obtain knowledge about the limits which are set by physical laws. This has been done in the case of maser noise with the result that only the spontaneous emission noise is unavoidable in principle. To advance further, one has to look for other amplification principles. This has been done by J. Weber.[1] It will be shown in this paper that an equal minimum amount of noise must be present in each amplifier which is sensitive to the phase as well as to the amplitude of the incident radiation.

To simplify the following calculations, the frequency characteristic shall be defined by the resolution time t instead of the bandwidth, that is, the time needed for another independent measurement of the same quantity after one measurement has been finished. The average output power of the maser divided by the gain is the sum of the signal power and an average of one quantum per resolution time

$$\overline{p} = p_{\text{sign}} + \hbar \, \omega / t \qquad (1)$$

The noise gives a background which is independent of the signal amplitude. On the other hand, it is known that it is possible in principle to count quanta without any background, for instance by a well-cooled photocell. In this case, the count noise will be proportional to the square root of the incident power. The phase information will be lost.

Consider a coherent radiation source in empty space and a quantum counter so far away that the radiation will be diluted and single counts will be observed. The weaker the radiation reaching the detector, the more time is needed to get a reasonable statistic. Now consider a phase-sensitive amplifier in the same situation but first placed near the transmitter in a strong coherent radiation field. Then it is possible, if necessary, to get a sine wave on the screen by heterodyning. What will happen if the amplifier is ideal and the distance between the transmitter and the amplifier is extremely enlarged? Neither a distinct sine wave nor single counts of either kind are to be expected, both possibilities violating the uncertainty relation[2] concerning phase and quantum number:

$$\delta \phi \, \delta n \geq 1 . \tag{2}$$

To get further information, consider another experimental situation. The amplifier now is used as a detector in a bridge circuit so that the incident power is rather weak again but so that it is possible to compare the amplifier output phase with the phase of the radiation source itself by a lock-in circuit. One will be able to measure with the lock-in amplifier the in-phase amplitude a_1 as well as the out-of-phase amplitude a_2. If these two quantities are known, the phase will be $\phi = \tan^{-1} a_2/a_1$, the incident power $p = (a_1^2 + a_2^2)/2$, and the number of quanta entering the amplifier input during the resolution time will be $n = (a_1^2 + a_2^2)t/2\hbar\omega$. To apply the uncertainty relation of Equation (2) to this problem, the uncertainties in phase and quantum numbers have to be calculated from the above formula and the experimental errors in the quantities a_1 and a_2. The prescript δ shall indicate the mean square error of each quantity. Assuming the experimental errors in a_1 and a_2 to be equal ($\delta a_1 = \delta a_2 = \delta a$), as they will be in most experimental cases, and applying the usual Gaussian formalism, the results are $\delta\phi = \delta a(a_1^2 + a_2^2)^{-\frac{1}{2}}$ and $\delta n = \delta a(a_1^2 + a_2^2)^{\frac{1}{2}} t/\hbar\omega$. From this and Equation (2), it follows that

$$\delta a \geq (\hbar \omega/t)^{\frac{1}{2}} . \tag{3}$$

To fulfill the uncertainty relation, the amplifier output must include some uncertainty, that is, noise in this case. The calculated minimum noise amplitude δa is independent of the incident radiation amplitudes a_1 and a_2. The mean output power divided by the gain is given by

$$\overline{p} = (\overline{a_1^2} + \overline{a_2})/2 = [(\overline{a_1})^2 + (\overline{a_2})^2]/2 + (\delta a)^2. \qquad (4)$$

The first term corresponds to the signal power, the second term indicates that a constant amount of noise power must be added. This corresponds to noise of the background type like hot resistor noise, maser noise, and others. Comparing Equations (1), (3), and (4), one sees that the effective noise power of the general phase-sensitive amplifier exactly equals the spontaneous emission noise of the maser. It follows that it is impossible to construct a phase-sensitive amplifier with a lower background noise than that of the ideal maser, whatever principle may be involved.

The spontaneous emission noise often is interpreted as to be stimulated by the zero-point fluctuations of the electromagnetic field. Therefore it seems to be only a different explanation of the same facts to say that either the spontaneous emission background of a maser is introduced by the amplifier itself or that it is a consequence of the zero-point fluctuations of the incident electromagnetic field.

REFERENCES

1. J. Weber, Phys. Rev. *108*, 591 (1957).
2. W. Heitler, *Quantum Theory of Radiation*, 3d edition, p. 65.

DISCUSSION

J. WEBER: The conclusion of Dr. Friedburg is not correct for all detectors and amplifiers. All of our *present* microwave amplifiers employ particles in excited states. These undergo spontaneous emission which is a purely random process; therefore it contributes noise. There are many ways of calculating the equivalent noise temperature $T = \hbar\omega/k$. All of these agree; also this result may be written immediately since it is the temperature which is constructed from $\hbar$, ω, and k by dimensional arguments. Dr. Friedburg's method of calculating T is a very novel one. Also this same result has been known for the free electron amplifier since 1954.* The free electron amplifier, it has been noted,** is really a maser.

It is, however, possible to construct a detector similar to a nuclear counter, which employs particles in their ground states. Such proposals have been made by Bloembergen† and by me.** Bloembergen's scheme employs 3 levels: 3 _____

$$2 \underline{}$$
$$1 \underline{}$$

A pumping signal ω_{32} is applied. This produces no effects, since level 2 is unoccupied.† If a microwave or infrared photon arrives, it raises particles to level 2, the pump raises them to level 3, where they spontaneously emit. This emission is detected by some optical means. Also a particle can repeatedly go from level 3 to 2 and back, giving an amplification. However, nothing can happen until a signal raises at least one particle into level 2.

An alternate scheme is to use 3 levels with the following values of m: _____ $m = 0$

_____ $m = 1$

_____ $m = 0$

If linearly polarized light is used to excite, it sends particles between the highest and lowest levels. It is arranged to have circularly polarized microwave or infrared photons. If *one* of these arrives, a transition to the middle state is possible. The spontaneous emission from the middle state down can go in a direction not allowed for a particle in the highest state. It can therefore be optically detected and amplified, for example by a photomultiplier tube.

The kind of amplifier which employs excited particles does not need to absorb energy to operate. I call this a voltage amplifier. It has a noise output *at all times*, whether a signal is incident or not. If one photon arrives during the averaging time of the receiver, we cannot be sure that it was not noise. Also it is very important to note that to apply $\delta n \delta \phi \geq 1$, $\delta n = 0$ is not allowed for a maser.

The photon counter, on the other hand, is expected to have zero output, until one photon appears. $\delta n = 0$ is allowed. Detection of this photon can be used to operate a meter, or ring a bell, or switch on an oscillator, or control the spectral character of some oscillator amplifier combination. If detection is possible, amplification is not necessary but can nonetheless be accomplished. One might argue that this isn't really amplification since phase information is not retained. However, in a maser at low signal levels phase information is not available either, except perhaps insofar as comparison of input and output may be concerned.

The purpose of amplification is to raise the level to the point where detection is possible. It makes more sense to talk about *detection limits* rather than amplification limits. It is quite clear that in principle lower detection limits are possible than provided by a maser.

No microwave photon counters have been built. We have no knowledge concerning the practical difficulties. Mr. U. E. Hochuli at the University of Maryland is investigating the fine structure of the optically excited states of gadolinium salts, in order to see what the possibilities are.

REFERENCES

*J. Weber, Phys. Rev. *94*, 215 (1954).
**J. Weber, Rev. Mod. Phys. *31*, 3, 681 (1959).
†N. Bloembergen, Phys. Rev. Lett. *2*, 84 (1959).

H. FRIEDBURG: In his comments, Dr. Weber said there should be no application of phase-sensitive amplifiers which could not also be done by using counting detectors. That is true insofar as detection of incoherent radiation or broad-band amplification is considered. It is not true in the case of narrow-band amplification of coherent signals. By connecting a lock-in circuit to a phase-sensitive amplifier, it is possible to reduce the noise bandwidth without any loss in signal power. If it is possible to compare the signal phase with the radiation source itself, the signal line appears to be infinitely narrow. Because of the attainable high frequency stability of transmitters, a nearly similar situation can arise if very weak satellite signals are to be detected.

LIMITS ON ELECTROMAGNETIC AMPLIFICATION DUE TO COMPLEMENTARITY

R. SERBER* and C. H. TOWNES**

Columbia University

THE ADVENT of maser amplifiers, which allow coherent amplification of electromagnetic waves consisting of only a few quanta, makes appropriate an analysis of the fundamental limits in the amplification process set by quantum mechanics. Coherent amplification implies reproduction and therefore measurement of phase as well as of intensity of an input wave. Fluctuations in intensity or numbers of quanta in maser-type amplifiers have already been extensively studied, but less attention has so far been given to fluctuations in phase. The question whether other advantageous types of coherent amplification can be achieved with still smaller fluctuations in intensity than those in a maser amplifier has also been raised,[1] and its answer can perhaps help clarify the properties of amplifiers demanded by fundamental physical principles.

Any amplifier or detector of electromagnetic radiation produces an output which is some representation of the intensity and possibly also the phase of an input electromagnetic wave. Such a device thus may afford simultaneous information on the number of quanta and the phase of the wave, and its performance must therefore be limited by an uncertainty relation between these two complementary quantities. The uncertainty Δn in the number of quanta making up the input wave and the uncertainty $\Delta \phi$ in

*Work partly supported by the Atomic Energy Commission.

**Work supported jointly by the U.S. Army Signal Corps, the Office of Naval Research, and the Air Force Office of Scientific Research.

its phase as deduced by examination of the output wave must not
be less than what is allowed by the expression

$$\Delta n \, \Delta \phi \geqslant \tfrac{1}{2}. \tag{1}$$

Thus any phase-sensitive amplifier must involve uncertainties in
determination of the number of quanta. If the amplification is
quite large so that the output is an electromagnetic wave containing many more quanta than the input, the output wave may be
treated classically with good accuracy, and any errors due to
examination of the output in either phase or numbers of quanta
will contribute no further error to measurement of the input. We
shall in all cases assume such a large amplification. Possible
amplifier characteristics and ideal amplifiers which reach the
limits set by Equation (1), including particularly masers, will be
discussed.

Although Equation (1) is a generally accepted one,[2] it is not
completely satisfactory because of rather basic difficulties in
the finding of an unambiguous quantum-mechanical definition of
the phase of an oscillator or electromagnetic wave.[3] This
manifests itself in part by the finite maximum of π for the uncertainty $\Delta \phi$ as usually understood classically and the possibility of infinite values implied by Equation (1).

Consider now the phase and uncertainty relations in a mechanical simple harmonic oscillator, which may serve as a model for an
oscillating electromagnetic field. If at some time $t = 0$ the oscillator is known to have a position x_0 and a momentum mv_0, then
for any arbitrary later time t_1,

$$x = x_0 \cos \omega t + \frac{mv_0}{m\omega} \sin \omega t$$

$$mv = -m\omega x_0 \sin \omega t + mv_0 \cos \omega t$$

where ω is the angular frequency, or $2\pi\nu$. If the scales of time
and of mass are chosen so that $\omega = 1$ and $m = 1$, and if q, p are
written for x and mv respectively, these equations become

$$q = q_0 \cos t + p_0 \sin t \tag{2a}$$

$$p = q_0 \sin t + p_0 \cos t. \tag{2b}$$

For an oscillating electromagnetic field, q and p may be considered to be electric and magnetic fields E and H respectively in appropriate units.

If the measured values of q_0 and p_0 or hence of E_0 and H_0 are not precise, the resulting error in q may be represented by

$$(\Delta q)^2 = \overline{q^2} - \overline{q}^2$$

which can easily be shown from Equation (2a) to be

$$(\Delta q)^2 = (\overline{q_0^2} - \overline{q_0}^2) \cos^2 t + (\overline{p_0^2} - \overline{p_0}^2) \sin^2 t$$
$$= (\Delta q_0)^2 \cos^2 t + (\Delta p_0)^2 \sin^2 t \qquad (3a)$$

if the fluctuations in q_0 and p_0 are not correlated. Similarly,

$$(\Delta p)^2 = (\Delta q_0)^2 \sin^2 t + (\Delta p_0)^2 \cos^2 t. \qquad (3b)$$

Thus uncertainty in q or p may oscillate with time by a large amount if Δq_0 and Δp_0 are different. Only if the two initial uncertainties Δq_0 and Δp_0 are equal do Δq and Δp remain constant. The same relations (3a) and (3b) also follow rigorously from a quantum mechanical argument.

Equation (2a) can be written

$$q = \sqrt{q_0^2 + p_0^2} \cos (t + \tan^{-1} p_0/q_0) \qquad (4)$$

so that the phase may be defined as $\phi = \tan^{-1} p_0/q_0$ $\qquad (5)$
or, by differentiation, the variation in phase is

$$\Delta \phi = \frac{q_0 \Delta p_0}{q_0^2 + p_0^2} - \frac{p_0 \Delta q_0}{q_0^2 + p_0^2}$$

if the uncertainties Δp_0 and Δq_0 are suitably small. Thus if fluctuations in Δp_0 and Δq_0 are not correlated,

$$(\Delta \phi)^2 = \frac{q_0^2 (\Delta p_0)^2 + p_0^2 (\Delta q_0)^2}{(q_0^2 + p_0^2)^2}. \qquad (6)$$

Any measurement which treats q and p, or E and H, equivalently, and which therefore gives $(\Delta p_0)^2 = (\Delta q_0)^2$, yields a phase uncertainty which from (6) is

$$(\Delta \phi)^2 = \frac{(\Delta q_0)^2}{q_0^2 + p_0^2} = \frac{(\Delta q_0)^2}{2W} \qquad (7)$$

where W is the total energy of the oscillator.

Consideration of possible values for Δp_0 and Δq_0 requires introduction of the uncertainty relations of quantum mechanics. Since $\Delta q \Delta p \geqslant \dfrac{\hbar}{2}$, if $\Delta q_0 = \Delta p_0$ then $(\Delta q_0)^2 = \dfrac{\hbar}{2}$ and $(\Delta \phi)^2 = \dfrac{\hbar}{4W}$ when Δq_0 has its minimum possible value. If $W = (n + \frac{1}{2})\hbar\omega$, or approximately $n\hbar\omega$ because Equation (6) applies accurately only when the number of quanta n is much larger than unity, Equation (7) then becomes, since ω is unity,

$$\Delta \phi = \frac{1}{2} \sqrt{\frac{\hbar}{W}} = \frac{1}{2\sqrt{n}}. \tag{8}$$

The uncertainty in energy ΔW when $(\Delta q_0)^2 = (\Delta p_0)^2$, is given similarly by $(\Delta W)^2 = q_0^2 (\Delta q_0)^2 + p_0^2 (\Delta p_0)^2 = 2W(\Delta q_0)^2 = W\hbar$. Hence

$$(\Delta n)^2 = \left(\frac{\Delta W}{\hbar}\right)^2 = \frac{W}{\hbar}, \quad \text{or}$$

$$\Delta n = \sqrt{n}. \tag{9}$$

From Equations (8) and (9), the minimum uncertainty in the product $\Delta n \Delta \phi = \frac{1}{2}$ allowed by Equation (1) is seen to apply. It will be shown below that an ideal maser amplifier, for example one in which the large majority of resonant molecules or atoms are in the upper state and the circuit losses are small, is an instrument to which the above discussion applies. That is $(\Delta q)^2 = (\Delta p)^2$, the uncertainties in phase and numbers of quanta are given by Equations (8) and (9), and the product $\Delta n \Delta \phi$ has the minimum value allowed.

The phase error in measurement may be minimized from Equation (6) with the restriction that $\Delta q_0 \Delta p_0 = \hbar/2$ by, for example, letting both q_0 and Δq_0 approach zero. However, q_0^2 cannot be less than $(\Delta q_0)^2$, and p_0^2 must be quite large since it cannot be less than $(\Delta p_0)^2$. Letting $q_0^2 \approx (\Delta q_0)^2$ and $p_0^2 \approx (\Delta p_0)^2 \approx \left(\dfrac{\hbar}{2\Delta q_0}\right)^2$, Equation (6) becomes $(\Delta \phi)^2 \approx \hbar^2/p_0^4 \approx 1/N^2$ since the energy $W = \hbar N = \frac{1}{2} p_0^2$ when $q_0^2 \to 0$. This gives

$$\Delta \phi \approx 1/N$$

and the uncertainty in number of quanta is simply

$$\Delta n \approx \frac{\frac{1}{2} p_0{}^2}{\hbar} = N . \qquad (10)$$

A "thought experiment" which corresponds to this case will be described below.

In the other limit where the number of quanta or total energy is measured very precisely so that $\Delta n \rightarrow 0$, q and p are not individually measured. Hence no information is obtained about ϕ or, formally, $\Delta \phi \rightarrow \infty$. This corresponds, of course, to a photon counter.

Additional discussion of the important case where $\Delta \phi = \dfrac{1}{2\sqrt{n}}$ and $\Delta n \approx \sqrt{n}$ in terms of zero-point fluctuations in a simple harmonic oscillator or in an electromagnetic field may perhaps be instructive. Consider an oscillator whose phase is very accurately known. The oscillator would need to be excited to a very high quantum state so that, in accordance with Equation (8), its phase could be determined with arbitrary precision. Radiation which it emits, or hence which it transmits to a previously unexcited resonant circuit might then be thought to have a precisely determined phase even though the number of quanta involved in the receiving resonant circuit is arbitrarily small. This may be thought to circumvent Equations (8) or (10), where the accuracy of phase determination is limited by the number of quanta. Such a conclusion is incorrect because of what might be described as the zero-point fluctuations of the receiving circuit.

Let the zero-point energy of the receiving circuit be $\frac{1}{2} h\nu$, and the associated electric field strength $\varepsilon = k \sqrt{\frac{1}{2} h\nu}$ where k is a suitable constant. This field strength ε is arbitrary in amplitude and phase. The field strength introduced into the circuit by the n quanta received is then $E = k \sqrt{n h \nu}$, and is presumably in precisely the same phase as the emitting oscillator. E and ε must add randomly, with $\dfrac{\varepsilon}{\sqrt{2}}$ the rms component of ε which is $90°$ out of phase with E. This gives a phase uncertainty

$$\Delta \phi = \frac{\varepsilon}{\sqrt{2} E} = \frac{1}{2\sqrt{n}} . \qquad (11)$$

The component $\dfrac{\varepsilon}{\sqrt{2}}$ of the zero-point fluctuations which is in phase with E also adds randomly to E since its sign is undetermined. This gives uncertainties in the energy W, or in E^2 to which W is proportional. Thus

$$[\Delta (E^2)]^2 = 2\,\varepsilon^2 E^2 = k^4 n\,(h\nu)^2 .$$

Since $\Delta n = \dfrac{\Delta (E^2)}{k^2\,\hbar\nu}$, one obtains

$$\Delta n = \sqrt{n} \; . \tag{12}$$

Hence the uncertainty in determination of phase and photon number for an electromagnetic field required by the uncertainty principle in the interesting case where $(\Delta E)^2 = (\Delta H)^2$ can be estimated in an elementary way from the residual random fields associated with zero-point fluctuations. It is interesting to note that this case gives the same fluctuation $\dfrac{1}{\sqrt{n}}$ for the fractional number of photons, $\dfrac{\Delta n}{n}$, and for twice the phase. It hence corresponds to similar fractional accuracy for phase and for number of photons.

UNCERTAINTY IN DETERMINATION OF PHOTON NUMBER AND PHASE BY A MASER AMPLIFIER

The fluctuations in output of a maser-type amplifier have been discussed in a number of papers,[4],[5],[6],[7],[8] and the complete distribution of output intensity as a function of input intensity is available. We are interested in the accuracy with which the number of photons in the input wave can be obtained from examination of the output wave. As indicated earlier, we may assume very large amplification has occurred so that the fractional accuracy in determination of output intensity is negligibly small. In all actual maser systems, thermal noise[4] has so far been dominant. However, some devices have approached within a small factor the case of an "ideal" maser amplifier where the effective noise temperature is given by $h\nu/k$, where k is the Boltzmann constant. For an ideal maser amplifier, the number of input quanta n would be obtained in terms of the output number m from the relation between their averages given by

$$\overline{m} = (\overline{n} + 1) K \tag{13}$$

where K is the amplification factor. This expression can be easily obtained, for example, from the results of Shimoda, Takahasi, and Townes for maser amplification in the case where the amplification factor K is large and the ratio of emission to absorption is also large.

To obtain a measure of the fluctuations in the predictability of n from m, we must examine the second moment of m,

$$\overline{m^2} = (\overline{n^2} + 3\overline{n} + 2) K^2. \tag{14}$$

From Equations (13) and (14),

$$(\Delta m)^2 = \overline{m^2} - \overline{m}^2 = (\overline{n^2} - \overline{n}^2 + \overline{n} + 1) K^2.$$

If now the input number n were completely definite so that $\overline{n^2} = \overline{n}^2$, the uncertainty in determination of n from the relation (13) would be given by

$$(\Delta n)^2 = \frac{(\Delta m)^2}{K^2} = n + 1$$

or $$\Delta n = \sqrt{n + 1}. \tag{15}$$

It should be noted that this uncertainty is what is introduced by the amplifying or measuring process and does not include any uncertainty in n due to fluctuations in the input wave itself, since we have assumed $\overline{n^2} = \overline{n}^2$.

Uncertainty in phase will first be deduced from fluctuation in intensity of a maser amplifier with the addition of relatively straightforward assumptions. Let the electric field at the output of a maser amplifier be

$$E = A \sin \omega t + B \sin (\omega t + \delta) \tag{16}$$

where B and δ vary with time and represent a fluctuation while A is constant, representing the average field intensity. The mean number of photons at the input indicated by the field E is

$$\overline{n} = k\overline{E^2} = k \left[\frac{A^2}{2} + \frac{\overline{B^2}}{2} + \overline{AB \cos \delta} \right] = k \left[\frac{A^2}{2} + \frac{\overline{B^2}}{2} \right] \tag{17}$$

where the phase δ is assumed to random, since its origin lies in zero-point fluctuations. Similarly, the mean square of the number of photons at the input is $\overline{n^2} = k^2 \left[\dfrac{\overline{A^4}}{4} + \dfrac{\overline{B^4}}{4} + \overline{A^2 B^2} \right].$

The uncertainty Δn is

$$(\Delta n)^2 = \overline{n^2} - \overline{n}^2 = \frac{k^2 \overline{A^2 B^2}}{2} . \tag{18}$$

From Equation (15) above, $(\Delta n)^2 = n + 1$. If n is much larger than unity so that the fractional fluctuations are small and $\overline{B^2} \ll \overline{A^2}$, then Equation (17) gives

$$\frac{\overline{A^2}}{2} = \frac{n}{k} . \tag{19}$$

Hence from Equation (18),

$$\overline{B^2} = \frac{n + 1}{kn} \approx \frac{1}{k} . \tag{20}$$

The output field (16) may also be written

$$E = \sqrt{(A + B \cos \delta)^2 + (B \sin \delta)^2} \; \sin \left[\omega t + \tan^{-1} \left(\frac{B \sin \delta}{A + B \cos \delta} \right) \right].$$

Hence

$$\phi = \tan^{-1} \left(\frac{B \sin \delta}{A + B \cos \delta} \right). \tag{21}$$

If now the fractional fluctuations are small so that $|B| \ll |A|$,

$$\overline{\phi} = 0$$

$$\overline{\phi^2} = \frac{\overline{B^2 \sin^2 \delta}}{A^2} = \frac{\overline{B^2}}{2 A^2} .$$

This gives, from Equations (19) and (20)

$$(\Delta \phi)^2 = \overline{\phi^2} = \frac{1}{4n} . \tag{22}$$

This gives when $n \gg 1$, as is to be expected,

$$\Delta n \, \Delta \phi = \tfrac{1}{2} .$$

Although Equation (22) indicates the result for phase fluctuations, a more rigorous and detailed examination is desirable since phase fluctuations in a maser amplifier have not been treated elsewhere. Consider an electromagnetic field of angular frequency ω interacting with an ensemble of molecules which may exist in two energy states separated by energy $\hbar\omega$. The wavefunction for the molecules may be written

$$\psi = b_1 u_1 + b_2 u_2 \tag{23}$$

where u_1 and u_2 are wavefunctions for the ground state and the excited state respectively. The approach of second quantization[9] will be used, in which case b_1 and b_2 are annihilation operators, and b_1^*, b_2^* are the corresponding creation operators. The oscillating electromagnetic field may be described in terms of a displacement coordinate q and a momentum p with

$$q = \sqrt{\frac{\hbar}{2\omega}} \, (a^* + a) \tag{24}$$

$$p = -i \sqrt{\frac{\hbar\omega}{2}} \, (a^* + a) \tag{25}$$

where a^* and a are respectively creation and annihilation operators for the photons.

The operators a^* and a have matrix elements which are all zero except that $a^*_{n+1,n} = \sqrt{n+1}$ and $a_{n-1,n} = \sqrt{n}$, where n is the number of photons. Hence

$$a^* a = n \tag{26}$$

$$a a^* = n + 1. \tag{27}$$

The operators b_2 and b_1 are similarly connected with the number of molecules in the upper and lower states.

If the energy of the upper state is taken as zero, the Hamiltonian for the system may be written

$$H = a^* a \hbar\omega - b_1^* b_1 \hbar\omega + \alpha \int \psi^* q \psi \, dr \tag{28}$$

where α is some constant appropriate to the strength of interaction between the molecules and electromagnetic field. From the wavefunction (23) and expression (24) for q, the Hamiltonian (28) can be written

$$H = (a^* a - b_1^* b_1)\hbar\omega + \beta (b_1^* b_2 + b_2^* b_1)(a^* + a) \tag{29}$$

where β is a constant. Here it is assumed that, as is usually the case for molecular systems, the interaction term in Equation (28) has no diagonal matrix elements. If only those terms in the Hamiltonian (29) are saved which conserve energy, it becomes

$$H = W_0 + \beta (b_1^* b_2 a^* + b_2 b_1 a) \tag{30}$$

where W_0 is the initial total energy, $(a^* a - b_1^* b_1)\hbar\omega$.

The system of interest is one in which the number of molecules in the upper state is very large and does not change by an appreciable fraction during the process of amplification, while the number of molecules initially in the lower state is zero. Hence we may take $b_2 = \sqrt{N}$ and $b_2^* = \sqrt{N+1}$ to be both constant and equal to $\sqrt{N}$, where N is the initial number of molecules in the upper state. The Hamiltonian (30) may then be further simplified as

$$H = W_0 + \beta \sqrt{N}(b_1^* a^* + b_1 a). \tag{31}$$

It may be noted that, since the total number of molecules is conserved, the system can be adequately followed in terms of the number in the lower state only.

The time variation of a may be found from $i\hbar \dot{a} = [a, H]$ which gives, since $[a, a^*] = 1$,

$$i\hbar a = \beta \sqrt{N} b_1^*$$

and similarly

$$i\hbar b_1 = \beta \sqrt{N} a^*.$$

The solutions to these equations are

$$a = a_0 \cosh \frac{\sqrt{\beta\beta^*}}{\hbar} N t - i\sqrt{\beta/\beta^*}\, b_{10}^* \sinh \frac{\sqrt{\beta\beta^*}}{\hbar} N t \tag{32}$$

$$b_1 = b_{10} \cosh \frac{\sqrt{\beta\beta^*}}{\hbar} N t - i\sqrt{\beta/\beta^*}\, a_0^* \sinh \frac{\sqrt{\beta\beta^*}}{\hbar} N t \tag{33}$$

where a_0 and b_{10} are values of a and b respectively at time $t = 0$.

If β is taken as real and $\gamma = \dfrac{\beta N}{\hbar}$, Equation (32) becomes

$$a = a_0 \cosh \gamma t - i b_{10}^* \sinh \gamma t. \tag{34}$$

The number of photons and fluctuations in number may now be found. From Equation (34),

$$a^* a = a_0^* a_0 (\cosh \gamma t)^2 + b_{10} b_{10}^* (\sinh \gamma t)^2$$
$$+ i \sinh \gamma t \cosh \gamma t (b_{10} a_0 - a_0^* b_{10}^*). \tag{35}$$

Hence, at time t, the average number of photons is

$$\overline{m} = <n_0 \, 0 \, | \, a^* a \, | \, n_0 \, 0 > = \overline{n}_0 \cosh^2 \gamma t + \sinh^2 \gamma t.$$

Here the initial number of photons has been indicated as an average $\overline{n}_0$ for the general case where n_0 is not definite. The initial number of molecules in the ground state is zero, as indicated by the zero in the matrix element. For large amplification $K = e^{2\gamma t}$

$$\overline{m} = (\overline{n}_0 + 1) K \tag{36}$$

Similarly, by evaluating the square of the operator (35), one obtains,

$$\overline{m}^2 = <n_0 \, 0 \, | (a^* a)^2 | \, n_0 \, 0 > = n_0^2 \cosh^4 \gamma t + \sinh^4 \gamma t$$
$$+ \sinh^2 \gamma t + \cosh^2 \gamma t (2 \overline{n}_0 + 1) \tag{37}$$

or, for large amplification

$$\overline{m}^2 = (\overline{n_0^2} + 3 \overline{n}_0 + 2) K^2. \tag{38}$$

Equations (36) and (38) give

$$\Delta m^2 = \overline{m^2} - \overline{m}^2 = (\overline{n_0^2} - \overline{n}_0^2 + \overline{n}_0 + 1) K^2.$$

Thence,

$$\Delta n_0^2 = \overline{n_0^2} - \overline{n}_0^2 + \overline{n}_0 + 1. \tag{39}$$

This expression has also been obtained in previous work.[6] m_0, the value of m at time $t = 0$, is of course the number of phonons n.

The uncertainty Δn after amplification is from Equation (39) composed of two parts, that due to the initial variation $\overline{n_0^2} - \overline{n}_0^2$ before amplification and the contribution $\overline{n}_0 + 1$ from the amplification or measuring process itself. Thus, if the initial number n

or m_0 is assumed to be definite, $\overline{n_0^2} - \overline{n}_0^2 = 0$ and the initial number is measured to an uncertainty

$$\Delta n = \sqrt{n + 1}. \tag{40}$$

The displacement coordinate and momentum are given in terms of a^* and a by Equations (17) and (18) which, combined with Equation (29), yield

$$q = \sqrt{\frac{\hbar}{2\omega}} \left[(a_0^* + a_0) \cosh \gamma t + i(b_0 - b_0^*) \sinh \gamma t \right]$$

$$p = -i\sqrt{\frac{\hbar\omega}{2}} \left[(a_0^* - a_0) \cosh \gamma t + i(b_0 + b_0^*) \sinh \gamma t \right]$$

when a time scale is chosen so that $\omega = 1$. In order for q or p to vary sinusoidally, there must be a distribution in the initial number of photons, since a_0^*, a_0, b_0^*, and b_0 have no diagonal elements and the initial number of molecules in the ground state has the definite value of zero. Then we may write

$$\overline{q} = \sqrt{\hbar/2\omega} \cosh \gamma t < 0 \,|\, a_0^* + a_0 \,|\, 0 > \tag{41a}$$

$$\overline{p} = -i\sqrt{\hbar\omega/2} \cosh \gamma t < 0 \,|\, a_0^* - a_0 \,|\, 0 > \tag{41b}$$

$$\overline{q_2} = \frac{\hbar}{\omega} \frac{(\cosh \gamma t)^2}{2} < 0 \,|\, (a_0^* + a_0)^2 \,|\, 0 > + \frac{\hbar}{\omega} \frac{(\sinh \gamma t)^2}{2} \tag{42}$$

$$\overline{p_2} = \hbar\omega \frac{(\cosh \gamma t)^2}{2} < 0 \,|\, (a_0^* - a_0)^2 \,|\, 0 > + \hbar\omega \frac{(\sinh \gamma t)^2}{2}. \tag{43}$$

Here use has been made of the relations $b_0^* b_0 = 0$ and $b_0 b_0^* = 1$ which are analogous to Equations (26) and (27) when the initial number of molecules is zero. From Equations (41a)-(43), we have

$$\Delta q^2 = \overline{q^2} - \overline{q}^2 = (\overline{q_0^2} - \overline{q}_0^2) \cosh^2 \gamma t + \hbar \frac{\sinh^2 \gamma t}{2\omega} \tag{44}$$

$$\Delta p^2 = (\overline{p_0^2} - \overline{p}_0^2) \cosh^2 \gamma t + \hbar \frac{\sinh^2 \gamma t}{2}. \tag{45}$$

For large amplification $K = e^{2\gamma t}$ these become

$$\Delta q^2 = (\overline{q_0^2} - \overline{q}_0^2 + \hbar/2\omega) K \tag{46}$$

$$\Delta p^2 = (\overline{p_0^2} - \overline{p}_0^2 + \hbar\omega/2) K. \tag{47}$$

Again if the process of amplification is treated as a measurement and only the uncertainty introduced by the measurement itself considered, Equations (46) and (47) give

$$\Delta q_0 = \Delta p_0 = \sqrt{\hbar/2}. \tag{48}$$

Here a time scale has been assumed as in Equations (2)–(10) such that $\omega = 1$. Thus, maser-type amplification can give the minimum possible product $\Delta q_0 \Delta p_0 = \hbar/2$.

In terms of the electric and magnetic fields E and H, which correspond to p and q, it may be observed from the above that a maser can, in principle, give the minimum allowable value of the uncertainty product $\Delta H \Delta E$ while at the same time minimizing the sum $(\Delta E)^2 + (\Delta H)^2$. The latter quantity is a minimum, subject to the uncertainty relation, when $\Delta E = \Delta H$.

The uncertainty in phase follows easily from Equation (48) and from the argument which leads to Equation (8),

$$\Delta \phi = \frac{1}{2\sqrt{n}}. \tag{49}$$

Hence from Equation (40),

$$\Delta n \Delta \phi = \frac{1}{2} \sqrt{\frac{n+1}{n}}.$$

Although the minimum uncertainty product $\Delta n \Delta \phi = \frac{1}{2}$ appears not to be obtained unless n is much larger than unity, it must be remembered that this relation is itself inexact because of the difficulty of defining ϕ or $\Delta \phi$ for small n. As indicated from Equation (48), maser amplification itself allows the minimum possible uncertainty product for the well-defined quantities Δq and Δp, which are proportional to the uncertainties in electric and magnetic fields of the electromagnetic signal.

MASER AMPLIFICATION WITH PHASE-COHERENT EXCITATION OF MOLECULES

In a beam-type maser, molecules entering the cavity are essentially all in the upper state, but before leaving the cavity they may be in some phase-coherent mixture of the upper and lower states which allows continued amplification even when a majority of the ensemble is in the lower state. This phenomenon shows up strikingly in the two-cavity maser,[10] when the beam of molecules is passed first through a cavity containing a resonant electromagnetic wave which puts them in a phase-coherent mixture of states. The molecules then traverse a second cavity containing an electromagnetic signal which they may amplify or absorb, depending on the relative phase of this signal with the exciting wave in the first cavity. We shall examine whether or not such an arrangement gives an improvement in phase or intensity determination.

Consider an ensemble of molecules initially all in the upper state. These are subjected to a strong electromagnetic field indicated by subscripts zero for a time t_0. This field, which might be called the carrier, is then removed and a second weaker signal field, characterized by subscripts unity, is imposed for a time t_1. At time t_0 we have, from Equation (33),

$$b_0' = b_0 \cos h\, t_0 - i a_0^* \sin h\, t_0. \tag{50}$$

At time $t_0 + t_1$, from Equations (32) and (50),

$$a = a_1 \cosh t_1 - i b_0'^* \sinh t_1 = a_1 \cosh t_1 - i b_0^* \cosh t_0 \sinh t_1 +$$
$$a_0 \sinh t_0 \sinh t_1. \tag{51}$$

Here it has been assumed that, although the number of molecules in the ground state after time t_0 is large, it is very much less than the number in the upper state. This validates the approximation involved in the Hamiltonian (31) and equations derived from it.

From Equation (51), the diagonal matrix element of a^*a, giving the average number of quanta in the field at time $t_0 + t_1$, is

$$n = n_1 (\cosh t_1)^2 + (\cosh t_0)^2 (\sinh t_1)^2 + n_0 (\sinh t_0 \sinh t_1)^2 +$$
$$\cosh t_1 \sinh t_1 \sinh t_0 \, |<a_1^* a_0 + a_0^* a_1>|. \tag{52}$$

The number n_1 is the initial number of photons in the signal and n_0 is the initial number in the carrier field. The operator b_0 is diagonal, but a_0 and a_1 are not diagonal if the phases of the two fields are defined.

An appropriate wave function for the carrier field can be represented by the sum of a number of functions characteristic of the Poisson distribution

$$c_m = \sqrt{\frac{n_0^m e^{-m_0}}{m!}}\; e^{-im(\phi_0 + \omega t)}. \tag{53}$$

This gives $q = \left| < -\dfrac{1}{\sqrt{2}}(a^* + a) > \right| = -\sqrt{2n_0}\,\sin(\omega t + \phi_0)$ so that ϕ_0 is the phase of a wave with an average number of photons n_0. Similarly, for the signal,

$$C_{1m} = \sqrt{\frac{n_1^m e^{-m_1}}{m!}}\; e^{-im(\phi_1 + \omega t)}. \tag{54}$$

If now the last term in Equation (52) is evaluated for the wavefunctions indicated by Equations (53) and (54), one obtains

$$\bar{n} = n_1 (\cosh t_1)^2 + (\cosh t_0 \, \sinh t_1)^2 + n_0(\sinh t_0 \, \sinh t_1)^2 +$$

$$2\sqrt{n_0 n_1}\, \cosh t_1 \, \sinh t_1 \, \sinh t_0 \, \cos(\phi_0 - \phi_1). \tag{55}$$

If $n_0 \sinh t_0$ is taken to be very large compared with $n_1 \cosh t_1$, and t_1 is very large, Equation (55) may be approximated as

$$\bar{n} = [n_0 \,(\sinh t_0)^2 + 2\sqrt{n_1 n_0}\,(\sinh t_0)^2 \times$$

$$\cos(\phi_0 - \phi_1) + n_1]e^{2t_1}. \tag{56}$$

Actually n_1 in Equation (56) may also be neglected, but it has been included to make evident the nature of this expression. It has the form of the intensity of two superimposed waves of amplitude $\sqrt{2n_0}\,(\sinh t_0)^2$ and $\sqrt{2n}$, respectively, and of phase ϕ_0 and ϕ_1. The resultant is amplified by the factor e^{2t_1}. It is important to note that, although the carrier field was removed before the signal was applied, after the signal has undergone a large amplification $(t_1 \gg 1)$, the carrier appears in the amplified wave.

Since the term $n_0 (\sinh t_0)^2$ in Equation (56) is large, it produces most of the fluctuations in the total number of quanta after amplification of the signal. The fluctuation Δn may be found by also computing $\overline{n^2}$ in a fashion similar to that used for $\bar{n}$. Again assuming that $n_0 (\sinh t_0)^2$ is much larger than n_1,

$(\Delta n)^2$ is given approximately by

$$(\Delta n)^2 = n_0 \; (\sinh t_1)^2 (\sinh t_0)^2 [(\sinh t_1 \; \cosh t_0)^2 + (\cosh t_1)^2 +$$

$$(\sinh t_1 \; \sinh t_0)^2]. \quad (57)$$

These fluctuations may be minimized if it is assumed that the carrier and hence $n_0 \; (\sinh t_0)^2$ is very large while $\sinh t_0 \ll 1$. Then

$$(\Delta n)^2 = n_0 \; (\sinh t_0 \; \sinh t_1)^2 [(\sinh t_1)^2 + (\cosh t_1)^2]. \quad (58)$$

If the phase difference $\phi = \phi_0 - \phi_1$ is to be evaluated from Equation (56), the error in phase may be obtained by differentiating this expression, so that

$$\Delta n = 2 \sqrt{n_1 n_0 \; (\sinh t_0)^2} \; \sin (\phi_0 - \phi_1) e^{2t_1}. \quad (59)$$

The uncertainty Δn is given by Equation (58), and the resulting uncertainty is $\Delta \phi$ is a minimum when $\sin (\phi_0 - \phi_1) = 1$. This gives, when the amplification is large so that $t_1 \gg 1$,

$$(\Delta \phi)^2 = \frac{1}{2 n_1}. \quad (60)$$

This is approximately the same as the uncertainty already obtained for an ordinary maser. The initial uncertainty in phase of the wave with wavefunction indicated by Equation (54) is $(\Delta \phi)_0^2 = \dfrac{1}{4 n_1}$, so the uncertainty due to the amplifying process alone is in fact precisely the same as if no carrier were used.

The number of photons in the signal may also be evaluated from Equation (56). The fluctuation is obtained by differentiation.

$$\Delta n = \sqrt{\frac{n_0}{n_1} (\sinh t_0)^2} \; \Delta n_1 \quad (61)$$

when $\cos (\phi_0 - \phi_1) = 1$.

This gives $(\Delta n_1)^2 = n_1 \quad (62)$

which is again the familiar result. Thus introduction of the carrier, or use of phase-coherent excitation prior to amplification, yields no essential change in the precision with which phase and number of quanta can be determined.

PRECISE DETERMINATION OF NUMBERS OF PHOTONS OR OF PHASE

Photon counters which can in principle count the number of photons in an electromagnetic wave with a negligibly small error are well known.   Examples are X-ray counters, photocells and photomultiplier tubes, as well as some more recently proposed devices.[1],[11]   To this list might be added, for detection of radiofrequency or microwave radiation, any molecular beam system where deflected molecules may be counted and deflection is affected by absorption of a quantum, and metastable atoms which may be lifted out of a metastable state by absorption of a low-frequency quantum, after which they may decay with radiation of a high-frequency quantum.[12] With the exception of X-ray counters, the actual attainment of devices which count individual quanta with little uncertainty is rather difficult, even though possible in principle. For such devices $\Delta n = 0$, and it is rather obvious that no information is obtained about the phase of the electromagnetic wave so that one may consider $\Delta \phi \rightarrow \infty$.

Devices which allow determination of phase with the highest possible precision while sacrificing accuracy in the number of photons are not so well known. The "thought experiment," indicated in Fig. 1, will show the characteristics of a precision measurement of phase.

A particle of charge e is allowed to pass between the plates of the condensor in Fig. 1 and its change in momentum as a re-

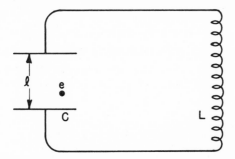

Fig. 1. Schematic of "thought experiment" for precise determination of phase of an oscillator

Charge e passes between condenser plates to measure electric field.

sult of any electric field E which is between the condensor plates may be measured. The momentum change is $p = eEt$, where t is the time required for passage of the particle between the plates. But p cannot be precisely determined, according to the uncertainty principle, because the particle is located in position to an accuracy $\pm l/2$ where l is the separation between the plates.* Hence at best

$$\Delta p = \hbar/l \tag{63}$$

or

$$\Delta E = \frac{\Delta p}{e\,t} = \hbar/etl. \tag{64}$$

Our purpose is to measure the phase of any oscillating field which may occur in the circuit of Fig. 1. This is most conveniently done at a time when the electric field is near zero, when the uncertainty in phase is given by

$$\Delta \phi = \frac{\Delta E}{E_m}. \tag{65}$$

Here E_m is the maximum field during the oscillation.

Evidently from Equations (64) and (65) $\Delta \phi$ can be made arbitrarily small by increasing the charge e. However, it must be at the cost of a large uncertainty in the energy or number of quanta in the circuit.

This process of phase measurement introduces an uncertainty in the energy of the circuit because the charge e may pass near either plate of the condenser, introducing a current of either sign. If the time t is much shorter than a period of oscillation, as it must be to obtain a simple measurement of the electric field at a particular time, then the current induced in the circuit by passage of the charge e close to either plate is

$$I = et/cL. \tag{66}$$

The uncertainty in energy which results is

$$\Delta W = h\nu\,\Delta n = \tfrac{1}{2}I^2 L = \tfrac{1}{2}CE^2 l^2 \tag{67}$$

---

*In addition to the uncertainty principle, another possible source of uncertainty in momentum would be image forces. However, these can be made small compared with the uncertainty given by (63) by choosing l sufficiently large.

where Δn is the uncertainty in number of quanta and E is the maximum field due to the oscillation which may be set up by passage of the charge e. If e is very large so that $\Delta \phi$ can be made arbitrarily small, then E becomes large and is equal approximately to E_m, the maximum field produced in the oscillating circuit. This makes also the total number of quanta n in the circuit comparable with the uncertainty Δn induced by the charge.

Thence from Equation (67), $E_m = \left(\dfrac{I^2 L}{C l^2}\right)^{\frac{1}{2}}$ which gives $\Delta \phi$ from Equation (64) and from Equation (65) as

$$\Delta \phi = \frac{l \, \Delta p}{e \, t I \sqrt{L/C}} = \frac{l \, \Delta p}{I^2 L \sqrt{LC}} = \frac{2 \pi \nu \, l \, \Delta p}{2 h \nu n} . \tag{68}$$

Here $\nu = \dfrac{1}{2 \pi \sqrt{LC}}$ and $\Delta n = \dfrac{\frac{1}{2} I^2 L}{h \nu}$ as in Equation (67). Since $l \Delta p = \hbar$ from Equation (63), this gives

$$\Delta \phi = \frac{1}{2n} . \tag{69}$$

Furthermore, $n = \Delta n$, so that again $\Delta \phi \Delta n = \frac{1}{2}$. Thus ΔE and $\Delta \phi$ may be made arbitrarily small, but at the cost of a correspondingly large uncertainty Δn in the total number of quanta in the circuit.

MEASUREMENT WITH ARBITRARY RATIO BETWEEN UNCERTAINTY IN PHASE AND UNCERTAINTY IN PHOTON NUMBERS

Combinations of the various devices described above allow in principle measurement of electromagnetic waves with any type of precision in either phase or number of photons allowed by the uncertainty relation $\Delta \phi \Delta n \geqslant \frac{1}{2}$. Assume an electromagnetic wave propagated from left to right in Fig. 2 which divides at the intersection so that a fraction x of the energy enters arm 1 and a fraction $(1 - x)$ enters arm 2. It might be thought that, if arm 1 ends in a photon counter which determines precisely the number of photons in this fraction of the wave and arm 2 ends in a device which measures phase precisely, then the phase and number of photons in the original wave are both precisely determined.

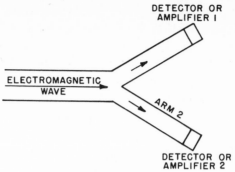

Fig. 2. Division of electromagnetic wave into two arms for measurement of phase and number of quanta with arbitrary ratio of accuracy

This is not the case because of fluctuations produced when the wave is divided at the junction between the two arms.

If the number n of photons in the original wave is given, the fluctuations in the number n_1 entering arm 1 can be obtained, for example, from Equation (15) of Shimoda, Takahasi, and Townes by letting $e^{-bt} = x$ and $a = c = 0$. The result is

$$\Delta n_1^2 = x(1 - x)\bar{n} + (\overline{n^2} - \bar{n}^2) x^2. \tag{70}$$

Assume the initial number n is definite, this is

$$\Delta n_1^2 = x(1 - x)n. \tag{71}$$

From symmetry, and also since the fluctuations in arm 2 must be equal to those in arm 1 in order to conserve energy, we also have

$$\Delta n_2^2 = x(1 - x)n. \tag{72}$$

The concomitant phase fluctuations may be found as was done for Equation (22). They are

$$(\Delta \phi_1)^2 = \frac{1 - x}{4 x n} \tag{73}$$

$$(\Delta \phi_2)^2 = \frac{x}{4(1 - x)n}. \tag{74}$$

The fluctuations given by Equations (61)-(74) may be regarded as due to a difference between waves associated with zero-point fluctuations in the two waveguide arms and those in the single guide. These waves differ because there is necessarily a mismatch at the junction. They produce, of course, fluctuations in both phase and energy.

Suppose that a perfect photon counter is used in arm 1 and a perfect phase detector in arm 2. Then the uncertainty in the total number of photons is given by

$$\Delta n^2 = \frac{\Delta n_1^2}{x^2} = \frac{(1-x)n}{x} .$$ (75)

The uncertainty in phase is determined by arm 2 alone, and

$$(\Delta \phi)^2 = (\Delta \phi_2)^2 = \frac{x}{4(1-x)n} .$$ (76)

Thus the product $\Delta n \Delta \phi = \frac{1}{2}$, while Δn varies between zero and infinity as x varies with $\Delta \phi$ taking on corresponding variations between infinity and zero.

Assume now a perfect photon counter in arm 1 and a perfect maser amplifier in arm 2. The phase information is given entirely by the maser arm, and

$$(\Delta \phi)^2 = (\Delta \phi_2)^2 + \frac{1}{4n_2} = \frac{x}{4(1-x)n} + \frac{1}{4(1-x)n} =$$
$$\frac{1+x}{4(1-x)n} .$$ (77)

The fluctuation in number of photons reaching the photon detector in the first arm is $\Delta n_1 = \sqrt{x(1-x)n}$ from Equation (71). This would give an uncertainty $\Delta n(1) = \dfrac{\Delta n_1}{x}$ in the total number of photons in the wave, or

$$[\Delta n(1)]^2 = \frac{1-x}{x}n .$$ (78)

But there is additional information about the number of photons from the maser amplifier in arm 2. The total fluctuation in the number of photons is that introduced by the junction plus that due to the maser amplifier. However, since the total number of photons entering both arms after the junction must be conserved, we may add the number detected in arm 1 to those found by the maser amplifier in arm 2 and cancel out fluctuations due to the junction. Then the uncertainty $\Delta n(2)$ in the total number is given by the maser fluctuation alone,

$$[\Delta n(2)]^2 = \frac{1}{4(1-x)n}. \tag{79}$$

Equations (78) and (79) represent independent measurements, so they can be combined to give a net uncertainty Δn less than either one, where

$$(\Delta n)^2 = \frac{1}{\dfrac{1}{[\Delta n(1)]^2} + \dfrac{1}{[\Delta n(2)]^2}} = \frac{1-x}{1+x}n. \tag{80}$$

Equations (77) and (78) give the final results, with again $\Delta\phi\,\Delta n = \frac{1}{2}$, and with Δn varying between 0 and n, the value given for the maser alone, as the fraction x varies between 1 and 0.

Similarly, the case of a perfect phase detector in arm 1 and a maser in arm 2 may be analyzed to give

$$(\Delta n)^2 = \frac{1+x}{1-x}n \tag{81}$$

$$(\Delta\phi)^2 = \frac{1-x}{4(1+x)}n. \tag{82}$$

CONCLUSION

The complementarity between phase ϕ and number of phonons n in an electromagnetic wave gives an approximate uncertainty relation $\Delta n\,\Delta\phi \geq \frac{1}{2}$ which limits the performance of any amplifier. An ideal maser-type amplifier introduces uncertainties $\dfrac{1}{2\sqrt{n}}$ and $\sqrt{n+1}$ in determination of ϕ and n respectively, or hence allows the limiting uncertainty product $\Delta n\,\Delta\phi = \frac{1}{2}$ if n is large enough for phase to be adequately defined. The minimum fluctuations introduced by the amplifying process itself correspond more precisely to equal magnitudes for the uncertainty in electric and magnetic fields while the product of these uncertainties has the minimum allowable value. These uncertainties can be connected with zero-point fluctuations of the fields. Ideal detectors which allow in principle $\Delta n = 0$, $\Delta \phi \to \infty$ or $\Delta \phi \to 0$, $\Delta n \to \infty$ may be combined with each other or with a maser amplifier to allow all possible ratios of Δn and $\Delta \phi$ while the relation $\Delta n \Delta \phi = \frac{1}{2}$ is still satisfied.

REFERENCES

1. J. Weber, Phys. Rev. *108*, 537 (1957).
2. W. Heitler, *The Quantum Theory of Radiation*, Oxford University Press (1936).
3. P. A. M. Dirac, *Quantum Mechanics*, Oxford University Press (1935).
4. J. P. Gordon, H. J. Zeiger, and C. H. Townes, Phys. Rev. *99*, 1264 (1955).
5. M. W. Muller, Phys. Rev. *106*, 8 (1957).
6. K. Shimoda, H. Takahasi, and C. H. Townes, J. Phys. Soc. Japan *12*, 686 (1957).
7. R. V. Pound, Annals of Physics *1*, 24 (1957).
8. M. W. P. Strandberg, Phys. Rev. *106*, 617 (1957).
9. L. I. Schiff, *Quantum Mechanics*, McGraw-Hill (1949).
10. A. Javan and T. C. Wang, Bull. Am. Phys. Soc. *2*, 209 (1957).
11. N. Bloembergen, Phys. Rev. Lett. *2*, 84 (1959).
12. Cf. experiment by W. Lamb and M. Skinner, Phys. Rev. *78*, 539 (1950).

DISCUSSION

M. STITCH: Is [noise in a system with multiple signal paths] a kind of "partition noise" with some randomness in the amount of energy that goes down each arm?

C. H. TOWNES: Yes, if one considered the energy as a stream of particles it would be partition noise. However, one must also allow for phase fluctuations introduced by division of a wave at a junction. In the case of partition noise for streams of electrons, the phase fluctuations are generally not considered.

USE OF VERY LOW NOISE AMPLIFIERS FOR RADIO ASTROMOMY

T. A. MATTHEWS

California Institute of Technology

RADIO ASTRONOMERS are interested in the development of very low noise amplifiers, since at frequencies greater than about 2000 Mc/sec the main limitation is the lack of ability to detect antenna temperatures below 0.01°K. Already several low noise amplifiers are being used. At Lincoln Laboratory, the detection of radio returns from the planet Venus last year depended largely upon the use of a cavity maser at a frequency of 440 Mc/sec.[1] This year they are repeating and elaborating upon the experiment using a parametric amplifier. At Jodrell Bank, the 250-foot dish is being used to detect radar returns from Venus, again with the use of a parametric amplifier. The Naval Research Laboratory has used a cavity maser operating at a wavelength of 3.37 cms to measure the radiation emitted by the planets Venus and Jupiter. They achieved a factor of improvement of 17 over a conventional receiver at this frequency.[2] In addition several other groups either will use, or are using, low noise amplifiers at frequencies above 1000 Mc/sec.

A brief discussion of the general observational techniques in use is helpful in evaluating the properties necessary for such devices to be fully effective in radio astronomy. For the purpose of this paper, it is convenient to divide radio astronomy into two main categories: 1. Discrete sources; 2. Line radiation.

The intensity of radiation from a discrete source does not vary rapidly with frequency, consequently we can use broad bandwidths to great advantage in reducing the noise fluctua-

tions.   The antenna temperature varies because of changes in
the amount of ground radiation, atmospheric emission, etc.;
consequently the observation of a radio source usually consists of a measurement of the difference of radiation at the
position of the source minus the radiation at one or more nearby
regions. Since we would like to compare two or more sources,
a complete observation takes at least 20 min and often longer.
Therefore the properties, in particular the gain, of the low
noise amplifier must remain constant for a similar period of
time.

The second category consists of observing the line radiation
from the hyperfine transition of neutral hydrogen in the ground
state, which exists in interstellar space.   The frequency of the
line is 1420 Mc/sec.   The desired information is the intensity
of radiation as a function of frequency, and also of position,
after subtracting any continuum radiation.   To make a detailed
study of the distribution in frequency, we need an I. F. bandwidth of 10 kc/sec, or less, at the $\frac{1}{2}$ power points.   For most
problems it is preferable to scan in frequency over a band of
one to two Mc/sec while looking in a fixed direction in space.
However, for problems where one is certain that the signal is
localized in position, scans in position at a fixed frequency can
be used to detect smaller signals.   Low noise amplifiers for
observing the line radiation may not be capable of scanning in
frequency while keeping the gain the same to a few percent at
all frequencies, as the observing technique may be confined to
using the latter method.

As the signal strength is small, any receiver system must
pay particular attention to methods of stabilizing receiver gain
and dealing with the effects of ground radiation.   Continuum
receivers are often designed to compare the signal with the
noise from a reference load at a known temperature.   This enables the receiver gain to be stabilized, but does not correct for
changes in ground radiation with antenna position.   In the case
of the hydrogen line observations, the effect of continuum radiation from discrete sources must also be taken into account.   In
order to take care of all of these effects, most 21 cm receivers
at present use a comparison between the radiation at a fre-

quency in the line and one outside the line, one to two Mc/sec away.

THE LOWER LIMIT OF USEFUL DETECTABLE ANTENNA TEMPERATURE

There is a limiting antenna temperature associated with each antenna, below which the information becomes rapidly less useful. This arises since, as the antenna temperature decreases, the number of observable sources increases. However there is only a fixed number of beam widths in a sphere; and so eventually, at some limiting antenna temperature, there will be more than one source in the beam. This is the confusion limit T_c, and it can be estimated with some confidence if we consider the effects of non-thermal sources only.

Under the assumption that the non-thermal sources have a uniform distribution in space, then the number of such sources per square degree, N_D, having a flux density greater than S_o, that can be observed by an antenna of effective area A, at a wavelength λ, is given by

$$N_D = K S^{-\frac{3}{2}} A^{-\frac{3}{2}} \lambda^{\frac{3n}{2}}$$

where the flux of a nonthermal source varies as $S_\lambda \propto \lambda^n$; the average value of n is approximately equal to one. On the other hand, the number of sources that can be resolved by the beam of the antenna is $N_R = D$, where D is the directivity of the antenna. For a filled aperture

$$N_R = \frac{4\pi A}{\lambda^2}.$$

The confusion limit is reached when $N_D = N_R$. Solving for S_c we find

$$S_c = K D^{-\frac{3}{2}} A^{-1} \lambda^n$$

which for a filled aperture becomes

$$S_c = K A^{-\frac{5}{3}} \lambda^{n+\frac{4}{3}}$$

or in terms of antenna temperature

$$T_c = KA^{-\frac{2}{3}}\lambda^{n+\frac{4}{3}}.$$

To evaluate the constant K, we note that a 90-foot diameter dish with about 50 percent efficiency, operating at $\lambda = 31$ cm, is confusion limited at $T_c = 0.1°K$. The formula can be used to predict when confusion sets in for the survey by Mills at $\lambda = 3.5$ m. The formula gives S_c (Mills) $= 16 \times 10^{-26}$ watts $m^{-1}(c/s)^{-1}$, whereas Mills[3] suggests a value of $S_c = 10 \times 10^{-26}$ watts $m^{-1}(c/s)^{-1}$. From an intercomparison with the Cambridge 3C survey, Dewhirst[4] suggests that the limit is near $S_c = 20 \times 10^{-26}$ watts $m^{-1}(c/s)^{-1}$. Certainly the formula is good to a factor two. Table 1 gives the calculated confusion antenna temperatures for a number of wavelengths and antenna sizes.

Table 1. The antenna temperature $T_c°K$ where confusion begins

λ cm	Antenna diameter in feet				
	30	50	90	140	300
60	2.2	1.1	0.50	0.28	0.10
30	0.43	0.22	0.10	0.055	0.020
15	0.086	0.044	0.020	0.011	0.004
10	0.026	0.013	0.0060	0.0033	0.0012
6	0.0099	0.0050	0.0023	0.0013	0.00046
3	0.0020	0.0011	0.00047	0.00026	0.000096

Since the effect of thermal sources has been neglected in these calculations, the numbers indicate the antenna temperatures we would like to detect in areas well away from the galactic plane.

GAIN STABILITY

Let us see how these limits fit the possibilities of low noise amplifiers. Following a discussion by Drake and Ewen[5] of the effects of receiver noise and gain stability on the minimum detectable temperature, ΔT_m, we have

$$\Delta T_m = K\left[\frac{T_R}{(Bt)^{\frac{1}{2}}} + \left(\frac{G_t}{G_o} - 1\right)(\Delta T + T_A)\right]$$

where

K is a factor approximately equal to one,

T_R = effective receiver noise temperature,
B = I.F. bandwidth,
t = time constant,
G_o = average amplifier gain,
G_t = rms fluctuation of the amplifier gain,
$\Delta T = T_2 - T_1$,
T_2 = antenna temperature as seen by the input of the low noise amplifier, when looking at the source. (It includes the effects of spillover, losses in the switch, and atmospheric emission.),
T_1 = the temperature at the input to the low noise amplifier when looking at the comparison region or load,
T_A = observed antenna temperature of the source or background.

Consider the first term in the bracket and let it equal T_o. If we assume a gain-bandwidth product of 100 Mc/sec, an effective single sideband noise temperature of 600°K for the following stage, G_o = 20 db, B = 1 Mc/sec, and t = 30 sec, then $T_o = 2 \times 10^{-3}$ °K.

T_o can be reduced still further when amplifiers having greater gains and bandwidths are available. For example, a traveling wave maser amplifier has been operated at $\lambda = 6$ cms with a gain of 30 db and a bandwidth of 10 Mc/sec.[6]

Reference to Table 1 shows that T_o becomes serious only at frequencies greater than 10,000 Mc/sec for antennas larger than 100 feet in diameter.

Consider now the second term: the most important part is ΔT. An equivalent temperature due to the system losses of about 30°K can readily be achieved; this can be reduced to 5°K or less, by careful design and by cooling the lossy elements. The atmospheric contribution comes from the emission of radiation by water vapor and molecular oxygen and varies from 2°K at 500 Mc/sec to about 6°K at 10,000 Mc/sec.[7] The value at the frequencies above 4000 Mc/sec depends largely on the amount of water vapor in the atmosphere and can vary widely. The spillover contribution can be reduced to under $10°K$,[8] but will probably be about $30°K$ for existing antennas. Thus T_2 can be as low as $20°K$, but will probably be as high as 60 to $80°K$. For the purpose of discussion we will assume $T_2 = 20°K$. Obviously T_1 should be very close to this value to achieve the desired sensitivity.

If the reference is a load, the temperature T_1 can be stabilized to $0.01°K$ or better. Even if the antenna is kept fixed, however, T_2 will fluctuate, because of changes in atmospheric emission due to changes in air temperature, barometric pressure, humidity, and clouds. Changes in atmospheric emission of $0.06°K$ at 500 Mc/sec and $0.3°K$ at 10,000 Mc/sec are expected to occur frequently in a period of one hour. We may expect changes of $\frac{1}{10}$ of this amount to occur in a few minutes. Thus it is unlikely that ΔT is less than $0.02°K$. This can be reduced significantly by using a separate identical feed looking at the dish, but displaced in position, as a reference source. The variations, particularly at 10,000 Mc/sec, will decrease in dry weather.

Using the previous discussion, we can now calculate the required gain stabilities to achieve different levels of detectable antenna temperature.

Table 2. Required gain stability for continuum radiation problems

ΔT °K	ΔT_m °K			
	0.1	0.01	0.001	0.0001
0.1	Factor 2	10%	1%	0.1%
0.01	...	Factor 2	10%	1%
0.001	...	...	Factor 2	10%

It is of interest to compare the values of T_c in Table 1 with the presently attained limits of detectability. At 8000 Mc/sec Drake and Ewen[5] using a TWT with a receiver noise temperature of $4300°K$, a bandwidth of 1000 Mc/sec, and a time constant of 80 sec, find a rms noise level of $0.1°K$. At 9000 Mc/sec, Alsop et al.[2] at NRL, using a cavity maser with an overall system noise temperature of $80°K$, a bandwidth of 5.5 Mc/sec, and a time constant of 5 sec, find the rms noise level is $0.04°K$. At 1000 Mc/sec, G. J. Stanley at the California

Institute of Technology, using a conventional crystal mixer and preamplifier with a double sideband noise temperature of $300°K$, a bandwidth of 10 Mc/sec, and a time constant of 20 sec, has found a rms noise level of $0.04°K$. Thus, for antenna sizes of about 100 feet in diameter, we are already at the confusion limit up to frequencies of 2000 Mc/sec, but are receiver noise limited above this frequency.

PROBLEMS FOR CONTINUUM MEASUREMENTS

It is not feasible to give details of all the specific problems that will be opened up with the availability of a stable low noise amplifier, nor indeed can one guess what future developments will be forthcoming in such a young science, but a summary of the major fields in which progress will become possible is instructive.

(a) *Position Measurements.* Perhaps the most obvious advantage of increased sensitivity at short wavelengths is that discrete sources can be observed with very narrow antenna beamwidths. The accuracy of position measurements can be greatly increased from the uncertainty in the position of moderately strong sources of an area 1×1 minutes of arc, currently being done at Cal Tech by J. G. Bolton with one 90-foot dish at 1000 Mc/sec. If the attendant mechanical problems can be solved, this accuracy should be increased by a factor 10 at 10,000 Mc/sec with the same dish. This is sufficient to identify most sources uniquely with optical objects, if indeed the optical objects can be seen with existing optical telescopes and techniques.

(b) *Size and Brightness Distribution Measurements.* The half-power beamwidth of a 90-foot antenna at a frequency of 10,000 Mc/sec is 4 minutes of arc. This will allow direct size measurements to be made on many thermal and non-thermal sources, and detailed contours of brightness distribution of sources larger than 10 minutes of arc. A pencil beam is of particular value since no assumptions need be made as to circular or other symmetry of the source, as is usually done to interpret the interferometric studies of brightness distribution. Already some very interesting results have come from the detailed studies made by Drake,[9] with a beamwidth of 6 minutes of arc at 10,000 Mc/sec, of the structure in the direction of the galactic center. Harris and Bolton at Cal Tech have used a 40 minutes of arc beamwidth, the former observing the detailed distribution in the Cygnus loop nebulosity; the latter, the structure of the radio source NGC 5128.

Another group of objects consists of the large faint regions of $H\alpha$ emission which appear on the Palomar Sky Atlas made by the 48-inch Schmidt. These regions will be observed at a level about five times the confusion limit at all frequencies. There will be a slight advantage in going to 3000 Mc/sec or 10,000 Mc/sec, since we can, in effect, look between the other point sources to find the large $H\alpha$ region, which is often several degrees across. The possibility of a detailed comparison between the optical and radio brightness distributions of sources is one of the most exciting possibilities of the near future.

(c) *Detection and Integrated Intensity Measurements of Miscellaneous Objects.* A rough calculation shows that all the planets out to and including Saturn should be detectable, with presently available equipment, at frequencies greater than about 500 Mc/sec. In actual fact, all of these but Mercury have already been detected at one or more frequencies. Uranus needs an improvement of a factor 10 in the presently detectable antenna temperature, Neptune a factor of 30; both of these will appear above the confusion limit. Pluto, however, is a factor 10 below the confusion limit for a 140-foot antenna used at 10,000 Mc/sec.

About a dozen galaxies have been detected, mainly at frequencies near 100 Mc/sec. Only five have been seen at frequencies of 1000 Mc/sec or higher. This number can be increased to at least two dozen as ΔT_m approaches T_c at the higher frequencies.

Observations indicate that the brightest of the planetary nebulae are probably present near the confusion limit of a 90-foot dish at 1000 Mc/sec. This agrees with the values of antenna temperature calculated from the best photoelectric optical data. Since these objects are optically thin regions of thermal emission, small in size with respect to the antenna beam widths we are considering, the expected antenna temperature varies only with the area of the antenna. Thus they will appear in large numbers as ΔT_m gets below 0.01°K. It is interesting to note that many objects which have been studied in great detail optically, are at or near our present detectable limits.

LINE RADIATION PROBLEMS

The present limits in detectability are due purely to receiver noise. A ΔT_m of approximately 1°K with a bandwidth of 5 kc/sec is about the best that can be done currently. However, for broad signals where the bandwidth can be increased to 500 kc/sec, ΔT_m becomes 0.1°K. Muller[10] at Leiden claims the ability to detect a ΔT_m of this amount.

It will be seen from the following paragraphs that the requirements for receivers which are to be used in line radiation measurements have somewhat less emphasis on the achievement of a very low noise temperature, and more emphasis on having high gain stability. The various types of observations that are made in the study of line radiation have been divided into several general groups and are discussed briefly below. The receiver requirements for each group of problems are given in Table 3. In several of these groups the receiver temperature, assumed to be 10°K, is still the limiting factor, but in others the observed signal or background radiation is the main source of noise. The time constant, t, needed in order to detect the minimum antenna temperature, ΔT_m, is given in column 5.

Table 3. Receiver characteristics for line radiation problems

Group	$(\Delta T + T_A)$ °K	ΔT_m °K	Bandwidth Kc/sec	t sec	Gain stability
a	75	0.1	5	145	0.1%
b	10	0.1	5	8	1.0
c	100	0.1	5	240	0.1
d	1	0.01	15	80	1.0
e	1	0.005	100	50	0.5

(a) A detailed study of the line profiles in the galactic plane would undoubtedly turn up much new and partially unexpected information. Such observations consist of studying details of

$\Delta T_m = 0.1°K$ on an emission profile of $T_A = 75°K$, while using a 5 kc/sec bandwidth. With these receiver parameters, the effects of individual clouds of gas should become visible. Detailed comparison can then be made between various features on the profiles and optical objects.

(b) When observations are taken more than 10 degrees of arc away from the plane of the galaxy, the peak antenna temperature goes down to about 10°K. To make a detailed study of these profiles, a ΔT_m of 0.1°K should be detectable with a 5 kc/sec bandwidth. A first survey has already been made by Erickson et al.[11] with a ΔT_m of 2°K. Their observations have opened the way to a detailed knowledge of the motions of the nearby hydrogen gas, and, hopefully, will also allow a determination of the size of the individual clouds of gas. Both of these questions require more numerous and detailed observations. As yet no detailed comparison has been made with the interstellar lines observed optically in stellar spectra. Such a comparison should provide information on the distribution, temperature, and abundance of different elements in space.

(c) Interstellar hydrogen between us and a radio source will absorb some of the continuum radiation from the source at particular frequencies, thus producing absorption lines. The region producing the absorption line is defined by the solid angle of the source. Since the source size is often much less than the antenna beamwidth, this is a method of achieving high angular resolution. For this reason, a study of absorption lines using a 5 kc/sec bandwidth (perhaps an even smaller bandwidth will be desirable), with the capability of detecting a ΔT_m of 0.1°K when looking at a source of $T_A = 100°K$, should show the effects of individual clouds or density variations in a large complex. A comparison with the expected emission profile for the region will give information on the spin temperature of the hydrogen gas.

One particular experiment of interest is the direct determination of the interstellar galactic magnetic field through the Zeeman splitting of the 21 cm line, as first suggested by Bolton and Wild.[12] From their paper, the minimum detectable magnetic field is given by $H_{min} = 1.7 \times 10^{-5} \Delta T_m$ gauss when using the sharp absorption lines produced by the gas in front of the radio source Cas A. With ΔT_m = 0.01°K we could see an H_{min} of 1.7×10^{-6} gauss, which is in the middle of the range of values for H estimated by indirect arguments.

(d) Observations have shown the presence of hydrogen gas moving perpendicular to the galactic plane over a wide range of velocities up to about 70 km/sec.[13] To investigate this hydrogen we must be able to see details of 0.01°K on a signal that has a peak antenna temperature of about 1°K. A bandwidth of 15 kc/sec is probably sufficient. These observations must be made by frequency scans, since this hydrogen seems to be present over most of the sky.

(e) In order to study the neutral hydrogen present in other galaxies, we would like to be able to detect a ΔT_m of 0.005°K or less, where the maximum antenna temperature is a few degrees Kelvin, while using a 100 kc/sec bandwidth. Already studies have been made of the neutral hydrogen in several galaxies. Such equipment could also be used to look for hydrogen in clusters of galaxies.

(f) The final group of problems comprises a search for the line radiation from other atoms and molecules in interstellar space. A list of possible lines has been given by Townes.[14] The most promising ones are those of deuterium at a frequency of 327 Mc/sec, and the lines of OH at 1665 and 1667 Mc/sec. The former is plagued by having a high galactic background temperature of about 50°K. Several unsuccessful attempts to see the deuterium line have already been made.[15],[16] It might be seen in emission, but it may also be seen as an absorption line in front of a radio source. The latter lines are in a good wavelength region, where the galactic background temperature is low. The main limitation, then, is receiver noise which has prevented the detection of OH in the only attempt made so far.[17] No figures are given for this category in Table 3.

From the values in column 6 of Table 3 we see that 0.1 percent gain stability is the best that is needed for the problems involving line radiation, if we have a receiver with a noise temperature of 10°K.

I wish to acknowledge my indebtedness to G. J. Stanley, as several of the ideas discussed in this paper are the result of fruitful discussions with him.

REFERENCES

1. R. Price, P. E. Green, Jr., T. J. Goblick, Jr., R. H. Kingston, L. G. Kraft, Jr., G. H. Pettengill, R. Silver, and W. B. Smith, Science *129*, 751 (1959).
2. L. E. Alsop, J. A. Giordmaine, C. H. Mayer, and C. H. Townes, *Paris Symposium on Radio Astronomy,* edited by R. N. Bracewell, Stanford University Press, p. 69 (1959).
3. B. Y. Mills and O. B. Slee, Australian J. of Phys. *10*, 162 (1957).
4. D. Dewhirst, private communication.
5. F. D. Drake and H. I. Ewen, Proc. IRE *46*, 53 (1958).
6. R. W. deGrasse, E. O. Schulz-DuBois, and H. E. D. Scovil, Bell System Technical Journal *38*, 305 (1959).
7. In a recent article, Hogg has calculated more accurate values of the atmospheric emission. He finds values which are 0.55 times the values given here. D. C. Hogg, J. Atmos. Phys. (in press).
8. R. W. DeGrasse, D. C. Hogg, E. A. Ohm, and H. E. D. Scovil, J. Atmos. Phys. (in press).
9. F. D. Drake, paper read at the Toronto meeting of the American Astronomical Society (1959).
10. C. A. Muller, *Paris Symposium on Radio Astronomy,* edited by R. N. Bracewell, Stanford University Press, p. 465 (1959).
11. W. C. Erickson, H. L. Helfer, and H. E. Tatel, *Paris Symposium on Radio Astronomy,* edited by R. N. Bracewell, Stanford University Press, p. 390 (1959).
12. J. G. Bolton and J. P. Wild, Astrophysical Journal *125*, 296 (1957).
13. H. C. Van de Hulst, Rev. of Mod. Phys. *30*, 913 (1958.
14. C. H. Townes, *Radio Astronomy,* edited by H. C. Van de Hulst, Cambridge University Press, p. 92 (1957).
15. G. J. Stanley and R. Price, Nature *177*, 1221 (1956).
16. R. L. Adgie, *Paris Symposium on Radio Astronomy,* edited by R. N. Bracewell, Stanford University Press, p. 352 (1959).
17. A. H. Barrett and A. E. Lilley, Astronomical Journal *62*, 5 (1957).

DISCUSSION

J. A. GIORDMAINE: The temperature of $0.03\,^\circ$K estimated for the noise level arising from fluctuations in atmospheric absorption at 3 cm. wavelength may be somewhat pessimistic. In recent observations using a maser amplifier at this wavelength (L. E. Alsop, J. A. Giordmaine, C. H. Mayer, and C. H. Townes Proc. IRE, June 1959), an rms fluctuation level of about $0.04\,^\circ$K was observed for periods of at least four minutes. This fluctuation level was in good agreement with the fluctuation level expected from ground radiation, lossy components, and the residual contribution of the crystal mixer. Thus it appears that the contribution from fluctuation of atmospheric absorption can be much less than 0.04°K.

T. A. MATTHEWS: The values of total atmospheric emission at 10,000 Mc/sec are based mainly on the amount of water vapor in the atmosphere under "normal" conditions. The expected short period variations are a certain fraction (estimated to be about $\frac{1}{100}$) of this total emission. If the total amount of water vapor in the atmosphere is less under the observing conditions, then the expected variations will also be less.

PARAMETRIC AMPLIFIERS AND THEIR COMPARISON WITH MASERS

H. HEFFNER
Stanford University

AT FIRST glance it may seem out of place to deliver a talk on parametric amplifiers at a conference on quantum electronics, for, after all, the principle on which the parametric devices work is a purely classical one. Nevertheless, I believe the subject is a pertinent one for two reasons; first because the parametric amplifier represents the strongest competition to the perhaps more intriguing quantum amplifiers, and second, it is likely that there are a number of quantum phenomena whose effects can be put to use in this simple classical manner. My purpose then is twofold, to give you an idea of the general characteristics of parametric operation and to present examples of the performance of certain parametric devices constructed in various laboratories throughout the country.

I shall resist the temptation to start this talk by a historical recounting of the many fascinating experiments performed on what we would now term parametric oscillators which were carried out in the middle and late eighteen hundreds. A list of names of these experimenters would include Airy, Melde, Lord Rayleigh, Maxwell, Marcel Brillouin, and in fact almost every one of the eminent nineteenth century physicists. The earliest of these experiments involved purely mechanical systems with observations that under certain conditions an excitation of one frequency could build up oscillations at a subharmonic frequency. It was not until later in the century that experiments on electromechanical systems were made, Lord Rayleigh being one of the first to show that electrical oscillations at a subharmonic frequency could be produced by mechanically varying the plate spacing of a capacitor in a tuned circuit.

So that we can all be aware of just what this oscillation phenomenon is and how it arises, let me illustrate it by what is essentially the configuration considered by Rayleigh[1] (Fig. 1).
I go through this explanation with some hesitation, for I am sure
that the behavior of this circuit is well known to all of you.
Thus let us consider this simple $L\,C$ resonant circuit in which
we imagine the plates of the capacitor are free to be moved back
and forth. If the plates were stationary, any energy in the circuit would of course oscillate back and forth between the induct-

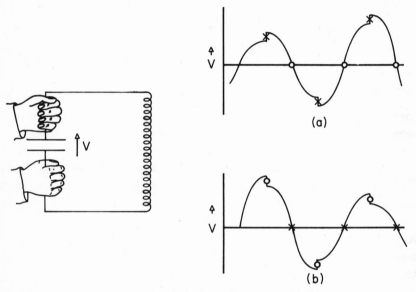

(a)

(b)

Fig. 1. A simple parametric oscillator

Here the crosses represent the sudden pulling apart of the condenser
plates, the circles the sudden pushing together.

ance and the capacitance at the natural resonant frequency, ω,
at one instant of time being stored wholly in the capacitor and a
half cycle later appearing entirely in the inductance. Let us
imagine that now when the energy is entirely in the capacitor,
that is, when both the voltage and the charge on the capacitor
are a maximum, we suddenly pull the plates apart. We must do
work in separating this charge and this work goes into increasing the electrical energy stored in the capacitor, or if you prefer,
the capacitance is reduced by the increased plate separation and

since $Q = CV$, the voltage must increase if charge is to be conserved. This process is illustrated by the first voltage jump
marked x in the upper right hand corner. Approximately a quarter
cycle of the natural oscillation period later, the energy is all
transferred to the inductance and at this point both the voltage
and the charge on the condenser are zero. Imagine that at this
instant we push the condenser plates back to their original spacing illustrated by the small circle. Since they are uncharged,
we do no work. A quarter cycle later, the energy is again in the
condenser and the voltage across it is now a negative maximum.
If at this instant we again pull the plates apart, we again do
work in separating the charge, the polarity of the voltage or the
charge being quite immaterial. Once more this work appears as
an increased voltage amplitude. If we repeat this regular pushing and pulling, electrical oscillations will build up from noise
to a level dictated either by our tiring muscles or by circuit nonlinearities which we have not included. If the circuit contained
loss, we would need only to push and pull a little harder to
reach the same level.

Notice two things. First, the frequency of our pushing and
pulling, or in modern parlance, the pump frequency, is twice that
of the natural resonance, that is, we have produced a subharmonic oscillation. Second, in this particular double frequency
case, there is a definite phase relation between the capacitance
variation, the pump, and the induced oscillations. If we imagine
pushing the plates together when the voltage is a maximum and
pulling them apart when it is zero as is illustrated in the bottom
right hand corner, work is done on us and the voltage is
attenuated.

The foregoing then represents a picture of the type of oscillations studied by Rayleigh and others during the late eighteen
hundreds. There were many contributions with the rise of the
great Russian school of nonlinear mechanics after the turn of
the century, but the references to this type of phenomenon by
European or American physicists became sporadic due to the intense preoccupation with the much more important quantum effects then beginning to be discovered.

With the advantage of our present knowledge, one very curious
fact sticks out. In spite of the great amount of work done in in-

vestigating these oscillations and in spite of very able men who
were so employed, no one seems to have recognized the fact
that this same mechanism which was capable of producing oscillations was also capable of amplifying a signal impressed on the
circuit. Perhaps this was because the concept of electrical amplification was a foreign one, nevertheless it was not until the
publication of an obscure engineering paper by Landon[2] in 1949
that the possibility of amplification by this means was not only
pointed out but demonstrated in a practical case. It is idle but
interesting to speculate how the course of radio would have been
changed had the principle of parametric amplification been recognized in the late nineteenth century. All the ingredients were
there, twenty-odd years before DeForest invented the triode.

A significant milestone in the history of parametric amplifiers
was the publication of a paper by Manley and Rowe[3] in 1956
in which they investigated the general properties of nonlinear
electrical energy storage elements, capacitors, and inductors.
The major result of their analysis was the derivation of two relations which govern the power flow at the various harmonic frequencies in a circuit containing a nonlinear reactance. Without
going into the derivation of these relations, let me try to indicate their generality and utility. Imagine that frequencies f_1 and
f_0 are applied to a lossless nonlinear reactance. The nonlinearity is capable of producing mixed frequencies $mf_1 + nf_0$ each
with a power flow $P_{m,n}$. The Manley-Rowe relations then are

$$\sum_{m=0}^{\infty} \sum_{n=-\infty}^{\infty} \frac{mP_{m,n}}{mf_1 + nf_0} = 0$$

$$\sum_{m=-\infty}^{\infty} \sum_{n=0}^{\infty} \frac{nP_{m,n}}{mf_1 + nf_0} = 0$$

These relations involve an integer times the power flow at one
of the possible frequencies divided by that frequency. Since it
is a sum which must add to zero, certain of the power flows can
be negative indicating a flow of power out of the nonlinear
element.

Peter Sturrock[4] has recently given an elegant derivation of
the Manley-Rowe relations in which he shows that they apply

very generally to any system describable by a Hamiltonian. These energy transfer relations and similar ones derivable in the same way are important not only to electrical circuit theory but also to instabilities in plasmas and the coupling of oscillations in particle accelerators. In fact, as early as 1929, R. V. L. Hartley[5] proposed this mechanism to describe the Raman effect.

Weiss,[6] by a very simple argument, has shown that the Manley-Rowe relations are obeyed in the maser if the total power is counted, that is, not only that going into the radiation field, but also that going into the lattice.

Let me illustrate the utility of the Manley-Rowe relations to parametric devices by considering two of the simplest, the up-converter and the regenerative amplifier. Imagine that we have a nonlinear reactance to which we apply pumping power at the frequency f_0 and which is attached to a circuit capable of accepting power only at two other frequencies, f_1 and f_2. First consider the case where the frequency f_2 is the sum of the pump frequency f_0 and the signal frequency f_1, that is, the integers m and n are both plus one. The two Manley-Rowe relations then are shown in Fig. 2. The bottom equation shows that if we supply pump power (P_0 positive) then the power at the mixed frequency P_2 must be negative, that is, it flows from the nonlinear element into the remainder of the circuit. Thus if we supply power P_1 at frequency f_1 we can abstract power P_2 at frequency

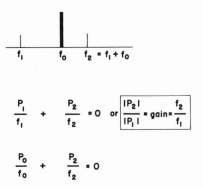

$$\frac{P_1}{f_1} + \frac{P_2}{f_2} = 0 \quad \text{or} \quad \boxed{\frac{|P_2|}{|P_1|} = \text{gain} = \frac{f_2}{f_1}}$$

$$\frac{P_0}{f_0} + \frac{P_2}{f_2} = 0$$

Fig. 2. A three frequency parametric up-converter with the appropriate Manley-Rowe equations

f_2 with a conversion gain given by the ratio of output frequency to input frequency. Hence up-converters give gain while down-converters give loss. It is worthwhile to emphasize here that we are dealing with frequency mixers which employ nonlinear energy storage elements. The conventional mixers employ nonlinear resistance and as such always produce conversion loss.

The second and perhaps more interesting illustration of the Manley-Rowe relations is that of the regenerative parametric amplifier. Consider again that we apply power P_0 at the pump frequency f_0 but that now the circuit is capable of accepting or supplying power only at the signal frequency f_1 and at a mixed frequency f_2 which is now the difference between the pump frequency and signal frequency rather than their sum as previously. For this new case the Manley-Rowe relations are shown in Fig. 3. The bottom equation again shows that if the pump power is

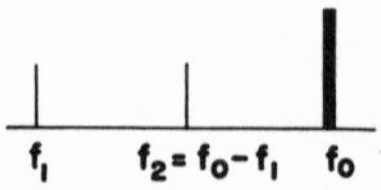

$$\frac{P_1}{f_1} - \frac{P_2}{f_2} = 0$$

P_1 and P_2 negative,
Potentially unstable

$$\frac{P_0}{f_0} + \frac{P_2}{f_2} = 0$$

Fig. 3. A three frequency regenerative parametric amplifier with the appropriate Manley-Rowe equations

positive, the mixed frequency power P_2 must be negative, that is flowing out of the nonlinear element into the circuit. The top relation again shows that the two powers are in the ratio of their frequencies but it differs from the up-converter case by a minus sign indicating that the power at the signal frequency, P_1, is also negative, flowing out of the nonlinear reactance. The implication of this fact is that if the circuit conditions are proper, the device can oscillate. If the circuit losses are too great, no oscillations occur, the powers all being zero, a situation which also satisfies the two Manley-Rowe equations.

The details of the circuit and of the nonlinear element govern the threshold of oscillation. Below the start oscillation value of pumping, the device is capable of amplifying a signal, the output being taken either at the same frequency or at the difference frequency. This difference frequency is termed the idling frequency. Notice that the double pump frequency circuit studied by Rayleigh and others is the degenerate version of this regenerative parametric amplifier obtained when the signal and idling frequencies become coincident.

There is another and to the engineer a more useful way of describing the operation of the regenerative parametric amplifier. That is in terms of the effective negative resistance seen by the signal or idling circuit. In Fig. 4 is shown the schematic dia-

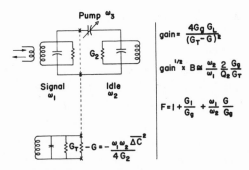

Fig. 4. *The equivalent circuit of the regenerative parametric amplifier with the equations for gain, gain-bandwidth product, and noise figure*

gram of a simple cavity-type parametric amplifier. The cavity resonances at signal and idle frequencies are represented by the two RLC circuits coupled by a nonlinear capacitance. For small signals, the nonlinear capacitance acted upon by the pump can be replaced by a time varying capacity. Then as far as either resonant circuit is concerned, the action of the remainder of the circuit at that resonant frequency can be described by a negative conductance. The value of this negative conductance, G, depends upon the product of signal and idle frequencies, the loading of the other resonant circuit, and the excursion of the nonlinear capacitance, that is, upon the amplitude of the pump power.

On the right are shown the expressions for gain, gain-band-width, and noise figure for this form of amplifier. The gain expression has the familiar appearance exhibited by all regenerative amplifiers, the denominator containing the difference between the total positive conductance, G_T, and the negative conductance, G. Exactly this same expression can be written for the cavity maser. There is one important practical difference in the gain behavior of the two amplifiers, however. In the maser, the negative conductance arises because of the population imbalance maintained by the pump, however, the value of this effective negative conductance is usually insensitive to the level of the pump power because the pump transition is operated at saturation. In the parametric amplifier, there is no such saturation effect so that the negative conductance and hence the gain is critically dependent upon the pump power level. For this reason, gain instabilities are a much more serious problem in the parametric amplifier.

The next equation gives a simplified form of the gain-band-width expression appropriate for most operating conditions. Here Q_2 is the Q of the idling circuit and ω_2/ω_1 is the ratio of idling to signal frequency. The form of this expression is reminiscent of that appropriate to the maser in which the magnetic Q replaces Q_2 and the frequency ratio is absent. Note that the gain-band-width product is increased the larger is made the ratio of idling frequency to signal frequency. Gain-bandwidths of 40 megacycles or so are easily obtained at S-band.

The last equation shows the expression for the noise figure of the parametric amplifier and is appropriate to the case where all parts of the circuit are assumed to be at the same temperature and the only type of noise introduced either by the circuit or the nonlinear element is thermal noise. If the nonlinear element introduces shot noise, a somewhat more complicated expression results. Let me discuss briefly the origin of each of the terms in this equation. The factor of unity is of course the result of incoming thermal noise which is amplified along with the signal. The second term is the result of noise introduced by the losses of the circuit at the signal frequency. Here, G_1 is a conductance representing these losses and G_g is the input conductance. Unless a circulator is used to isolate the load from the amplifier, we should include another term which represents the effect of thermal noise which is generated in the load, travels to the amplifier, is there amplified and returned to the load. So far, all of these terms appear in the equivalent noise figure expression for the maser. It is the last term which has no counterpart in the maser. It represents thermal noise generated in the idling frequency circuit and converted to noise at the signal frequency. The ratio of signal to idle frequency appearing in this term represents the power conversion ratio, as we have seen by the Manley-Rowe relations.

For this case of the amplifier used with a circulator, the noise figure expression can be put into a simpler form

$$F = \frac{\omega_{pump}}{\omega_{idle}} \frac{Q_{ext}}{Q_{loaded}}.$$

Here the terms have been combined and the various conductance ratios appear in the ratio of external Q to loaded Q. For very heavy coupling, this ratio becomes unity in the limit and the minimum noise figure of the parametric amplifier is simply the ratio of pump frequency to idle frequency,

$$F_{min} = \frac{\omega_{pump}}{\omega_{idle}}.$$

Notice that for the case of the degenerate parametric amplifier in which signal and idling frequencies are the same and equal to half the pump frequency, this expression indicates the minimum noise figure is numerically two, that is, three db. That such a result is reasonable is easily seen by considering signal and idling frequencies to be almost coincident. Then there are two adjacent channels in which noise is amplified but only one channel in which the signal appears and is amplified. Since both channels are equivalent, the amplifier will have a noise figure of 3 db even if it adds no noise itself. If the signal appears simultaneously in both signal and idle bands symmetrically spaced about half the pump frequency, then this 3 db limitation no longer holds. Such a situation holds in radio astronomy and the degenerate amplifier will probably find application for this purpose.

Measurements of the noisiness of degenerate amplifiers made by applying noise to both signal and idle channels are called double channel noise figures. One must add 3 db to them if the amplifier is to be used for communication purposes in the conventional way.

As in the case of the cavity maser, the simple cavity type of parametric amplifier has an undesirably small bandwidth. As in the case of the maser, one solution to this problem is to employ a traveling-wave structure. A drawing of an idealized version of such a structure is shown in Fig. 5. Here we have a transmis-

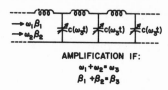

AMPLIFICATION IF:

$$\omega_1 + \omega_2 = \omega_3$$
$$\beta_1 + \beta_2 = \beta_3$$

Fig. 5. A traveling wave parametric amplifier

sion line with an inductance L per unit length and a nonlinear capacitance C per unit length. If a strong pump signal is applied, we may treat the nonlinear capacitance as an equivalent time varying capacitance varying at the pump frequency. Tien[7] and Suhl have analyzed in great detail the behavior of this circuit. I shall indicate only one of their results, namely that exponential gain is obtained if the sum of the signal and idle frequencies is equal to the pump frequency and if at the same time the sum of their phase constants is equal to the phase constant of the pumping wave of capacitance variation. Because of this last requirement, the traveling wave version may be made nonreciprocal, giving gain in only one direction. The noise figure expression for these amplifiers has the same form as that for the cavity amplifier.

The practical difficulties in building a broad band amplifier of this sort at microwave frequencies are formidable, first of all because most of the parametric elements are lumped, making it a difficult job to design a periodically loaded line in which the phase constant relationship is obeyed over a wide band of frequencies. Secondly, one finds that if the structure is capable of propagating one or more of the upper sidebands, that is, the pump frequency plus the signal frequency or the pump frequency plus the idle frequency, the gain can be drastically reduced. Never-theless, useful forms of such amplifiers can be and have been built.

There is another and simpler technique for broadbanding the parametric amplifier. It involves using the single nonlinear element of the cavity version, but instead of providing singly tuned resonant circuits at the signal and idling frequencies, more complicated filter type structures are employed. In this way Herrmann and Seidel[8] have managed to obtain bandwidths as large as 40 percent. Siegman has pointed out that the same technique can be applied to the cavity maser to obtain amplifi-cation over the full line width of the paramagnetic material. Amplifiers broadbanded in this way still have gain instability problems characteristic of regenerative amplifiers.

So far we have been concerned with the general behavior of amplifiers employing nonlinear energy storage elements. Let us now turn to the types of nonlinear elements suitable for use at microwave frequencies.

The first proposal for a practical microwave parametric ampli-fier was made by Suhl, who considered using ferrite as the non-linear medium. One form of this amplifier simply couples several cavity resonances together through the $M \times H$ nonlinearity in the equation of motion of the ferrite magnetization. In this type of amplifier, the ferrite can be looked upon as simply a nonlinear inductance which is caused to vary at the pump frequency. The situation is complicated, of course, by the spin wave instabili-ties at high pump powers which limit the opening up of the pre-cession angle or in this picture limit the amount of inductance change which can be obtained. Since the amount of inductance change available determines the gain-bandwidth product of the amplifier, one finds himself caught between conflicting require-ments when he tries to design a ferromagnetic amplifier of this sort. The first requirement is for reasonable pumping powers which dictates as small a linewidth ferrite as possible, while the second requirement for a reasonable gain-bandwidth product dic-tates as large a linewidth as possible. Typically, the amplifiers of this type which have been constructed employed ferrites with linewidths of a few tens of oersteds and required kilowatts of pumping power.

The situation is improved somewhat if a spin wave resonance is used for one or both of the resonances. The improvement is due to the increased filling factor thus obtained, but it apparently comes at the expense of noise figure. Berk has reported such an amplifier which had a noise figure in the vicinity of 11 db. I suspect that all such amplifiers of this type which use a spin wave resonance for signal or idle frequencies will exhibit high noise figures. I believe that this effect is due to the virtual infinity of spin wave modes which allow many spin waves having frequencies which are integer combinations of pump, signal, and idle to couple their noise into the signal circuit.

Not long after Suhl proposed the ferrite version of the parametric amplifier, Hines[9] built a degenerate version of the amplifier at microwave frequencies using a back biased semiconductor diode as the nonlinear element. Of all the nonlinear elements proposed and used, the diode has proved to be the most attractive from almost every point of view. It requires no magnetic field, it produces low noise amplification without the use of liquid helium, and it can be operated with only milliwatts of pumping power.

In the back biased regime, the diode acts as a voltage sensitive capacitance. It also has a small loss due primarily to the spreading resistance so that its equivalent circuit can be well represented by a series RC combination as shown in Fig. 6.

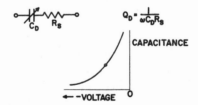

Fig. 6. The equivalent circuit, quality factor, and capacitance variation of a backbiased diode

Also shown here is a typical sort of capacitance *versus* voltage variation. One of the important figures of merit for the diode as a parametric element is its Q. The higher the Q, the smaller is the effect of the thermal noise contribution of the spreading resistance to the amplifier noise figure. An alternative description of the diode's quality is the cut-off frequency defined as that frequency at which the Q has become unity. Diodes are now being commercially constructed which have cut-off frequencies in excess of 100 kilomegacycles, which means that they have Q's in excess of 100 to 1000 megacycles.

The only appreciable source of noise in the diodes seems to be simple thermal noise. Because of the minute current drawn in the back biased condition, typically a microampere or so, shot noise is no problem. Thus cooling of the diode and of the amplifier as a whole can considerably reduce the noise figure. This fact arises not only because the amount of thermal noise is less at a lower temperature, but also because in certain materials, such as germanium, but not silicon, the mobility and hence the diode Q is increased at moderately reduced temperatures.

Diode parametric amplifiers have been built at various frequencies between 1 mc and 10,000 mc. They have been used as up-converters, regenerative parametric amplifiers, and as combinations of the two. Both traveling wave types and cavity versions have been constructed. Even superregenerative operation has been tried. There has even been some experience gained in using diode parametric amplifiers in radar systems.

I have tried to summarize the most important characteristics of these amplifiers, namely their measured noise temperatures, in Fig. 7. Here the ordinate is noise temperature in degrees Kelvin with 10 degrees at the bottom of the scale and 1000 degrees at the top. The abscissa is frequency in megacycles starting at 100 megacycles. Each dot represents the reported measurement of a particular cavity-type diode amplifier. The circled dots indicate that this is a degenerate version and that the measurements are of the double channel type. Thus for these amplifiers, the indicated noise temperature would be appropriate for radio astronomy purposes, but would not if they were to be used for the reception of conventional communication signals. The letter C next to two of the circles indicates that the diode was cooled, typically to temperatures between 80 and 90 degrees Kelvin. For comparison, I have indicated the best current performance of two traveling wave tubes, one at 3000 and one at 10,000 megacycles.

You notice that most of these amplifiers have noise temperatures below 100 degrees and the lowest of them has a noise

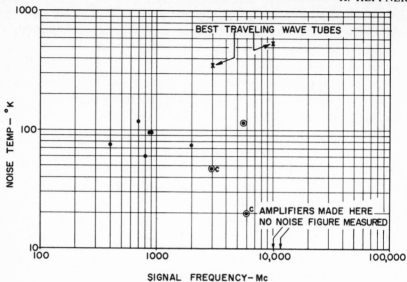

Fig. 7. The current (1959) noise performance of parametric amplifiers employing semiconductor diodes

The circled points represent double channel noise measurements and the letter C implies the diode was cooled to 80°–90° K.

temperature of 20 degrees. It is a degenerate amplifier using a special gallium arsenide diode cooled to about 90 degrees. It operates at 6000 megacycles and was constructed by Uenahara.[10]

I believe it is still too early to be able to draw a curve in this figure and say, "This line represents the capability of parametric amplifiers." Too much depends upon the outcome of research and development now going on in new semiconductor materials and fabrication techniques. I believe, however, that we shall see diode parametric amplifiers even at 10,000 megacycles with noise temperatures below 100 degrees and moreover that either by the broad banding technique or by use of traveling wave circuits, any of these amplifiers may be designed to have bandwidths in the vicinity of 10 percent.

Many of you will notice that I have made no mention of the electron beam parametric amplifier. I have omitted it not only because of lack of time but also because I believe in its present form it is not as attractive for use at frequencies much above S-band. In spite of this and many other omissions, I hope I have given some idea of what parametric amplifiers and are how they compare with masers. Though I believe that they will be important as devices, I suspect they will also have a fundamental importance in understanding energy conversion mechanisms in a wide variety of nonlinear physical phenomena.

REFERENCES

1. Lord Rayleigh, Phil. Mag. S. *5* (1883).
2. V. D. Landon, "The use of Ferrite-Cored Coils as Converters, Amplifiers, and Oscillators," RCA Rev. *10*, 387 (1949).
3. J. M. Manley and H. E. Rowe, "Some General Properties of Nonlinear Elements, Part I. General Energy Relations," Proc. IRE *44*, 904 (1956).
4. P. A. Sturrock, "Action-Transfer and Frequency-Shift Relations in the Nonlinear Theory of Waves and Oscillations," Microwave Laboratory, Stanford University, Internal Memorandum, M. L. No. 625 (August, 1959).
5. R. V. L. Hartley, "Oscillations in Systems with Nonlinear Reactance," Bell System Technical Journal *15*, 424 (1936).
6. M. T. Weiss, "Quantum Derivation of Energy Relations Analogous to Those for Nonlinear Reactances," Proc. IRE *45*, 1012 (1957).
7. P. K. Tien, "Parametric Amplification and Frequency Mixing in Propagating Circuits," J. Atmos. Phys. *29*, 1347 (1958).
8. H. Seidel and G. F. Herrmann, "Circuit Aspects of Parametric Amplifiers," Wescon Convention Record, Part II, p. 83 (August, 1959).
9. M. E. Hines, paper delivered at the fifteenth Annual Converence on Electron-Tube Research, held at Berkeley, California (June 26–28, 1957).
10. M. Uenahara, Paper delivered at the seventeenth Annual Conference on Electron Tube Research, held at Mexico City (June 24–27, 1959).

DISCUSSION

R. KOMPFNER: It may be of interest to note that the first suggestion that parametric amplification is inherently low-noise, even with variable-compacitance semiconductor devices, was made by A. von der Ziel around 1950.

M. T. WEISS: Dr. Berk used a modified semistatic operation for his ferrite microwave amplifier with the idler resonant circuit being the ferrite uniform precession. No spin waves were used.

The 11 db noise figure measurement is apparently entirely due to circuit problems with the ferrite contributing very little to this noise.

A. YARIV: A comparison of the effective source temperatures of maser and parametric amplifiers was carried out using the following models:

1. The maser amplifier uses a reflection cavity at temperature T_c coupled to a matched load through an ideal circulator.

2. The parametric amplifier uses a microwave circuit identical to that of the maser amplifier and operates in the degenerate mode, i.e., $\omega_{pump} = 2\omega_{signal}$. The parametric element is assumed lossless. Assuming high gain operation and denoting the cavity Q and the external Q as Q_c and Q_{ex} respectively, we get for the effective source temperature T_e:

$$(T_e)_{maser} \cong \frac{T_c}{Q_c/Q_{ex}} + |T_m| \tag{1}$$

$$(T_e)_{P.A.} \cong \frac{T_c}{Q_c/Q_{ex}} \tag{2}$$

where T_m is the negative maser temperature which is equal to zero when all the molecules are in the upper energy level.

This analysis leads to the conclusion that in the ideal limit the parametric amplifier has a lower noise temperature than the maser. A serious problem that has to be settled before this conclusion can be trusted is the following.

The maser analysis takes into account quantum effects, which are represented by $|T_m|$. The parametric amplifier analysis is wholly classical and assumes that pure reactive modulation is lossless and consequently introduces no noise. This assumption should be examined in the light of the theory of statistical fluctuations.

J. ROTHSTEIN: Lossev, in the 1920's, did many experiments with point contact rectifiers using silicon carbide, zincite, zinc blende, lead sulfide, etc., in which oscillation or amplification were obtained. While many of his results had a thermal origin, others seem not to have been so, and he may well have done the first semiconductor parametric amplifier experiments.

C. H. TOWNES: It appears to be very difficult to draw any absolute line of distinction between parametric and maser amplifiers. Several types of criteria have been set up to distinguish between these two types of amplifiers, but each criterion appears to break down when examined closely. For example, it is sometimes proposed that a maser is not phase sensitive, whereas phase coherence is an important property of parametric amplifiers. However, the two-cavity beam-type maser discussed by Javan and Wang* gives a clear example of phase sensitivity. Here the beam of excited ammonia molecules traverses a first cavity where some transitions are induced by a carrier. It then proceeds, carrying a phase coherence, through a second cavity where the signal is introduced. If the signal is in phase with the carrier, it is amplified; if it is out of phase it may be attenuated. Another criterion commonly referred to is that a maser must have more systems in an upper state than in a lower state, i.e., be at a "negative temperature." But the two-cavity maser amplifies in the second cavity without any such requirement. More than half the molecules may have made transitions before entering the cavity, but they possess a phase coherence which distinguishes them from a normal Boltzmann distribution and which allows amplification. To make it still plainer that this two-cavity device is a maser, it need only be observed that a normal single-cavity beam-type maser exhibits the same properties as the beam passes through the last part of the cavity, assuming that a majority of the energy is extracted from the beam into the electromagnetic wave.

I would propose that a distinction between masers and parametric amplifiers be drawn, if one is needed, by characterizing systems where the discreteness of energy levels is important and is determined essentially by atomic or molecular properties as masers, and those where the energy levels are essentially

*A. Javan and T. C. Wang, Bull. Am. Phys. Soc. II, *2*, 209 (1957).

continuous and hence classical as parametric amplifiers. This leaves amplifiers using ferromagnetic resonances in the camp of masers, where I believe they can rightfully repose, although they are commonly referred to as parametric. Here the discrete energy levels are of importance, but the system can be adequately discussed classically, as can any simple spin system.

Perhaps in the end some looseness in terminology is not harmful as long as it is realized that the usual categories of maser and parametric amplifier are somewhat artificial and may overlap.

THE MASER AS A PARAMETRIC AMPLIFIER

E. T. JAYNES

Microwave Laboratory and Department of Physics,
Stanford University

MANY PEOPLE have noted an amusing similarity between the maser and the parametric amplifier, whose behavior is also governed by "pseudo-quantum" laws, such as the Manley-Rowe equations, reminiscent of $E = \hbar\omega$. Relations giving a proportionality between energy and frequency have a long history in physics, and are characteristic of many purely classical systems. The best-known example is the adiabatic theorem, which played an important role in the early development of quantum theory. One finds that in any classical periodic system, the action integral over one period is an approximate invariant under slowly varying perturbations. The derivation of this law is particularly simple in the case of a harmonic oscillator with slowly varying spring constant. Here the oscillator coordinate satisfies the equation of motion $\ddot{x} + \omega^2 x = 0$. If now we allow ω to be a slowly varying function of time, the BWK approximation to the solution is

$$x(t) = \frac{1}{\sqrt{\omega}} \exp[i \int \omega(t)dt] \tag{1}$$

and so the energy is

$$E = \tfrac{1}{2}m\dot{x}^2 + \tfrac{1}{2}m\omega^2 x^2 = (\text{const.})\,(\omega). \tag{2}$$

This adiabatic theorem has recently found several applications, ranging from a simple derivation of the Slater perturbation formula in microwave theory to the calculation of orbits in particle accelerators.

Now consider a quantum-mechanical system such as a molecule in a maser, interacting with an electromagnetic field. We wish to show that the Schrödinger equation describing the time-evolution of this system has a close mathematical analogy to classical parametric systems, and in fact discloses a particular form of classical Hamiltonian for which the action conservation law becomes rigorous, independently of the magnitude or rate of change of the perturbations. Let the stationary state vectors of the quantum-mechanical system be u_n for the energy levels $E_n = \hbar \omega_n$, and expand the time-dependent wave function in the usual way,

$$\psi(t) = \sum_n a_n(t) \, u_n. \tag{3}$$

The equations of motion are then

$$i\hbar \dot{a}_m = \sum_n H_{mn} a_n = E_m a_m + \sum_n V_{mn}(t) \, a_n \tag{4}$$

where $V_{mn}(t)$ are the matrix elements of the interaction with fields, for example the product of dipole moment operator with electric field $E(t)$. By introducing the quadratic form which represents the expectation value of the energy,

$$H = \sum_{mn} \mathrm{H}_{mn} \, a_m^* \, a_n \tag{5}$$

we can write the equations of motion in a form resembling the classical Hamiltonian equations:

$$i\hbar \dot{a}_m = \frac{\partial H}{\partial a_m^*}, \qquad i\hbar \dot{a}_m^* = -\frac{\partial H}{\partial a_m}. \tag{6}$$

To increase the resemblance, we introduce the real quantities $p_n(t)$, $q_n(t)$ defined by

$$a_n = \frac{p_n - i\omega_n q_n}{(2\,\hbar\omega_n)^{\frac{1}{2}}}. \tag{7}$$

In terms of them, the quantity (5) becomes

$$H(q,p) = \frac{1}{2} \sum_n (p_n^{\ 2} + \omega_n^{\ 2} q_n^{\ 2})$$

$$+ \frac{1}{2} \sum_{mn} [a_{mn}(p_m p_n + \omega_m \omega_n q_m q_n) + 2 b_{mn} \omega_m q_m p_n] \tag{8}$$

where $a_{mn}(t)$, $b_{mn}(t)$ are proportional to the real and imaginary parts of V_{mn}, and the Equations of motion (4) and (6) reduce to

$$\dot{q}_m = \frac{\partial H}{\partial p_m}, \qquad \dot{p}_m = -\frac{\partial H}{\partial q_m}. \tag{9}$$

Equations (8) and (9) are, of course, nothing but the Schrödinger equation, in unconventional notation.

In consequence of the fact that H_{mn} is Hermitian, the Equation of motion (4) has a rigorous constant of the motion

$$\sum_m |a_m|^2 = \text{constant} \tag{10}$$

which in quantum theory we interpret as "conservation of probability." Using Equation (7), we find that in terms of p_n, q_n this conservation law becomes

$$\sum_n \frac{p_n^2 + \omega_n^2 q_n^2}{2\omega_n} = \sum_n \frac{W_n}{\omega_n} = \text{constant} \tag{11}$$

where W_n is the energy stored in the n'th mode. Equation (11) is also easily verified directly from Equations (8) and (9).

If we had been shown only the final Equations (8), (9), and (11), and not the argument which I have used to derive them here, a very different interpretation would seem natural. In Equations (8) and (9) we have an assemblage of classical harmonic oscillators perturbed by some external environment in a manner described by the matrices $a_{mn}(t)$, $b_{mn}(t)$. Since the Hamiltonian (8) is quadratic in the p_n, q_n, for any particular values of the a_{mn}, b_{mn} we could find a new set of normal modes; the effect of the environment is to vary the spring constants. The set of harmonic oscillators is not coupled directly to its environment, but parametrically. Thus to every kind of level scheme which one might use in a maser, there corresponds a purely classical parametric system which would behave in just the same manner and what is most important, would react back on the perturbing environment in the same way as does the atom or molecule.

As a consequence of this analogy, the decision whether a maser or a parametric amplifier is best for any given application might involve the following reasoning. For many jobs which a maser can do, we can in principle find a classical parametric system which would do the same job. So it must be the practical considerations, such as availability of materials with certain relaxation times, stability of parameters, efficient parametric circuit elements, etc., which lead us to prefer one kind of device to another. Many years ago, W. W. Hansen proposed a theorem which may or may not apply to this case; given two different ways of accomplishing something, both of which will work in principle, that one will be best which receives the greatest number of man-hours of development work.

DISCUSSION

I. R. SENITZKY: I would like to make two comments.

1. The spontaneous emission properties of the molecule have not been completely considered, since the field has not been quantized. Thus, a molecule may be regarded as a classical parametric system only if some of the quantum-mechanical properties are neglected.

2. It seems that the essential difference between a maser and a parametric amplifier (ignoring now the quantum-mechanical aspects mentioned above) is that a maser is a collection of many loosely-coupled systems, while a parametric amplifier is a single system. Thus, there is negligible correlation between the idler oscillations of the many molecules of the maser, while the parametric amplifier has a single idler oscillation. Any effects, therefore, which are due to idler oscillation (such as the ones mentioned in my talk yesterday) will be entirely different in a maser than in a parametric amplifier.

E. T. JAYNES: 1. Surely. When we write $E(t)$, we are implying semiclassical radiation theory. However, as I showed in a report last year, this theory does give spontaneous emission, with the correct Einstein A-coefficients, if we take the expectation value of dipole moment as the source for a classical electromagnetic field. Field quantization is not necessary for spontaneous emission.

2. The "idler oscillations" involve the absolute phase of the wave function $\psi(t)$, which is not observable. In the classical Hamiltonian, [Equation (8)], this corresponds to the fact that the interaction term involves coordinates and momenta in a form which contains only the difference frequencies $\omega_m - \omega_n$, not the sums $\omega_m + \omega_n$.

M. WEISS: In addition to deriving the Manley-Rowe relations by means of conservation of the number of quanta, it is also possible to derive the Tien phase relations for a traveling wave parametric amplifier by requiring the conservation of momentum. Thus,

$$\left(\frac{h\nu}{v\varphi}\right)_{pump} = \left(\frac{h\nu}{v\varphi}\right)_{signal} + \left(\frac{h\nu}{v\varphi}\right)_{idler}$$

results in

$$\beta_{signal} + \beta_{idler} = \beta_{pump}.$$

It is to be noted that for momentum in a dispersive medium one must use the phase velocity. This quantum analog is particularly useful in the derivation of the phase relations of more than three frequency traveling wave parametric amplifiers.

G. GOULD: Professor Townes has mentioned an early electron maser, the triode. The Barkhauser-Kurz oscillator is more easily understood. Electrons oscillate approximately harmonically in a one-dimensional potential well between plate and cathode. The electrons are injected into a band of levels whose vibrational quantum numbers are $n \cong [E/h\nu] - \frac{1}{2} \sim 10^8$. An oscillating electric field induces transitions to empty lower and higher levels, depending on phase. Those which absorb power are removed, leaving a net induced emission of photons to the e.m. field.

Similarly, in the magnetron type of maser, stimulated emission of radiation takes place as the electrons undergo transitions to states of lower angular momentum quantum number.

M. W. P. STRANDBERG: An analytic definition which seems to make physical sense has been given by Strandberg [Phys. Rev. (1958), "Spin-Lattice Relaxation"]. A solid state maser or pa-

ramagnetic amplifier by this definition is one in which the pumping field interacts with a system which has such a short phase
memory that only the diagonal elements of the density matrix are
affected, for example, a system with $T_2 \ll T_1$. A parametric
amplifier is one such that the pumping field is able to impose
phase coherence on the system, so that both diagonal and off-
diagonal elements of the density matrix are affected.

CROSS RELAXATION AND MASER PUMPING BY A FOUR SPIN FLIP MECHANISM

P. SOROKIN, G. J. LASHER, and I. L. GELLES

International Business Machines Corporation, Poughkeepsie, New York

BLOEMBERGEN AND co-workers[1] have recently analyzed the processes of energy transfer between adjacent resonances in both nuclear and electronic spin systems. These authors consider that multiple spin reversals of neighboring spins which are induced by the dipolar and exchange interactions between the ions are primarily responsible for the transfer of energy between resonances. For a given multiple spin flip process to be important in the establishment of spin-spin equilibrium, a necessary requirement is that total Zeeman energy be nearly or exactly conserved by the process. This led Bloembergen *et al.* to suggest that in certain instances a relatively high order process which conserves Zeeman energy may be more probable than a simple flip-flop between two spins whose resonance frequencies are sufficiently different that there is no appreciable overlap between the lines.

It occurred to us that the paramagnetic resonance[2] of nitrogen centers in diamond could be used to verify quantitatively the occurrence of a higher order spin flip process, the reason being that the simple resonance spectrum of three narrow, equally spaced lines is compatible with only one multiple spin reversal process which exactly conserves Zeeman energy. This process (Fig. 1) consists of simultaneous double flip-flops and was invoked by Bloembergen and co-workers to explain qualitatively the cross-saturation results reported by Townes *et al.*[3] in a copper salt. Two spins of the center line

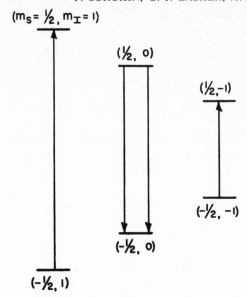

Fig. 1

Electron spin resonance energy level diagram for nitrogen centers in diamond ($H_0 \parallel [100]$) showing the four spin flip mechanism which establishes spin-spin equilibrium. The hyperfine splitting is 94.2 mc/sec.

make a downward transition while a spin belonging to each satellite makes an upward transition. The net rate of the process is proportional to $[(n_o^+)^2 \, n_{-1}^- \, n_{+1}^- - (n_o^-)^2 \, n_{-1}^+ \, n_{+1}^+]$, where the n's are level populations, subscripts referring to nuclear spin quantum numbers and superscripts to electron spin quantum numbers. In the linear approximation of small population differences, the rate becomes

$$R = \frac{1}{2\,T_{21}} \, [(n_{+1}^+ - n_{+1}^-) - 2(n_o^+ - n_o^-) + (n_{-1}^+ - n_{-1}^-)]. \quad (1)$$

If a saturating microwave field is suddenly applied to one of the three lines of the nitrogen spectrum, a weak probing microwave signal at either of the two other lines should register a change in absorption in a time T_{21}. Specifically, if T_{21} is much less than other relaxation times of the system, then making the pump incident upon the center line should force the absorption at either satellite to drop to zero. Setting the pump at the position of one of the satellites, on the other hand, should reduce the center line absorption to $\frac{3}{5}$ its thermal equilibrium value but should *increase* the absorption measured at the other satellite by the factor $\frac{6}{5}$. These predictions follow from Equation (1).

We observed precisely this behavior at liquid-helium temperatures in those diamonds of our collection which had the greatest concentration of nitrogen centers. A double resonance method was used, with two independent X-band microwave sources functioning as pump and probe. The microwave cavity used the two orthogonal, degenerate cylindrical TM_{110} modes which could be continuously split in frequency from 0 to ~ 600 mc/sec. Both pump and probe klystrons were AFC stabilized on their respective cavity modes. A counter monitoring the difference frequency of the two sources allowed the pump and probe to be set precisely on any two lines. A fast microwave switch in the pump line made it possible to turn the pump power on or off rapidly. Figure 2 shows oscilloscope traces whose vertical component is proportional to the absorption of the probe signal. When the pump is turned on, the absorption jumps to a new value and then relaxes slowly to the equilibrium pump-on value. The jump in absorption is interpreted as the change in spin population caused by the four spin flip mechanism. The magnitude of the jump in all three cases agrees with the predicted value. The slow change in absorption which follows the jump is caused by other relaxation mechanisms T_s, T_x, T'_x, T_N [4] working under the constraint that R of Equation (1) equals zero. The role of the other relaxation processes is now being studied and a more complete report of these experiments will be made in the future.

In connection with this experiment one of us (G. L.) has noted that the four spin flip transition may be used in special cases to establish c.w. maser operation by inverting the population of one of the satellite lines. For simplicity, consider a spin system of three equally spaced resonances for which the direct ($\Delta m_s = \pm 1$) spin lattice relaxation is the only contact with the lattice. This spin lattice relaxation is represented by

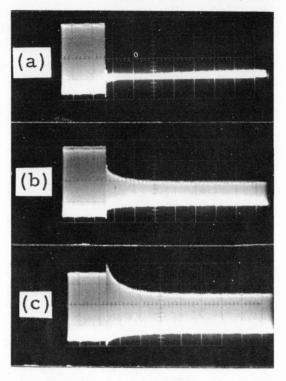

Fig. 2

Probe absorption vs. time showing effect of turning on the pump;
(a) probe on high field satellite, pump on center line, (b) probe on
center line, pump on low field satellite, (c) probe on high field satellite, pump on low field satellite. The sweep speed is 0.5 sec/cm.
(T = 1.6°K).

rate equations of the form:

$$\left(\frac{dn_{a,\,b}^{+}}{dt}\right)_{SL} = -\left(\frac{dn_{a,\,b}^{-}}{dt}\right)_{SL} = -W_{a,\,b}\left(e^{\frac{h\nu}{kt}}n_{a,\,b}^{+} - n_{a,\,b}^{-}\right) \qquad (2)$$

where the subscripts a and b refer to the two satellite lines
which do not necessarily arise from the nuclear states of the
same electronic spin system. If one assumes that the four spin
flip probability $\dfrac{1}{2T_{21}}$ is much greater than the spin lattice relaxation probability $W_{a,\,b}$ and that the center line of the triplet

is completely saturated by a microwave field, then in the steady state:

$$n_a^- - n_a^+ = N_a \left(\frac{e^{\frac{h\nu}{kt}} - 1}{e^{\frac{h\nu}{kt}} + 1} \right) \left(\frac{W_a N_a - W_b N_b}{W_a N_a + W_b N_b} \right), \tag{3}$$

where $N_{a,b} = n_{a,b}^- + n_{a,b}^+$.

Equation (3) holds also when the subscripts a and b are interchanged and therefore shows that if an asymmetry exists in the NW product of the two satellite lines, the one with the smaller NW product will have its spin population inverted. If the system is chosen so that the low field satellite is inverted, then a maser could be built with a pump frequency slightly lower than the amplifying frequency. The pump power levels required should not in principle be higher than those encountered in the usual method of three-level maser excitation.

Our thanks are due J. P. Anderson for building much of the double resonance equipment. We would like to thank Dr. W. V. Smith for helpful conversations.

REFERENCES

1. Bloembergen, Shapiro, Pershan, and Artman, Phys. Rev. *114*, 445 (1959).
2. Smith, Sorokin, Gelles, and Lasher, Phys. Rev. (in press).
3. Giordmaine, Alsop, Nash, and Townes, Phys. Rev. *109*, 302 (1958).
4. See, for example, F. M. Pipkin, Phys. Rev. *112*, 935 (1958).

DISCUSSION

A. KIEL: The relationship $R\left[(n_o^+)^2 n_{-1}^- n_{+1}^- - (n_o^-)^2 n_{-1}^+ n_{+1}^+\right]$ where R is the 4-fold cross-relaxation rate is not unique. For example, it could as well be written in terms of ratios of the n's.

However, in the linearized theory (the rate equations are highly nonlinear) which holds when $h\nu/kT \ll 1$, one always gets

$$R = \frac{1}{2T_{21}}\{(n_{+1}^+ - n_{+1}^-) - 2(n_o^+ - n_o^-) + (n_{-1}^+ - n_{-1}^-)\}.$$

THE EXCITATION OF AN L-BAND RUBY MASER*

W. H. HIGA

*California Institute of Technology, Jet Propulsion Laboratory
Pasadena, California*

WE HAVE measured the pump power required to operate a ruby maser at 1,000 mc for the 90° orientation of the ruby. Figure 1 shows the pump power required for various frequencies at the threshold of oscillation for the signal frequency.

It is noted that there are three minima at

$$f(1-3) = 10.6 \text{ kmc}$$

$$f(2-3) = 9.65 \text{ kmc}$$

and

$$f = 10.20 \text{ kmc.}$$

The second of these is of special interest since it occurs at the idle frequency $f(2-3)$ where one normally expects only the opposite effect. The explanation for this has been given by Geusic[1] in terms of harmonic spin-coupling. Figure 2 shows the energy level diagram for the 90° orientation used. It is to be noted that maser action at $f(1-2)$ may be achieved by pumping at either $f(1-3)$ or $f(1-4)$ in the high field mode. It is further noted that in the vicinity of 1,700 gauss

$$f(1-4) \approx 2f(2-3)$$

Mims and McGee[2] found that whenever a spin system has a transition frequency which is a multiple of another transition frequency then the two spin systems may become strongly

*This paper represents one phase of research carried out at the Jet Propulsion Laboratory under contract No. NAS w-6, sponsored by the National Aeronautics and Space Administration.

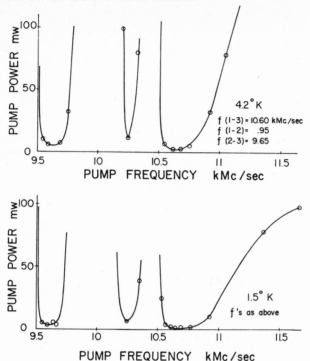

Fig. 1. Pump power versus pump frequency for an L-Band maser in high field mode

coupled. Hence pump power at $f(2\text{-}3)$ can cause saturation of the $f(1\text{-}4)$ transition. The detailed mechanism for harmonic spin-coupling is yet to be explained.

If it is assumed that pumping at the idle frequency $f(2\text{-}3)$ is equivalent to pumping simultaneously at $f(2\text{-}3)$ and $f(1\text{-}4)$ due to spin-coupling, then it is possible to carry out a Bloembergen[3] type analysis for the population levels. Using Bloembergen's notation, it is found that

$$n_1 - n_2 =$$

$$\frac{Nh}{4kT} \frac{w_{12}f_{12} + w_{13}f_{12} + w_{13}f_{23} - w_{24}f_{23} - w_{24}f_{34} - w_{34}f_{34}}{w_{12} + w_{13} + w_{24} + w_{34} + W_{12}}.$$

This equation holds for large W_{23} and W_{14}, and for this case these two quantities cancel in the resulting equation.

Whatever the detailed mechanism for harmonic spin-coupling
may be, it is certainly a nonlinear process. It is perhaps not
too farfetched to assume the existence of nonlinear coupling
in two spin systems with nearly the same transition frequencies.[4] It would then be possible, for instance, to saturate
two transitions by pumping at a frequency which is the average
of the two independent frequencies. This appears to be a
plausible explanation for the minimum at 10.2 kmc in Fig. 1.
This frequency is very nearly the average of $f(1{\to}3)$ and $f(2{\to}3)$.

It is perhaps of some interest to point out further that a four-
level maser of the type suggested by Javan[5] was also operated
successfully. Here a few milliwatts of power at $f(3{\to}4)$ and

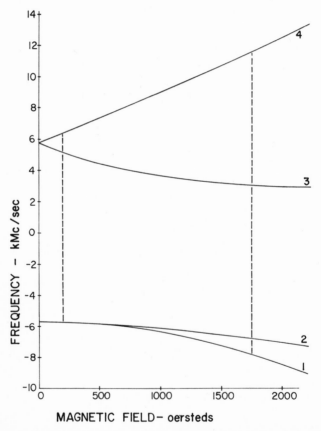

Fig. 2. Energy level diagram for ruby in 90° orientation

$f(1-3)$ were applied simultaneously to achieve signal amplification at $f(1-2)$ as before. Moreover, it was demonstrated that the two pumps augmented each other. The Javan amplifier, however, requires that the relaxation rates be properly related, and it was found that the four-level maser would obtain only for a dilute (.01 to .02 percent) concentration of chromium in the ruby. When the temperature was lowered from $4.2°K$ to $1.6°K$, the pumping at $f(3-4)$ was observed to have no effect on the system. For higher concentrations of chromium, it was observed that pump power at $f(3-4)$ actually caused antimaser effect.

Finally, we remark that low field operation (see Fig. 2) of the L-band maser was possible at $4.2°K$ for linear polarization of the RF magnetic field parallel to the constant field. This is expected from the matrix elements as in the high field mode but polarization is much more critical here.

REFERENCES

1. J. E. Geusic (to be published).
2. Mims and McGee (to be published).
3. N. Bloembergen, Phys. Rev. *104*, 324 (1956).
4. N. Bloembergen *et al.*, Phys. Rev. *114*, 445 (1959).
5. A. Javan, Phys. Rev. *107*, 1579 (1957).

DISCUSSION

A. PENZIAS: The explanation by Geusic was experimentally verified by Arams (Airborne Instruments Laboratory) who monitored the harmonic transition and found that it was indeed saturated by pumping at half frequency.

In the paper just given, each of the observations corresponded to a different X-band mode of the cavity. Perhaps the greater efficiency of the 10.25 transition is merely a result of the better coupling of this particular mode to the spin system.

W. HIGA: In reply to Mr. Penzias, we would like to state that cavity resonance probably enhanced the cross-saturation effect described in the text. In any case, his point is well taken, and an effort will be made to repeat the experiment with a tunable maser.

CROSS RELAXATION AND MASER ACTION IN $Cu(NH_4)_2(SO_4)_2 \cdot 6H_2O$

F. R. NASH AND E. ROSENWASSER
Columbia University

MASER ACTION has been observed in $Cu(NH_4)_2(SO_4)_2 \cdot 6H_2O$ under the most unusual circumstances.

The concentration of the Tutton salt was 1 percent in a host of $Zn(NH_4)_2(SO_4)_2 \cdot 6H_2O$.

The schematic energy level diagram is shown in Fig. 1. for $S = \frac{1}{2}$ and $I = \frac{3}{2}$ for the external field ($\sim$ 3000 oersteds) along the rhombic axis of the crystal.[1]

The levels are not equally spaced although the allowed transitions ($\Delta m_s = \pm 1$, $\Delta m_I = 0$) labeled ①, ②, ③, and ④ are equally spaced. The experiments described below were carried

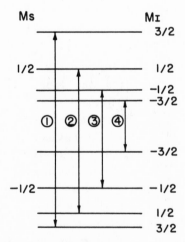

Fig. 1. Schematic energy level diagram for $S = \frac{1}{2}$ *and* $I = \frac{3}{2}$

out with an angle of ~ 45° between the external field and the rhombic crystal axis.[2] The separation between the above four transitions was ~ 100 oersteds. Actually there is another group of four closely spaced lines which occur at lower frequencies which arises because of the two nonequivalent lattice sites for the Cu^{+2} ion.[3]

It has been observed that saturation of ② produced emission at ①. Saturation of ③ produced emission at ① and ② and the former was very close to oscillation. Thus for the same input saturating power ③ was more effective in inverting ① than ②. Furthermore ③ was more effective than ② in reversing ①. This effect is unidirectional, in that saturation of ① produces only slight saturation in ② and nothing in ③ or ④. The same holds for saturation of ② and ③. Saturation of ④ produces complete saturation of ①, ②, and ③ but no inversion.

It was possible to "burn a hole" in ①; i.e., one could saturate the wing of the line without saturating the center. More strikingly, one could saturate the wing of ② nearest ① and invert ① without saturating the center of ②. Thus it appears that two cross-feed mechanisms are operative; one which spreads energy throughout a given line and one which carries energy to neighboring transitions.

Decay of the inverted spin system could be measured with a stop watch and the spin-lattice relaxation time was found to be several seconds. All the measurements mentioned so far were made at 1.4°K and a frequency of 8700 Mc. The spin-lattice relaxation time was noted at 4.2°K and appeared to be 10 times faster indicating a temperature dependence other than expected for a single spin-phonon interaction. The relaxation time at 1.4°K and 25 KMc is thought to be between 0.2 sec and 0.5 sec yielding a frequency or magnetic field dependence of H_o^{-n} where $2 < n < 3$.

A schematic of the experimental setup is shown in Fig. 2.

The cavity is a single mode TE_{101} piece of X-band waveguide. The display of the scope is the cavity mode made visible by a scope swept 2K45 monitoring klystron. The long relaxation times involved allowed the following procedure to be employed.

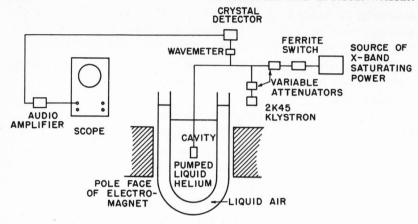

Fig. 2. Experimental schematic

The magnetic field is varied manually until a particular transition is observed. The ferrite switch is then thrown so that the fixed frequency power saturates the particular transition. After saturation has been achieved, the switch is again thrown so that the power is cuf off. Variation of the magnetic field would then permit one to look at neighboring lines.

Emission was not observed directly at 25 KMc but evidence will be cited to show that there was probably inversion. If one saturated ① and then observed the results of shutting off the saturating power it was seen that ① was already half decayed. However, if one saturated ② and simultaneously switched off the power and switched the magnetic field so as to observe ①, it was observed that ① appeared completely saturated. A natural interpretation is that in the latter case ① had been inverted before observation was possible.

REFERENCES

1. Bleaney, Bowers, and Ingram, Trans. Royal Soc. *A 228*, 147 (1955).
2. Ingram, Proc. Phys. Soc. *A 62,* 664 (1949).
3. Giordmaine, Alsop, Nash and Townes, Phys. Rev. *109*, 302 (1958).

DISCUSSION

P. SOROKIN: That the strongest inversion effect occurs where line (3) is saturated [line (1) being inverted as a result] would appear to be understandable in terms of the four spin flip mechanism we have just discussed. Lines (1), (3), and (5) form the required triplet for this mechanism, the spacing $(\nu_1 - \nu_3)$ being very close to $(\nu_3 - \nu_5)$. Line (5) can relax via flip-flops with spins of line (6) which overlaps it. Thus an asymmetry in the NW product of lines (5) and (1) exists which would, in fact, predict that line (1) would be the one inverted when line (3) is saturated.

F. NASH: If line (5) couples to (6), (7) and (8) by single flip-flops, then why doesn't the wing of (2) couple to the center of (2) by the same process?

GENERATION AND AMPLIFICATION OF MICROWAVES BY FERROMAGNETS

A. G. FOX
Bell Telephone Laboratories, Holmdel, New Jersey

IT IS now a little over two and a half years since H. Suhl first proposed the use of ferrites for microwave amplification. Soon after the proposal was made, M. T. Weiss experimentally demonstrated such an amplifier. It may be appropriate at this time to review the progress that has been made in this field to date. Within the same period of time, we have seen maser amplifiers developed into sufficiently practical devices that they are now being used in radio astronomy. Traveling wave types have been built which yield much broader bandwidths than are possible with cavity types. Semiconductor diodes of the variable capacitance type have been used to build simple, compact reactance amplifiers with attractively low noise figures even at room temperature. These, also, have been built in both cavity and traveling wave structures. Compared to this progress, it would appear that the ferrite amplifiers have been stillborn, or are, at most, in the incubator stage. At this time we have no really practical ferrite amplifier which can be operated cw with low pumping power and for which noise figure measurements have been made. Yet this poor showing is in spite of the fact that we now have available yttrium iron garnet (YIG) with a linewidth comparable to that of a paramagnetic material and a spin density much higher than that of paramagnetic materials. With Q's in the range of 6,000 even at room temperature, it would appear that this should be the ideal nonlinear coupling medium to use for reactance amplifiers. What then are the difficulties?

Semiconductor diodes have much lower Q's than the YIG. They all have some d-c leakage current, and this means that there is effectively a resistance shunting the variable capacitance. The Q's resulting from this are typically in the range of 10–100. However, the diodes have one big advantage. When they are made the capacitive element of an LC circuit, it is clear that at one point in the oscillation cycle substantially all of the energy will be stored electrostatically in the diode capacitance. Thus the filling factor can be very close to 1. In the case of the ferrites, on the other hand, filling factors have rarely been achieved which are much larger than .01. When it is attempted to use a large sample of ferrite in a waveguide cavity, the field becomes so highly distorted that not only is the required geometry of the field vectors destroyed, but spurious magnetic resonances within the sample are set up.

It appears that the very properties which make the ferrite so attractive as a low-loss reactive medium are the same properties which make it so difficult to employ properly. The large available magnetic moment is, of course, the result of exchange forces between atoms tending to line up the electron spins coherently. These same exchange forces can in many instances provide stronger coupling effects within the sample than the desired coupling between the spins and the radiation field. Thus the ferrite, instead of being a simple circuit element operating as a coherent unit in the way that a variable capacitance diode does, is a complex many-body system permitting a large number of internal modes of resonance. If these internal modes are excited, it is possible to reduce or entirely prevent the desired operation of the ferrite as an amplifying element.

These internal resonances can be excited by the same basic mechanism which produces the desired amplification of two signal fields externally applied. I will assume that all of you are familiar with the principle of magnetic amplification, and refer to Fig. 1 as a reminder of the field geometry required in such an amplifier. It is assumed here that a circularly polarized pumping field h_p at frequency f_p has set the magnetization in uniform precession about the d-c field H at a precession angle of θ. If a signal field h_1 at frequency f_1 is applied parallel to the d-c field,

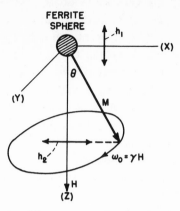

Fig. 1. Field geometry for ferrite amplifier

changes in magnetization m_2 will appear in the plane at right angles to H at signal frequency, $f_2 = f_p - f_1$. On the other hand, if the signal field h_2 were applied in the plane normal to H, this will disturb the uniform precession so that M wobbles alternately above and below the equilibrium precession angle θ, and this will produce changes in magnetization parallel with H at frequency f_1. If, then, modes of energy storage are available so that these magnetization components at the two signal frequencies can radiate energy into the modes, thereby building up fields h_1 and h_2 at these two frequencies, an intermodulation process can take place so that both signals will be amplified. It is important to make θ as large as possible, for clearly if it is very small, changes in θ produced by h_2 will produce negligible changes in M parallel with H. Thus, the larger θ can be made, the stronger will be the coupling provided between the two signal fields, and the easier it will be to overcome circuit losses so that amplification or oscillation can result. Typically, however, θ is no more than about 1 degree, even under conditions of high pumping power.

It is important to emphasize that any energy storage mechanism which can produce the required geometry of signal fields at a pair of frequencies whose sum is equal to the pump frequency can operate as an oscillator if the precession angle is sufficiently large. The higher the Q of these modes, the smaller will be the precession angle required in order to start oscillation.

Let us consider briefly various types of energy storage which can exist for a ferrite sample. Electromagnetic energy storage can be simply provided by a waveguide cavity of the proper design, and this is the means usually employed for coupling signal frequency fields into the ferrite sample. We usually like to think of these electromagnetic fields being uniform over the sample and resulting in uniform precession of all the spins throughout the sample.

However, it is possible to have spins in different parts of the sample oriented in somewhat different directions at any instant of time, as shown in Fig. 2A. To take a simple example, we have assumed that the spins (M) in the upper half of the sphere have a precession angle slightly greater than that of the uniform precession mode (M_o) while those in the lower half of the sphere have an instantaneous precession angle slightly less than the uniform precession angle. Thus, as far as the r-f components of magnetization are concerned, we can say that superimposed on the uniform precession are the transverse magnetization components shown in Fig. 2B. Magnetic lines of force close outside this sphere, as shown, and it is evident that for this configuration the external field energy will be much less than for the uniform precession mode. Since spin orientation changes slowly from point to point throughout the sphere, it is clear that exchange forces play an insignificant role in determining the resonant frequency of this mode, and that it is determined primarily

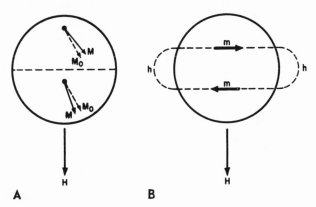

Fig. 2. Schematic of a simple magnetostatic mode

by the total magnetostatic field energy. For more complex magnetostatic modes, the external field energy is in general smaller
and by the time the variations in magnetization are large in
number, exchange forces begin to be important, and the magnetostatic energy may be insignificant in comparison. Most of the
magnetostatic modes and all of the spin modes are so loosely
coupled to external fields that it is not possible to use them for
transferring useful power to and from the sample. On the other
hand, since the energy is confined so tightly to the sample, it is
apparent that the filling factor will be very high for all such
modes, so that, provided they have the correct field geometry for
amplification, they can start to oscillate at lower pump power
than is required for amplification using electromagnetic modes
for the signal frequency.

Still another form of excitation which can be of importance is
the acoustic mode of resonance. We can imagine a sphere of
ferrite oscillating in shape like a bouncing basketball so that it
is alternately flattened and elongated along the d-c magnetic
field. Magnetostrictive coupling can then result in components
of magnetization parallel with the axis of distortion, namely,
along H. Thus, acoustic oscillation of the sphere can produce
signal components along the d-c field, and this together with a
resonant mode at right angles to the d-c field provided by either
an electromagnetic mode or some one of the magnetostatic or
spin modes, can result in oscillation. Such oscillations have
been observed at acoustic frequencies in the range from 1 mc to
20 mc. They typically appear as a fundamental with a series of
evenly spaced harmonics. A corresponding series appears as
upper and lower sidebands of the pump frequency, with the upper
sidebands usually very much weaker.

We come finally to a picture of a ferrite sample behaving as
shown schematically in Fig. 3. Here we see a single ferrite
crystal performing as a coupling element between a large number
of possible mode pairs whose frequency sum is equal to the pumping frequency. In general, a particular pair such as f_1 and f_2
are intended for useful signal amplification. As a result, this
particular pair must be loaded by external circuit couplings so
that power can be delivered to the sample and removed from it.

If all of these modes had the same filling factor and unloaded Q, the loading for f_1 and f_2 would alone be enough to insure that any of the other modes were likely to break into oscillation before the desired modes could provide amplification. Matters are made still worse if f_1 and f_2 modes are provided by resonant cavities yielding filling factors small compared to 1, because most of the other modes are likely to have filling factors near to 1. Thus the ferrite, rather than operating as a simple element coupling only the desired modes, is a complex system tending to oscillate at any or all modes other than the desired ones. As a

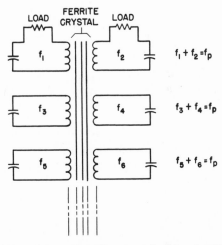

Fig. 3. Schematic of modes coupled by ferrite samples

result, when the pump is applied to a ferrite specimen and the power is increased, long before the precession angles are attained that would be predicted on the basis of the low-power linewidth, spin modes, magnetostatic modes, or acoustic modes are excited which bleed power from the uniform precession mode and tend to limit further increase in the precession angle. This is one of the most important reasons why very large pumping powers are required in order to obtain relatively small θ's.

Even though it has been commonly assumed that the use of YIG, because of its small losses, would permit amplification at lower pumping power than for other ferrites, this is not necessarily so. It is true that, provided we operate below saturation, the YIG will give larger θ's for a given pumping power. However, if in order to obtain the largest gain-bandwidth product we are forced to use the largest possible θ, the higher loss ferrites may prove better. Thus, Suhl[1] has shown that the precession angle tends to be limited by the onset of spin mode excitation to

$$\theta_c \approx \sqrt{\frac{\Delta H_k}{M}}$$

where ΔH_k is the linewidth of the spin mode excited and M is the saturation magnetization. Therefore, material with a broader linewidth will permit a larger maximum value for θ. However, a broad amplifier bandwidth is not a direct consequence of using a low-Q ferrite. If it were not for the excitation of spin waves, the narrowest possible linewidth for the uniform precession mode would be desired. The bandwidth of the amplifier would then be determined by how heavily the ferrite was loaded by the radiation field.

In conclusion, those who are working in the field of ferrite amplifiers have been disappointed at the lack of results shown to date, but have learned many new and fascinating things about the behavior of ferrites which may eventually make it possible to achieve the results we are looking for. It is tantalizing to have in the yttrium iron garnet a material with such remarkably attractive properties and not be able to make these properties perform to better advantage. There surely must be ways of using it if we are only clever enough. Several possible approaches might be employed. For example, if there were any way of building the garnet crystal so as to provide a higher damping for the spin modes than for the uniform precession mode, this would be enormously helpful in allowing the use of larger precession angles for a given pumping power. There is also the possibility that by suitably shaping the sample, the spin mode spectrum may be shifted so as to provide fewer possibilities for excitation by the uniform precession mode. A third possibility is that if we can learn enough about some of the low order magnetostatic modes to be able to couple to them efficiently from our waveguides, we might be able to employ them for excitation of the sample by the signal frequencies. In this case, we might hope for filling factors approaching 1 which would give us a couple of orders of magnitude improvement over what we now have when using electromagnetic modes.

REFERENCE

1. H. Suhl, Proc. IRE *44* (October, 1956).

DISCUSSION

A. E. SIEGMAN: The magnetostatic modes are relatively long-wavelength and the spin modes relatively short-wavelength modes. Did you state that they blend into each other in a continuous fashion?

A. G. FOX: Yes, I meant to imply that magnetostatic modes grade continuously into the spin modes as the wavelength is reduced. A detailed analysis of these modes is complicated, and has only been performed for the low-order magnetostatic modes and for the higher order spin modes. But there is no reason why there should not be a smooth transition from one type to the other in that range where the magnetostatic energy is comparable to the exchange energy.

NONLINEAR EFFECTS IN FERRITES

R. W. ROBERTS, W. P. AYRES, and P. H. VARTANIAN
MELabs, Palo Alto, California

DURING THE past ten years, the number of applications of ferrites in microwave circuits has been growing at a very fast rate. These applications have made use of the linear nonsymmetrical tensor permeability of the ferrite when operated near ferromagnetic resonance. Recently, a new class of applications has appeared, based on the nonlinear properties of this tensor permeability. Though the actual number of such devices being used in systems is very small today, it is anticipated that, as in the past, the introduction of a new nonlinear element will prove to be extremely useful in electronic circuits.

The nonlinear properties of the ferrite show up immediately from a consideration of the basic gyromagnetic equation of motion of the magnetization vector when biased near resonance. The equation is the familiar

$$\frac{dM}{dt} = \gamma (M \times H) \qquad (1a)$$

of which the z component equation is given by

$$\dot{m}_z = \gamma (m_x h_y - m_y h_x). \qquad (1b)$$

This equation shows the cross-product terms responsible for the nonlinear behavior of the ferrite. For if the ferrite is precessing in a uniform precession mode with the m_x and m_y components having a frequency dependence of ω_1 and an r-f field with a frequency dependence of ω_2 is impressed on the sample, one can see that the z component of magnetization will have frequency components at the sum and difference frequencies. But this is not the total picture since an auxiliary equation states that in the absence of spin waves, the total magnetic moment of the sample must be conserved. Therefore, if sum and difference frequencies exist in the z component, in general they will be present in the x and y components also. This then forms the basis of several interesting applications of ferrites at microwave frequencies. For instance, mixers, up-converters, and down-converters can be built using this frequency mixing principle. If suitable positive feedback can be incorporated in the spin system, regeneration will occur and parametric amplification will result. If the two frequencies are made equal then the sum frequency will be equal to $2\omega_1$ and second harmonic generation will result. Though not entirely obvious from this discussion, higher order terms can lead to higher harmonics also. In this paper I would like to discuss some experimental results that have been obtained with two of these applications: harmonic generation and parametric amplification.

HARMONIC GENERATION

Second harmonic generation can be pictured as arising from a noncircular orbit of the precessing magnetization vector $\overline{M}$. Since $\overline{M}$ is of constant amplitude, its tip must move on a spherical surface and a z component at twice the fundamental frequency will arise. Solution of the equation of motion taking into account second order terms gives for the amplitude of this harmonic term:

$$m_{z_{2\omega}} = \frac{\gamma M_o}{4\omega\Delta H} h_x^{\,2} \qquad (2)$$

M_o = Saturation moment of sample
ω = Fundamental frequency
h_x = r-f field at fundamental frequency
ΔH = Effective linewidth of sample

Though this equation is only approximate and neglects several factors which experiments have shown are not negligible, two relations can be seen immediately:

1. The output power is proportional to the square of the input power over the range of validity of Equation (2).

2. The output power is proportional to the ratio of $M_o/\Delta H$.

Considerable work has been carried out in the past four years in frequency doubling covering the range of 3 kmc to 140 kmc. The results of these experiments have, in general, verified these predictions. Initial experiments were carried out with a fundamental of 3 kmc and a second harmonic of 6 kmc. These results verified the square law dependence of second harmonic output over the remarkable range of 42 db. Experiments carried out with a fundamental of 9 kmc have verified that conversion efficiencies as high as 3.5 db with high power outputs can be obtained.

The ability of a ferrite to generate relatively large amounts of power at a harmonic frequency have led to its use at millimeter-waves where high powers are difficult to achieve. In particular, we have generated peak powers of 20-50 watts at 140 kmc. It is believed that this is the highest power available at this frequency. These experiments have, in general, borne out the relationships expected from the basic equation for doubling. Figure 1 shows an input-output curve for a doubling experiment at these frequencies using a single crystal yttrium iron garnet sphere of 0.040-inch diameter. The powers are plotted on a db scale with arbitrary reference levels. The slope is almost exactly 2:1 as expected from the square law dependence of second harmonic to fundamental. The dependence of second harmonic output on the ratio $M_o/\Delta H$ has been verified qualitatively over a range of better than 20:1.

However, experiments at these frequencies have also pointed out the limitations of our knowledge of the process and what factors govern conversion efficiency.

One factor which is not included in any equation for frequency doubling is the degree of coupling achieved for both the fundamental and the second harmonic. That this factor can be quite important has been shown in the wide range of conversion efficiencies obtained from a single sample with variations in sample location. Some of these variations are understandable from a consideration of the sample position with respect to the field configuration. For instance, Fig. 2 shows a ferrite geometry used for doubling from 70 to 140 kmc and an output curve as a

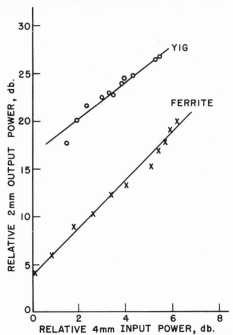

Fig. 1. 2 mm output vs. 4 mm input for single crystal YIG sphere and for ferramic G ferrite post

The power scales are plotted in db with arbitrary reference levels.

function of sample position. The sample was moved from one side of the guide wall to the other, and as might be expected from a consideration of the field pattern of the 140 kmc wave, maximum output was obtained with the sample in the middle of the guide where coupling of the z component of magnetization to a TE_{01} mode for the second harmonic would be best.

Other variations in conversion efficiency have been seen which are not so easily explained. For instance, we have noted considerable variation in output for changes in sample length of as little as 0.001 inch. Some of these variations most probably result from distortion of the microwave fields caused by the ferrite sample. The simple theory assumes fundamental fields at the sample are known, implying that the ferrite only perturbs them. This condition can't be fulfilled when large samples are used to obtain high conversion efficiencies. Instead one tries

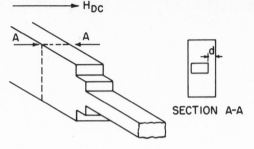

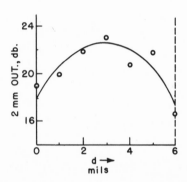

Fig. 2. Variation of 2 mm output as cylindrical ferrite sample is moved across test section

to match the ferrite to the source so that all incident power is absorbed in the sample.

In our present work we are trying to learn more about these factors which affect conversion efficiency and how to optimize the coupling of both the 2 mm and 4 mm energy. A large part of our effort goes into refining the experiment to eliminate the large variations of 2 mm generation with sample shape and position. In addition, we are building a 1 mm crystal detector to attempt to measure the output at 210 kmc.

PARAMETRIC AMPLIFICATION

The parametric amplifier is another application that utilizes the nonlinear properties of a ferrite. Although most applications of the parametric amplifier today are based on the nonlinear capacitance of a back-biased diode, the ferrite amplifier is of considerable interest, not only for high frequency, low noise applications but also for the insight it gives us on the behavior of ferrites.

Operation of the ferrite parametric amplifier can be visualized as two mixing processes similar to those described earlier taking place simultaneously in the ferrite sample. The signal field interacts with the spin system of the ferrite which is presumed to be precessing at the pump frequency. This interaction produces a component of magnetization varying at the difference or idle frequency. This component of magnetization can then couple to some suitable structure resonant at the idle frequency, producing an r-f field at this frequency. This field can then interact with the spin system and in like manner produce a component of magnetization at the difference frequency which in this case is the same as the original signal frequency. This component of magnetization will, in turn, produce a field at the signal frequency. Thus, the entire amplifier is a closed loop where the straight-through gain is the product of the conversion efficiencies of the two mixing operations and the feedback factor is determined by the cavity modes and Q's of the signal and idler resonant structures. Since the conversion efficiency of each mixing operation depends on the first power of the pump field, the straight-through gain will depend on the square of the pump field. Therefore, for a given set of cavity Q's, there will be some value of pump power which will cause the overall loop gain to exceed unity and free oscillations will result. At pump powers just below this threshold value, regenerative amplification can be achieved.

Suhl originally proposed three possible modes of operation for the ferrite parametric amplifier.

1. Electromagnetic—in which an external resonant circuit is supplied at both the signal and idler frequencies.
2. Semi-static—in which an external resonant circuit is supplied at the signal frequency but the idler resonance is supplied by a spin wave mode in the ferrite.
3. Magneto-static—in which both the signal and idler resonances are supplied by spin wave modes.

In all of these modes of operation, the ferrite is biased to ferromagnetic resonance at the pump frequency. The first two methods have been made to operate while the third is generally deemed inoperable. A variation on the semi-static method is the modified semi-static in which the ferrite is biased to resonance at the idler frequency, thus furnishing the idler resonance. The external cavity then supplies only the signal resonance, and, for efficiency, a pump frequency resonance.

Another mode of operation which I would like to describe in detail is the dielectric resonance mode. In this type of amplifier the idler resonance is furnished by biasing the ferrite to ferromagnetic resonance as in the modified semi-static mode. The signal resonance, however, is furnished by a dielectric rod resonance in the ferrite rather than by an external cavity resonance. Thus, the cavity structure of the amplifier has only a single resonance—that of the pump frequency. Figure 3 shows

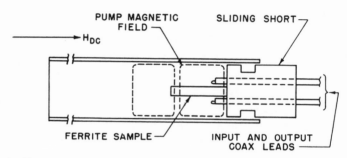

Fig. 3. Ferrite parametric amplifier operating in dielectric resonance mode

a schematic drawing of this amplifier. The pump cavity is a cylindrical TE_{115} cavity with a sliding short in one end for tuning. The ferrite is in cylindrical form with typical dimensions of 0.350-inch diameter by 2-inch length, and is mounted coaxially with the cavity and on the face of the shorting plug. This amplifier was operated successfully with a pump frequency of 9 kmc and a signal frequency of 7.2 kmc. Net gains of about 45 db were achieved with pump powers of approximately 5 kw. The signal frequency was determined almost entirely by the dimensions of the ferrite sample. Ferrite rods of approximately 2-inch length were used and the diameter was varied from 0.325 inch to 0.385 inch. In all cases the signal frequency was found to vary inversely with rod diameter and to be independent of rod length.

This pattern is consistent with a TM_{010} mode resonance in the rod with a uε of 11.9. This mode is a radial mode with no length dependence thus fitting the observed data. Although the signal frequency was independent of sample length, it was noted that when the sample was shorter than a half guide wavelength at the pump frequency, no oscillations could be obtained. Presumably this is due to a reduced filling factor at the pump frequency.

As was mentioned earlier, the amplifier can be made to oscillate simply by increasing the pump power. In between these two conditions the amplifier behaves as a super-regenerative amplifier. That is, the overall loop gain is greater than unity and the amplifier is in an oscillating condition but the time constant associated with the buildup of these oscillations is longer than the applied pump pulse. This situation is shown in Fig. 4

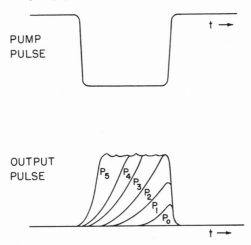

Fig. 4. Pump and output pulse waveforms showing decrease in rise time as signal input power is increased

where the top trace is the applied pump pulse and the bottom is a composite of the output pulse for various signal powers. It can be seen that with no input there is a small output pulse. As the input power is increased, the output increases until a limiting value is reached. Further increases in input power decrease the rise time of the output, effectively widening the pulse. The exact cause of the limiting action on the output is not understood at this time. It is rather surprising that it is such a sharp effect. The variation of rise time with input power affords a convenient way to measure the magnetic Q of the amplifier. If the rise time is plotted against the power input in db, there will be a straight line portion of the resulting curve. The slope of this portion times a conversion factor is just the reciprocal Q of the system, which is, of course, a negative quantity. Values of magnetic Q obtained in this manner vary from -390 to -960 with varying pump power levels.

At present our work is aimed at reducing the pump power required for amplification. A certain amount of reduction can be expected from improved coupling of the pump to the cavity. Even more should be expected from using a narrow linewidth material such as yttrium iron garnet. However, efforts to date with this material have been unsuccessful.

DISCUSSION

M. T. WEISS: How much 4 mm power was required to produce 50 watts of 2 mm power?

R. W. ROBERTS: The conversion efficiency was less than 10 percent. I can't give the exact value, since the power source used is classified.

R. L. KYHL: What was the average power output in frequency doubling?

R. W. ROBERTS: Peak power falls off at increased PRF's due to heating in the ferrite. Therefore, the average power corresponding to the 50 watts output is of the order of 50 μ watts. At PRV's around 350 pps the peak power drops to around 10-20 watts but the average power increases to approximately 300 μ watts.

A. OKAYA: The microwave resonance modes of a dielectric rod are quite complicated. I suppose that field leakage from the rod contributes an even greater complication. How did you identify the mode as TM_{010}?

R. W. ROBERTS: The TM_{010} mode is the simplest one that fits the observed data. I agree that the actual mode is perturbed to some extent.

G. S. HELLER: In our ferrite doubling experiments we have not noticed deterioration due to spin wave excitation even for narrow linewidth garnets. Have you observed similar results?

R. W. ROBERTS: We have observed saturation effects; i.e., a deviation from square law of the output as a function of input. These effects appear to be due, at least partly, to other parameters of the experiment. I would expect that there would be some effect due to spin wave excitation, but the results are not clearcut enough to say so with definiteness.

G. S. HELLER: Is there really a difference between the "dielectric rod resonance" which you speak about and a "magnetostatic mode"? If one had an exact solution of the electromagnetic problem of a rod in a cavity (this has been done by myself for special cases) would not the system of modes obtained include all the magnetostatic modes?

R. J. STRAIN: In reference to Dr. Heller's question, the difference between the magnetostatic mode and the dielectric mode is mainly one of predominance of effect. The dielectric mode will simply be one of a dielectric rod perturbed by the magnetic dipoles, whereas the other is principally a case of an atmosphere of interacting magnetic dipoles, perturbed by propagation effects. The difference is largely one of size and operating region.

Incidentally, Steier* has been concerned with this intermediate region.

B. LAX: The dielectric resonance mode represents one in which the electromagnetic field becomes concentrated in the ferrite, effectively increasing the filling factor.

*Steier and Coleman, J. A. P., Sept. 1959.

TEMPERATURE AND CONCENTRATION EFFECTS IN A RUBY MASER

T. H. MAIMAN

Hughes Aircraft Company, Research Laboratories, Culver City, California

IN ORDER to obtain the maximum performance from a solid-state maser, both the line width and the paramagnetic-ion concentration of the working material must be considered. It will be shown that the optimum values for these quantities for a given maser are a function of the operating temperature.

We consider a reflection-cavity-type maser and make use of the equivalent-circuit representation shown in Fig. 1. By straightforward circuit analysis we can show that

$$B(A - 1) \cong \left(\frac{2 \, \nu_m}{Q_M + Q_R} \right) \left(1 - \frac{Q_M}{Q_C} \right) \tag{1}$$

where

A = voltage gain
B = the 3-db bandwidth
ν_m = maser frequency
Q_M = magnitude of the magnetic Q of the maser material
Q_C = unloaded Q of the cavity (including dielectric losses in the material)

$Q_R = \dfrac{\nu_m}{\Delta \nu}$ = the Q of the magnetic resonance line

$\Delta \nu$ = the line width of the material for the maser transition.

In terms of the material parameters, the magnetic Q is

$$Q_M = \frac{h \, \Delta \nu}{8\pi \, (n_2 - n_1) <\mu^2> F} \tag{2}$$

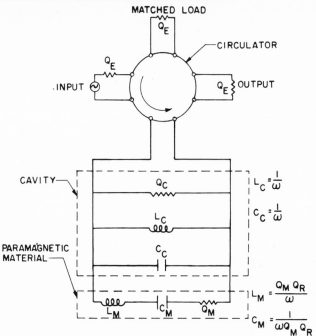

Fig. 1. Equivalent circuit of reflection-cavity maser

where

$(n_2 - n_1)$ = difference in paramagnetic-ion density between the upper and lower levels of the maser transition,

$<\mu^2>$ = average (squared) dipole moment for the maser transition

F = the filling factor.

In most practical cases, $Q_M << Q_C$; therefore, we can rewrite Equation (1) in order to show the explicit dependence on line width:

$$B(A - 1) \simeq \frac{2\,\nu_m{}^2\,(\Delta\nu)}{Q_M\,Q_R\,(\Delta\nu)^2 + \nu_m{}^2} \tag{3}$$

(the product $Q_M Q_R$ is independent of $\Delta\nu$). Taking $\Delta\nu$ as a variable parameter, we find an optimum value:

$$\Delta\nu_{opt} = B_{max}\,(A - 1) = \frac{\nu_m}{\sqrt{Q_M\,Q_R}}. \tag{4}$$

Although it is not generally feasible to *reduce* the line width of a given material, it is possible to *increase* it at a fixed crystal concentration by making the external magnetic field inhomogeneous; that is, if $Q_R > Q_M$, the gain-bandwidth product can be *increased* by artificially increasing $\Delta\nu$ to conform to Equation (4).

To illustrate, we consider an X-band ruby maser operated in the push-pull pumping mode at $4.2\,^\circ K$. Measurements of line width versus concentration are shown in Fig. 2. The heavy curve is experimental and approaches a linear dependence on concentration shown by the light curve. If we assume equal

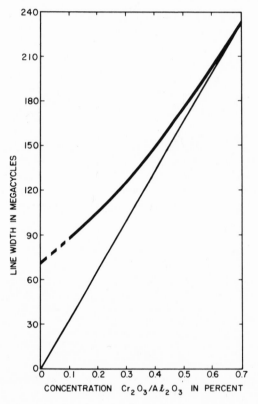

Fig. 2. Line width of $-\frac{1}{2} \longrightarrow +\frac{1}{2}$ transition in ruby at $H_o = 4000$ gauss, $\theta = 55\,^\circ$

thermal relaxation times and push-pull pumping, then

$$Q_M \cong \frac{kT\,\Delta\nu}{2\pi\,N_o\,\langle\mu^2\rangle\,(\nu_p - \nu_m)}. \tag{5}$$

Here ν_p is the pump frequency and N_o is the total chromium ion density. With the values

$$T = 4.2\,^\circ K$$
$$\nu_p = 23.5 \text{ kMc}$$
$$\nu_m = 9.3 \text{ kMc}$$
$$\langle\mu^2\rangle = 2.0 \times 10^{-40}\,\text{ergs}^2/\text{gauss}^2$$

and from Fig. 2, Q_M and Q_R were calculated and are shown in Fig. 3. The gain-bandwidth product would then be expected to be increasing even at concentrations as high as 0.5 percent.

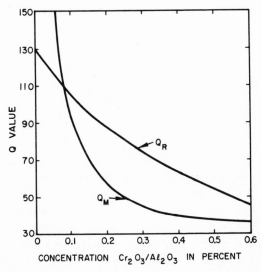

Fig. 3. X-band Q values for ruby in the push-pull pumping mode (T = 4.2 °K)

The experimental situation is quite different. Measured values agree with calculated values only for chromium concentrations of less than approximately 0.1 percent. For larger concentrations, the gain-bandwidth product falls off rapidly. At low concentrations, a negative spin temperature of about $2.7\,^\circ$K is observed, but in a 0.2 percent crystal the lowest negative spin temperature is of the order of $150\,^\circ$K; we were not even able to produce negative spin temperature with a 0.6 percent crystal. An explanation based on cross-relaxation effects follows.[1],[2]

In sufficiently dilute paramagnetic crystals, cross-relaxation times are long compared with thermal relaxation times and do not essentially interfere with normal maser operation. However, as the spin density is increased, the cross-relaxation rate is also increased and can become competitive with the thermal processes. In the limit, an equilibrium emissive condition is prevented. An extension of a maser equation derived by Bloembergen et al.[1] to a push-pull, four-level system including cross relaxation is

$$(n_3 - n_2) \propto \frac{\nu_p - \nu_m \left(1 + \dfrac{T_1}{4\,T_{21}}\right)}{\left(1 + \dfrac{T_1}{4\,T_{21}}\right)} . \tag{6}$$

We have assumed coupling between the pump and idler transitions, and have taken all of the thermal relaxation times to be equal. It is seen that it is only the ratio of thermal-relaxation time to cross-relaxation time that enters into the formula. One expects that if the lattice temperature is raised, the thermal-relaxation rate will increase but that the cross-relaxation rate will remain essentially unchanged. In this situation, even in a reasonably concentrated crystal, the cross-relaxation time may be large compared with the thermal-relaxation time, and therefore we may expect normal maser operation with crystal concentrations which exhibit reduced or no maser action at low temperatures.

The above argument is supported by the fact that we have observed amplification and oscillation in a 0.6 percent ruby at $77\,^\circ$K, but as noted above, we were not even able to produce negative temperatures in the same crystal at $4.2\,^\circ$K. With the 0.2 percent crystal operated at $77.4\,^\circ$K, a negative spin temperature of $51\,^\circ$K was produced, which is a value that one would expect when cross-relaxation effects are small. Since in this latter crystal the negative spin temperature obtained by cooling with liquid helium was 150°K, it is seen that this crystal actually exhibited poorer maser performance at the lower temperature than at the higher one!

To further test the idea of cross-relaxation mechanisms in concentrated crystals, the following experiment was performed. The pump power to the maser was pulsed with 10 msec pulses at a repetition rate of ten per second. The time required to saturate the pump transition is an inverse function of the pump power and can be made arbitrarily short, depending on the amount of pump power available. One then expects that if the pump transition is saturated in a short time compared with the cross-relaxation time, for a time the order of T_{21} normal maser operation (low spin temperatures) will be attained and that the inverted population will then decay through cross relaxation. This was indeed what was observed (see Fig. 4). In the 0.2 percent crystal a large inver-

Fig. 4. Output of maser using 0.2 percent crystal when the pump power is pulsed

The time scale is 5 msec per division.

sion was initially produced but then decayed in about 2 msec to the value found in the steady-state experiments. The cross-relaxation time in a 0.6 percent crystal was too short to measure directly in this way, but indirect measurements at 77°K indicate a value of several microseconds.

From these measurements we see that normal maser operation is obtained in the steady state in somewhat more concentrated crystals at high temperatures than at lower temperatures and therefore that some of the loss in gain-bandwidth product which results from high-temperature maser operation can be partially regained.

A compact, liquid-nitrogen-cooled maser was constructed along lines out-lined in references 4 and 5 using a 0.2 percent ruby crystal (see Figs. 5 and 6). The gain-bandwidth product obtained, 14 Mc, was in agreement with calculations. Maser operation was also observed with this crystal (small net gain) at a temperature of 195 °K with dry ice used as a coolant.

The operation of a solid-state maser at temperatures well above the liquid-helium range affords an experimental check on noise theory since in this case the spin temperature of the maser is a large fraction of the total effective amplifier noise temperature. By reference to the circuit diagram in Fig. 1 and by analysis along lines outlined by Pound,[3] we find that the effective noise temperature of a reflection-cavity maser (excluding input losses) is

$$ T_e = \left[\frac{G-1}{G}\right] \left[\left(\frac{Q_M}{Q_C - Q_M}\right) T_C + \left(\frac{Q_C}{Q_C - Q_M}\right) T_S\right] $$

Fig. 5. Complete liquid-nitrogen-cooled, X-band ruby maser

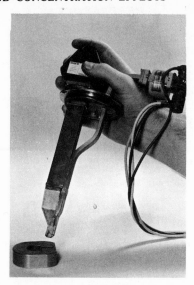

Fig. 6. Liquid-nitrogen-cooled maser showing permanent magnet and internal construction

where

G = maser power gain
Q_M = magnitude of the magnetic Q
T_s = magnitude of the spin temperature of the maser transition
T_C = cavity temperature.

Using the values

$$Q_C = 4000$$
$$Q_M = 1000$$
$$T_s = 51°K$$
$$T_C = 77.4°K$$

we calculate $T_e = 93°K$. The measured value, $100°K \pm 10°K$, was in good agreement with this.

The author gratefully acknowledges the technical assistance of I. J. D'Haenens in constructing the apparatus and in making the measurements; he also appreciates helpful discussions with R. H. Hoskins and D. P. Devor.

REFERENCES

1. N. Bloembergen, S. Shapiro, P. S. Pershan, and J. O. Artman, Phys. Rev. *114*, 445 (1959).
2. S. Shapiro and N. Bloembergen, Cruft Laboratory, Harvard University, Technical Report No. 306 (June 18, 1959).
3. R. V. Pound, Annals of Physics *1*, 24 (1957).
4. T. H. Maiman, Signal Corps Contract No. DA 36-039 SC-74951, Second Quarterly Progress Report (March 1, 1958 through May 30, 1958) et seq.
5. T. H. Maiman, NSIA-ARDC Conference on Molecular Electronics, Washington, D. C., p. 71 (November 13-14, 1958).

DISCUSSION

F. NASH: What was the overlap of the lines and what was their separation?

T. MAIMAN: The line width was in the range of 100–200 Mc when the cross-relaxation effects were observable and the separation was the maser frequency (9000 Mc).

C. H. TOWNES: The observation that higher concentrations of Cr may be used at higher temperatures does seem, as indicated, to represent a decrease in the ratio $\dfrac{T_1}{T_{21}}$ However, one should keep open the possibility that T_{21} as well as T_1 may change with temperature, since T_{21} may involve some phonon processes.

SOME MEASUREMENTS OF THE DECAY OF PARAMAGNETIC SATURATION IN SYNTHETIC RUBY

J. C. GILL

Royal Radar Establishment, Malvern, England

METHOD OF MEASUREMENT

THE DECAY of paramagnetic saturation in synthetic ruby has been examined by observing the return of resonance absorption after the application of a "saturating" pulse of microwave energy.

Measurements were made at 9375 Mc/s, using a reflection cavity spectrometer with superhet receiver and oscilloscope display. The klystron used in the spectrometer to monitor the absorption delivered 10 milliwatts maximum power, and a second klystron generated the high-power pulses (up to 20 watts peak) necessary to produce saturation.

In most cases the decay time constants were estimated from the display by adjusting the velocity of the oscilloscope time-base so that the observed decay coincided with an exponential curve superimposed on the screen. Decay times exceeding 5 microseconds, the recovery time of the receiver after the saturating pulse, could be measured with a probable error of the order of ±10 percent. Most of this rather large error was due to vibration caused by the boiling liquids surrounding the cavity.

EXPERIMENTAL RESULTS

(a) *Measurements at* $77°K$. Seven samples of ruby, with chromium concentrations between .014 percent and .89 percent, were examined at the temperature of liquid nitrogen. The concentrations were determined spectrographically.

Within the limits of experimental error, the observed decay curves had the form

$$A = A_0 \left(1 - \exp \frac{-t}{T}\right),$$

A being the absorption at a time t after the end of the saturating pulse, and A_0 being the absorption when recovery from the pulse is complete. A single relaxation time T may, therefore, be specified.

No dependence of T on the length of the saturating pulse was found for pulses up to the maximum available length of 5 msec. There was also no observable change in T when the monitor power in the spectrometer was reduced to 1 percent of its maximum. The effects on the relaxation time of any heating of the specimen, either by the high-power pulses or by the microwave field used to measure the absorption, and of transitions induced by the latter, are thus too small to be of importance.

The relaxation times measured for the $-\frac{1}{2} \rightarrow +\frac{1}{2}$ transition, with the direct magnetic field parallel to the crystalline c-axis, are given in Table 1, and are shown in Fig. 1.

Table 1

Chromium concentration, %	.014	.024	.076	.24	.39	.55	.89
Relaxation time T (microseconds)	61	49	31	21	14	< 5	< 5

The times for the $-\frac{3}{2} \rightarrow -\frac{1}{2}$ transition, the only other accessible with a field less than 3500 gauss parallel to the axis, were not significantly different.

There is a marked dependence of relaxation time on chromium concentration, the time decreasing as the concentration increases. In the two most concentrated crystals (0.55 percent and 0.89 percent) the relaxation was so rapid, compared with the recovery of the receiver, that accurate measurement was not possible. Some signs of a finite decay time were, however, visible for the 0.55 percent sample.

(b) *Measurements at other temperatures.* A few measurements of relaxation times at other temperatures have been made by Dr.

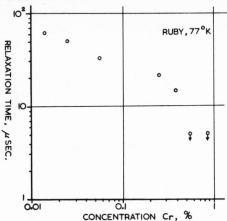

Fig. 1. Relaxation time in ruby as a function of concentration

A. F. Harvey, of R.R.E. They refer to the $-\frac{1}{2} \rightarrow +\frac{1}{2}$ transition in ruby containing approximately .04 percent chromium, with the magnetic field parallel to the crystal axis. Once again, the decay curves appear to be explicable in terms of single relaxation times.

The relaxation times measured at five different temperatures are shown in Fig. 2. At the lowest temperatures they vary ap-

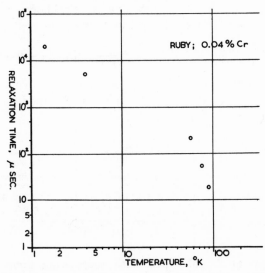

Fig. 2. Relaxation time in ruby as a function of temperature

proximately as the reciprocal of the temperature, the variation becoming more rapid at higher temperatures.

COMMENT

The dependence of relaxation time on temperature is similar to that predicted by Van Vleck,[1] for the exchange of energy between a system of isolated spins and the crystal lattice. It is, however, apparent from the dependence of relaxation time on concentration that a complete explanation of the relaxation process is not possible without consideration of the effects of the spins on each other.

The author wishes to thank Dr. A. F. Harvey, for making available the results of his measurements, and Mr. R. A. Mostyn, of the Chemical Inspectorate, for analyzing the ruby specimens.

Crown Copyright reserved, reproduced by permission of the Controller of Her Britannic Majesty's Stationery Office.

REFERENCE

1. J. H. Van Vleck, Phys. Rev. 57, 426 (1940).

DISCUSSION

A. PROKHOROV: A. Manenkov and A. Prokhorov measured T_1 in Al_2O_3 diluted by Cr_2O_3 by the C.W.S. method. In order to obtain T_2, we supposed that $T_2 = \dfrac{1}{\pi \Delta \nu}$, this is supported by the fact that saturation effects obey ordinary law even at low concentration. I shall compare the results obtained by J. C. Gill and by us.

	T_1	
Concentration	J. C. Gill	A. Manenkov A. Prokhorov
1.4×10^{-4}	6.1×10^{-5}	38×10^{-5}
3.9×10^{-3}	1.4×10^{-5}	6.6×10^{-5}
	4.4 times	5 times

The decrease of T_1 obtained with increasing concentration is practically the same by both methods.

ON THE SATURATION AND RELAXATION BEHAVIOR OF SOME PARAMAGNETIC SALTS

E. BOLGER

Kamerlingh Onnes Laboratory, Leiden

THE IMPORTANCE of so-called cross relaxation, through which the populations of different energy levels of a spin system come into equilibrium, has been stressed by Bloembergen *et al.*[1] The cross-relaxation rate will be independent of the lattice temperature while this is not expected to be the case for the various spin-lattice relaxation rates U_{ij}.

Three situations may arise with respect to the degree of equilibrium in the spin system.

I. $U_{cr} \ll U_{ij_{\min}}$, the smallest value of U_{ij} for the ion. The relaxation behavior is determined by the U_{ij}'s and can be calculated using the formalism of Lloyd and Pake.[2] Maser action may be obtained.

II. $U_{ij_{\min}} < U_{cr} < U_{ij_{\max}}$
For some levels there may still be maser action but for other levels, such as those corresponding to $U_{ij_{\min}}$, the relaxation behavior is mainly determined by U_{cr}.

III. $U_{cr} \gg U_{ij_{\max}}$
The spin system is in complete equilibrium at a temperature T_s. The magnetization will change according to a simple exponential decay, determined by the total energy transfer of the different transitions.

The saturation behavior can be calculated by considering the power balance for the sample. The absorbed power can be written as

$$P_m = \frac{QW}{T_s} \tag{1}$$

where W is the r.f. induced transition rate. The power transferred between the spin system and the lattice (T_L) is

$$P_{tr} = \eta\, T_L \left(\frac{1}{T_L} - \frac{1}{T_S} \right). \tag{2}$$

When C is the curie constant and H the magnetic field, the internal energy of the spin system is represented by

$$U_S = \frac{b + CH^2}{T_S} \tag{3}$$

then the power balance becomes

$$P_m = \frac{QW}{T_S} = \frac{dU_S}{dt} + \eta\, T_L \left(\frac{1}{T_L} - \frac{1}{T_S} \right). \tag{4}$$

The steady-state solution of Equation (4) is

$$1/X'' \propto T_S = T_L + QW/\eta. \tag{5}$$

For the plot of T_S vs W one expects a straight line with a slope of Q/η. Steady-state saturation of paramagnetic resonance thus yields the value of η.

The transient solution of Equation (4) with $W = 0$ contains an exponential of t with a time constant τ_1 which equals

$$\tau_1 = \frac{b + CH^2}{\eta T_L}. \tag{6}$$

The classical nonresonant relaxation method[3] and pulse saturation experiments yield the value of τ_1.

Because of the temperature dependence of the U_{ij}'s one may continuously go over from one situation to another.

EXPERIMENTS WITH A PULSE MODULATED SATURATING FIELD

When pulse modulating (on-off) the pump power in a three-level maser experiment, the signal absorption will become modulated when the magnetic field is adjusted to an operating point. Such a point exists in Cr/Co $K_3(CN)_6$ for $\nu_{13} = \nu_{pump} =$

3850 Mc; $\nu_{12} = \nu_{signal} = 1420$ Mc, $H = 480 \phi$ and the angle of H to the a-axis $= 11°$ (in ac-plane). The levels are numbered in order of increasing energy. For a Cr/Co percentage of 0.035 (sample A), maser action was obtained. The characteristic times of the decay of the absorption τ_{off} during the off time of the pump are shown in Fig. 1. In the liquid-helium range we found for sample A $\tau_A \propto T^{-1}$ and above this range to 20°K $\tau_A \propto T^{-3.3}$. From these experiments and the steady-state maser experiments, one finds at 1.4°K when the fourth level does not take part in the relaxation process:

$$U_{12} = 0.6 \ S^{-1} \quad U_{23} = 2.6 \ S^{-1} \quad U_{13} = 8.1 \ S^{-1} \ .$$

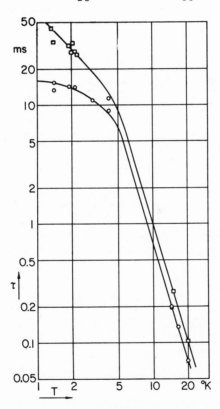

Fig. 1. τ_{off} *for* Cr/Co K$_3$ (CN)$_6$

□ τ_A

○ τ_B

For a non-masering crystal with a Cr/Co percentage of 0.1 percent (sample B) τ_{off} can be represented by

$$1/\tau_B = 1/\tau_A + 1/31 \ \text{ms}^{-1}.$$

This curve has been drawn in Fig. 1.

Experiments were also performed in ruby (Cr/Al of 0.1 percent) at two different operating points.

$R_I)$ $\nu_{13} = \nu_{pump} = 10.7$ KMc; $\nu_{12} = \nu_{sign} = 1430$ Mc, H = 430 ϕ < Hc-axis = 23°; non-masering operating point.

$R_{II})$ $\nu_{13} = \nu_{pump} = 8.5$ KMc; $\nu_{23} = \nu_{sign} = 1430$ Mc, H = 2100 ϕ < Hc-axis = 21°. At this operating point maser action was obtained.

The characteristic times are plotted as a function of temperature in Fig. 2, and for R_{II} is seen to be proportional to T^{-1}. For R_I, $\tau_{off} \propto T^{-1}$ below 4°K and a constant above this temperature to 20°K.

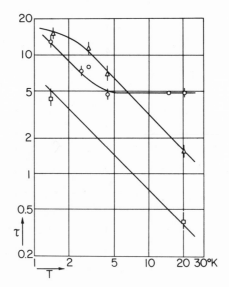

Fig. 2. τ_{off} *for ruby*

$\triangle$ τ_{off}; pump 8.5 KMH$_2$.

$\bigcirc$ τ_{off}; pump 10.7 KMH$_2$.

These results can be explained in the following way. For Cr/Co $K_3(CN)_6$ sample A, situation I is realized; for sample B below 4°K situation II exists with $1/U_{cr} = 31$ ms. At lower temperatures, one expects τ_B to increase again.

For the ruby, point R_{II}, situation I is realized, while for point R_I we have situation II between 4°K and 20°K (one measures U_{cr} directly) and situation III below 4°K. At higher temperatures situation I may be realized, so that at higher temperatures it is possible to use more concentrated maser materials than at lower temperatures.

For further information on the work on masers carried out by our group see the references.[4],[5]

EXPERIMENTS WITH STEADY STATE SATURATION

To check formulas (5) and (6), experiments were carried out on the following substances:
KCr alum, H // (111) and H // (100), undiluted and diluted with the Al salt, $CuK_2(SO_4)_2 6H_2O$, anisotropy and temperature dependence of η, $Cu(NH_4)_2(SO_4)_2 6H_2O$, $CuK_2Cl_4 2H_2O$, $CuSO_4 5H_2O$, $Mn(NH_4)_2(SO_4)_2 6H_2O$, $Co(NH_4)_2(SO_4)_2 6H_2O$, temperature dependence of η. Experimentally one determined $P_{ext}/P_m \propto 1/\chi'' \propto T_S$ as a function of the power P_{ext}, the power dissipated in the load of a transmission cavity. We have $P_{ext} \propto W$ and $\eta = dP_{ext}/d(P_{ext}/P_m)$ taken for one gram ion of magnetic ions. The saturation graphs P_{ext}/P_m vs P_{ext} according to Equation (5) are expected to be straight lines. This was indeed the case for diluted materials, but for the undiluted ones a new effect is found. All saturation graphs appear to be curved. A few examples are shown in Fig. 3 and Fig. 4. When we call the value of η at low powers η_s, at high powers η_f and η derived from the nonresonant relaxation measurements with Equation (6), η_{rel}, then the results for CrK alum are shown in Fig. 5 and Fig. 6. η_{rel} is determined on powders so that we can compare the temperature dependence and order of magnitude. We may conclude that $\eta_f = \eta_{rel}$, which is most unexpected as the spin temperature changes. $\Delta T_S/T_S$ used in the relaxation measurements is at most 10^{-3}.

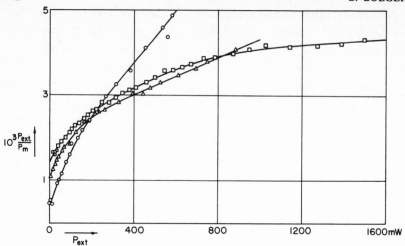

Fig. 3. Saturation graphs of CrK *alum;* H / / (*111*)

□ $T = 3.36°K$ △ $T = 2.55°K$ ○ $T = 1.49°K$

For direct processes one expects η to be independent of temperature and concentration at high magnetic fields. This is seen to be the case for η_s. The most likely explanation for the curvature of the saturation graphs is a spatial distribution of the values of η, due to impurities acting as an energy sink.

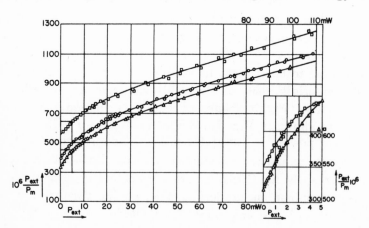

Fig. 4. Saturation graphs of $CoNH_4$ *tutton salt;* H / / K_1 *axis*
(*Scales differ for the inlay*)

△ $T = 1.33°K$ ○ $T = 1.61°K$ □ $T = 2.06°K$

However, this explanation is not completely consistent with the experimental results. For further details reference is made to Bölger (1959).[6] On the basis of the interpretation of their results, Eschenfelder and Weidner[7] stated the occurrence of large discrepancies between the values of τ determined by the relaxation and by the saturation method. To obtain τ from the measured value

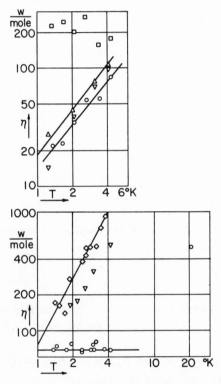

Fig. 5. η *as a function of* T *for undiluted* CrK *alum;* H $//$ *(111)*

$\diamond\ \eta_f$ $\quad$ $\circ\ \eta_s$ $\quad$ $\nabla\ \eta_{rel}$

of η, they considered the power transfer to the lattice to be due to the saturated transition only. As for the concentrations used by them situation III is realized, all transitions play a role, and for the diluted salts there is no discrepancy any more when using Equation (6) for the relation between τ and η. (cf.[6]).

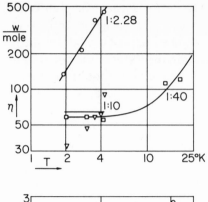

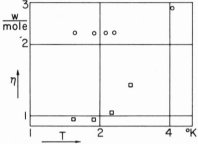

Fig. 6. η *as a function of* T *for diluted* CrK *alum;* H / / *(111)*

O Cr : Al = 1 : 2.28   ∇ Cr : Al = 1 : 2 η_{rel}

□ Cr : Al = 1 : 40   _____ Cr : Al = 1 : 10 Eschenfelder
                                                      and Weidner

For the concentrated salt $\eta_f = \eta_{rel}$ was mostly realized in the salts investigated, but for $CoNH_4$ tutton salt we found $\eta_s = \eta_{rel}$.

This work was carried out in cooperation with B. J. Robinson and J. M. Noothoren van Goor and was a part of the research program of the foundation ''Fundamenteel Onderzoek der Materie.''

I thank Professor C. J. Gorter for his stimulating interest and many helpful discussions.

REFERENCES

1. Bloembergen, N., Shapiro, S., Pershan, P. S., and Artman, J. O., Phys. Rev. *114*, 445 (1959).
2. Lloyd, J. P. and Pake, G. E., Phys. Rev. *94*, 579 (1954).

3. Gorter, C. J., *Paramagnetic Relaxation*, Elsevier (1947).
4. Bölger, B. and Robinson, B. J., Arch. des Sci. Geneve *11*, 187 (1958) and Commun. Kam. Onnes Lab. Suppl. no. 114.
5. Bölger, B., Robinson, B. J. and Ubbink, J., to be published in Physica and Commun. Kamerlingh Onnes Lab., Leiden.
6. Bölger, B., thesis Leiden (1959).
7. Eschenfelder, A. H. and Weidner, R. T., Phys. Rev. *92*, 869 (1953).

DISCUSSION

H. GERRITSEN: Your method seems to be a nice way of measuring the cross-relaxation time. Did you measure this at different concentrations?

B. BÖLGER: The values of η have been determined as a function of concentration for CrK alum. At low r.f. powers η is found to be independent of the concentration and temperature.

SPIN-LATTICE RELAXATION VIA HARMONIC COUPLING*

W. S. C. CHANG**

Department of Electrical Engineering, The Ohio State University

EXPERIMENTS AT the Stanford Electronics Laboratory and elsewhere have shown that the spin-lattice relaxation time of ruby varies rapidly depending upon the pair of levels observed and the exact operating point. Some but not all of this variation can be explained by Bloembergen's cross-relaxation theory,[1] which predicts strong coupling between two transitions which have the same or nearly the same resonance frequency. Recently, Geusic and Mims of the Bell Telephone Laboratories observed that saturation of one transition in ruby can result in saturation of a second transition if the second transition frequency is either a harmonic or a subharmonic of the first transition frequency.[2] He proposes that the two transitions, at frequencies f_{ij} and f_{kl}, may exhibit cross-relaxation effects when $f_{ij} \approx n f_{kl}$ through a process in which n spins flip in one direction on the $k \to 1$ transition simultaneously with one flip of a spin in the opposite direction on the $i \to j$ transition. This process merely redistributes energy among the various levels of the spin system, and does not involve any energy exchange with the lattice. However, it can lead to effects which appear to be spin-lattice relaxation if only one of the transitions is observed. It can well be termed "harmonic cross-relaxation."

A series of experiments has been performed in this laboratory to investigate the harmonic cross-relaxation process, using a

*Prepared under Air Force Contract AF33(600)–27784 with Stanford University.

**Work done at Electron Devices Laboratory, Stanford Electronics Laboratory, Stanford University.

traveling-wave-maser apparatus to permit wideband measurements.[3] These results presented here substantiate the harmonic cross-relaxation process in two ways: 1. as a mechanism to shorten the relaxation time of the idle transition in a three-level maser; and 2. as a mechanism to shorten the time needed by a pair of energy levels to recover the Boltzmann equilibrium distribution after saturation. The results indicate that if harmonic coupling is present, at least for harmonics through the third, the harmonically related transitions will first come to thermal equilibrium with each other at a relatively rapid rate (~ 10 msec) and then both together will thermalize with the lattice at a slower rate (~ 100 msec). The two characteristic relaxation times are clearly observed.

The experiments were performed exclusively on ruby. It is reasonable to assume, however, that the phenomenon will appear generally in multilevel spin systems.

MEASUREMENTS WITH A TRAVELING-WAVE APPARATUS

Conventional practice in paramagnetic resonance measurements is to use a high-Q microwave resonant cavity. This method is effective but limited to fixed frequency. In the present work, an apparatus developed as a practical traveling-wave maser amplifier[3] is used in place of a cavity. Traveling-wave masers were first developed at the Bell Telephone Laboratories[4] and later at Stanford University. The traveling-wave measurement technique is advantageous in that it offers sensitivity approaching that of the cavity technique, combined with very broad bandwidth (nearly two to one in frequency in a single apparatus).

The power gain (or magnetic resonance absorption) of a traveling-wave maser is given by[3], [4]

$$G_{\text{in decibels}} = \frac{27 N}{Q_m (v_g / c)}$$

where N is the length of the circuit in free-space wavelengths and (v_g / c) is the ratio of the group velocity of the slow-wave circuit to the velocity of light. The magnetic Q_m of the circuit is defined, much the same as in the cavity case, as ω times the stored energy per unit length divided by the power emitted (or absorbed) by the magnetic material per unit length. When the magnetic spin system is saturated, the spin temperature and Q_m go to ∞ and the gain or loss is zero.

Following Geusic *et al.*,[5] we consider an inversion ratio I for a three-level maser as the ratio of gain with pump power on to magnetic resonance absorption with the pump power off. If T_{spin} is the magnitude of the spin temperature of the maser's signal transition and $T_{lattice}$ is the lattice or bath temperature, one can show that

$$I = \frac{\text{Gain (db)}}{\text{Absorption (db)}} = \frac{Q_m \text{ (absorption)}}{Q_m \text{ (gain)}} = \frac{T_{lattice}}{T_{spin} \text{ (pump on)}}.$$

The inversion ratio is related to the spin-lattice relaxation times T_1 of the maser's signal and idle transitions by

$$I = \frac{1 + [T_{1(sig)}/T_{1(idle)}] [f_{idle}/f_{sig}]}{1 + [T_{1(sig)}/T_{(idle)}]}.$$

Note that a short idle relaxation time optimizes the inversion ratio, and that measurement of the inversion ratio yields information about relative relaxation times.

For small gain or loss ($G < 10\text{db}$), the ratio $(P_{out} - P_{in})/P_{in}$ is proportional to $1/T_{spin}$. Therefore, observation of P_{out} vs. time for constant P_{in} when the spin system is perturbed in some manner permits dynamic observation of the relaxation of T_{spin} to $T_{lattice}$. Plots of P_{out} vs. time on semilog paper yield relaxation times in the usual manner.

Typical arrangement of the experimental setup is shown in Fig. 1. Generators G and G_s are at the same frequency, which is within the 2500 Mc/s to 3800 Mc/s passband of the maser's slow-wave circuit, while G_p is at the much higher externally tunable resonance frequency of the pump cavity which encloses the slow-wave circuit. The generator G_s supplies high-power saturating pulses repeated once per second for use in saturation measurements. This rate is chosen to be considerably slower than the observed relaxation times. The generator G supplies very low power probing pulses $2\mu\text{sec}$ wide at a 1000 pps or faster rate, in order to monitor the gain or loss of the apparatus. The generator G_p can be operated at frequencies from 9 to 18 kMc/s, either as a high-power pumping source for the maser ex-

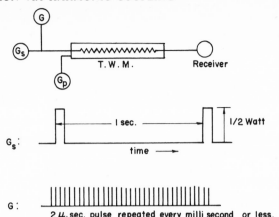

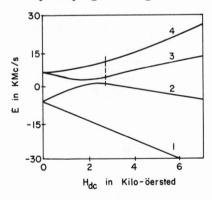

Fig. 1. The T.W.M. system for measurement of T_1

periments, or as a low-power probing signal for monitoring a higher-frequency transition during saturation measurements.

HARMONIC CROSS-RELAXATION IN A THREE-LEVEL MASER

The effect of harmonic cross relaxation on a three-level maser was investigated by measuring the inversion ratio I of a ruby traveling-wave maser at various operating points near 3000 Mc/s, $\theta = 23.5°$, and $H_o = 2650$ oersteds. The operating region is shown in Fig. 2. By varying the angle θ and/or the d-c field

Fig. 2. Energy of Cr^{+++} *in* Al_2O_3 *(ruby) near* $\theta = 23.5°$

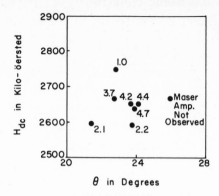

Fig. 3. The gain-bandwidth products map

H_o slightly, operation can be obtained in this region at any desired signal frequency near 3000 Mc/s with independent choice
of any desired pump frequency near 10,000 Mc/s. Earlier cavity
measurements[6] in this region had shown a critical dependence
of inversion ratio upon the exact operating point, as shown in
the measured gain-bandwidth products for the cavity maser recorded in Fig. 3. Systematic investigation of this region with
the traveling-wave maser yields the profile map of inversion
ratio as a function of pump and signal frequency shown in Fig.
4. It should be emphasized that any point in this plot can be

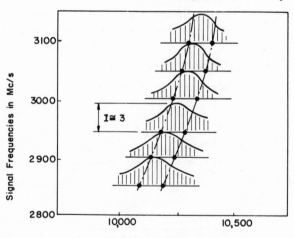

Fig. 4. The profile map of the inversion ratio vs. frequencies

made a maser point, in the sense of having simultaneous magnetic resonance at signal and pump frequencies, by proper adjustment of θ and H_o. However, only in the narrow band shown
is any appreciable inversion obtained, the maximum inversion
ratio being approximately 3. It follows that the relaxation time
$T_{1(idle)}$ of the 3 $\longleftrightarrow$ 4 transition must be short compared to
$T_{1(sig)}$ of the 2 $\longleftrightarrow$ 3 transition only in this region. In an iso-
frequency plot of the pump and signal resonances, the high-
inversion-ratio region of Fig. 4 corresponds to a nearly constant
value of $\theta \approx 23.5^\circ$.

The anomalous behavior of the inversion ratio in this region
can be explained as due to shortening of the idle of 3 $\longleftrightarrow$ 4 relaxation time by harmonic coupling. In and only in the high-

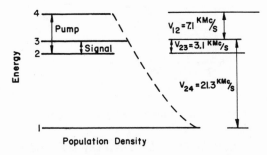

Fig. 5. Energy level distributions for f_s = 3,100 Mc/s *and* f_p =
10,200 Mc/s

inversion-ratio region, the frequency of the 1 $\longleftrightarrow$ 3 transition is
exactly three times the resonance frequency of the 3 $\longleftrightarrow$ 4 or
idle transition. Figure 5 shows a typical case, while Fig. 6
shows how $f_{13} = 3 f_{34}$ only at the $\theta = 23.5^\circ$ point for a typical
fixed signal frequency of 3200 Mc/s. The frequency width of
the high-inversion-ratio region is approximately 100 Mc/s, which
is roughly the same as the ruby resonance line widths. One can
deduce that the T_1 of the idle transition is "short-circuited" by
harmonic cross relaxation to 1 $\longleftrightarrow$ 3 transition over a bandwidth
roughly the same as the line width. This shows experimentally
that harmonic coupling is an effective way to modify relaxation
times to achieve high inversion in a three-level maser.[7]

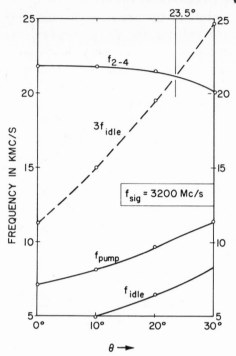

Fig. 6. Other frequencies for fixed signal frequency

EFFECT OF HARMONIC COUPLING ON DYNAMIC
RELAXATION

Figure 7 shows a typical energy-level diagram for ruby (at $\theta = 30°$) in which harmonic coupling can readily be studied using the traveling-wave maser apparatus. If the operating frequency on the $3 \longleftrightarrow 4$ transition varied from 3000 Mc/s up to 4000 Mc/s (with the d-c magnetic field tracking appropriately), one passes through three points where harmonic coupling may occur: a fourth harmonic case at 3250 Mc/s to the $1 \longleftrightarrow 3$ transition; a second harmonic case at 3300 Mc/s to the $2 \longleftrightarrow 3$ transition; and another second harmonic case at 3650 Mc/s to the $1 \longleftrightarrow 2$ transition. The fourth harmonic coupling case is not resolvable. However, near both of the second harmonic coupling points, the $3 \longleftrightarrow 4$ transition is experimentally observed to recover from saturation with two characteristic relaxation times, one of order 5–50 msec and one of order 200–400 msec. The saturation of the $3 \longleftrightarrow 4$ transition is caused by a pulse from generator G_s. Resonance absorption only is being discussed here—no pumping power or maser action is present. A typical picture of the recovery to equilibrium of the absorption (as monitored by the generator G and receiver) after a 1 msec saturating pulse is sketched in Fig. 8(a). These two relaxation times are always present for G_s pulses shorter than 1 msec at power levels up to 1 watt, whether the $3 \longleftrightarrow 4$ transition is fully saturated or not. If a longer saturating pulse (~ 60 msec) is used, only the long relaxation time is observed, again exclusive of whether or not the $3 \longleftrightarrow 4$ transition is fully saturated.

The higher frequency transition to which the harmonic coupling couples can also be simultaneously monitored with low power pulses from the generator G_p. One finds that the harmonic transition is not affected by short (1 msec) pulses from G_s at powers up to $\frac{1}{2}$ watt. However, the harmonic transition is observed to be saturated by a long (100 milliwatt 60 msec) pulse

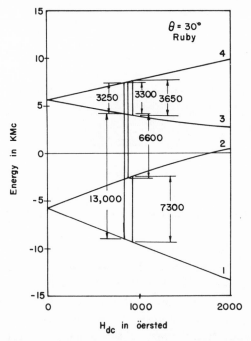

Fig. 7. Energy levels of ruby at $\theta = 30°$

from G_s. The harmonic transition then recovers to equilibrium with a relaxation time which in all cases is identical with the longer relaxation time measured also on the original or $3 \longleftrightarrow 4$ transition. Typical behavior of the harmonic transition is shown in Fig. 8(b).

The long and short relaxation times have been measured systematically at $\theta = 30°$ as a function of frequency. The results are plotted in Fig. 9. Comparing this with Fig. 7, one sees that the shorter relaxation time is drastically reduced whenever there

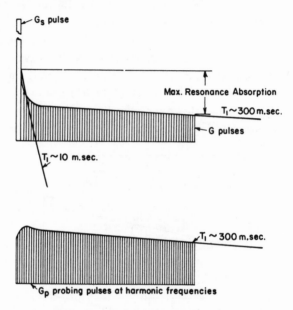

Fig. 8. The harmonic cross-relaxation effects

is a possibility of harmonic coupling, while the longer relaxation time is unaffected.

Based on these results, it is concluded that the two harmonically coupled levels thermalize with each other at the rapid rate, and then both together thermalize with the lattice at the longer rate. An equivalent thermal-flow diagram is shown in Fig. 10. A saturating pulse longer than the cross-relaxation time brings both transitions to the same temperature and only the long relaxation time is observed.

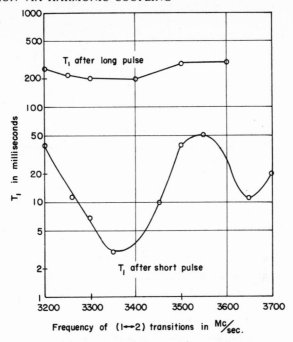

Fig. 9. Variation of T_1 *at* $\theta = 30°$ *for ruby*

At a d-c magnetic field orientation slightly away from 30°, three relaxation times were observed at 3200 Mc/s in one experiment. Figure 11 shows a plot of P_{out} vs. time for this case. This and similar plots are made by picking off points with a pair of dividers on a photograph of the receiver scope face.

This can be explained as being due to the 3 ⟷ 4 transition being harmonically coupled, with different cross-relaxation times, to both the 1 ⟷ 3 and 2 ⟷ 3 transitions. One harmonic

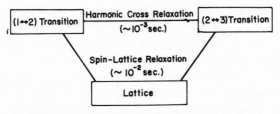

Fig. 10. Harmonic cross relaxation

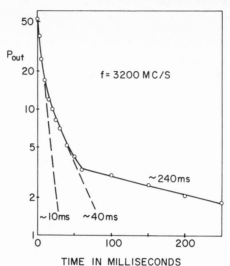

TIME IN MILLISECONDS

Fig. 11. A relaxation measurement showing three time constants

cross-relaxation time is ~ 10 msec, another is ~ 40 msec, and the "true" spin-lattice relaxation time is ~ 240 msec.

The longest relaxation time cannot be caused by the lattice-to-bath relaxation as suggested by Townes and co-workers.[8] Spin-lattice relaxation times of similar magnitude were observed for negative spin temperatures at other values of θ during maser operation. Bath temperatures in these experiments were 1.4°K to 1.6°K.

CONCLUSION

One can argue that there are always three different relaxation times in a four-level system without bringing any cross-relaxation processes into the picture. Therefore, one might see different relaxation times without cross relaxation. However, the facts that the fast relaxation time changes rapidly in harmonic coupling regions and that the harmonically coupled level becomes partially saturated argue that some harmonic coupling mechanism is present.

Although experiments at $\theta = 30°$ were primarily discussed here, many similar effects were observed at other values of θ. However, at some angles the harmonic cross-relaxation effect is very weak. This might be expected because the mixing of states is different for different orientations in ruby.

From the fact that the long relaxation time is not affected by harmonic coupling, one might conclude that the harmonic coupling is predominantly a spin-spin effect. If it were a spin-phonon-spin effect, one might expect to find the longer relaxation time modified by the simultaneous presence of the phonons involved in the harmonic process.

The author wishes to thank A. E. Siegman and H. Heffner for many suggestions and discussions. Leonard Dague contributed greatly to construction of the traveling-wave maser, and Per Skullestad assisted in performing the experiments.

REFERENCES

1. N. Bloembergen, S. Shapiro, P. S. Pershan, and J. O. Artman, Phys. Rev. *114*, 445 (1959).
2. J. E. Geusic, private communication. It was later learned that the harmonic coupling effect was first observed by Mims.
3. A. E. Siegman, J. Cromack and W. S. C. Chang, 1959 IRE WESCON Conv. Rec., in press.
4. R. W. DeGrasse, 1958 IRE WESCON Conv. Rec., Pt. 3, 29 (1958); DeGrasse, Schulz-DuBois, and Scovil, Bell System Technical Journal *38*, 305 (1959).
5. Geusic, Schulz-DuBois, DeGrasse and Scovil, J. Appl. Phys. *30*, 1113 (1959).
6. W. S. C. Chang, J. Cromack and A. E. Siegman, J. Electr. Cont., in press.
7. It is believed that recent anomalous maser observations by F. R. Arams, Proc. IRE *47*, 1373 (1959), are due to this same mechanism.
8. Giordmaine, Alsop, Nash, and Townes, Phys. Rev. *109*, 302 (1958).

DISCUSSION

N. BLOEMBERGEN: The harmonic cross relaxation is essentially the same as the cross-relaxation effects discussed by Sorokin in this symposium. Consider n spin flips at frequencies ω_n, taken as positive if spin energy increases, and negative if spin energy decreases during the transition. The condition for multiple spin flips to occur is $\Sigma\, \omega_n \approx 0$. A number of the ω_n may be equal to one another or may be equal to zero.

R. KOMPFNER: I believe that the discovery of harmonic cross-coupling relaxation of electron spins in ruby was first made by W. B. Mims at Bell Telephone Laboratories. He also gave the correct explanation of this effect and pointed out its potential applications to masers.

J. P. GORDON: W. B. Mims at Bell Labs has investigated concentration and angular dependence of harmonic spin coupling using a single frequency pulse technique. Using low ($\ll$ .05 percent) concentration ruby, anomalous T_{21} and T_1 effects could be seen only at angles such that $2:1$ frequency ratios were very accurately satisfied. The cross-relaxation effects were temperature independent and went approximately as the square of the concentration. At concentrations above .05 percent significant cross-relaxation effects were seen at all angles, indicating a rapid equalization of spin temperature. A letter to the editor of the IRE has been submitted discussing this work.

B. BÖLGER: What concentration did Geusic use when he observed his 11th harmonic?

H. E. D. SCOVIL: .05 percent.

A. E. SIEGMAN: Swarup in the Canadian Journal of Physics (1959) has reported that the line shape in chromicyanide changes from clearly Lorentzian to clearly Gaussian as the chrome concentration increases above ~ 0.1 percent. This may be related to the concentration dependence of the various relaxation phenomena in the same range of concentration.

RELAXATION PROCESSES IN DILUTE POTASSIUM CHROMICYANIDE*

P. F. CHESTER, P. E. WAGNER, and J. G. CASTLE, JR.

Westinghouse Research Laboratories

THE BEHAVIOR of the $-\frac{1}{2}, \frac{1}{2}$ line in $K_3Cr_xCo_{1-x}$ $(CN)_6$ with $x = .0002, .001, .0025, .004, .01,$ and $.02$ has been examined in the helium temperature range with a 9 KMc/sec spectrometer. Line profiles recorded at $2.1\,°K$ revealed in all cases a Lorentzian shape out to three half widths. The width at half intensity varies with concentration as shown in Fig. 1. The expected variation on the assumption of a truly Lorentz line is shown by the dashed line. It would appear that the line is inhomogeneously broadened at the lowest concentration and becomes less so as the concentration is increased. This is supported by our ability to invert a hole in the .1 percent material but not in the 1 percent.

Measurements of relaxation time were made by monitoring the recovery of the whole line with a delayed field sweep after inversion by field-sweep rapid passage. The technique has been described elsewhere.[1],[2] A typical oscilloscope presentation showing the recovered and inverted lines on alternate traces is shown in Fig. 2. The peak-to-peak voltage difference, corrected for instrumental nonlinearity, gives the deviation from equilibrium directly.

In each case the crystal was oriented with the magnetic field in the a-c plane at an angle of $47.5\,°$ to the c axis. This corresponds to the maximum field for the $-\frac{1}{2}, \frac{1}{2}$ line. In this position the nearest lines are the $-\frac{3}{2}, -\frac{1}{2}$ line ~ 1.2 KMc/sec away and

*This work was supported in part by US Air Force Contract AF 33(616)-5258 and AF 19(604)-5589.

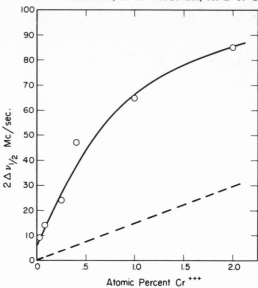

Fig. 1. Observed width of $-\frac{1}{2} \longrightarrow \frac{1}{2}$ *line in* $K_3(CoCr)(CN)_6$ *as a function of* Cr^{+++} *concentration*

the $\frac{1}{2}$, $\frac{3}{2}$ line ~ 3.1 KMc/sec away. The $-\frac{3}{2}$, $\frac{1}{2}$ line is separated from the $-\frac{1}{2}$, $\frac{3}{2}$ line by ~ 1.2 KMc/sec. The $-\frac{1}{2}$, $\frac{1}{2}$ line was inverted and its recovery observed as a function of time afterwards.

THE TIME DEPENDENCE OF RECOVERY

A result typical of the four lowest concentrations is shown in Fig. 3. It will be noted that inversion is not perfect, the peak emission being only ~ 35 percent of the equilibrium absorption. At each temperature the data are fitted very well by a single exponential.

On the present picture of spin-lattice relaxation this result is surprising, since there is more than one path available for relaxation. With 4 levels, one would expect in general to see a compound-exponential recovery with three time constants. One possible explanation is that the $-\frac{1}{2}$, $\frac{1}{2}$ relaxation path dominates over the others. Another possible explanation is that the $-\frac{1}{2}$, $\frac{1}{2}$ relaxation path is relatively slow and that relaxation by other paths is very rapid so that a quasi-equilibrium sets in be-

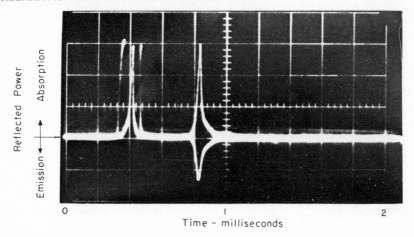

Fig. 2. Inversion of 2–3 line in .1 percent chromicyanide using field sweep

Superposed traces with and without inverting pulse.

fore the first observation of the $-\frac{1}{2}$, $\frac{1}{2}$ line. From this point on, the relaxation rate would be limited by the $-\frac{1}{2}$, $\frac{1}{2}$ path.

Whatever the exact combination of spin-lattice paths involved, the fact that the curve of Fig. 3 is linear throughout the whole

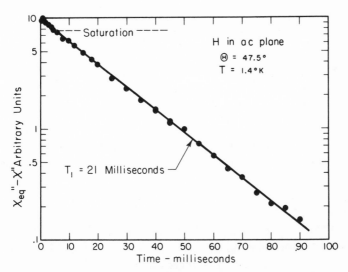

Fig. 3. Recovery of 2 → 3 line in $K_3Cr_{.001}Co_{.999}(CN)_6$ after inversion

range of observation, including the region of infinite spin temperature, implies that there is no significant imprisonment of phonons in this material at temperatures down to 1.3 °K and concentrations up to .4 percent Cr^{+++}.

Between .4 percent and 1 percent Cr^{+++}, the nature of the recovery appears to change. A typical recovery curve for 1 percent material is shown in Fig. 4. The rate of recovery is seen to be more rapid and no longer proceeds with a single time constant. Even the longest time constant is shorter than those

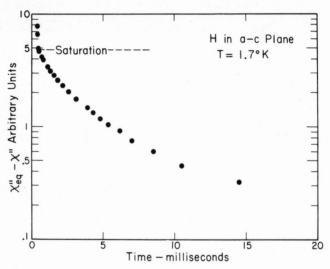

Fig. 4. Recovery of $2 \rightarrow 3$ line in $K_3Cr_{0.01}Co_{0.99}(CN)_6$ after inversion

observed in the more dilute materials at the same temperature. It seems highly improbable that imprisonment could be responsible for this new behavior, for several reasons. The concentration change is only by a factor of 2.5 and this is offset by an increase in line width by a factor of 1.5. A greater change in population difference is made by cooling the .4 percent material from 4.2 °K to 1.3 °K and this does not result in a curved recovery. Moreover, in the absorptive region, imprisonment is expected to reduce rather than increase the rate of recovery. An estimate of phonon mean free path against reabsorption by a spin in the 1 percent material assuming the same T_1 as measured for .4 percent yields the value 3.5 mm at 4.2 °K. In this sample the mean distance of a spin from the surface is about .3 mm.

The true T_1 for 1 percent would have to be less than one tenth the T_1 for .4 percent if the 1 percent recoveries are to be explained by imprisonment. The behavior of the one percent material probably has a different explanation.

THE TEMPERATURE AND CONCENTRATION DEPENDENCE OF T_1

In the discussion so far it has been assumed that the relaxation is by a single phonon process. To check this, the temperature dependence of T_1 was measured for several concentrations. The results are plotted in Fig. 5. In the case of the one percent material, the values plotted refer to the slowest of the observed rates, which in general accounted for only a small fraction of the total recovery.

For any given concentration below one percent, T_1 is seen to vary slightly more rapidly than T^{-1}. This is consistent with a single phonon process dominating at the lowest temperatures and a Raman process setting in near 4 °K. The precise temperature dependence of relaxation for the one percent material is difficult to define because of the multiplicity of relaxation times observed in this material.

The concentration dependence of T_1 below .4 percent is slight. Above this concentration, however, there is a marked change. At any given temperature the slowest rate in one percent material is twice as fast as in .4 percent; the fastest observed rate is ten times as fast. Apparently, the mechanics of the relaxation process undergo a qualitative change between .4 and 1 percent. Further light is shed on this matter by the results to be described next.

THE PROXIMITY EFFECT

A series of experiments was carried out at constant temperature (1.7 °K) in which the value of H and its angle with the c axis in the a-c plane were varied so as to alter the frequency

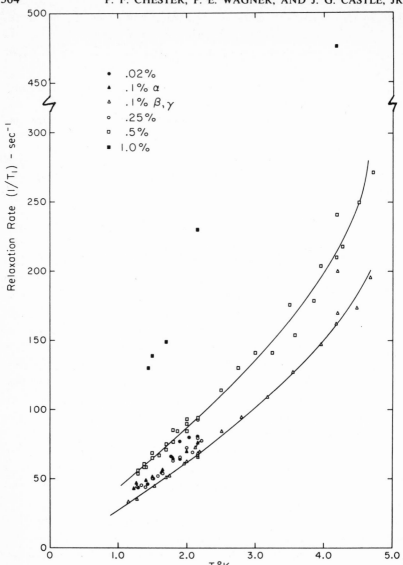

Fig. 5. Relaxation Rates as a Function of Temperature

separation between the $-\frac{1}{2}$, $\frac{1}{2}$ line and the $-\frac{3}{2}$, $-\frac{1}{2}$. At each setting a measurement of T_1 was made for the $-\frac{1}{2}$, $\frac{1}{2}$ line. The results for four concentrations are plotted in Figs. 6, 7, 8, and 9. Note the different frequency scales. The appearance of the

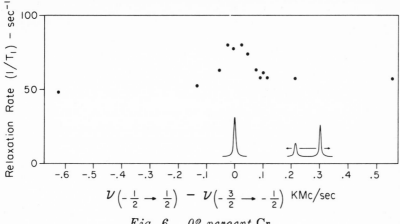

Fig. 6. .02 percent Cr

lines is shown to scale in each case. In most cases the $-\frac{3}{2}$, $-\frac{1}{2}$ line appeared split. We were unable to make it coalesce by small adjustments of angle while observing the resonance. It is believed that the splitting is a property of the crystal and not due to misorientation.

We shall first discuss the behavior of the .02, .1, and .4 per-cent material. A general feature is an increase in the rate of re-laxation as the lines approach each other. When the lines are made to coincide and are inverted together, the relaxation time takes on an intermediate value. This "proximity effect" ex-

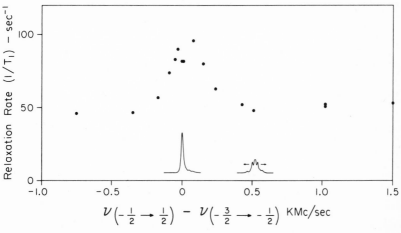

Fig. 7. .1 percent Cr

tends over a frequency range of ~ 150 Mc/sec for .02 percent, ~ 600 Mc/sec for .1 percent, and ~ 1100 Mc/sec for .4 percent. In the large majority of cases, the recovery within the proximity region takes place with a single time constant over the whole range of observation which was always greater than 90 percent of the recovery. In a few cases of very close proximity, there were signs of a second shorter time constant for the first several percent of recovery.

For reasons discussed above we must reject "hot phonons" as an explanation of the proximity effect. Cross relaxation[3] in principle can explain the effect although some details are left obscure. The process of inversion heats the $-\frac{1}{2}$, $\frac{1}{2}$ transition and cools the $-\frac{3}{2}$, $-\frac{1}{2}$ transition. When the frequencies of the two transitions are far apart, relaxation takes place solely by the emission and absorption of phonons, presumably involving all the transitions whose population ratios have been disturbed from their equilibrium ratio. When the frequencies of the $-\frac{1}{2}$, $\frac{1}{2}$ and $-\frac{3}{2}$, $-\frac{1}{2}$ transitions come within a few linewidths of each other, simultaneous spin flips are possible. For example, a $-\frac{3}{2}$ spin may flip up to $-\frac{1}{2}$ while a $+\frac{1}{2}$ spin simultaneously flips

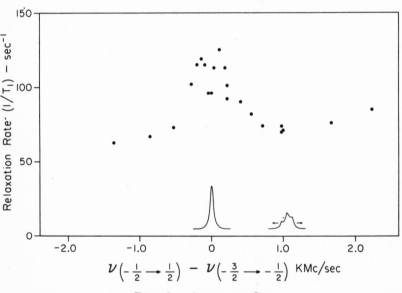

Fig. 8.   .4 percent Cr

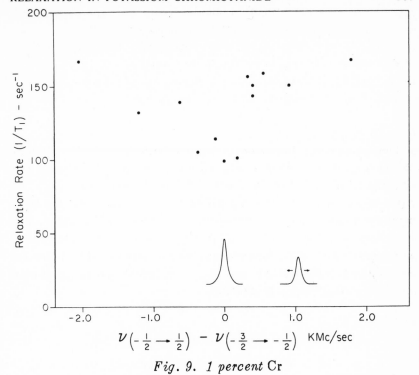

Fig. 9. 1 percent Cr

down to $-\frac{1}{2}$. The effect of this cross relaxation is to increase the observed rate of recovery of the $-\frac{1}{2}$, $\frac{1}{2}$ line. However, in general, one would expect it to show up as an additional time constant.

The effect of simultaneous rapid passage on the superposed lines is to invert both of them. Perfect inversion should result in the $-\frac{1}{2}$ population remaining unchanged and the $-\frac{3}{2}$ and $+\frac{1}{2}$ populations being interchanged.[4] Thus both intervals would be heated to approximately the same temperature and no cross relaxation would be possible. In this case, the recovery would be expected to be slower than with cross relaxation present although not necessarily as slow as the individual lines at wide separation. This can be seen in Figs. 7 and 8.

The behavior of the 1 percent material is not as clear-cut. There still appears to be a reduction in the relaxation rate at coincidence. The extent of the region of enhanced relaxation rate is not clearly defined, probably due to the fact that at this concentration cross relaxation occurs between other lines (e.g., the $-\frac{3}{2}$, $\frac{1}{2}$, and the $-\frac{1}{2}$, $\frac{3}{2}$) and completely alters the pattern of relaxation. It should be noted that none of the recoveries in the 1 percent material are simple exponentials; the rates plotted in Fig. 9 are the slowest of the observed rates.

CONCLUSION

The relaxation behavior of $K_3(CoCr)(CN)_6$ in the liquid-helium region has been examined in a way which reveals the absence of phonon imprisonment and the presence and extent of cross relaxation. In the more dilute material, the time and temperature dependence of relaxation were measured under conditions free of cross relaxation. A single relaxation time, having an approximately T^{-1} dependence, was observed. The behavior of the more concentrated material is different, probably due to the influence of cross relaxation.

REFERENCES

1. P. F. Chester, P. E. Wagner, and J. G. Castle, Jr., Proceedings of the Solid State Maser Symposium, Fort Monmouth, N. J., p. 42 (June, 1958); Phys. Rev. 110, 281 (1958).
2. P. F. Chester, P. E. Wagner, J. G. Castle, Jr., and G. Conn, Rev. Sci. Instr. (to be published).
3. N. Bloembergen, S. Shapiro, P. S. Pershan, and J. O. Artman, Phys. Rev. 114, 445 (1959).
4. P. E. Wagner, J. G. Castle, Jr., and P. F. Chester, paper in this volume.

DISCUSSION

J. A. GIORDMAINE: Do you conclude from your experimental work that the relaxation time of two coincident lines is appreciably different from that of either single line far from coincidence?

P. F. CHESTER: Yes. It is appreciably faster — say 40 percent, but one would not necessarily expect it to be the same.

RELAXATION EFFECTS IN A MASER MATERIAL, $K_3(CoCr)(CN)_6$*

S. SHAPIRO[†] and N. BLOEMBERGEN

Gordon McKay Laboratory, Harvard University

INVESTIGATION OF paramagnetic relaxation[1] by means of microwave resonance techniques[2] has received new impetus[3],[4],[5] with the advent of solid-state masers.[6],[7] It has recently been shown[8] that cross-relaxation terms have to be added to the conventional rate equations. The present paper is a sequel to BSPA. Some general expressions for the dependence on pump power of the susceptibility at various frequencies are derived and the temperature dependence in the presence and absence of cross saturation is discussed. A brief description of the experimental method is then given. Experimental data are then discussed. Evidence is presented that the various spin-lattice relaxation times in $K_3(CoCr)(CN)_6$ are all inversely proportional to the absolute temperature in the liquid-helium range. The theoretical dependence of the susceptibility on pump power is verified. Experiments at different Cr^{+++} concentrations and different crystallographic orientations show a controllable influence of the cross-relaxation mechanism. Implications for the operation of a solid-state maser are discussed.

*The research reported in this paper was made possible through support extended to Cruft Laboratory, Harvard University, by the National Security Agency under Contract Nonr–1866(28). It was performed in partial fulfillment of the requirements of the Ph.D. degree at Harvard by S. S.

†Present address: Arthur D. Little, Inc., 15 Acorn Park, Cambridge, Mass.

THE DEPENDENCE OF MICROWAVE SPIN SUSCEPTIBILITIES ON PUMP POWER, TEMPERATURE, AND CROSS RELAXATION

A complete description of the magnetic properties of a system of spin levels requires the use of the spin density matrix formalism.[9] When the spin-spin phase memory time T_2 is short, in particular when $\gamma H_{pump} T_2 \ll 1$, the time dependence of the diagonal elements is described by the well-known rate equations for the population of the various spin levels. The susceptibility near the various resonant frequencies is proportional to the difference in population of the two levels defining the resonance. The rate equation for the population of the ith level can be written in the general form

$$dn_i/dt = \sum_j (-w_{ij}n_i + w_{ij}n_j) + \sum_{jkl} w_{ijkl} N^{-1}(n_j n_l - n_i n_k)$$

$$+ \sum_j W_{ij}(n_j - n_i). \quad (1)$$

$N = \sum_i n_i$ is the total number of magnetic ions

$$w_{ij} = w_{ji} \exp \{- h\nu_{ij}/kT\} \quad (2)$$

is the probability per unit time for a spin transition from level i to level j, separated by an energy difference $h\nu_{ij}$ under the influence of lattice vibrations at a temperature T.

$$W_{ij} = W_{ji} = \tfrac{1}{4}\hbar^{-2} |M_{ij}|^2 H_{ij}^2 g(\nu_{ij}) \quad (3)$$

is the transition probability per unit time induced by pump power applied at the frequency ν_{ij}. M_{ij} is the matrix element of the component of the magnetic moment operator parallel to $H(\nu_{ij})$, and $g(\nu_{ij})$ is the normalized shape function of the resonance absorption line.

The imaginary part of the suspectibility near a resonant frequency may be derived by equating the power absorbed to $(\tfrac{1}{2}) \omega\chi'' H^2$.

$$\chi''(\nu_{ij}) = \tfrac{1}{4}\hbar^{-1} |M_{ij}|^2 g(\nu_{ij}) \Delta n_{ij} \quad (4)$$

where $\Delta n_{ij} = n_i - n_j$ is the difference in population between the lower and upper levels.

w_{ijkl} is the probability per unit time for a cross-relaxation process in which one ion makes the transition $i \longrightarrow j$ and simultaneously a neighboring spin $k \longrightarrow l$. This process is only of importance if the difference in energy $h(\nu_{ij} - \nu_{kl})$ is very small and can be taken up by the dipolar interaction of the spin assembly, as discussed in BSPA. It is permissible to put the exponential factor exp $\{- h(\nu_{ij} - \nu_{kl})/kT_s\}$ equal to unity in this term. The introduction of cross-relaxation terms is meaningful, when the resonances at ν_{ij} and ν_{kl} are close but well resolved. The cross-relaxation time is usually shorter than the spin-lattice relaxation time $(w_{ijkl} > w_{ij})$, if the resonances at ν_{ij} and ν_{kl} are separated by two to five times the dipolar interaction. The cross-relaxation terms are usually completely negligible for larger separations, so that frequently only one or two of the w_{ijkl} have to be considered.

It should be mentioned that spin-lattice relaxation processes may also involve transitions of two spins, the balance of energy being taken up by the lattice. This occurs if the dipolar interaction between two spins is modulated by the lattice vibrations. In this case spin-lattice relaxation terms quadratic in the occupation numbers occur. In practice the dominant spin-lattice relaxation will occur via the orbital modulation and spin-orbit coupling of individual ions. Therefore no confusion should arise by reserving the w_{ijkl} exclusively for the cross-relaxation terms.

The rate Equations (1) may be linearized in the high temperature approximation, when the differences in population are small, $\Delta n_{ij} \ll N$. By expanding the Boltzmann factor in Equation (2) and omitting terms of order $(\Delta n_{ij})^2$ in Equation (1), a set of linear equations in Δn_{ij} is obtained. The steady state solution may readily be written in a determinantal form.[10] The dependence of the susceptibility on the pumping power at the frequency ν_{kl} takes the general form

$$\chi''_{ij} (H^2_{kl}) - \chi''_{ij} (\infty) = \{\chi''_{ij} (0) - \chi''_{ij} (\infty)\} \{1 + C_{kl} H^2_{kl}\}^{-1} . \quad (5)$$

This equation remains valid in the presence of cross-relaxation and pumping power at other frequencies. The constant C_{kl} is a function of all other pump powers and all relaxation parameters w. For the transition kl, Equation (5) reduces to the usual self-saturation curve with the asymptotic value $\chi''_{kl}(\infty) = 0$.

When all w's have the same temperature dependence $f(T)$, then $C_{kl} \propto f^{-1}(T)$ and $\chi''_{ij}(\infty)$ has the same temperature dependence as $\chi''_{ij}(0)$, i.e., Curie's law is obeyed.

This situation is expected to occur at very high temperatures, where all $w_{ij} \propto T^2$ because of Raman phonon processes, and at very low temperatures, where all $w_{ij} \propto T$ because of single phonon processes, with the important proviso that temperature-independent cross relaxation is negligible. If cross-relaxation terms are not small compared to the spin-lattice terms, the temperature dependence of $\chi''_{ij}(\infty)$ is complex and may even decrease with decreasing temperature. In particular, lowering of the lattice temperature T may result in the transition from a regime where $w_{ij} > w_{ijkl}$ to one where $w_{ijkl} > w_{ij}$.

These general considerations are now applied to the particular case of the four spin levels of a Cr^{+++} ion, corresponding to the situation encountered in the experiments described in the following sections. It is assumed that only the ν_{24} resonance is pumped and that the level spacings and line widths are such that only the cross relaxation between the resonances ν_{12} and ν_{23} need be considered. In addition to the six w_{ij}'s, only W_{24} and w_{1232} have to be considered. The steady-state solution for the population differences is given for two special cases.

a. Complete saturation, no cross relaxation, $w_{24} \gg w_{ij}$, $w_{1232} = 0$.

$$\Delta n_{24} = 0$$

$$\Delta n_{23} = -\frac{N\hbar}{4kT} \times$$

$$\left\{ \frac{(w_{12} + w_{13} + w_{14})(w_{34}\nu_{34} - w_{23}\nu_{23}) + w_{13}(w_{14}\nu_{34} - w_{12}\nu_{23})}{(w_{12} + w_{13} + w_{14})(w_{34} + w_{23}) + w_{13}(w_{12} + w_{14})} \right\} \quad (6)$$

This transition can be emissive. If the relaxation from level 3 to level 1 is negligible, $w_{13} = 0$, the condition for maser action is the same as for a simple three-level system,[6]
$$w_{34}\nu_{34} > w_{32}\nu_{32}.$$

$$\Delta n_{12} = \frac{Nh}{4kT} \times$$

$$\left\{ \frac{w_{13}(w_{34}\nu_{14} + w_{23}\nu_{12}) + (w_{23} + w_{34} + w_{13})(w_{14}\nu_{14} + w_{12}\nu_{12})}{(w_{12} + w_{13} + w_{14})(w_{34} + w_{23}) + w_{13}(w_{12} + w_{14})} \right\}$$

The resonance at ν_{12} never becomes emissive.

b. Complete saturation, rapid cross relaxation, $w_{24} > w_{1232} \gg w_{ij}$

$$\Delta n_{24} = 0$$

$$\Delta n_{12} = \Delta_{23} =$$

$$+ \frac{Nh}{4kT} \left\{ \frac{2w_{13}\nu_{13} + w_{12}\nu_{12} + w_{23}\nu_{23} + w_{14}\nu_{14} - w_{34}\nu_{34}}{w_{12} + 4w_{13} + w_{14} + w_{23} + w_{34}} \right\} \quad (7)$$

In this case both resonances ν_{12} and ν_{23} may become emissive when

$$w_{34}\nu_{34} > 2w_{13}\nu_{13} + w_{12}\nu_{12} + w_{23}\nu_{23} + w_{14}\nu_{14}. \quad (8)$$

This condition is more difficult to satisfy than the condition that Equation (6) be negative. On the other hand, if because of cross saturation, Δn_{23} becomes positive, $\Delta n_{34} = -\Delta n_{23}$ will surely be negative. The action of the transition ν_{12} is similar to the action of the transition in another ionic species at the same frequency. Scovil et al.[11] describe such an influence of Ce^{+++} on the population of the Gd^{+++} levels in a mixed crystal.

Finally, it should be emphasized that Equation (1) does not include the most general form of cross relaxation. As pointed out in BSPA, processes in which more than two transitions take place simultaneously are possible. One then has third-order transition probabilities w_{ijklmn}, which are not negligible if $\nu_{ij} + \nu_{kl} + \nu_{mn}$ is zero or comparable with the dipolar interactions. The cubic terms in the rate equations can again be linearized in the population differences Δn in the high temperature approximation. Fourth-order terms with $w_{ijklmnop}$ can be introduced in a similar fashion and have been used in BSPA to explain cross-saturation effects in copper tutton salt. Their existence has been demonstrated most strikingly in the case of nitrogen impurities in diamond in a paper by Sorokin *et al.,*[12] presented in this volume.

EXPERIMENTAL METHOD

Crystals of $K_3(CoCr)(CN)_6$ were grown from aqueous solution by controlled evaporation. The relative $[Cr^{+++}]$ concentration in the solution was 0.5 percent and 2 percent. Small single crystals were placed in a maser-type cavity of a design described previously.[13] A small size of crystal is chosen since the purpose is to obtain reliable values for the microwave susceptibilities. Heavy loading of the cavity, useful in maser operation, is avoided. The field intensity over the sample at both microwave frequencies was uniform to within 5 percent.

The cavity was tunable at X-band by a movable diaphragm coupling which could slide with quarter-wave sections in standard X-band guide. The X-band pump power was supplied by a Varian V-58 klystron. L-band signal power was supplied by a 5981 klystron or a Navy Model LAG signal generator run from an external power supply. Although L-band tuning by capacitive loading of the quarter-wavelength resonator proved feasible, the present experiments were carried out at a few fixed L-band frequencies with fixed resonators.

The klystrons at both frequencies were locked to the sample cavity resonance with a repeller voltage modulation feedback system similar to that developed by Kip.[14] Influence of the dispersive components of the susceptibility was eliminated.

A rotatable electromagnet supplied the d-c magnetic field. In the present experiments the crystals were oriented in such a way that the magnetic field could rotate in the ac-plane. In this plane the two ions in the unit cell are magnetically equivalent, so that only four energy levels have to be considered. The variation of the splittings ν_{12}, ν_{23} and ν_{24} is plotted in Fig. 1 as a function of the magnitude of the magnetic field H_o for various angles θ between the a-axis and H_o in the ac-plane. The curves have been calculated from published tables for the energy levels.[15] It is seen that the resonances ν_{12} and ν_{23} coincide for $\theta = 0$ at about 1700 Mc/s, but can be made to deviate considerably at other angles at the same frequency. As the angle θ

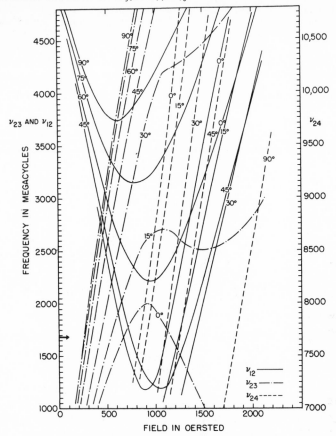

Fig. 1

The resonant frequencies ν_{12}, ν_{23}, and ν_{24} between the four levels of Cr^{+++} in $K_3(CoCr)(CN)_6$ as a function of the magnetic field strength H_0 in the crystallographic ac-plane, for different angles between H_0 and the a-axis. The graph was calculated from published tables for the energy levels.[15] The arrow indicates the L-b and operating frequency.

is varied, the value of H_o is adjusted to keep ν_{23} at the indicated L-band frequency. The X-band resonant frequency ν_{24} does not vary too much under these conditions. Pumping at ν_{24} remains possible. Calculation of the other resonant frequencies ν_{13}, ν_{14}, and ν_{34} shows that these resonances remain all well separated from each other and the other resonances. It is thus possible to create an experimental situation in which only one cross-relaxation process w_{1232} with variable strength is of importance.

Incident power at both frequencies can be monitored with the aid of directional couplers and thermistors. The reflected power at L-band is modulated at 15 cps by modulation of the d-c magnetic field, and it is displayed after rectification by a 1N21C crystal on an oscilloscope or after passage through a narrowband receiver on a pen-recorder. The coaxial line contains a low-pass filter to eliminate X-band power. The L-band susceptibility is measured as a function of X-band pump power. Self-saturation curves at X-band are taken by measuring the reflected power in the X-band guide in a similar manner. With the small samples used, the reduction from change in reflected power to change in susceptibility of the sample is straightforward. The power at L-band was sufficiently low that saturation at the signal frequency was negligible $W_{23} \ll w_{ij}$.

EXPERIMENTAL RESULTS

The general dependence of the susceptibilities on pump power is illustrated in Fig. 2. The drawn curves have the theoretical form of Equation (5). The experimental points of both the L-band and the X-band susceptibility (self-saturation) are in good agreement[16] with the theory presented above.

Strandberg[17] has pointed out that considerable deviations from Equation (5) should be expected if the phonon-bath contact were a bottleneck rather than the spin-lattice relaxation. The extent of phonon-heating and the heat conductivity would change with pump power. There is apparently no experimental evidence for this.

The rather large negative asymptotic value for the L-band susceptibility indicates the suitability of this material for maser operation. In early papers on masers,[18] graphs of gain vs. pump power did not show any indication for such an asymptotic behavior. The explanation for the shape of those gain-vs.-pump power curves, which have no fundamental significance, can be based on the following two reasons. As χ'' approached its asymptotic value, $\chi''(\infty)$, the maser approached the point of

instability versus oscillation due to the choice of external coupling of the maser cavity. In the second place, the pump field
intensity was not uniform over the sample. As the pump power
increased, successively larger regions of the crystal became
emissive.

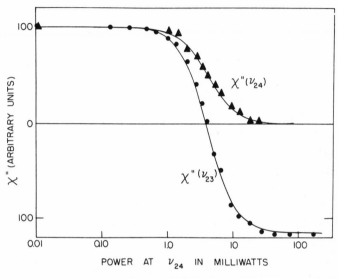

Fig. 2

The susceptibility χ'' at the frequencies ν_{23} and ν_{24} respectively, as a function of pump power applied at ν_{24}. The crystal
$K_3(0.995\ Co,\ 0.005\ Cr)(CN)_6$ was maintained at 2.5 °K. The
magnetic field $H_o = 1175$ oersteds makes an angle $\theta = 10°$ with
the a-axis in the ac-plane. The drawn curves have the theoretical form of Eq. (5). The final spin temperature $T_f = 2.2°$ K at
ν_{23} and $T_f = \infty$ at ν_{24}.

There will still be an asymptotic value for the effective susceptibility at high pump power level. The approach to this
limiting value will be more gradual than the curves in Fig. 2.
The detailed shape depends on the field configurations at both
the pump and the maser frequency in the cavity. Since the effects of spatial spin diffusion in the nonuniformly saturated
crystal is negligible, the effective susceptibility at ν_{ij}, includ-

ing the filling factor, as a function of pump power at ν_{kl} is given by

$$4\chi''_{ij,\,\text{eff}}\,(H^2_{kl}) \iiint_{\text{cavity}} \sum_{\alpha} (H^{\alpha}_{ij}{}^2/8\pi)dV =$$

$$\doteq \hbar^{-1}\,g(\nu_{ij})\,[\Delta n_{ij}(0) - \Delta n_{ij}(\infty)] \iiint_{\text{sample}} \frac{\left\{\sum_{\alpha} M^{\alpha}_{ij}\,H^{\alpha}_{ij}\right\}^2 dV}{1 + C'_{kl}\left\{\sum_{\alpha} M^{\alpha}_{kl}\,H^{\alpha}_{kl}\right\}^2} +$$

$$+ \hbar^{-1}\,g(\nu_{ij})\,\Delta n_{ij}(\infty) \iiint_{\text{sample}} \left(\sum_{\alpha} M^{\alpha}_{ij}\,H^{\alpha}_{ij}\right)^2 dV. \quad (9)$$

The summation α is over the three Cartesian coordinates. H^{α}_{ij} and H^{α}_{kl} are functions of position in the cavity. $\Delta n_{ij}(0)$ and $\Delta n_{ij}(\infty)$ are the differences in population of levels i and j in thermal equilibrium and at infinite pumping power at the frequency ν_{kl}. These quantities as well as C'_{kl} are not a function of position.

The approach of χ'' (eff) to an asymptotic value is important for maser operation. It implies a good stability against amplitude and frequency fluctuations in pump power[19] which is not shared by certain parametric amplifiers.

In Fig. 3 data for the temperature dependence of the asymptotic value $\chi''(\infty)$ are shown. Instead of $\chi''(\infty)$ a final spin temperature T_f defined by

$$T_f = T\,\Delta n_{23}(0)/\Delta n_{23}(\infty) = T\,\chi''(0)/\chi''(\infty)$$

is plotted. Clearly, $\chi''(\infty)$ is proportional to $\chi''(0)$ or inversely proportional to T. Curie's law is valid.

The power required to reach the value halfway between $\chi''(0)$ and $\chi''(\infty)$ is proportional to the absolute temperature. These data are therefore consistent with the explanation that all w_{ij} are determined by single phonon processes and are all proportional to T, whereas cross-relaxation terms are absent for the crystalline orientation used ($\theta = 30°$). This result is in agreement with the data of Eschenfelder[2] on Cr^{+++} in an alum.

As explained above, cross relaxation should become important, when the angle θ approaches zero, as $\nu_{12} = \nu_{23}$ for $\theta = 0°$. In

Fig. 4 $\chi''(\infty)$ is shown as a function of $\nu_{12} - \nu_{23}$ at two different concentrations. The result of cross relaxation is that maser action is suppressed, $\chi''(\infty) \geqslant 0$. This occurs at small values of θ and at high magnetic concentration for all values of θ.

This result is physically understandable because one has to compete with various relaxation mechanisms to and from level 1, if cross-relaxation w_{1232} is important. This is expressed mathematically by Equations (6) and (7). Apparently the condition (8) is not satisfied. At $\theta = 0$ one measures, of course, not χ''_{23}, but $\chi''_{23} + \chi''_{12}$. This does not change the argument for the ratio

$$\frac{\chi''_{12}(\infty) + \chi''_{23}(\infty)}{\chi''_{12}(0) + \chi''_{23}(0)} = \frac{T_f}{T}$$

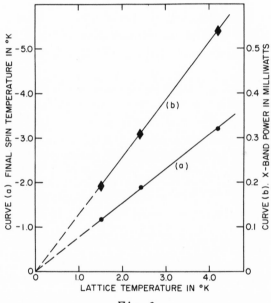

Fig. 3

Curve a. The final spin temperature $T_f = T\chi''(0)/\chi''(\infty)$ at ν_{23} as a function of the lattice temperature. Curve b. The pump power at ν_{24} required to produce 50 percent saturation at ν_{23}, i.e., to obtain a value $\chi'' = \frac{1}{2}(\chi''(0) + \chi''(\infty))$, as a function of the lattice temperature. The magnetic field $H_o = 1390$ oersteds in the ac-plane makes an angle $\theta = 30°$ with the a-axis of the crystal K₃(0.995 Co, 0.005 Cr)(CN)₆.

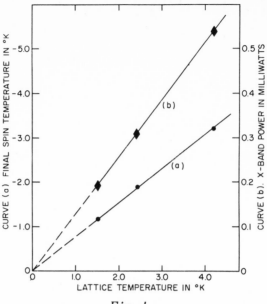

Fig. 4

The inverse of the final spin temperature $T_f^{-1} \propto \chi''(\infty)$ is plotted as a function of the separation between the resonances at ν_{12} and ν_{23}. The separation $\nu_{12} - \nu_{23} = 1000$ Mc/s corresponds to $\theta = 14°$. The magnetic field is varied in the ac-plane of $K_3(CoCr)(CN)_6$ in magnitude and direction so as to keep $\nu_{23} \approx$ 1700 Mc/s. Curve (a) is for 0.5 percent Cr^{+++} concentration, curve (b) is for 2 percent Cr^{+++} concentration. Cross-relaxation effects are important near zero separation at the lower concentration and at all separations at the higher concentration.

since the susceptibilities of the two transitions are described by the same temperature because of the coincidence of the resonant frequencies.

The difference in T_f at 1000 and 3000 Mc/s separation, is probably caused by the variation of the matrix elements $M_{ij}(\theta)$ and the consequent variation in the ratio of the $w_{ij}(\theta)$ at $\theta = 14°$ and $\theta = 32°$ respectively. The matrix elements[15] do not change much for $\theta < 10°$, and the rapid change in T_f in this region is caused by the onset of cross relaxation. One may crudely estimate that w_{1232} becomes of the same order as the $w_{ij}(\sim 10^{+3}$ sec^{-1}) at separation $\nu_{12} - \nu_{23} = 400$ Mc/s. In the more concentrated sample cross relaxation is important at all separations.

The marked concentration dependence of T_f because of the onset of cross saturation provides the clue for the action of light ruby as an amplifier and dark ruby as an attenuator in the same traveling-wave maser.[20]

Another interesting observation has been made about the temperature dependence of $\chi''_{23}(\infty)$ at $\nu_{12} - \nu_{23} = 600$ Mc/s. Cross relaxation in this orientation is comparable with spin-lattice relaxation at $4.2\,^\circ$K according to Fig. 4. When the crystal is cooled and the w_{ij} become smaller, cross relaxation should become dominant. It was indeed observed that lowering the temperature T caused an increase in $|T_f|$. In other words, maser action became poorer at the lower temperature. Cross relaxation provides a natural explanation for this effect, which has a reverse trend from the usual Curie behavior shown in Fig. 3.

The magnitude of w_{1232} may be estimated theoretically from an approximate formula given by BSPA,

$$w_{1232} = (2\pi)^{-\frac{1}{2}} \hbar^{-2} |\mathcal{H}_{1232}|^2 [\Delta\nu_{12}^2 + \Delta\nu_{23}^2]^{-\frac{1}{2}} \times$$

$$\exp\left\{-(\nu_{12} - \nu_{23})^2/2(\Delta\nu_{12}^2 + \Delta\nu_{23}^2)\right\}. \quad (10)$$

The resonant lines at ν_{12} and ν_{23} are assumed to have a Gaussian shape with second moments

$$\Delta\nu_{12}^2 \text{ and } \Delta\nu_{23}^2$$

respectively, due to the dipolar interaction between neighboring Cr^{+++} ions, $\mathcal{H}_{1232}$ is the matrix element of the dipolar interaction of Cr^{+++} and its neighbors responsible for the double transition.

The second moments may be estimated from the observed line shape at the two resonances, if the contribution of the nuclear spins is subtracted. The calculated second moments $(\Delta H)^2$ of the local fields may be converted to a frequency scale by multiplication with $(\partial\nu/\partial H)^2$, evaluated at the appropriate resonant frequency. In this way the values $(\Delta\nu_{12}^2 + \Delta\nu_{23}^2)^{\frac{1}{2}} = 115$ Mc/s and 350 Mc/s for 0.5 percent and 2 percent Cr^{+++} concentration are found. It should be remembered that these are the nominal concentrations in the solution and the concentration in the crystals may be different. Since the local fields from the Cr^{+++} ions is comparable or larger than the field arising from the nuclear spins, the use of Equation (10) is justifiable. For the average value of $\hbar^{-2}|\mathcal{H}_{1232}|^2$ one may take approximately $0.1(\Delta\nu_{12}^2 + \Delta\nu_{23}^2)$. In this way w_{1232} at a separation $\nu_{12} - \nu_{23} = 400$ Mc/s is estimated to be 10^{+4} sec^{-1}, in the crystal at 0.5 percent concentration. At $\nu_{12} - \nu_{23} = 1000$ Mc/s, $w_{1232} = 10^{-10}$ sec^{-1}, which is negligibly small. The intricacies of cross relaxation in dilute magnetic materials have not been considered in detail, but it is gratifying that a reasonable order of magnitude for the onset of cross relaxation is obtained.

For the crystal with the higher concentration, at 1500 Mc/s separation, the estimate $w_{1232} = 10^{+3}$ sec^{-1} is made. The Gaussian function would give negligible cross relaxation at 3000 Mc/s. The tail of the resonances is probably not adequately represented by the Gaussian function (10) and no detailed explanation is offered for the constancy of T_f over a wide range of separations.

The fact that the two samples with different concentration give the same result for $\theta = 0°$ is gratifying. Here there is complete overlap and the cross relaxation is always very short $w_{1232} \gg w_{ij}$. Equation (7) should be valid in this case at all concentrations and a result independent of concentration is obtained. The term in w_{1232} is essential to explain both curves of Fig. 4, because it is inconceivable that the ratios of the $w_{ij's}$ would have a strong mixed dependence on concentration and orientation.

Extrapolation of the data presented here shows why undiluted magnetic salts are unsuitable for maser operation in the conventional microwave region although not necessarily at higher frequencies. There will always be sufficient overlap of resonances in the whole system of spin levels to reach internal thermal equilibrium, as proposed by Casimir and du Pré.[21] When such a system is pumped at any frequency, the system will warm up as a unit to infinite temperature. Validity of the Casimir-du Pré hypothesis of thermodynamic equilibrium and maser operation are mutually exclusive.

The bandwidth of a maser at gain unity cannot be increased, by increasing the magnetic concentration, beyond a certain limit of approximately one third the distance between adjacent resonances. This limitation can be circumvented by loading the maser with a number of single crystals in slightly different orientations.[20]

REFERENCES

1. C. J. Gorter, *Paramagnetic Relaxation*, Elsevier, New York (1947).
2. A. H. Eschenfelder and R. T. Weidner, Phys. Rev. *92*, 869 (1953).
3. Giordmaine, Alsop, Nash and Townes, Phys. Rev. *109*, 302 (1958).
4. Davis, Strandberg and Kyhl, Phys. Rev. *111*, 1268 (1958).
5. K. D. Bowers and F. Mims, Phys. Rev. (to be published).
6. N. Bloembergen, Phys. Rev. *104*, 324 (1956).
7. Scovil, Feher and Seidel, Phys. Rev. *105*, 762 (1957).
8. Bloembergen, Shapiro, Pershan and Artman, Phys. Rev. *114*, (1959). This paper is referred to as BSPA.
9. A. M. Clogston, J. Phys. Chem. Solids *4*, 271 (1958).
10. J. P. Lloyd and G. E. Pake, Phys. Rev. *94*, 579 (1954).
11. Schulz-duBois, Scovil and de Grasse, Bell System Technical Journal *38*, 335 (1959).
12. Sorokin, Lasher, and Gelles, paper in this volume.
13. Artman, Bloembergen and Shapiro, Phys. Rev. *109*, 1392 (1958).
14. A. F. Kip, private communication.
15. W. S. Chang and A. E. Siegman, Technical Report No. 156-1 for $K_3(CoCr)(CN)_6$. Stanford Electronics Laboratories, Stanford University.
16. The pump power scale in Fig. 8 of BSPA does not match with the scales of Figs. 9-11. This is due to an error in calibration, which was eliminated in taking the data presented here. The calibration error does not impair the argument in BSPA, which is only concerned with the relative displacements of the two self-saturation curves in Fig. 8.
17. M. W. P. Strandberg, Phys. Rev. *110*, 65 (1958).
18. A. L. McWhorter and J. W. Meyer, Phys. Rev. *109*, 312 (1958).
19. Giordmaine, Alsop, Nash and Townes, Proc. IRE. *47*, 1062 (1959).
20. De Grasse, Schulz-duBois and Scovil, Bell System Technical Journal *38*, 305 (1959).
21. H. B. G. Casimir and F. K. du Pré, Physica *5*, 507 (1938).

DISCUSSION

J. G. CASTLE: How precisely have you measured the proportionality with temperature of the relaxation times? Could you, for example, see a deviation of 20 percent?

S. SHAPIRO: Yes.

J. G. CASTLE: Did you find, as we did, that the cross relaxation becomes comparable to spin-lattice relaxation at a frequency separation of about 10 line widths?

N. BLOEMBERGEN: Cross relaxation was controlled by changing the concentration and frequency separation of spin resonances. At liquid-helium temperature it was found that cross relaxation becomes comparable to spin-lattice relaxation if the frequency separation is 5 to 8 times the width of the resonance.

OPERATION OF A CHROMIUM-DOPED TITANIA MASER AT X AND K BAND

H. J. GERRITSEN and H. R. LEWIS*
RCA Laboratories

A MASER has been operated using TiO_2 in which 0.12 percent of the Ti ions were replaced by chromium ions. The strong paramagnetic resonances observed in this material have been explained in terms of a spin Hamiltonian for Cr^{3+} ions,[1] which indicates that at least a large fraction of the Cr goes in as a trivalent ion, replacing the Ti^{4+}.

In the maser experiments, use was made of the fact that, due to the high dielectric constant of the material, a crystal of TiO_2 can act as a resonant cavity. For a certain range of values of the area and volume, a fairly good match is observed for those dielectric resonances, by just placing the crystal inside a waveguide. At liquid-helium temperature, many resonances were observed in a crystal of about 0.2 cm^3 in accordance with a dielectric constant of the order of 100. The losses in the material are quite small at liquid helium and the Q values of the resonances are typically of the order of 30,000 for loose coupling and decrease of course when one couples stronger to the waveguide by changing the position of the crystal in the waveguide. The structure used is shown schematically in Fig. 1. The guide in which the crystal is placed is X band waveguide and propagates both signal and pump power.

At X band, maser amplification and oscillation were obtained at two different modes of operation namely: pump between levels 1 and 3 and signal between 1 and 2 and pump between levels 2 and 4 and signal between 3 and 4. In the first mode, the mag-

*This work was supported by the U. S. Army Signal Corps.

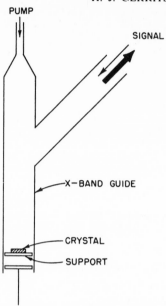

Fig. 1. Structure for observing amplification in Cr^{+++}-*doped rutile*

netic field was in the YZ plane (see the reference for the mean-
ing of this notation), making an angle of $12°$ with the c-axis and
was 5600 gauss. The signal frequency was at 10.3 kMc/s and
the pump frequency at 35.3 kMc/s. The temperature of this and
the other experiments to be described was $4.2°$K and the helium
was in direct contact with the crystal. At pump powers above
about 25 mW oscillations were observed with a frequency of 10.3
kMc/s.

The second mode has the energy levels as shown in Fig. 2.
For this mode of operation, amplification and oscillation were
observed at several frequencies in the range from 8.2 to 10.6
kMc/s. A typical case is where the magnetic field is in the YZ
plane, making an angle of $78°$ with the c-axis. Here the pump-
frequency was at 35.6 kMc/s and the signal frequency at 9.3
kMc/s. The magnetic field was 3200 gauss. An amplifying
bandwidth of 1.7 Mc/s was observed and a power gain of 23 db,
leading to a product of voltage gain times bandwidth of 24 Mc/s.
Because the coupling to the guide was still so loose that oscillations could be obtained by applying sufficient pump power and

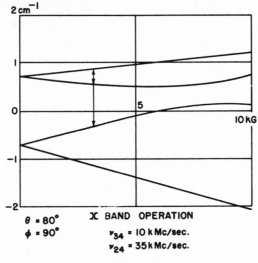

Fig. 2

also because it was found out later that there was some saturation present due to the signal, this figure is thought to be only a preliminary lower limit value.

The energy level diagram used in the K band experiment is shown in Fig. 3. The actual values were: pump frequency 49.9

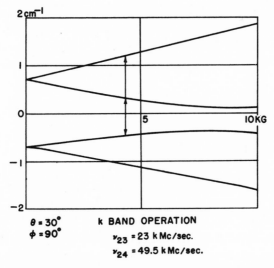

Fig. 3

kMc/s, signal frequency 22.3 kMc/s, magnetic field 4500 gauss making an angle of 33° with the c-axis in the YZ plane. The same set up was used as for the X band experiment, so that the K band power is tapered into the X band guide.

The pump power available was only about 2 mw and this was not sufficient to get much saturation between levels 2 and 4. However, some amplification was obtained, showing that the ratio of the relaxation times is favorable. This is quite important for this operation, where signal and idler frequencies are not much different. What helps here to a certain extent is the fact that the idler frequency turns out to be the same as that for the 3-4 transition of the second ion in the unit cell, for which the magnetic field is in the XZ plane. Thus some shortening of idler relaxation due to self-doping can be expected.

It is believed that with this material the range of signal frequencies possible can be extended up to about 40 kMc/s while the large dielectric constant should make it quite suitable for traveling-wave masers.

REFERENCE

1. H. J. Gerritsen, S. E. Harrison, H. R. Lewis, and J. P. Wittke, Phys. Rev. Lett. *2*, 153 (1959).

THE PARAMAGNETIC RESONANCE SPECTRUM OF Fe^{3+} IN TiO$_2$ (RUTILE)*

A. OKAYA, D. CARTER, and F. NASH

Department of Physics, Columbia University

THE PARAMAGNETIC resonance of Fe^{3+} in single crystals of rutile has been measured at X and M band frequencies. The concentration by weight of Fe^{3+} to TiO$_2$ was 0.04 percent.

The ground state of Fe^{3+} is $^6S_{\frac{5}{2}}$. There are three Kramers doublets separated by the crystalline electric field. The frequencies between the doublets were measured directly at zero magnetic field. The results are summarized below.

$$T = 78°K$$

$$\Delta M_s = \pm\tfrac{3}{2} \longrightarrow \pm\tfrac{1}{2} \qquad 43.3 \pm .1 \text{ kMc,}$$
$$\Delta M_s = \pm\tfrac{5}{2} \longrightarrow \pm\tfrac{3}{2} \qquad 81.3 \pm .1 \text{ kMc}$$

The spin Hamiltonian used to explain the data is

$$H_{op} = g\beta H \cdot S + D[S_Z^2 - \tfrac{1}{3}S(S+1)] + E(S_x^2 - S_y^2) +$$
$$+ a/6[S_x^4 + S_y^4 + S_Z^4 - \tfrac{1}{5}S(S+1)(3S^2 + 3S - 1)].$$

The Z axes for the two impurity sites in rutile are along [110] and [$\bar{1}$10]. (The axes a, b, and c are perpendicular to the unit cell faces with c as optic axis. a = [100]; b = [010]; c = [001].) The constants which fit the experimental data to within 2 percent are given below.

$$D = +20.35 \pm .20 \text{ kMc}$$
$$E = +2.14 \pm .06 \text{ kMc}$$
$$a = +0.8 \pm .4 \text{ kMc}$$
$$g = 2.00 \pm .02$$

*Work supported by U.S. Air Force Contract AF 49(638)-631.

The g factor was found to be isotropic within 1 percent.

The sign of the constants was determined from intensity measurements of the $+\frac{1}{2} \longrightarrow -\frac{1}{2}$ transition at 9 KMC for $T =$ 4.2°K and 1.5°K.

Typical energy levels are shown in Fig. 1.

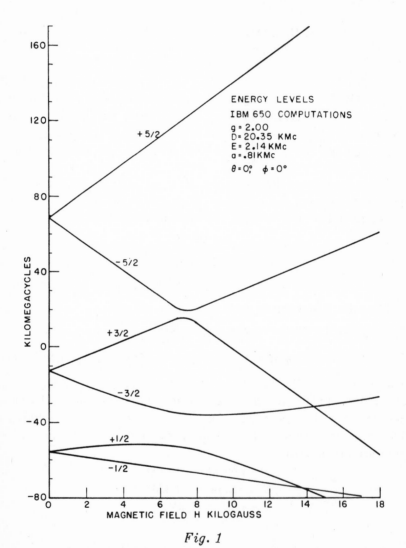

ENERGY LEVELS
IBM 650 COMPUTATIONS
g = 2.00
D = 20.35 KMc
E = 2.14 KMc
a = .81 KMc
$\theta = 0°$ $\phi = 0°$

Fig. 1

Energy level diagram for one impurity site with H *parallel to* Z

The linewidth has a variation from approximately 25Mc to 84Mc for $T = 1.5\,^\circ K$ and X-band frequencies. The approximate value of relaxation time T_1 by the pulse-decay technique at $1.5\,^\circ K$ is 5 msec.

Further investigation of the levels, their widths, and relaxation times is now in progress, with an eye to operating a milli-meter wave maser. The final results will be published in the near future.

THE PUZZLE OF SPIN-LATTICE RELAXATION AT LOW TEMPERATURES

J. H. VAN VLECK
Department of Physics, Harvard University

THE PRESENT discussion will be confined to spin-lattice relaxation at very low temperatures, where it is generally assumed that direct rather than Raman processes predominate. The mechanism of spin-spin relaxation, i.e., the process by which a common spin temperature is achieved, is now pretty well understood, as is the interpretation of the anomalies in the dispersion curves at high frequencies which are connected with the breaking of the equilibration between Zeeman and spin-spin temperatures. The key word to the subject of spin-spin equilibration is cross relaxation, a term coined by Bloembergen and his collaborators, and a phenomenon which has been abundantly and brilliantly treated in other papers of this conference. The key word, or more likely words, to the understanding of spin-lattice relaxation at low temperatures is, in my opinion, yet to be found.

When Casimir and du Pré[1] developed their by now classical theory of paramagnetic relaxation in 1938, based on the idea of a spin and a thermostat lattice temperature, physicists at first felt that the subject was in order. However, before many years it became apparent that while this model worked on the whole very well at liquid-air temperatures, it was unsatisfactory in the helium region on two counts.

In the first place experimentally the dependence of the relaxation time on temperature and field strength is quite wrong. One can show by very general arguments based on the invariance of the diagonal sum, that in the Casimir-du-Pré thermodynamic model, the relaxation time ρ should have the form[2]

$$\rho = \frac{b + C H^2}{a_0 + a_2 H^2 + a_4 H^4} \frac{1}{T} \tag{1}$$

where b, C, a_0, a_2, a_4 are constants independent of field strength and temperature. Actually, a large number of experimental measurements[3] made at Leiden show the variation with temperature is usually much more rapid than Equation (1) predicts. Furthermore, it is found that except at very high field strengths, one usually has $d\rho/dH > 0$ whereas with any theoretically reasonable choice of the constants, one would expect $d\rho/dH < 0$. The physical reason why theoretically $d\rho/dH < 0$ is a simple one. The density of phonon states is proportional to ν^2, and if the dominant term in the spin energy $h\nu$ exchanged with the lattice is the Zeeman energy $g\beta H$, then the spin system becomes, so to say, on "speaking terms," with more and more lattice oscillators as the field strength is raised, and so should relax more rapidly.

In the second place, on the theoretical side, also, one can demonstrate[4] that the thermodynamic model in the original Casimir-du-Pre form, should not be applicable in the helium region. The difficulty is that in the ordinary model, the phonons which exchange energy with the spin system span a rather narrow frequency range. Because of the ν^2 factor in the formula for phonon density, there are simply not enough oscillators to carry the spin energy to the walls of the containing thermostat, even if this energy is conveyed with the velocity of sound. The temperature of the phonons which are *en rapport* with the spins is then more nearly the spin than the thermostat temperature, and the relaxation time is greatly lengthened. To get out of this difficulty, one must assume that somehow the oscillators which are *en rapport* with the spin system are also in good thermal contact with the other, much more numerous oscillators of higher frequency and of higher heat capacity. However, one can show both theoretically[4] and experimentally that the exchange of energy between low frequency oscillators and those of higher frequency is a very slow process. Theoretically, in an ideal crystal, the exchange takes place only because of anharmonic terms, and in the helium range, the theoretically calculated values are much too small. The calculation of this exchange which the author essayed in 1941 should be regarded as reliable only as regards orders of magnitude. I did not allow for the dispersion in the velocity of sound, a refinement considered by Herring[5] in connection with other problems. The calculation of the energy exchange ought really to be revised to include dispersion effects, but presumably they only make matters worse, as they make it more difficult to satisfy the conditions on conservation of energy and momentum necessary for energy exchange between lattice oscillators.

Within the last year or so, very striking experimental evidence has also been presented that the energy exchange between lattice oscillators is a slow process. I refer to the work of Bommel and Dransfeld,[6] and of Jacobsen[7] on the propagation of ultrasonic waves in a crystal. Their experiments show clearly that these waves can go appreciable distances without attenuation, whereas if they dissipated their energy by sharing it with other oscillators, it would be impossible to propagate ultrasonic energy in a narrow band without attenuation. Furthermore, the most recent experiments on the acoustical excitation of spin resonance by Jacobsen, Shiren, and Tucker[8] show that there is sharp tuning as regards the band of lattice oscillators which are on speaking terms with the spin system. It is also found that ultrasonic waves are reflected by walls with only moderate loss, suggesting that the bath-lattice contact may be poorer than that calculated on the basis that phonons convey energy directly to the walls with the velocity of sound.

Although I pointed out in 1941 that at low temperatures there should be a bottleneck in paramagnetic relaxation because of the paucity of oscillators[4] for transporting energy to the walls, nobody seems to have taken this idea very seriously until it was revived by Gorter, van der Marel, and Bölger in 1955.[3] They show that much of the Leiden data on paramagnetic relaxation are qualitatively understandable on the idea that at low fields the ensemble of phonons on speaking terms with the spins have a certain critical band width. The width is presumably higher at higher concentrations, and so the fact that the relaxation time actually increases with decreasing concentration is qualitatively understandable. However, any attempt to interpret relaxation times simply in terms of a lattice-bath bottleneck soon meets with difficulties, for the mean relaxation time should then increase drastically with the size of the sample. Eisenstein[9] has examined the influence of size theoretically and shows that there should be a size-dependent distribution of relaxation times rather than a single time. Although some size effects are found, experimentally they are not as large as would be expected if we think of the phonons simply as porters conveying energy from the spins to the wall with the velocity of sound. One is thus at something of an impasse. What is the way out of it?

1. One possibility one might consider is that the calculations underlying Equation (1) are incorrect. The most outspoken claim to this effect is one made over 20 years ago by Temperley.[10] The dipolar coupling between the spins creates satellite transitions where several spins turn over at once. It is his contention that these satellites greatly increase the spin-lattice conductivity because of the greater density of phonon states at high frequencies. However, in my opinion this argument is incorrect provided the thermodynamic model based on well-defined spin and lattice temperatures is retained. The arguments leading to the result (1) are very general, being based on the invariance of the diagonal sum. It is perfectly true that there are multiple jumps, but the spin enhancement effects coming from these higher order transitions are just counterbalanced by a depletion of the customary single jumps [except for correction terms of the order of the square of the ratio of the internal to the applied field, which have been examined by Miss Wright[11]].

At this stage we may digress to mention that experimental confirmation of the general type of calculation based on the diagonal sum method is furnished by the experiments of Hebel and Slichter[12] on nuclear relaxation in metals. I have not discussed nuclear relaxation, as the subject of this conference is paramagnetic relaxation presumably of the electronic variety. I may, however, note in passing that the subject of nuclear relaxation seems to be better understood than the electronic in the helium region. Over ten years ago, Bloembergen[13] showed conclusively that paramagnetic impurities were the key mechanism in nonconductors. He was able to achieve a much more quantitative theory than one would expect a priori for a mechanism which is primarily a "dirt effect." More quantitative succinctness is possible in the case of metals. By using the method of diagonal sums, Hebel and Slichter show that the dependence of the nuclear relaxation time ρ_N in a metal should be of the form

$$\rho_N = \frac{\beta_0 + \beta_2 H^2}{\alpha_0 + \alpha_2 H^2}\ \frac{1}{T}. \qquad (2)$$

There are lower powers of the field strength in the denominator of (2) than (1) because two extra powers of the field strength are eliminated inasmuch as the nuclear spin system exchanges energy with the translational motion of electrons rather than phonons. Consequently the density of the latter does not enter as a factor. Hebel and Slichter show that Equation (2) is confirmed experimentally both as regards the dependence on field strength and temperature. The same kind of dependence on field strength is, incidentally, found for electronic paramagnetic relaxation stemming from the Raman processes which are all-important in the liquid air region but supposedly negligible in the helium domain. The experimental confirmation of Equation (2) can be regarded as substantiating the standard mathematical diagonal-sum methods of calculation for the thermodynamic model, but their basis seems sound, anyway.

2. At one time I suggested that perhaps the effective band width of energy exchange between spin and lattice was increased because of the spin-lattice relaxation itself. This suggestion has been pursued somewhat further by Townes and collaborators.[14] However, the whole process is too reminiscent of someone lifting himself up by his own bootstraps. In the language of the communication industry, it would correspond to the bandwidth being widened in virtue of the conversation itself! The matter has been thoroughly considered in a paper by P. W. Anderson.[15] He shows that the whole problem is mathe-

matically equivalent to that of trapped resonance radiation, which has been treated by Holstein.[16] His analysis reveals that it is incorrect to attribute a bandwidth because of the interaction itself. Anderson also shows that there can indeed sometimes be some spin diffusion caused by spin-lattice interaction, but this is presumably a small effect. The mere fact that masers are able to function successfully, not to mention the experiments of Bloembergen *et al.*,[17] is indirect evidence that the important cross-relaxation mechanism is directly between spins and not one involving the lattice. Since there is no upper limit to the energy of the phonons, a negative temperature would never be possible in a process with the phonons as middlemen, for the absence of a ceiling to the energy of the phonons means that the temperature is always kept positive.

3. A more realistic suggestion is that cracks or lattice imperfections can transfer energy between lattice oscillators. Of course, the acoustical experiments we have mentioned earlier show that this effect cannot be too large, but still there is evidence[18] in $MnCl_2 \cdot 4H_2O$ that the relaxation time actually decreases when one goes below the lambda point. This presumably means that the helium is able to flow right into the crystal and so give better thermal contacts. Also the relaxation time decreases when powdered specimens rather than large pressed specimens are used, but it is inconclusive whether this effect is to be attributed to better phonon-phonon energy exchange, or to a larger spread of spin frequencies. Although cracks can sometimes be a factor, I doubt if they are the major explanation of the impasse in the theory.

4. What is obviously needed is a large spread of frequencies to break the lattice bottleneck, and it is perfectly true that as suggested by Temperley,[10] there are processes where several spins flip simultaneously to compensate the creation or destruction of a phonon of comparatively large energy. In the thermodynamic model, as already mentioned, this effect does not shorten the relaxation time materially, as the single processes are correspondingly depleted. When, however, the conventional routes are bottlenecked by saturation of its phonons to practically the spin temperature, the multiple-flip channels

are a help in getting energy out of the spin system to the bath. Thus a Temperley effect in a very liberally interpreted sense of the word may exist if one uses the partially bottlenecked model rather than the thermodynamic one which he had in mind. It is somewhat doubtful, however, whether enough relief is afforded to break the bottleneck, for the multiple processes have only a small probability. The calculated relaxation times with the conventional thermodynamic model without bottleneck effects are of about the right order of magnitude, so those yielded by the multiple-flip detours will most likely turn out too large. More explicit theoretical calculations are obviously desirable.

5. Another possibility is that the effect of impurities is important. An ion, such as a ferrous ion, whose angular momentum is poorly quenched, can have exceedingly short relaxation times, and so have a very large effect on the relaxation constants, as it is in thermal contact with other ions by well-known spin diffusion, or cross-relaxation processes. A mechanism of this sort is in many respects analogous to the well-substantiated Bloembergen[13] theory of nuclear relaxation in nonconducting salts. The biggest objection to this type of explanation is that, although some dependence of the relaxation time on the sample is observed experimentally, it is usually not large. Leiden experiments show that even controlled impurities abundant to the extent of five percent or so do not change the relaxation time more than a factor of about two or three.

6. A more likely explanation than chemical impurities is irregularities. By an irregularity, I mean an unusual situation for a paramagnetic ion, so that it is subject either to a more effective crystalline field or greater exchange coupling than on a normal lattice site, and so capable of conducting energy very rapidly to the phonons. Some ions, for instance, might be short their water of hydration, be at a grain boundary, or something of the kind — a sort of analog of the dislocation effects now deemed so important in crystallography.

One possibility is that the irregularities are such that the ion has an unusual Stark splitting of such a character that it can turn over larger quanta to the lattice than is normally the case. If there is a wide distribution of these different splittings, the lattice bottleneck difficulty is removed. It is essential that the irregularities have short relaxation times, for otherwise it would be impossible for only relatively few of them to influence the behavior of the whole salt. This will be the case, for instance, if the irregularities have much lower lying electronic levels than normal. The conductivity due to the Raman type of interaction with the lattice varies inversely as at least the sixth power of the energy gap between the ground and electronic levels.[2] So under certain conditions it is possible for even the Raman type of relaxation to be important in the helium region. Since the corresponding relaxation time is proportional to the seventh power of the temperature, the drastic variations of relaxation time with temperature in the helium region are qualitatively explained.

Another possibility is that the irregularities have very high exchange coupling. One can imagine that there are "exchange pockets" where there are groups of three or more paramagnetic ions closer together than usual. Since exchange forces vary exponentially with distance, they are sensitive to lattice modulations. A pair of atoms, however, is not enough. The spin-lattice coupling is diagonal in the resultant spin, and a system of two atoms has only a single state of each multiplicity, and there can be exchange of energy with the lattice only if one includes spin-orbit effects, i.e., anisotropic exchange. For example, a system of two spins $S = \frac{1}{2}$ has one triplet and one singlet, but if there are three such spins there are two doublets, and the energy difference between them can be passed on to the lattice. If this difference is of the order kT, the dependence of relaxation rate on temperature will be much more rapid than in the usual calculations predicated on the assumption $h\nu \ll kT$, for at very low temperatures the probability of any energy exchange process involving an energy exchange of the order $h\nu$ will fall off like $e^{-h\nu/kT}$ if $h\nu \gg kT$. The experimental work of Bloembergen and Wang[19] shows very clearly that tightly coupled exchange systems can transfer energy very rapidly to the lattice, faster sometimes than even the spin-spin relaxation time. The atoms of salts such as are used for maser operations are as a whole, of course, not able to effect this rapid exchange, since the Curie temperatures are small compared to kT. The fundamental question is whether it is physically reasonable that there be the pockets with three or more ions abnormally close together and so endowed with large exchange forces.

With either the abnormal Stark or exchange proposals, there is the difficulty of getting enough energy transport from the average atom to one which is a fast relaxer. The intermediary for doing this would have to be dipolar coupling. The irregularities are associated with large quanta, whereas the dipolar quanta are small. There are two possible ways that the necessary exchange might be effected, neither especially plausible. One is a high order cross-relaxation process wherein multiple spin flips give a change in dipolar energy just counterbalancing a single transition of the irregularity. The other is that the dispersion in the energy of the irregularity resulting from spin-lattice coupling is so great as to be comparable with the average change in dipolar energy associated with a spin flip of a normal atom. This is the same sort of mechanism as that by which according to the Bloembergen theory the small nuclear spin quanta are kept in equilibrium with the larger electronic spin quanta that alone are capable of reacting appreciably with the lattice. It is, however, doubtful if the irregularities relax so fast that the spread in Fourier spectrum associated with the diagonal elements of their magnetic moment is comparable with the dipolar quanta. In any case this spectrum would not be so wide that the effective time of diffusion of spin energy to the lattice is inversely proportional to the relaxation time of the irregularities as it is in Bloembergen's nuclear theory.[13]

The idea that energy is somehow transmitted via the irregularities does have the merit that it gives a relaxation time which decreases with increasing concentration. If we assume that the percentage of irregularities is kept constant, the distance from a typical atom to the nearest irregularity is smaller at high concentrations, and so the spin diffusion time is shorter. The generalized Temperley effect also gives the right trend with concentration, as at high concentrations the higher order processes or multiple flips are relatively more important.

The best way of summarizing things is to look once more at Equation (1) and its relation to the experimental data. Although we have given the impression that it fails completely, there are some indications that it holds asymptotically at high field strengths and low concentrations. In fact, at sufficiently low concentrations, the relaxation time seems to be approaching independence of the concentration, as required by the thermodynamic theory. If we assume that the bottleneck is in the spin-bath transfer, and is determined by the oscillator density, then at high field strengths one would expect, as Gorter and collaborators show, the relaxation time to follow a formula of the type

$$\rho \propto \frac{c}{HT^2}.\tag{3}$$

On the other hand Equation (1) implies

$$\rho \propto \frac{1}{H^2T}\tag{4}$$

when the dipolar broadening is small compared to the Zeeman energy. Existing Leiden data do not extend to low enough c or high enough H to decide between Equations (3) and (4), but at high H, low c, the experiments clearly give $d\rho/dH < 0$. The measurements of Foner and collaborators reported in another paper of this conference with very high pulsed fields favor Equation (3) rather than Equation (4), but the near independence of concentration at high fields shown in the Leiden experiments agrees better with Equation (4).

At low field strengths, and high concentrations, the relaxation time is found to be proportional to $b + CH^2$, i.e., to show the same dependence on H as though the denominator in Equation (1) were constant. In the thermodynamic theory, the relaxation time is the quotient of the spin specific heat $(b + CH^2)/T^2$ to the spin-lattice conductivity. Thus the experimental data indicate that at low field strengths the spin-bath conductivity is independent of field strength, and increases with concentration and rapidly with temperature. This situation is only possible if there is some other channel of communication between the spin system and the bath than the conventional direct process involving resonance between Zeeman or small Stark splittings and phonon frequencies. Prima facie evidence as to the existence of such a channel is furnished by the fact that in the ultrasonic experiments reported by Jacobsen and collaborators in this conference, an acoustically excited phonon band is able to saturate the spin system only to a temperature which is orders of magnitude lower than one calculates from the conventional theory of spin-lattice coupling.

In short, it thus appears experimentally that at high field strengths, the conventional term proportional to H^4 (or H^3) takes over in the denominator in Equation (1), or in other words the field strength is bringing higher and higher Zeeman frequencies and so more oscillators into play. On the other hand, at low field strengths, there must be some kind of "high frequency by-pass," such that the modulation of this frequency by the applied field is of minor consequence. This by-pass must be sensitive to temperature, and become relatively more effective at high concentrations, presumably indicating some sort of spin diffusion or cross-relaxation process as its bottleneck. However, the precise nature of this process still remains a puzzle.

The writer is much indebted to Professor Bloembergen, and to Drs. Bölger and Weger, for valuable discussions and suggestions.

REFERENCES

1. H. B. G. Casimir and F. K. du Pré, Physica 5, 507 (1938); 6, 156 (1939).
2. J. H. Van Vleck, Phys. Rev. 52, 426 (1940).
3. C. J. Gorter, L. C. Van der Marel, and B. Bölger, Physica 21, 103 (1958).
   L. C. Van der Marel, J. Van den Broek, and C. J. Gorter, Physica 23, 361 (1957); 24, 101 (1958).
   B. Bölger, dissertation, Leiden, 1959, to appear in Proc. Roy. Netherlands Acad. Sci.
4. J. H. Van Vleck, Phys. Rev. 59, 724 and 730 (1941).
5. C. Herring, Phys. Rev. 95, 954 (1954).
6. H. Bommel and K. Dransfeld, Phys. Rev. Lett. 1, 234 (1958); 2, 298 (1959); 3, 83 (1959).
7. E. H. Jacobsen, Phys. Rev. Lett. 2, 249 (1958).
8. E. H. Jacobsen, M. S. Shiren, and E. B. Tucker, Phys. Rev. Lett. 3, 81 (1959).
9. J. Eisenstein, Phys. Rev. 84, 548 (1951).
10. H. N. V. Temperley, Proc. Camb. Phil. Soc. 35, 156 (1939); 43, 118 (1946).
11. A. Wright, Phys. Rev. 76, 1826 (1949).
12. L. C. Hebel and C. P. Slichter, Phys. Rev. 113, 1504 (1959).
13. N. Bloembergen, Physica 15, 386 (1949).

14. J. A. Giordmaine, L. E. Alsop, F. R. Nash, and C. H. Townes, Phys. Rev. *109*, 302 (1958).
15. P. W. Anderson, Phys. Rev. *114*, 1002 (1959).
16. T. Holstein, Phys. Rev. *72*, 1212 (1947); *83*, 1159 (1951).
17. N. Bloembergen, S. Shapiro, P. S. Pershan, and J. O. Artman, Phys. Rev. *114*, 445 (1959).
18. M. A. Lasheen, J. Van den Broek, and C. J. Gorter, Physica *24*, 1061, 1076 (1958).
19. N. Bloembergen and S. Wang, Phys. Rev. *93*, 72 (1954).

DISCUSSION

P. F. CHESTER: Should not Van Vleck's exchange pocket mechanism result in a weaker temperature dependence than T^{-1} if it involves single phonons of frequency equal to or greater than $\dfrac{kT}{h}$?

J. H. VAN VLECK: I would expect it to give a stronger temperature dependence than T^{-1}. Even the Raman mechanism, which gives a much more drastic temperature dependence, may become of importance as soon as the exchange quanta become larger than ordinarily considered. In general, if we have a process involving energy transfer of the order of kT, there will be a considerable sensitivity to temperature, since the Boltzmann factors of the contributing states will change materially with T.

J. G. CASTLE: Since the experimental observation of single time constants in recovery in multilevel spin systems indicates that the principal transfer of Zeeman energy from the spins of randomly diluted impurities is accomplished by processes other than through stochastic, independent collisions with the single phonons of the pure lattice, is it likely that collisions are not abrupt and that the effective vibrations sample the spin populations collectively at a single ion site?

J. H. VAN VLECK: In the ordinary thermodynamic theory of Casimir and du Pré, there is only a single relaxation time because it is assumed that the various spin levels are kept at a common temperature by spin-spin interaction, presumably arising from dipolar coupling. If the density of paramagnetic ions is so low that no processes of this type can be operative, and there is no cross relaxation, then the observation of a single relaxation time poses a problem, and just what happens is not clear.

A. M. CLOGSTON: How large would the exchange interaction need to be to be effective? I would expect that indirect exchange would lead to an exchange energy equal to one or two degrees between a substantial fraction of the spins occupying normal lattice sites.

J. H. VAN VLECK: Energies of this magnitude would be very effective in spin-lattice energy transfer. The main difficulty is to find a cross-relaxation or other mechanism whereby these spins with unusually large exchange splittings are kept in equilibrium with the great bulk of the paramagnetic ions which have much smaller splittings.

P. F. CHESTER: Single exponential recoveries in multilevel systems have now been observed in at least three independent investigations. While this is to be expected under certain special conditions, the number of experiments is now large enough to make one suspect this explanation in all of them, and consequently a more radical approach to the relaxation problem might be required.

B. BÖLGER: When selective heating of phonons around the Larmor frequency ω_L takes place, a process to be considered is the combination of a number of phonons at frequency ω_L to form a phonon at the sum frequency.

The rates for this process are proportional to T^n, where T is the temperature and n is the number of phonons at ω_L that combine.

Furthermore, I have calculated the Temperley effect as a function of the field for the case of $S = \frac{1}{2}$ by a diagonal sum method. At $H = 0$ the power transferred from the spin system to the lattice (for the terms $\alpha\ H^4$) is enhanced by a factor of about 30.

M. S. SHIREN: In our experiments on the direct interaction of ultrasonics, with spin resonances in impurity-doped quartz the magnitude of the interaction is as much as 1000 times smaller than expected from the assumption that the spins relax to thermal vibrations within the resonance linewidth. Since the applied ultrasonics are at the spin resonance frequency, I believe our results lend support to Professor Van Vleck's hypothesis that the relaxation proceeds mainly through high frequency modes.

W. LOW: If Van Vleck's mechanism of "exchange pockets" is correct, then one would expect large changes in relaxation times, for different ions. The exchange energy of two neighboring ions is a function of the particular ground state of the ion, i.e., it will depend whether $d\varepsilon$ or $d\gamma$ electrons are involved.

I would suggest that experiments should be undertaken to measure the relaxation time in dilute rare earth crystals. In these f^n systems the exchange energy between neighboring ions is negligibly small. Such ions would give a much better test of present relaxation theories.

C. H. TOWNES: Although the weight of experimental evidence shows that in most of the substances which have been closely examined there is no important "phonon bottleneck," it is perhaps worthwhile to point out that relaxation mechanisms which are understood at present would give an even more serious phonon bottleneck than is generally realized, and that such a bottleneck seems necessarily to imply a broadened band of phonons — that is, lattice modes heated up in a bandwidth appreciably broader than the width of the spin resonance.

Usually a rough calculation of the time required for a phonon to transport energy to the surface of a crystal is made by dividing the distance to the surface by the velocity of sound. The total maximum rate of transport of quanta from a paramagnetic resonance to the external bath then depends on this time and the number of modes within the bandwidth of the spin resonance. Such a calculation results in the conclusion that, at least in some cases, the phonon modes cannot deliver energy to the bath sufficiently fast to prevent their heating up as the electron spins relax.

A more complete calculation makes the situation much more impressive. Delivery of energy is of course slowed up by a small factor by acoustical mismatch at the crystal boundary. It is often slowed up very much more by the short mean free path of the phonons at the resonance frequency of the spins. This mean free path can be calculated with reasonable sureness if the relaxation time for the spins is known and is assumed to be due primarily to single-phonon processes. Frequently the phonon mean free path is so short compared with the crystal dimension that it progresses to the surface by diffusion at a rate which is several orders of magnitude slower than that obtained from a direct path. Thus the phonon bottleneck is typically worse than what is usually calculated by a factor as large as about 10^3.

In case the phonon mean free path is short compared to the crystalline dimension and the phonon must deliver its energy to the bath, there will also be phonon broadening. This has already been discussed in some detail in terms of the uncertainty broadening of the phonon modes.[a] It was also pointed out[b] that a more detailed calculation, of the general type which Holstein carried out for broadening of spectral lines, gives quantitatively the same results. Anderson's recent conclusions[c] that the first view is not valid and is not equivalent to the Holstein type of broadening seems to be based primarily on a misunderstanding. However, the important point here is that in any case a broadening of the magnitude previously discussed[a] is present, unless additional relaxation mechanisms are assumed.

Since in the several cases where experimental evidence seems clear a phonon bottleneck is not observed, one must assume either:

1. the observed relaxation rate of spins is not due to single phonon processes, but to some other unknown mechanism which scatters the energy over a wide spectrum of frequencies, or

[a]Giordmaine, Alsop, Nash, and Townes, Phys. Rev. *109*, 302 (1958).

[b]C. H. Townes, Bull. Am. Phys. Soc. *3*, 105 (1958).

[c]P. W. Anderson, Phys. Rev. *114*, 1002 (1959).

2. phonons themselves are very rapidly converted to a wide spectrum by some unknown mechanism. The phonon mean free life would need to be, at very low temperatures, somewhat shorter than $T_1 \dfrac{n}{T}$, where N is the spin density and n is the density of lattice modes within the width of the spin resonance. In typical cases this gives lifetimes shorter than $10^{-6} - 10^{-8}$ seconds. When paramagnetic impurities are not present, it seems very unlikely that phonons of microwave frequencies have lifetimes this short in the crystals which have been studied, since it is known experimentally that, at least in quartz, these lifetimes are many orders of magnitude longer.[d] Hence if this alternative applies at all, the short phonon life-time should be associated with the presence of the paramag-netic atoms. Van Vleck's proposal for "exchange pockets" of particular properties represents qualitatively a mechanism of this character.

It may be appropriate here to point out the possibility of a phonon maser, if the rate of decay of phonon modes to other frequencies or to the bath is not excessively high. Let the paramagnetic centers, or spins, be in a negative temperature state with the excess population in the upper state indicated by N. Assume these spins relax with a time constant τ_s by single phonon processes when the lattice is at absolute zero. Let the number of lattice modes to which the spins relax be $m\Delta\nu$. Here $\Delta\nu$ is the bandwidth to which the spins relax either directly, or the width to which the energy spreads in a time shorter than τ_s by any process after initial phonon emission. Then the rate of increase in the number Q of phonons in this band width $\Delta\nu$ is

$$\frac{dQ}{dt} = -\frac{m\Delta\nu}{\tau_L} \left(\frac{kT_L}{h\nu}\right) + \frac{N}{\tau_s} \left(1 + \frac{kT_L}{h\nu}\right). \tag{1}$$

Here it is assumed for simplicity that the lattice modes in question are at a temperature such that $kT_L \gg h\nu$, while the bath is at a much lower temperature. From this equation, $\dfrac{dQ}{dt}$ is positive

[d] E. H. Jacobsen, "Research in Phonons at Microwave Frequencies," paper in this symposium.

as long as

$$\frac{N\tau_L}{m\Delta\nu\tau_s} > \frac{1}{1 + \dfrac{h\nu}{kT_L}} . \tag{2}$$

Hence

$$\frac{N\tau_L}{m\Delta\nu\tau_s} > 1 \tag{3}$$

is the condition for maser action, or an instability in which the phonon temperature will increase indefinitely until nonlinearities become important.

The condition (3) for producing a phonon maser does not seem difficult to fulfill on the basis of present knowledge (or ignorance) about relaxation mechanisms. This is particularly true since N is normally very much greater than $m\Delta\nu$. Such a system may become a valuable method for producing a coherent phonon oscillation at microwave or very much higher frequencies. Phenomena of this type may possibly already occur in some two-level masers, which are operated in pulses.

Another type of phonon maser can be imagined in which the spins are driven coherently and continuously by an electromagnetic field while they couple to drive a particular lattice mode for which there is a relatively large volume of the crystal oscillating in the same phase.

Expression (2) is also useful in understanding the bearing of a phonon bottleneck on the possibility of maintaining a negative temperature in the spins for an ordinary electromagnetic maser. As long as $\dfrac{n\tau_L}{m\Delta\nu\tau_s} > 1$, where n includes all spins in the resonance line, which may possibly be inhomogeneously broadened, there can exist a phonon bottleneck which will slow up relaxation of the spins when they are at a positive temperature, and prevent continuous maintenance of a negative temperature in the spins. This is rather similar to what Bloembergen[e] seems to

[e]N. Bloembergen, Phys. Rev. *109*, 2209 (1958).

have had in mind in indicating that the existence of maser action is positive evidence against a phonon bottleneck. It perhaps needs to be emphasized, however, that, as the earlier paper of Giordmaine et al.[a] pointed out, maser action can under appropriate conditions still occur over a narrow bandwidth if spins in only a small fraction ε of the line are maintained at a negative temperature. Thus if the number of these spins is $N = n\varepsilon$, then there may be a phonon bottleneck for the line $\left(\dfrac{n\tau_L}{m\Delta\nu\tau_s} > 1 \right)$ for a substance in which $\dfrac{N\tau_L}{m\Delta\nu\tau_s} < 1$, if the fractional bandwidth ε is sufficiently small. Actual experimental results have shown, however, that masers are obtained in a number of crystals with bandwidths comparable with the entire width of the spin resonance.

N. BLOEMBERGEN: Not only experimental evidence, but also theoretical considerations are in favor of a homogeneously saturated or inverted line.[f] The possibility of a small fraction ε to be inverted appears slight on the basis of present knowledge. One may therefore conclude that salts which show electromagnetic maser action cannot serve as phonon masers. The reverse is probably also true. Either the phonons constitute a thermal reservoir for the spins, as observed in many cases, or the spins constitute a thermal reservoir for the phonons. In this latter situation, for which no conclusive experimental example is available, a phonon maser would be possible. The observation by Jacobsen[g] that the ultrasonic microwave energy density necessary for the onset of saturation of a spin resonance is several orders of magnitude larger than the thermal energy density of the phonons in $\Delta\nu$ appears to support the conclusion that spin-lattice relaxation does not take place via single phonon processes in $\Delta\nu$.

[f]Bloembergen, Shapiro, Pershan, and Artman, Phys. Rev. 114, 445 (1959).

[g]E. H. Jacobsen, paper in this symposium.

OPTICAL PROPERTIES OF PARAMAGNETIC SOLIDS*

W. LOW

Department of Physics, The Hebrew University, Jerusalem

THIS SURVEY article intends to discuss the salient features of the spectra of the transition elements in single crystals. These transition elements show characteristic spectra in the infrared and visible range, the details of which are not only characteristic of the particular ion but also of the crystalline environment. Finkelstein and Van Vleck[1] were the first to point out that these absorption lines can be considered to arise from transitions from the ground state to the various Stark levels of the ground and excited states. In their original paper on Cr^{3+} they were able to assign some of the observed transitions. However, the agreement between the calculated energy level scheme and the observed transitions showed discrepancies of the order of several thousand cm^{-1}.

In recent years a number of laboratories have started to investigate experimentally and theoretically the spectra of the transition elements in various crystal symmetries. Considerable progress in the understanding of the energy level scheme has been achieved in the $3d^n$ group, the iron group. [2],[3],[4],[5],[6],[7] In this article it will be shown that many of the transitions can be uniquely assigned and that the energy level scheme can be calculated to within a few hundred cm^{-1}.[8] In the rare earth group, beautiful experimental results have been obtained by the Johns Hopkins group in Professor Dieke's laboratory. Judd in a number of publications[9],[10] has interpreted the finer details of these spectra and has been able to fit the Stark splittings to within a few cm^{-1}. The other transition groups have not been

*Supported in part by the U.S. Air Force through its European Office.

studied in detail. Their absorption spectra can be correlated qualitatively but no quantitative calculations have been made.

This article is concerned only with the iron and rare earth group. It summarizes the main methods and the results of the energy level calculations. It also discusses the intensity and line width of many of these transitions. It is hoped that this survey might be helpful to those scientists who are working on masers utilizing optical pumping techniques.

ENERGY LEVEL CALCULATIONS

The various transition groups exhibit very different spectral behavior. The iron group ions which usually crystallize in a slightly distorted octahedron, show several wide absorption bands in the visible range. The position of these bands has no correlation with the position of the term values of the free ion. The rare earth group, on the other hand, show transitions from the infrared to the visible spectral range. These transitions correspond very closely to those of the free ion. Each level, however, seems to show additional crystal fine structure, which is small compared with the term separation. The line widths are usually very sharp and in some cases sharper than some of the line spectra in gases.

The difference in the spectra of the two transition groups is caused by the difference in the strength and the symmetry of the "crystal field" set up by the surrounding ions. This crystal field potential is considered to be static and to arise from the surrounding charge distribution. The exact nature of the charge distribution need not be known, only its symmetry. This crystal field potential can be expanded in a series involving spherical harmonics.

$$V(r, \theta, \phi) = \sum_n \sum_{m=n}^{-n} A_n^m \, r^n \, Y_n^m (\theta, \phi)$$

where

$$Y_n^m(\theta,\phi) = (-1)^n \left[\frac{1}{4\pi} \, \frac{(2n+1)(n-|m|)!}{(n+|m|)!} \right]^{\frac{1}{2}} P_n^m (\cos \theta) \, e^{im\phi}. \quad (1)$$

The three potentials important for our discussion are:

Cubic field (six or eight coordinated complexes) for d electrons

$$V = Dr^4 \left[Y_4^0 + \sqrt{\tfrac{5}{14}} (Y_4^4 + Y_4^{-4}) \right] \tag{2}$$

For f electrons one has to use additional terms in Y_6^0 and Y_6^4.

Tetrahedral symmetry (four coordinated complexes) for d electrons

$$V = Cr^3 (Y_3^2 + Y_3^{-2}) + Dr^4 \left[Y_4^0 + \sqrt{\tfrac{5}{14}} (Y_4^4 + Y_4^{-4}) \right] \tag{3}$$

In the rare earth the crystal symmetry is usually C_{3v} or C_{3h}. The C_{3h} potential for f electrons can be written

$$V = A_2^0 r^2 Y_2^0 + A_4^0 r^4 Y_6^0 + A_6^0 r^6 Y_6^0 + A_6^6 r^6 Y_6^6. \tag{4}$$

The constants, $\overline{Dr^4}$, $\overline{Cr^3}$, $\overline{A_n^m r^n}$, involve radial integrals. These cannot be evaluated from first principles and are determined from the optical spectra. The magnitude and the sign of these constants determines the order and the extent of the splitting into the various Stark levels. The number of the levels into which each term is split is determined by the angular part of the potential. It can of course be predicted from group theory.[11] It should be noted that the sign of $\overline{Dr^4}$ is opposite for d^p and d^{10-p} systems. Also, the sign and magnitude of the six and eight coordinated systems are different. A point charge calculation shows that the ratio of the cubic crystal field strength is $9 : -8 : -4$ for the six, eight, and four coordinated complexes. The change in sign causes the order of the Stark levels of a given term to be reversed for the six coordinated structure in comparison with a body centered structure.

Inspection of the spectra show that the transition groups can be divided into the following approximate schemes:

Iron group: octahedral complexes $\qquad e^2/r_{ij} \geqslant V_c > \xi$ medium field strength

$\qquad\qquad$ four and eight co-
$\qquad\qquad$ ordinated complexes $\qquad e^2/r_{ij} \gg V_c \geqslant \xi \qquad (5)$

Rare earth group: $\qquad\qquad\qquad\qquad e^2/r_{ij} > \xi > V_c$ weak field strength

Uranium group: $\qquad e^2/r_{ij} > \xi \geqslant V_c$

Palladium and platinum group: $\qquad V_c \geqslant e^2/r_{ij} > \xi$ strong field
strength

Here V_c is the crystal field potential, e^2/r_{ij} the mutual repulsion between electrons and ξ the spin-orbit interaction.

The energy levels can be calculated as follows. First one determines the point symmetry, i.e. the form of the crystal field potential. This is best done by measuring the paramagnetic resonance spectra of these ions as these spectra are very sensitive to small departures from high symmetry. The symmetry can of course in some cases be determined from the optical spectra as well. Next the energy level matrices are computed. In general they will involve the following parameters: B, C the electrostatic parameters introduced by Racah,[12] α a small correction called the Trees correction found necessary to explain the atomic spectra,[13] ξ the spin-orbit interaction, and the various $A_n^m \overline{r^n}$, the crystal field parameters. It turns out that the electrostatic parameters are not necessarily the same for an ion in a crystal as for the "free ion." Moreover the values of B, and C vary from one crystal to the next. In order to determine these parameters uniquely, many absorption lines have to be observed. The spin orbit coupling in the crystal is determined from an observation of the crystal fine structure components in the iron group. This is, however, observed only in exceptional circumstances in the iron group. In the rare earth group, the spin-orbit components are of course widely separated and the crystal field effects smaller than this separation.

The obvious coupling schemes for the iron group and the rare earth group are the strong and weak field schemes. The strong field matrices have been calculated for the d^n configuration by Tanabe and Sugano.[14] Tanabe and Kamimura[15] have also shown how one can calculate the spin-orbit matrices in this coupling scheme. The essence of the procedure is as follows. One assigns the electrons into e and t electrons. In general the energy of a configuration is $t^p e^{n-p}$ where n is the total number of electrons. In this scheme the cubic crystal field matrices are easy to calculate and are found to be diagonal. The electrostatic interaction matrices involving B and C (Sugano *et al.* did not take α into account) have to be calculated and are non-diagonal, connecting different crystal field configurations. Next the spin-orbit matrices have to be calculated in the cubic field scheme.

A different approach, which saves considerable computation time, has been followed by Racah *et al.*[5] They use the weak field scheme in which J is a good quantum number. The matrices in the S, L, J scheme are well known from atomic spectroscopy. One now has to calculate the cubic crystal field matrix in the S, L, J scheme and then transform from the J, M to the J, Γ scheme. Of course the same results are obtained in both schemes. The latter scheme has the advantage that the electrostatic matrices already exist, that many of the Racah coefficients have been tabulated, and that a program for the electronic computer was available.

The matrices were diagonalized by putting in approximately correct parameters and letting the computer find new values for these parameters yielding the least mean square deviation from the experimental results. Table 1 gives some of these results for Co^{2+} in MgO (six coordinated structure), Co^{2+} in CaF_2 (eight coordinated structure), and Cr^{3+} in MgO, all d^7 or d^3 complementary configurations. Table 2 gives the computed and observed energy levels for one particular case, Co^{2+} in CaF_2. In this spectrum the crystal fine structure was resolved. The computations were made by letting all parameters with the exception of α be free parameters. For the other ions both α and ξ were held fixed. We assumed that the peak of an absorption band in which the fine structure was not resolved coincides with the barycenter of the spin orbit components. No weighting factor, such as the number of the degeneracy, was taken into account since the selection rules governing the intensities of the transitions within a spin multiplet are not well known. It was not considered appropriate to improve on this scheme at this stage.

The following can be inferred from the results on the iron group.

1. The agreement between theory and experiment is very good and substantiates essentially the assumption of a static crystal field potential. It should be noted that the experimental accuracy

*Table 1. Comparison of electrostatic parameters in a
crystal and in the free ion**

Parameters		Free Ion Values[†]	Crystal Values	Deviation (percent)
Co^{2+} in MgO	B	1027 ± 11	874 ± 19	~ 15
	C	3880 ± 43	3891 ± 103	
	α	83 ± 4	70	
	ξ	506 ± 68	-500	
	Dq		-941 ± 25	

Average deviation $\Delta = \pm 400$

Parameters		Free Ion Values	Crystal Values	Deviation (percent)
Co^{2+} in CaF_2	B	1027 ± 11	1008 ± 8	~ 2
	C	3880 ± 43	3815 ± 41	
	α	83 ± 4	77	
	ξ	506 ± 68	-480 ± 80	
	Dq		350 ± 11	

Average deviation $\Delta \approx 180$ cm^{-1}

Parameters		Free Ion Values	Crystal Values	Deviation (percent)
Cr^{3+} in MgO	B	918	646 ± 42	28
	C	4113	2876 ± 114	30
	α	90	85	
	ξ	270	210	
	Dq		1548 ± 25	

Deviation ~ 350 cm^{-1}

*G. Racah, G. Schonfeld and W. Low to be published.
[†]G. Racah, private information.

of many of these levels is only to 50–100 cm^{-1}. Moreover, all
these transitions are electric dipole in character coupled with
odd parity vibrations (discussed below). One can infer that
these vibrations do not shift the excited levels very differently
than the ground state.

2. The effect of a strong Jahn-Teller distortion is not notice-
able either in the ground state (from paramagnetic resonance
data) or in the excited states. In the d^8 and d^7 configurations,
the Jahn-Teller effect will not of course remove the Kramers
degeneracy of the Γ_6 or Γ_7 doublets. Distortion, however, might
have produced a splitting in some of the Γ_8 quartet states. Similarly in the even number electron case of Ni^{2+}, d^8 electrons, the
agreement between the computed values and the experimental
transitions was very good.

3. There is a strong correlation between the reduction of the
electrostatic parameters and the crystalline field strength (Dq).

Table 2. Energy Levels of Co^{2+} in CaF_2*

Level Designation			Experimental values in cm^{-1}	Calculated levels in cm^{-1}	Deviation in cm^{-1}
^4F	Γ_2		0	-46	46
^4F	Γ_5	Γ_8	3180 ± 50	3290	-110
		Γ_6			
^4F	Γ_5	Γ_8	3500 ± 50	3645	-145
		Γ_7			
^4F	Γ_4	Γ_6	5800 ± 25	5628	172
	Γ_4	Γ_8	6100 ± 75	6041	59
	Γ_4	Γ_7	6600 ± 25	6611	-11
		Γ_8			
52% ^2G + 23%	^4P	Γ_4	17800 ± 50	17935	-135
62% ^4P + 25%	^2G	Γ_4	18550 ± 25	18598	-48
38% ^2G + 46%	^4P	Γ_4	19220 ± 75	18905	315
	^2G	Γ_1	19590 ± 50	14668	-70
	^2G	Γ_5	20450 ± 50	20561	-111

*The experimental values are taken from R. Stahl-Brada and W. Low, Phys. Rev. *113*, 575 (1959).

The computed values are by G. Racah, G. Schonfeld, and W. Low (to be published).

The stronger the crystal field, the more B and C are reduced from their free ion values. In the case of Co^{2+} in CaF_2 where the crystal field is fairly weak these parameters are nearly equal to those of the free ion. In general the reduction is larger for trivalent ions, and the crystal field is also much stronger.

The interpretation of the spectra in tetrahedral symmetry is more complicated.[16] The odd part of the potential U_3 couples different configurations. The matrix elements $< d \mid\mid U_3 \mid\mid p >$ and $< d \mid\mid U_3 \mid\mid f >$ are fairly large. It turns out that the individual Stark levels are differently affected by this perturbation. This explains the experimental observations that, while the individual energy levels can be assigned in the tetrahedral case, the position of the energy levels as well as the relative separation of the spin components do not fit the theory outlined above.

The rare earth calculations are somewhat more difficult although not very different in character. First of all the atomic spectra of many of the trivalent ions have never been measured. What data there is suggests that an intermediate coupling scheme should be used. The matrices are usually large, in particular in these low symmetry crystals. Judd[10] was able to correlate the fine structure splitting of many of the individual levels to within 1 cm^{-1}. The overall splitting of such a structure is of the order $100\text{-}200 \text{ cm}^{-1}$. In all these calculations no allowance was made for the influence of the electron-distribution of the rare earth ion on the surroundings. This effect could conceivably be different for various excited states. The positions of the surrounding charges could well be changed in the excited states and this in turn would affect the crystal field parameters. The very good agreement of one set of crystal field parameters for many levels shows that this effect is negligible.

One of the interesting and disturbing results of Judd's calculation is the fact that there seems to be no correlation between some of the $A_n^m \overline{r^n}$ from one ion to the next. Previously, paramagnetic resonance data were interpreted by assuming that these parameters vary in a smooth manner, for example $\overline{r^n} \sim (Z - \sigma)^{\frac{n}{4}}$. Apparently the screening effect σ, which prevents the full effect of the crystal field to be felt by the rare earth ion, may differ considerably from ion to ion and may depend on the nature of the various excited states. It is, therefore, not advisable to extrapolate the fine structure separations from one ion to the next and each individual ion has to be measured and interpreted separately.

INTENSITIES AND LINE WIDTH

The oscillator strength f is defined by the relation

$$f = \frac{mc}{\pi N e^2} \int k(\nu) \, d\nu \qquad (6)$$

where N is the number of absorbing ions per cm^3, ν the frequency, $k(\nu)$ the absorption coefficient. The measurement of the absorption coefficient is usually quite difficult in dilute single crystals. Most absorption coefficients have been measured on solutions. In this case one measures the extinction coefficient ε defined by $I/I_0 = 10^{-\varepsilon c_0 x}$ where c_0 is the concentration in moles per litre, x the thickness of the solution in cm, and I/I_0 the fractional intensity of light transmitted through the sample. The f number in terms of the extinction coefficient is given by

$$f = \frac{2.3 \times 10^3}{N_{\text{avog.}}} \frac{mc}{\pi N e^2} \int \varepsilon(\nu) \, d\nu.$$

We shall make the assumption that the f value of an absorption band does not differ much in a crystal from that in the solution. The evidence for this assumption is a little sporadic, but what evidence there is seems to support this assumption. We shall also assume for simplicity that the f number is not a function of the concentration. There has been no systematic study of this either in solutions or in crystals.

Experimental results. The transitions are so called forbidden transitions   This will be discussed in more detail in the theoretical section. Correspondingly, the intensities of the transitions are relatively small.

a. Iron group spectra. Typical f number and line width for the spin-permitted transitions are given in Table 3.   A number of single crystals have been investigated.   The f number of Co^{2+} in $CoCl_2 \cdot 6H_2O$ is about 10^{-4}. The spin-forbidden transitions, corresponding to the quartet-doublet transitions are about one hundred times weaker or about 10^{-6}–10^{-7}.[17] In Mn^{2+} where all transitions from the ground state ^6S are to quartet states the f number is 4–7×10^{-8}.[18] Some spin-forbidden transitions have somewhat larger f numbers. This can arise if these transitions are near a spin-permitted transition and the spin-orbit coupling mixes the two levels. Examples of such larger intensities for the spin-forbidden transitions occur in Ni^{2+} in MgO.[3] Fluorescence has also been observed in a powdered sample of Ni^{2+} in MgO.[19]   The fluorescence at $21{,}270$ cm^{-1} corresponds to the spin-forbidden transition $\Gamma_5(^1D) \rightarrow {}^3\Gamma_2(^3F)$. The decay time is 1.2×10^{-5} sec, a characteristic magnitude for such transitions.

The crystal probably most studied is the ruby crystal, i.e. Cr^{3+} in Al_2O_3. The well known fluorescence in the red at about $14{,}400$ cm^{-1} has been studied by Jacobs.[20]   The decay time given is 2.08×10^{-3} sec, at $77°K$. The fluorescence arises from transitions from a close lying doublet, separated by about 30 cm^{-1}, to the ground state. An approximate energy level diagram is shown in Fig. 1. The fluorescent transition is from the doublet $\Gamma_3(^2G)$ to the ground state $\Gamma_2(^4F)$.

Most gems containing chromium fluoresce in the red. The effect of the concentration of chromium on the fluorescent yield has not been studied. There are some indications that at higher

Table 3. Absorption spectra of hydrated transition metal ions*

Ion	System	Maximum ε	Energy at maximum cm^{-1}	$f \times 10^4$	Bandwidth at half-maximum extinction, cm^{-1}
Ti^{+++} $3d^1\ ^2D$	CsTi(SO$_4$)$_2$·12H$_2$O	4	20,300	0.8	4600
V^{+++} $3d^2\ ^3F$	NH$_4$V(SO$_4$)$_2$·12H$_2$O	3.5	17,800	0.6	3200
		6.6	25,700	1.1	3300
V^{++} $3d^3\ ^4F$	solution	0.45	11,800	0.1	4000
		0.65	17,500	0.2	5000
Cr^{+++} $3d^3\ ^4F$	KCr(SO$_4$)$_2$·12H$_2$O	7.8	17,500	1.6	3600
		10.5	24,700	2.2	4400
Cr^{++} $3d^4\ ^5D$	solution	6.8	14,000	1.8	6000
Mn^{+++} $3d^4\ ^5D$	CsMn(SO$_4$)$_2$·12H$_2$O	5	21,000	1.1	5000
Mn^{++} $3d^5\ ^6S$	solution	0.008	18,900	9×10^{-4}	2500
		0.006	23,000	7×10^{-4}	2500
		0.017	25,000	5×10^{-4}	500 (double)
		0.010	28,000	8×10^{-4}	1400
		0.009	29,750	6×10^{-4}	500
		0.006	32,400	7×10^{-4}	4000
Fe^{+++} $3d^5\ ^6S$	solution	0.1	12,600	approx 20×10^{-4}	2200
		0.1	18,200	approx 20×10^{-4}	3800
		0.4	24,500	approx 20×10^{-4}	1500 (double)
Fe^{++} $3d^6\ ^5D$	FeSO$_4$·7H$_2$O	1.6	10,000	0.4	6000 (double)
Co^{++} $3d^7\ ^4F$	CoSO$_4$·7H$_2$O	1.7	8,350	0.3	3600
		3.4	19,800	0.9	5000
Ni^{++} $3d^8\ ^3F$	NiSO$_4$·7H$_2$O	2.5	8,600	0.45	3000
		1.8	14,700	0.35	4300
		4	25,500	0.6	3200
Cu^{++} $3d^9\ ^2D$	CuSO$_4$·5H$_2$O	5	13,000	1.4	5300

*O. G. Holmes and D. S. McClure, J. Chem. Phys. 26, 1688 (1957).

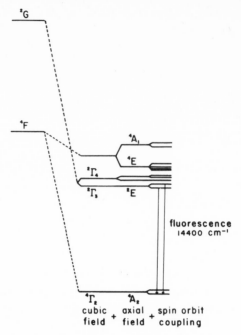

Fig. 1. Energy level diagram of ruby

concentration a quenching effect sets in. This is of course a well known phenomena in phosphorescent substances.

Tetrahedrally coordinated ions in solutions have f numbers which are about a hundred times larger than those in octahedrally coordinated complexes. The two examples in Table 4 will illustrate this.

Table 4

Ion	Tetrahedral coordination f number		Octahedral coordination f number
Cu^{2+}	2×10^{-3}	$(^2T_2 \rightarrow {}^2E)^{21}$	1.4×10^{-4}
Co^{2+}	6×10^{-3}	$(^4A_2 \rightarrow {}^4T_1)^{22}$	10^{-5}

This increase in intensity is also observed in single crystals of ZnO and in spinels in which many ions occupy the tetrahedrally coordinated "A" site. It is significant that in tetrahedral symmetries the spin permitted transitions are relatively sharp.

An investigation of the line width of the spectra shows the following regularities:

1. Transitions between levels of the same spin multiplicity are usually very wide. There seems to be a correlation between line width and the crystal field strength (Dq). A good example is Co^{2+} in MgO and CaF_2. In MgO the line width is several thousand cm^{-1} and the crystal field strength moderately large $(Dq = -940 \ cm^{-1})$. In CaF_2 $Dq = 350 \ cm^{-1}$ and the line width at most a few hundred cm^{-1}. The line width in the latter case is sufficiently narrow so that the fine structure is resolved. The line width, therefore, depends on the absolute magnitude of the crystal field strength.

2. Transitions between levels of different spin multiplicity are weaker and often narrower. The line width of these transitions seem to be correlated with the quantity $d(h\nu)/d(Dq)$, as first pointed out by Orgel.[23] If this is zero, i.e. if the frequency of the transition is not dependent on Dq, we get sharp lines. Examples of this are the 14,400 cm^{-1} line in ruby and some of the sharp lines in Mn^{2+}. Similar effects have been noticed in a number of paramagnetic resonance spectra of the ground state. Forbidden transitions which are not dependent on the axial parameter D to a first order are usually sharper than those which depend on D.

3. A comparison of the line width of sharp lines in different symmetries shows large variations. For example the line width of Co^{2+} in the cubic CaF_2 at about 14,000 cm^{-1} is much wider than the corresponding line of Cr^{3+} in corundum.[24] Possibly the line width is also connected with the coupling mechanism of the odd and even vibrations in the electronic transition.

b. Rare Earth Spectra. It is well known that many trivalent salts of the rare earth fluoresce. Many phosphors contain rare earth ions, notably Sm, Ce, Eu, and Gd. The rare earth spectra are characterized by sharp lines even at room temperature. These lines become much sharper as the temperature is lowered, some of these having a line width less than a fraction of a cm^{-1}. The f numbers of these individual transitions are about 10^{-5}-10^{-6}. This corresponds to a natural life time of about 10^{-2}-10^{-3} sec. Geissler and Hellwege[25] have determined the life time of $Tb(BrO_3)_3 \cdot 9H_2O$ as $\tau_0 = 0.014$ sec.

In the hydrated single crystals, Dieke and Hall[26] have determined the fluorescent decay times. They are given in Table 5. There are some discrepancies between Dieke and Hall's results and those of Geissler and Hellwege. For the other rare earth ions in these hydrated crystals, no fluorescence was detected. Presumably the decay time is very short. Recently Carlson and Dieke[27] have observed strong fluorescence from Pr, Nd, Sm, Eu, Gd, Tb, Dy, Er, and Tm in single crystals of anhydrous $LaCl_3$ at low temperatures. Nd^{3+}, which was carefully examined, showed more than 200 fluorescent lines, many of these coming from different excited states.

*Table 5. Observed decay times in crystalline rare earth salts**

Salt	$T = 293\,°K$	τ in μsec $77\,°K$	$4\,°K$	$\tau 77/\tau 293$	$\tau 4/\tau 77$
$Gd(C_2H_5SO_4)_3 \cdot 9\,H_2O$	7400*	7500*		1.01	
$GdCl_3 \cdot 6\,H_2O$	4800*	7800*		1.62	
$Tb(C_2H_5SO_4)_3 \cdot 9\,H_2O$	410	430		1.05	
$TbCl_3 \cdot 6\,H_2O$	467	487	492	1.04	1.01
$Eu(BrO_3)_3 \cdot 9\,H_2O$	119	120		1.00	
		curved			
$EuCl_3 \cdot 6\,H_2O$	120	120		0.98	
		37*			
$Dy(C_2H_5SO_4)_3 \cdot 9\,H_2O$	~ 10	~ 10			
$DyCl_3 \cdot 6\,H_2O$	~ 10	~ 10			
$Dy(BrO_3)_3 \cdot 9\,H_2O$	~ 10	~ 10			
$SmCl_3 \cdot 6\,H_2O$	~ 10	~ 10			

*G. H. Dieke and L. A. Hall, J. Chem. Phys. 27, 465 (1957).

We have observed the fluorescence of Eu^{2+} in a number of single crystals such as CaF_2, KCl, and $SrCl_2$. The $SrCl_2$ grown under conditions in which there was an excess of Sr shows a strong red afterglow.[28] $CaF_2:Eu^{2+}$ shows the familiar absorption bands near 31,000 cm^{-1} ($f \sim 6 \times 10^{-3}$), and near 45,000 cm^{-1} ($f \sim 3 \times 10^{-2}$). Fluorescence occurs from the 31,200 cm^{-1} level to the ground state. This crystal has been considered by a number of laboratories as a possible "maser" material.

The following observations can be inferred, in the main, from the results of the Johns Hopkins group.

1. There is a correlation between the magnitude of the crystal field parameters and the intensity of the fluorescence spectra.

The anhydrous chlorides have smaller crystal field splittings and sharper lines than the corresponding hydrated crystals. This indicates that the ions in the anhydrous $LaCl_3$ approximate the spectra of the free ions, and that these ions are well isolated from the surrounding matrix. The deexcitation of energy through the lattice interaction is relatively weak and the fluorescent decay time approaches the natural life time. It is probable that the strong fluorescence observed in SrS phosphors is connected with the very small crystal field in this lattice. It is important to find other crystal systems in which the crystal fields are small. CaF_2 is presently being investigated in the author's laboratory.

2. A comparison of the fluorescent decay time of various rare earth ions in a crystal series, such as the ethylsulfates, shows that the longest times are observed for the ions occupying the middle of the $4f^n$ group, i.e. Gd^{3+}, Eu^{3+}, Tb^{3+}, Eu^{2+}. The energy level diagrams of these rare earth ions show a large gap between the first excited state and the ground state. All the other ions have a number of energy levels all the way from the infrared to the ultraviolet. Apparently radiationless dissipation of the excitation energy is more likely when the energy difference between the levels is small. Large transfers of energies seem to be improbable.

We have been mainly concerned with fluorescence to the ground state. Absorption may well take place in other regions of the spectrum or even in the absorption edge of the crystal. These excited states may in turn transfer the energy selectively to other excited states and populate selectively some of its fine structure.[29] Only a difference of population is important for maser operation and not the absolute magnitude of the population. More systematic work on the absorption and fluorescence of excited states should be undertaken.

Theory. The transitions usually observed are between Stark levels of terms belonging to the same configuration. All these levels have the same parity. Electric dipole transitions are therefore strictly forbidden. This is not changed in a crystal field having a center of symmetry, even under the combined action of spin-orbit coupling and the crystal field. Van Vleck[30] was the first to point out that there may exist several mechanisms which may permit these transitions. These are:

1. Magnetic dipole transitions.
2. Electric quadrupole transitions.
3. a. Electric dipole transitions in a crystal field having a center of symmetry by means of coupling with odd parity vibrations.
   b. Electric dipole transitions in a crystal field having no center of symmetry.

Most of the observed spectra can be classified to belong to the electric dipole type. Some of the rare earth ions spectra are magnetic dipole in character. These two types can be distinguished as follows. One measures the absorption spectra, for example in a uniaxial crystal, with the propagation vector parallel ("a" spectrum) as well as perpendicular to the crystal axis. In the latter case one measures it with the E vector parallel ("σ" spectrum) or perpendicular ("π" spectrum) to the crystal axis. If the "a" and "σ" spectra coincide then this is an electric dipole transition. If the "a" and the "π" coincide we have a magnetic dipole transition. One can also distinguish between magnetic and electric quadrupole transitions. However, the electric quadrupole transitions are very weak and none have been observed with certainty.

The f value for magnetic dipole transitions can be estimated to be of the order of 10^{-6}. The electric quadrupole transitions have an f number of about 10 times less.[31]

The electric dipole transitions can arise because of two mechanisms. In the first case, odd parity vibrations coupled with the electronic transition mixes p and d levels (presumably also d and f levels) in the iron group, and f and d levels in the rare earth group. The intensity is then stolen from the next excited configuration via the vibrations. For a number of cases, the f number has been calculated, in particular Ti^{3+}, Cu^{2+};[32] Ni^{2+}, V^{3+};[33] Mn^{2+};[34] and Co^{2+}.[35]

The theoretical calculations cannot be relied upon too well. They involve radial integrals, magnitudes of the odd vibrations, and separation of excited configurations from the ground state, all of which are not well known in the solid state. However, with plausible estimates the authors obtain the right orders of magnitude for the intensities.

Unfortunately, nearly all the observed f numbers are of ions in crystal symmetries which depart from octahedral symmetry. Many of the measurements have been made on non-centro-symmetric crystals. It is not unlikely that these lower symmetries may profoundly influence the absolute magnitude of the f numbers as well as the relative intensities. The effect of covalent bonding, which is present in nearly all these complexes, has not been taken into account.

In the second case, for example in the case of tetrahedral symmetry, there are two mechanisms which give rise to the increased intensities of the transitions. Ballhausen and Liehr[36] take into account the strong covalent character of tetrahedral complexes. In this case one sets up the tetrahedral wave functions which are a combination of the d orbitals and those of the surrounding ligands. The increased intensity comes from the mixing of the Stark levels and those of the charge transfer band. By assuming a fair amount of covalent bonding, Ballhausen and Liehr find reasonable agreement between the calculated and measured f numbers.

Low and Weger[16] have shown that the odd part of the potential U_3 causes a large admixture of the next excited odd configurations. While intensities have not been calculated, it is very likely that this may also in part explain the large f numbers in tetrahedral complexes.

Another example of a non-centro symmetry is ruby, $Al_2O_3 : Cr^{3+}$. This has the effect that certain optical transitions become allowed. An approximate estimate shows that the relative magnitude of the intensity of the various spin-permitted transitions can be explained on the basis of the absence of a center of symmetry.

The relative intensity as well as the f number of rare earth ions have not been calculated in detail.

REFERENCES

1. R. Finkelstein and J. H. Van Vleck, J. Chem. Phys. *8*, 790 (1940).
2. W. Low, Phys. Rev. *109*, 275 (1959).

3. W. Low, Phys. Rev. *109*, 256 (1959).
4. R. Stahl-Brade and W. Low, Phys. Rev. *113*, 775 (1959).
5. S. Sugano and Y. Tanabe, J. Phys. Soc. *A, 13,* 880 (1958).
6. S. Sugano and I. Tsujikawa, J. Phys. Soc. *A, 13,* 899 (1958).
7. M. H. L. Pryce and W. A. Runciman, Trans. Faraday Soc. *26*, 34 (1958).
8. G. Racah, G. Schonfeld and W. Low (to be published).
9. B. R. Judd, Proc. Roy. Soc. *A, 241,* 414 (1957).
10. B. R. Judd, Proc. Roy. Soc. *A, 251,* 134 (1959).
11. H. Bethe, Ann. d. Physik 3, *133* (1929).
12. G. Racah, Phys. Rev. *62*, 438 (1941).
13. R. E. Trees, Phys. Rev. *83*, 274 (1951); *84*, 1089 (1951).
14. Y. Tanabe and S. Sugano, J. Phys. Soc. Japan *9*, 753 (1954).
15. Y. Tanabe and H. Kamimura, J. Phys. Soc. Japan *13*, 394 (1958).
16. W. Low and M. Weger, Phys. Rev. (in press).
17. R. Pappalardo, Phil. Mag. *4*, 219 (1959).
18. R. Pappalardo, Phil. Mag. *2*, 1397 (1959).
19. F. A. Kroger, H. J. Vink, J. Van der Boomgaard, Physica *18*, 77 (1952).
20. J. Jacobs, Ph.D. thesis, Johns Hopkins (1958).
21. L. Helmholtz and R. F. Kruh, J. Am. Chem. Soc. *74*, 1176 (1952).
22. C. J. Ballhausen and C. K. Jorgensen, Acta Chem. Scand. *9*, 397 (1955).
23. L. E. Orgel, J. Chem. Phys. *23*, 1824 (1955).
24. W. Low (unpublished).
25. H. F. Geissler and K. W. Hellwege, Z. Physik *136*, 293 (1953).
26. G. H. Dieke and L. A. Hall, J. Chem. Phys. *27*, 465 (1957).
27. E. Carlson and G. H. Dieke, J. Chem. Phys. *29*, 229 (1958).
28. W. Low (unpublished).
29. The author is indebted to Dr. S. Yatziv for discussing and suggesting this idea.
30. J. H. Van Vleck, J. Phys. Chem. *41*, 63 (1937).
31. L. J. F. Broer, C. J. Gorter, J. Hoogenschagen, Physica *11*, 231 (1945).
32. A. D. Liehr, C. J. Ballhausen, Phys. Rev. *106*, 1161 (1957).
33. A. D. Liehr and C. J. Ballhausen, Mol. Phys. *2*, 123 (1959).
34. S. Koide and M. H. L. Pryce, Phil. Mag. *3*, 607 (1958).
35. S. Koide, Phil. Mag. *4*, 243 (1959).
36. C. J. Ballhausen and A. D. Liehr, Molecular Spectr. *2*, 342 (1958).

DISCUSSION

A. L. SCHAWLOW: For Cr^{3+} in MgO, the R line has been observed at 6981 Å, both in emission and absorption, by F. Varsanyi, D. L. Wood, and A. L. Schawlow. Although the line width depends somewhat on concentration and method of preparation, it is usually well under 1 cm^{-1}. Because it is so narrow, it is hard to find in absorption unless really high resolution is available.

W. LOW: It is quite possible that the Cr^{3+} red line is MgO is as sharp as you say. It is clearly observable in fluorescence. However, the same line in Co^{2+} in CaF_2 is much broader.

I do not think that there were many paramagnetic impurities present in the CaF_2. At any rate, we did not detect any by means of paramagnetic resonance.

W. V. SMITH: In comparing tetrahedral and octahedral coordinations of cubic symmetries with transition group ions, is it correct that the *stronger* lines are also the *narrower* ones?

W. LOW: Yes, because crystal field splitting is less in tetrahedral coordination, leading to narrower lines.

CYCLOTRON RESONANCE AND IMPURITY LEVELS IN SEMICONDUCTORS*

B. LAX

Lincoln Laboratory, Massachusetts Institute of Technology

FOR SOME time, semiconductors have been seriously considered as a possible medium for generating infrared and millimeter radiation. Some success has already been attained in generating incoherent radiation in the infrared. Consequently, it is a logical step to consider semiconductors as likely candidates for use as quantum amplifiers and oscillators. A number of proposals have been made in the literature and elsewhere. I would like to review these, comment on them, and also add one or two suggestions of my own. The basic phenomena that are involved in most of these proposals concern cyclotron resonance and impurity levels.

CYCLOTRON RESONANCE

Perhaps the first idea that was entertained was that of generating millimeters by the harmonics of the heavy holes in germanium. Dexter, Zeiger, and Lax[1] observed and identified weak absorption of second and third harmonics of the heavy hole resonance as shown in Fig. 1. It can be shown theoretically that, for motion of carriers in a magnetic field on warped energy surfaces of the type

$$\varepsilon = -\frac{\hbar^2}{2m_o}\ AK^2 \pm \sqrt{B^2 k^4 + C^2 (k_x^2 k_y^2 + k_x^2 k_z^2 + k_y^2 k_z^2)} \tag{1}$$

*The work reported in this paper was performed by Lincoln Laboratory, a center for research operated by Massachusetts Institute of Technology with the joint support of the U. S. Army, Navy, and Air Force.

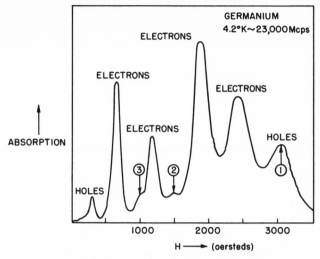

Fig. 1 Cyclotron resonance in germanium

The numbers refer to the fundamental, second, and third harmonics of the heavy hole resonance.

R. N. Dexter, H. J. Zeiger, and B. Lax, Phys. Rev. 104, 637 (1956).

where the + sign refers to light holes and the − sign to heavy holes, this is possible.[2] The surfaces for the light and heavy holes of silicon are shown in Fig. 2 with a large anisotropy for the heavy hole. If a Fourier expansion of the wave vector $\vec{k}$ in multiples of the cyclotron frequency $\omega_c = eH/m^*c$ is made, then along certain directions of H relative to the crystal axes second and third harmonic amplitudes become finite. Quantum mechanically, this means that the selection rules for cyclotron resonance corresponding to transitions $\Delta n = \pm 1$ between Landau levels has been supplemented by additional transitions corresponding to $\Delta n = \pm 2$ and 3. Consequently, DZL looked for emission at 6 mm in germanium when it was strongly irradiated with 1.2 cm in a resonant cavity. No such signal was detected at 6 mm.

More recently, a scheme to use the anharmonic properties of cyclotron resonance of the heavy hole was again considered by Tager and Gladun.[3] They proposed that a pump frequency $\omega_p = n\omega_c$ with sufficient power be employed to permit a large number of carriers to make transition to the higher states and then excite carriers at frequencies $\omega_s = \ell\omega_c$, where $\ell < n$ or $\ell > n$. The latter corresponds essentially to the scheme tried by Dexter, Zeiger,

and Lax, and the former constitutes a proposal for a cyclotron resonance maser. Neither idea is new and each has many problems associated with it which have been overlooked by Tager and Gladun.
First of all, pumping of microwave energy into a quantum system
with energy levels equally spaced whether transitions corre-
spond to $\Delta n = \pm 1$ or $\Delta n = \pm 2, \pm 3$, etc., does not create population inversion which is necessary for a maser. Under steady-
state conditions it merely increases the average energy of the
electrons, but the distribution $\partial f/\partial \varepsilon$ remains negative. Even if
by some scheme it would be possible to raise carriers up into
the band and obtain population inversion, the fact that the levels
are equally spaced still prevents maser action. As the electric
field at the signal frequency is turned on there is an equal probability that induced transitions absorb energy, $\Delta n = 1$, as well
as those that emit, $\Delta n = -1$. This has the effect of spreading
the distribution both up and down in energy. The net effect is
that the system absorbs energy.

To overcome the two difficulties just mentioned, the author
has several suggestions to make. Since equally spaced levels

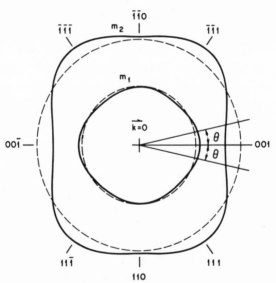

Fig. 2 Energy contours of the valence band in silicon in the
(100) plane at k = 0, *showing the region of negative masses in*
the cone of $\theta = 12°$ *about the* [100] *axis*

are undesirable, it is necessary that in any cyclotron resonance device, we employ a system in which this is not the case. Fortunately, experimental and theoretical results have shown that in semiconductors several such situations exist. The first one involves the warped surfaces of germanium or silicon in which it has been shown by Luttinger and Kohn[4] that there is a quantum effect in which the lowest magnetic levels are unequally spaced. The level scheme, which has been worked out by Goodman[5] and also by the Lincoln group[6] is shown in Fig. 3. The ex-

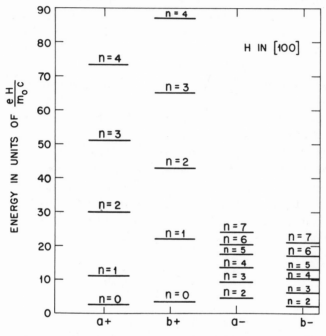

Fig. 3 Magnetic levels for the valence band in germanium

istence of these unequal levels was first demonstrated by the microwave results of Fletcher, Yager, and Merritt[7] and confirmed by the oscillatory magneto-absorption experiments of Zwerdling and Lax.[8] This system of levels is rather complex and has two sets of families corresponding to light and heavy holes. Neglecting transitions between the light and heavy hole bands, if by some process carriers were excited to quantum level $n = 1$ and then transitions induced downward to either of the two levels $n = 0$, radiation would be emitted in the millimeter or far infrared regions of the spectrum. The situation for the heavy holes which have higher masses and are more nearly equally spaced is not favorable. That such excitation is possible in germanium optically has been the object of the magneto-absorption studies of the Lincoln group.[8],[9] It is of course necessary that large magnetic fields be employed to get well-defined separation between individual magnetic or Landau levels. Furthermore, it has been shown that even at very low temperatures, the widths of the lines are of the order 10^{-3} ev. corresponding to a lifetime $\tau = 10^{-12}$ sec. To obtain a suitable separation, fields of the order of 40,000 or more are desirable. Under these circumstances, the induced emission for $n = 1$, $n = 0$ corresponds to a frequency of 10^{12} c.p.s. or a wavelength of 300 microns in the far infrared.

Another situation where unequal spacing of Landau levels can occur is in indium antimonide as demonstrated by the infrared cyclotron resonance experiments with pulse magnetic fields.[10] The apparent effective masses of electrons as obtained from the data increased with magnetic field. From this it was deduced that the energy band was non-parabolic with the curvature decreasing with energy. It has been shown by Kane[11] from perturbation theory that the energy-momentum relation for the electron can be given by an expression essentially equivalent to the following:

$$\varepsilon \approx \frac{\left[\varepsilon_g^2 + 2\,\varepsilon_g\,(p^2/m_o^*)\right]^{\frac{1}{2}} - \varepsilon_g}{2} \tag{2}$$

where ε_g is the energy gap, p is the momentum and m_o^* is the effective mass for the electron at the bottom of the band. If the quadratic equation in ε from which Equation (2) was obtained is used as the Hamiltonian and a magnetic potential is introduced whereby $\vec{p} \longrightarrow \vec{\pi} = \vec{p} - \dfrac{eA}{c}$ and this is then solved, the solution of the corresponding effective mass equation gives an expression for the magnetic levels:[12]

$$\varepsilon_n \approx \frac{\left[\varepsilon_g^2 + e\,\varepsilon_g\,(n + \tfrac{1}{2})\,\hbar\,\omega_c\right]^{\frac{1}{2}} - \varepsilon_g}{2} \tag{3}$$

where the component of the momentum p_z along the magnetic
field is neglected, ω_c is the cyclotron frequency corresponding
to the mass at the bottom of the band, and n is the Landau quantum number. If the above results are used to interpret the pulsed
cyclotron resonance data where the transition corresponds to
$\Delta n = 1$ between $n = 0$ and $n = 1$, the apparent effective mass that
is obtained agrees remarkably well with the experimental results. Consequently, the energy levels can be drawn for various
magnetic fields as indicated by Fig. 4. Large magnetic fields

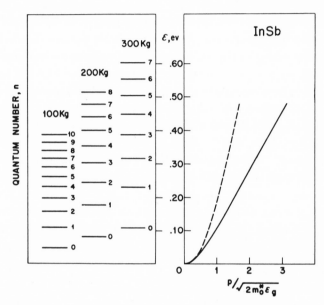

*Fig. 4 Magnetic levels for the conduction band in indium
antimonide*

which are now available are desirable in order to take advantage
of the non-parabolic bands. Thus at 10^5 gauss and room temperature the spacing between $n = 0$ and $n = 1$ level is 0.06 ev.
corresponding to 20 microns, and that between $n = 1$ and $n = 2$ it
is 0.05 ev. corresponding to 25 microns. At 3×10^5 gauss, the
corresponding spacings would be 0.12 ev. or 1 microns between
$n = 0$ and $n = 1$, and 0.09 ev. or 14 microns between $n = 1$ and
$n = 2$. The situation is somewhat more complex since the levels
are also split by a spin-orbit effect via the valence band leading

to an anomalous g-factor[6] of -50. However, this does not alter the situation insofar as the existence of unequal spacings between levels are concerned.

It has been demonstrated that in several semiconductors it is possible to obtain a level structure of the desired spacing needed for a cyclotron resonance maser. The magneto-absorption experiments[8],[9] in these semiconductors also show that it is possible to excite carriers into these levels selectively across the gap. Consequently, the possibility of a population inversion between two magnetic levels is feasible. Furthermore, stimulated emission between these levels is possible in a cavity or interferometer of the appropriate design. The question that must be examined is the quantitative aspects of both the excitation and the stimulated emission in such a system. Germanium appears more attractive than indium antimonide for excitation since at the low temperatures it is possible to excite holes into the selected level close to the maximum spectral emission of a tungsten filament lamp. This occurs at the energy of the direct gap at approximately 1.4 microns as compared to about 5 microns in InSb at low temperatures. The amount of power available in a spectral band from a large spectrometer, corresponding to the line width of .001 ev., may be 10 to approximately 100 milliwatts. Even if the higher value is assumed, the number of carriers that could be excited into a magnetic level optically would correspond to $n_{ex} = \dfrac{P\tau}{h\nu} \approx 10^6$ for $\tau = 10^{-12}$ sec. The number required for an oscillator or amplifier necessitates that the power produced by stimulated emission be greater than that absorbed by the standing waves in a cavity. The expression for this has been given by Schawlow and Townes[18] and is

$$n_{in} \geq \frac{h\,(1-\alpha)\,Ac}{\nu\,\tau 16\,\pi^2\,\mu^2} \tag{4}$$

where A is the wall area, c the speed of light, α the reflection coefficient of the cavity walls, and μ is the electric dipole moment. The electric dipole moment is equal to approximately 10^{-14} e.s.u. since the effective mass in consideration is approximately $0.1\,m_o$. If we assume that $A = 1$ cm^2 and the frequency of resonance is at a few hundred microns, the n_{in} would be equal to about 10^8 which is somewhat larger than the number that we are able to excite. Consequently, for this situation, a cyclotron maser even neglecting other possible complications, which we have ignored, does not appear feasible. However, we have taken a value of τ at infrared frequencies in germanium which is much shorter than the best values obtained at microwaves, i.e., $\tau \approx 10^{-10}$ sec. If the latter can be achieved at higher frequencies, the possibility of a millimeter or infrared maser becomes more promising.

The possibility of optical excitation of a cyclotron resonance maser which can operate at microwave, millimeter, and even far infrared frequencies has been considered by some of us at Lincoln Laboratory. An important consideration for its potential success depends on the existence of bands whose curvature varies quite rapidly as a function of energy. We have just shown that such a situation exists in indium antimonide. However, for the optically excited cyclotron resonance maser, germanium and silicon offer better possibilities. First of all, the materials in pure form have relaxation times from 10^{-10} to 10^{-11} seconds. The curvature of the valence bands in silicon and germanium is known to vary appreciably from the theoretical work of E. O. Kane.[14] This therefore offers the possibility of tuning the resonance over a wide range of frequencies by selecting the proper combination of magnetic fields and appropriate portions of bands. If the former is of the order of 100,000 gauss, then the operating range of the maser may vary from microwave frequencies into the far infrared as high as 30 microns. The optical excitation can be accomplished as follows: A strong optical source which can be a tungsten filament lamp is permitted to pass through a filter near its peak at 1 micron with a bandwidth of a few percent, thereby supplying energy for excitation of approximately one watt or more for the direct transition in germanium. This could create a possible inverted population of holes in the valence band. Another alternative is that the electrons which are created in the conduction band at $k = 0$ will fall rather quickly into the various [111] conduction bands by emitting longitudinal phonons of approximately 0.03 ev. in energy. Then the descent to the bottom of the conduction band would be simi-

larly achieved by interband transitions to the other conduction
bands with the simultaneous emission of more phonons. The distribution of the carrier population in either case would assume
the character shown in Fig. 5. The dotted curve indicates the
existence of a sink or deep trap which quickly removes the carriers whereas the solid curve indicates an accumulation of carriers at the band edges. Nevertheless, if part of the distribution
is "inverted," Zeiger has pointed out that such a system will
be emissive if the microwave cavity is tuned to the resonance of
the effective masses when the distribution f has a positive slope

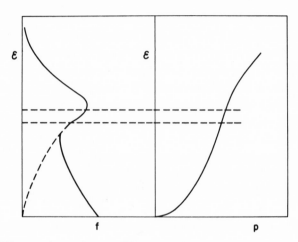

*Fig. 5 Illustration of possible negative resistance for cyclotron
resonance in a non-parabolic energy band indicated by the
horizontal dotted lines*

The dotted line for the distribution assumes a "sink" for carriers at
the bottom of the band.

or negative temperature, i.e., $\dfrac{\partial f}{\partial \varepsilon} > 0$. Then the system is emissive provided that the effective masses above and below differ
sufficiently to give selective resonance for this region. We have
already indicated that in germanium this is possible in the valence band[14] and perhaps also in the conduction band, where it
is known from magneto-absorption[15] that the curvature of the
conduction bands start increasing at an energy of 0.1 ev. above
the bottom of the band. If we assume a lifetime $\sim 10^{-11}$ sec

corresponding to the usual microwave resonance linewidth then the number of carriers in the inverted population would be approximately 10^8. The number of carriers necessary for emission and for overcoming the losses of the system may be evaluated from an expression analogous to that of Equation (4) which for a microwave cavity may be written as

$$n \geq \frac{h\,V}{4\pi\,\mu^2\,Q_c\,\tau} \tag{5}$$

where V is the volume of the cavity and Q_c the quality factor of the cavity which may be as high as 10^4. The estimated number of carriers required for stimulation would then be of the order of 10^7. It appears that such a cyclotron resonance maser is feasible. However, since the negative temperature region is not sharply defined, the number of carriers required for emission may be larger than that of Equation (5). In addition, we have again neglected some practical problems such as that of focusing an intense light source down into a helium bath and on to a sample of suitable size inside a microwave cavity. It was also assumed that the sample was in equilibrium with the helium bath in order that the large fraction of the 1 watt, transformed into phonons emitted by the electrons as they cool down, is dissipated by the bath.

Other cyclotron resonance devices which have been discussed are those involving an oscillating r.f. magnetic field which is parallel to the d.c. magnetic field. The first of these was that of a harmonic generator conceived and constructed by Maiman.[16] He considered two modes of operation, one in which his modulating frequency $\omega_m = \omega_c$, the cyclotron frequency, and the harmonic generation or signal frequency $\omega_s = 2\,\omega_c$. The other mode required that the modulating frequency be one half the cyclotron frequency $\omega_m = \omega_c/2$ and that generation occur at ω_c. A gas discharge system was built using the latter scheme in which 9 watts of input power at 1000 Mcps was converted to 1.3 milliwatts at 2000 Mcps. Still another version of this technique has been suggested by Tager and Gladum[3] for parametric amplification and generation of high frequency oscillations. They suggest that the pump frequency be the modulating magnetic field $\omega_m = 2\,\omega_c/n$ where n is an integer and that the system, which is then unstable

at ω_c, be used to amplify at this frequency in a polarization perpendicular to the d.c. magnetic field. Another conceivable system for a parametric device is one in which the pumping field is
at the cyclotron frequency, the idler or modulating field ω_m is
lower, and hence the signal frequency $\omega_s = \omega_c - \omega_m$ is the difference.

The last scheme using cyclotron resonance for amplification
or generation involves the so-called negative mass system which
had its origin in the proposal of Kroemer.[17] The related cyclotron resonance phenomena has been investigated by Dousmanis
and co-workers[18] more recently. The theoretical aspects of the
negative mass phenomena have been considered by Kittel,[19]
Kaus,[20] by Mattis and Stevenson[21] and also by Zeiger.[22]

One important aspect that differentiates the negative mass
system from a positive mass as in a semiconductor is that, even
for parabolic bands in which the magnetic levels are equally
spaced, a distribution which has a peak as shown in Fig. 6,
would have emissive properties for the negative mass, but not
for the positive. The explanation, which has been essentially
given by Mattis and Stevenson, and also by Zeiger, resides in

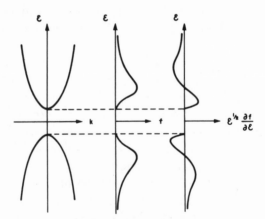

*Fig. 6 Unbalanced nonequilibrium distribution for positive and
negative carriers*

In parabolic bands $\delta = -\dfrac{e^2\tau}{m^*}\displaystyle\int \varepsilon^{\frac{1}{2}}\dfrac{\partial f}{\partial \varepsilon}\,d\varepsilon$ is shown to be positive for

positive mass carriers, i.e., *absorptive* and can be negative for negative mass carriers, i.e., *emissive*.

the fact that the density of states $n(\varepsilon)$ for the positive mass increases with increasing energy and therefore the integral for the current, which involves $n(\varepsilon)\,\partial f/\partial\varepsilon$, is negative and hence the conductivity is positive which results in absorption. This means that the net effect is a transfer of energy to the electrons which are then shifted to higher energies. Similarly, for the negative mass or the valence band, $\dfrac{\partial f}{\partial\varepsilon}$ is negative for energies where the density of states is relatively small and becomes positive when the density of states are high. This will give a positive value for the integral of $\dfrac{\partial f}{\partial\varepsilon}$ and the density of states, resulting in a negative conductivity or one which is emissive.

The experiment of Dousmanis and co-workers involved the observation of cyclotron resonance in negative mass region of the heavy holes in germanium, i.e., a cone approximately $15°$ about the [100] axis similar to that shown in Fig. 1. They used circular polarization and detected a decrease in the absorption below the baseline for masses $\sim 0.22\ m_o$. This dip was interpreted as evidence for the emissive properties of the negative mass. It has been shown by the theoretical analysis[19],[20],[21],[22] that emission can only occur if the equilibrium distribution is disturbed and if the distribution for the negative masses is at least partially inverted. The use of optical excitation in the experiments can possibly produce such inversion and account for the results of Dousmanis. Although the theory and experiment indicate that emission can be obtained from a negative mass system under appropriate conditions, the number of carriers excited into an inverted population optically appear to fall below that required to overcome the losses of the resonant system.

IMPURITY LEVELS

In semiconductors, discrete or quantized levels can be achieved not only by a magnetic field, but also by the creation of impurity levels which are essentially complicated delicate hydrogen-like structures of carriers imbedded in a dielectric medium. Such structures have been extensively studied by Burstein and co-workers,[23] Newman[24] and also by Hrostowski and Kaiser[25] in silicon, and in germanium by Fan and Fisher.[26] Theoretical investigations of impurities have been made by Kohn and Luttinger[27] and others.[28] More recently, the Zeeman effect of these levels have been studied in germanium by Boyle[15] and also by Fan and Fisher,[26] and in silicon by the Lincoln group.[29] These studies reveal a number of properties which indicate that the energy levels may possibly be utilized for generation of infrared radiation.

N-Type Impurities. Electrons both in germanium and silicon move on surfaces whose energy momentum relation is spheroidal. One can then write an effective mass Schrödinger equation which has the form:[27],[28]

$$- \left[\frac{\hbar^2}{2m_t} \left(\frac{\partial^2}{\partial x^2} + \frac{\partial^2}{\partial y^2} \right) + \frac{\hbar^2}{2m_l} \frac{\partial^2}{\partial z^2} \right] \Psi - \frac{e^2}{\kappa r} = \varepsilon \Psi. \qquad (6)$$

The solution to this equation is usually obtained by a variational method in which the exponential has the form $e^{- \sqrt{A^2 (x^2 + y^2) + B^2 z^2}}$. One of the interesting properties that results is that the 3-fold degeneracy which exists for spherical bands is removed, so that a p_o state whose wave-function is parallel to the principal or z axis falls below the 2-fold degenerate $p_{\pm}$ states along the x and y coordinates. Still another new feature of these states which is of importance for the ground or s states is that the multiplicity of the energy surfaces for the conduction band minima, six for silicon and four for germanium, results in a set of states which are linear combinations of the envelope functions. For silicon it appears that the singlet of the tetrahedral grouping is lowest and the other five states of the E and T_1 groups are higher in energy. This is due to the fact that for deeper impurity levels such as bismuth and others, the effective mass equation breaks down near the Coulomb center. For the singlet which is a symmetrical combination, the wave function peaks at the Coulomb center and hence it is likely that its energy is reduced below that theoretically predicted by the effective mass equation. For the other states which vanish at the Coulomb center, the perturbation is much smaller and their binding energy is closer to that of the theoretical value. A similar situation appears to exist in germanium where the lowest state is a singlet and the higher s state is a triplet. In germanium, the binding energy obtained from theory is 0.0092 ev., whereas the experimental binding energies of impurities are as shown in Table 1.

Table 1. Ionization energies of Group V impurities in germanium in units of 10^{-3} ev.

Impurity in germanium	As	Bi	Sb	P
Optical ionization	14.0	12.5	9.8	12.8
Approximate separation between singlet and triplet	4.8	3.3	0.6	3.6

After Fan and Fisher, J. Phys. Chem. Solids *8,* 270 (1959)

Since the triplet is hardly perturbed by the deviation from the effective mass approximation, it can be interpreted that the above states are singlets and the approximate separation between the singlet and triplet are as shown above. It is significant in arsenic, bismuth, and phosphorous and negiigible in antimony. These results are of great importance for the interpretation of spin resonance of bound states in germanium in which the g-factor is isotropic for the singlet and multi-valued and anisotropic for the triplet.[30] The existence of the triplet implies a metastable state in which transitions to the singlet are forbidden. The anisotropic and complex character of the g-value of the triplet state would suggest that this set of states would not be particularly useful for applications in a maser at microwave frequencies. However, the singlet state whose g-value is isotropic would be more useful. Some of these properties of the g-factor in germanium have been observed by Feher, Wilson, and Gere[31] who have shown that in phosphorous, with impurities of the order of $10^{17}/cm^3$, the linewidth at $4°K$ is of the order of 4 oersteds with H along the [100] axis, although much broader with the magnetic field in other directions. This suggests that by using spin resonance, germanium might possibly be utilized in a two-level maser. There is an analogous situation in silicon in which the ground state donor levels are split due to the departure from the effective mass theory, with the symmetric state being lowest for the reasons cited in germanium and the other five states being higher in energy and closer to the theoretical value. It should be mentioned at this point that silicon was the first solid-state material in which stimulated emission was exhibited[32] and of course has been used in a two-level maser by Feher and co-workers.[33]

P-type Impurities—Internal Levels. The impurity levels for p-type materials are much more complex. Strictly speaking, it is necessary to solve a determinantal effective mass equation which involves a 6×6 matrix, although one of the 2-fold degenerate bands is split away due to spin orbit coupling. The solution for such a system has been considered by Schechter.[34],[35] This system can be shown to have an extremely interesting property which until recently has not been recognized. In attempting to solve for the impurity levels, particularly in silicon where the spin orbit splitting is comparable or smaller than the binding energy of the ground state, it is necessary that one treat the problem as the solution of the 6×6 matrix equation. To do this as a first approximation, we can consider the solution for the envelope functions of a 4×4 matrix and then separately of a 2×2 matrix for the split-off band. Then if one treats the overlapping terms in the 6×6 matrix as a perturbation, it can be shown that there is mixing of the impurity levels of the corresponding ground and excited states respectively for these two bands and coupling between them. If one then evaluates the matrix elements for transitions between these two sets of states, it can be shown that transitions do exist. Furthermore, the presence of discrete levels inside the bands above the split-off band which we shall call internal levels do exist and are detectable. This phenomenon now has been experimentally verified by Zwerdling, Button, and Lax[36] in both aluminum and boron-doped silicon. It can be shown that the transition probability is given by W, the square of the matrix element, which can be represented as follows:

$$W \sim \left[\frac{H'_{ab}(1)}{\varepsilon_{ab}(1)} p_{12}(b) + \frac{H'_{ab}(2)}{\varepsilon_{ab}(2)} p_{12}(a) \right]^2 \qquad (6)$$

where H'_{ab} is a matrix element represented by the coupling of the levels due to the overlap terms in the 6×6 matrix equation, ε_{ab} is the energy spacing between the impurity levels of bands a and b, the numbers 1 and 2 refer to the ground and excited states of either band, and p_{12} is the momentum matrix between the ground and excited states in each band. The important result demonstrated here is that the matrix element above represents the transition from the ground state of band a to an excited state of band b as shown in Fig. 7. Of course, similarly, an allowed transition also exists from the ground state of band b to an excited state of band a. Consequently, this system permits transitions between impurity levels in a manner analogous to that in paramagnetic materials, so that at low temperatures it is possible to get population inversion between states 2 and 1 of band b or between states 1 of band b and states 2 of band a. Unfortunately, at the wavelength where this is possible, the energy of the in-

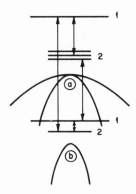

Fig. 7 *Impurity levels of valence bands*

Levels of band a are normal levels, those of band b are the *internal* impurity levels.

frared radiation is much too small to permit a large number of excess carriers for inversion. Hence in silicon this is not very practical. In germanium, the situation is somewhat more favorable from the viewpoint of the pumping energy since the spacing of the levels is approximately 0.3 ev. which is about 3 times that of the spacing between the similar states in silicon. This of course reduces the transition probability by one order of magnitude. However, this is compensated by the fact that the dipole moment is larger in germanium since the dielectric constant is larger and effective mass is smaller so that the transition probability is comparable. In addition, the energy which varies as

λ^4 should now increase by 2 orders of magnitude. Nevertheless, even at 4 microns where this occurs, the electron concentration and lifetime are still too small to permit an impurity maser to operate.

CONCLUSION

Although at present the quantitative aspects indicate that cyclotron resonance and impurity masers of the type discussed here in such semiconductors as germanium, silicon, or InSb, appear marginal or submarginal, the ideas outlined here only represent a preliminary beginning in this respect. Consequently, the possibility of using other semiconductors or other phenomena in semiconductors which may result in a workable device does exist. First of all, we know that the phenomenon of emission due to radiation recombination semiconductors has been observed.[37],[38] The recombination of hole-electron pairs emits radiation close to that of the energy gap in germanium and silicon. Luminescence has been observed in intermetallics[38] and before that in other semiconductors.[39] As a matter of fact, Aigrain[40] suggested that one might be able to use the injection and the recombination of electron hole pairs across the gap for an infrared maser. This problem has been considered quantitatively by Zeiger, who has shown that the matrix element for the indirect transition is so small that a very large number of carriers in conduction and valence band would be needed for maser action. The transition probability can be obtained from the absorption coefficient of the inverse process in which an electron is taken from the valence band to the conduction band via an intermediate state involving emission or absorption of a phonon. It is not surprising that the probability is low since it is an indirect process. It is conceivable that similar recombination processes across the gap where a direct transition is involved can be utilized in a more efficient system since the probability is usually many orders of magnitude higher. Perhaps it is just a question of finding a suitable material.

In reviewing various suggestions for semiconducting masers, the possibility of electrical excitation should be mentioned. This has been independently considered by Autler and Zeiger[41] and also by Basov and co-workers.[42] The proposal involves the excitation of carriers at liquid-helium temperatures into the conduction band by avalanche breakdown in the presence of an applied DC electric field. Hopefully, it is expected that the electrons would accumulate in an excited state permitting allowed transitions to the ground state. Presumably if an inverted population can be thus achieved, a maser in the far infrared would result. Neither group has demonstrated either theoretically or experimentally that such an inversion would result. Furthermore, in arsenic-, phosphorous-, or bismuth-doped germanium the electrons might accumulate in the triplet state which would act as a metastable state since transitions are not allowed to the singlet, which is lowest. In antimony-doped germanium, this would not occur, and in p-type germanium this also would not be a problem.

In conclusion, it should be stated that the proposals for semiconducting masers reviewed in this paper vary from unlikely to those that may be possible. However, in each case a number of unknowns appear regarding transition processes and in many semiconductors basic parameters of the band structure are lacking. Consequently, before a successful maser using cyclotron resonance or impurity levels is achieved, more experimental and theoretical investigation will be necessary on a wide variety of materials in order that the proper prescription be selected.

The author is grateful to Dr. J. G. Mavroides for his contributions in the preparation of this paper and in particular for his help in the calculation of the cyclotron data presented here. He has also enjoyed several informative discussions with Dr. H. J. Zeiger and is thankful for his criticisms and suggestions.

REFERENCES

1. R. N. Dexter, H. J. Zeiger, and B. Lax, Phys. Rev. *104*, 637 (1956).
2. H. J. Zeiger, B. Lax, and R. N. Dexter, Phys. Rev. *105*, 495 (1957).
3. A. S. Tager and A. D. Gladun, ZETF *35*, 808 (1958).
4. J. M. Luttinger and W. Kohn, Phys. Rev. *97*, 869 (1955).
5. R. R. Goodman, Ph.D. thesis, University of Michigan (1958, unpublished).
6. L. M. Roth, B. Lax, and S. Zwerdling, Phys. Rev. *114*, 90 (1959).

7. R. C. Fletcher, W. A. Yager, and F. R. Merritt, Phys. Rev. *100*, 747 (1955).

8. S. Zwerdling and B. Lax, Phys. Rev. *106*, 51 (1957).

9. S. Zwerdling, B. Lax, L. M. Roth, and K. J. Button, Phys. Rev. *114*, 80 (1959).

10. R. J. Keyes, S. Zwerdling, S. Foner, H. H. Kolm, and B. Lax, Phys. Rev. *104*, 1804 (1956).

11. E. O. Kane, J. Phys. Chem. Solids *1*, 249 (1957).

12. B. Lax, R. J. Keyes and J. G. Mavroides (to be published).

13. A. L. Schawlow and C. H. Townes, Phys. Rev. *112*, 1940 (1957).

14. E. O. Kane, J. Phys. Chem. Solids *1*, 82 (1956).

15. W. S. Boyle, J. Phys. Chem. Solids *8*, 321 (1954).

16. T. H. Maiman, "Solid State Millimeter Wave Generation Study," Hughes Aircraft Co. (1956–57).

17. H. Kroemer, Phys. Rev. *109*, 1856 (1958); Proc. IRE *47*, 397 (1959).

18. G. C. Dousmanis, Phys. Rev. Lett. *1*, 55 (1958); G. C. Dousmanis, R. C. Duncan, Jr., I. J. Thomas, and R. C. Williams, Phys. Rev. Lett. *1*, 404 (1958).

19. C. Kittel, Proc. Nat. Acad. Sci. *45*, 744 (1959).

20. P. Kaus, Phys. Rev. Lett. *3*, 18 (1959).

21. D. C. Mattis and M. J. Stevenson, Phys. Rev. Lett. *3*, 18 (1959).

22. H. J. Zeiger, private communication.

23. E. Burstein, G. Picus, B. Henvis, and R. Wallis, J. Phys. Chem. Solids *1*, 65 (1956); G. Picus, E. Burstein, and B. Henvis, J. Phys. Chem. Solids *1*, 75 (1956).

24. R. Newman, Phys. Rev. *99*, 465 (1955); Phys. Rev. *103*, 103 (1956).

25. H. J. Hrostowski and R. H. Kaiser, J. Phys. Chem. Solids *4*, 148 (1958).

26. H. Y. Fan and P. Fisher, J. Phys. Chem. Solids *8*, 270 (1959).

27. W. Kohn and J. M. Luttinger, Phys. Rev. *97*, 1721 (1955).

28. For a more complete list, see W. Kohn, Solid State Physics *5*, 257 (1957).

29. S. Zwerdling, K. J. Button, and B. Lax, Bull. Amer. Phys. Soc. Ser. II, *4*, 145 (1959); W. Kleiner, R. N. Brown, and B. Lax, Bull. Amer. Soc. Ser. II, *4*, 145 (1959).

30. L. M. Roth and B. Lax, Phys. Rev. Lett. *3*, 217 (1959).

31. G. Feher, D. K. Wilson, and E. A. Gere, Phys. Rev. Lett. *3*, 25 (1959).

32. J. Combrisson, A. Honig, and C. H. Townes, C. R. Acad. Sci. *242*, 2451 (1956).

33. G. Feher, J. P. Gordon, E. Buehler, E. A. Gere, and C. D. Thurmond, Phys. Rev. *109*, 221 (1958).

34. W. Kohn and D. Schechter, Phys. Rev. *99*, 1903 (1955).

35. D. Schechter, Ph.D. thesis, Carnegie Institute of Technology.

36. S. Zwerdling, K. J. Button, and B. Lax, (to be published).

37. J. R. Haynes and H. B. Briggs, Phys. Rev. *86*, 647 (1952); R. Newman, Phys. Rev. *91*, 1313 (1953); P. Aigrain and C. Benoit à la Guillaume, J. Phys. Rad. *17*, 709 (1956).

38. R. Braunstein, Phys. Rev. *99*, 1892 (1955); E. E. Loebner and E. W. Poor, Jr., Phys. Rev. Lett. *3*, 23 (1959).
39. See Symposium on Luminescence (Paris, May 1956) J. Phys. Rad. *17* (1956).
40. P. Aigrain, International Conference on Solid State Physics and its Applications to Electronics and Telecommunications, Brussels, Belgium (1958, to be published).
41. S. H. Autler and H. J. Zeiger, private communication.
42. N. G. Basov, B. M. Bul, and U. M. Popov, JETP (USSR) *37*, 587 (1959).

DISCUSSION

M. J. STEVENSON: Dr. Lax stressed in his discussion the non-uniform Landau level spacing for amplification use. In the particular case of negative mass cyclotron resonance, I would like to add that the concept of amplification at the negative mass cyclotron resonance frequency depends on an inverted population distribution over a restricted energy coupled with a variation in the effective mass of the carriers as a function of energy so that the emission from the inverted population region takes place at a frequency different from the absorption by the rest of the carriers that have Boltzmann type distribution. If the resonance lines are sufficiently resolved, emission of radiation could occur. One of such possible mechanisms is very rapid recombination of low energy carriers which would act to invert the distribution function under some circumstances.

The negative mass of the carriers is only incidental, since the negative mass holes in Ge or Si are only two of several systems characterized by nonuniform effective mass. The greater matrix element for transitions to lower energy levels is helpful but not sufficient to produce emission without population inversion.

B. LAX: The excitation of population inversion in the negative mass experiments of Dousmanis appears to be correct. However, although this is emissive, it does not mean that a cyclotron resonance maser is therefore possible. On a quantitative basis it may be submarginal, since the number of carriers excited may not be enough to overcome the losses in the system.

F. S. BARNES: [asked a question about DC pumping across a P-N junction].

B. LAX: DC pumping across a P-N junction is essentially electrical pumping. The equivalent result can be achieved by a discharge or avalanche in a semiconductor. This has been proposed by Autler and Zeiger for germanium and independently by Basov. However, it is not obvious that one can get the necessary population inversion between the excited and ground state for an infrared maser. This is an interesting idea, but requires measurement of transition processes involved.

F. S. BARNES: [asked a question about light emmitted from the junction].

B. LAX: That is different. It involves recombination of hole electron pairs. Haynes has done this type of experiment in Ge and Si. Aigrain has also considered such a process for a maser. However, Zeiger has shown that for such an indirect process, the dipole matrix element is too small.

E. BURSTEIN: It may be of interest to mention another possible process for producing inverted spin populations which makes use of the negative g-factors that occur for conduction electrons in some semiconductors. It involves the transfer of electrons from a negative g-factor crystal into a second crystal having a positive g-factor. As an example, consider a junction of n-type InSb, which has an electronic g-factor of about -50 with p-type Si, in which the g-factor is approximately $+2$. By applying a positive potential to Si relative to InSb, electrons will move across the boundary from InSb into Si. In the InSb, the $M = +\frac{1}{2}$ state is the lower state and therefore, under thermal equilibrium conditions, the more highly populated state. If the transfer from one medium to the other is carried out so that the orientation of the magnetic moment remains unchanged, this will lead to an inverted population which would be detected by spin resonance measurements on either free electrons or on electrons which become bound to uncompensated donor centers in the p-

type Si. An experimental and theoretical program to study the factors which control the transport of the electronic magnetic moments across the boundary between two solids or between a solid and a vacuum, is being carried out in collaboration with M. Hirsh and co-workers at the I.T.T. Laboratories, Nutley, N.J.

B. LAX: The g-factor of the electron in InSb varies as the electron rises in the band, going from negative to positive as the mass changes. If the electron is removed too slowly, then it will already be inverted inside the crystal. The transition time for the process is unknown; hence it is difficult to state whether such a phenomenon is possible or not.

COMBINED PARAMAGNETIC RESONANCE— INFRARED RADIATION STUDIES IN SILICON*

A. HONIG
Syracuse University

THE SIMULTANEOUS utilization of paramagnetic resonance and infrared excitation has some interesting applications to the study of solids. In a general sense, the paramagnetic resonance selects out particular impurities whose electronic excited state spectrum in the infrared can then be investigated, even in the presence of abundant extraneous impurities. Spin-relaxation modifications resulting from particular excitations can serve as the detectable quantity in many cases. We are at present investigating the excited states of impurities in silicon with this technique. In addition to the above-mentioned bound-state problems, we have also been investigating the spin interactions between photoionized conduction electrons and bound electrons in silicon. Since we can excite the electrons to any desired initial energy by appropriately choosing the infrared frequency, hot electron relaxation effects are studied in conjunction with the usual exchange and lattice relaxations. "By-products" of the relaxation studies, which have been pointed out by us previously,[1] include information on spectral infrared absorption coefficients, electron diffusion distances, and trapping lifetimes.[1,2] I would like to limit myself here to discussion of a few recent developments in the *bound electron—conduction electron* relaxation picture.

*This research is supported in part by the Air Force Office of Scientific Research.

The apparatus used in most of the studies was constructed by R. Levitt, and is depicted in Fig. 1. Infrared energy can be focused from the monochromator onto the windowed light pipe running adjacent to the X-band wave guide, or can emanate from a blackened plunger which slides inside the light pipe. The latter provides black body radiation at any temperature be-

Fig. 1. Photograph of the paramagnetic resonance and infrared monochromator assembly

tween 1.25°K and 300°K, and has been useful for some of the experiments in which it was desired to excite with long wavelength infrared and to exclude room temperature background radiation (suitable long wavelength pass filters were not at the time available to us). For example, with the plunger at 95°K, only 5 percent of the total radiant energy is at wavelengths shorter than 20 microns, while 20 percent of the total energy is useful for ionization of phosphorus impurities. Taking account of the increased number of photons per unit energy interval and the increased free carrier absorption coefficient at longer wavelengths, over 90 percent of the electrons will be excited from phosphorus impurities to energies below 0.02 e.v. This of course still represents a fairly high kinetic energy compared with the lattice temperature (10^{-4} e.v.).

We return now to consideration of the relaxation processes. Pines, Bardeen, and Slichter[3] presented a theory in which the bound electron spins relax via spin exchange with conduction electrons; the latter, however, must themselves first relax to the Boltzmann distribution. Anderson[4] suggested that even in the absence of conduction electron relaxation to the Boltzmann distribution, the exchange time between bound and conduction electrons can be directly measured by creating an inequality in the magnetization associated with the essentially noninteracting hyperfine lines. Electron exchange equalizes the magnetizations of the hyperfine lines in a time which we call T_{ex},[5] because the conduction electron spin distribution is created impartially from both hyperfine states, and thus represents their *average* magnetization. $1/T_{ex}$ is given by $\sigma_s v n_e$, where σ_s is the cross section for singlet exchange scattering, v is the thermal velocity, and n_e is the steady-state population of conduction electrons. From the total σ estimated by PBS, one obtains $1/T_{ex} = 1.5 \times 10^{-6} \, n_e/\text{sec}$, allowing for statistical weights.[6] If n_e is optically produced, we have the usual expression

$$n_e = S \, T_R \tag{1}$$

where S is the rate of generation of electrons per cm^3, and T_R is the lifetime against trapping, which is presumed to be inversely proportional to the amount of compensation. From a knowledge of the free carrier infrared absorption coefficient[7] and a measurement of the incident infrared flux, we obtained S. n_e was determined from the measured value of T_{ex} using the PBS relation. Inserting these values into expression (1) yielded a trapping lifetime[2] within order of magnitude agreement with lifetimes obtained from photoconductivity measurements by Sclar and Burstein[8] and with theoretical calculations of M. Lax,[9] seemingly indicating the validity of the exchange scattering cross section estimated by PBS. Recently, Feher[4] measured n_e directly from the Hall effect, and also got a dependence between T_{ex} and n_e in order of magnitude agreement with the PBS calculation.

We would like to point out now that even if there were no electron exchange interaction of the type considered by PBS and Anderson, the same experimental effects could be obtained through another mechanism, which consists simply of *interchange* of electrons resulting from ionization and subsequent recapture. T_{ex} would be given in this case by the mean lifetime of a phosphorus atom against ionization, since recapture occurs rapidly. The mean lifetime against ionization is n_D/S, where n_D is the concentration of neutral donor impurities. The measured value of T_{ex} was found in all samples looked at thus far to agree with *this* mechanism, which makes the contribution of true exchange unknown. To compare the exchange and interchange mechanisms, we note that the exchange mechanism of PBS depends only on n_e. Thus, by increasing the lifetime T_R while maintaining S and n_D constant, n_e can be increased. On the other hand, the interchange mechanism depends only on S/n_D and not on n_e or T_R. Experiments on two samples of phosphorus-doped silicon, both with about 10^{15} P/cc but differing by greater than a factor of ten in compensation (and hence in T_R and n_e) yielded approximately the same exchange relaxation time under the same photon flux, indicating a dominant interchange mechanism. Putting in the actual numbers suggests that the PBS σ_s is too large by at least a factor of five. Of course, this conclusion rests on assumptions relating the trapping lifetime to amount of compensation, which have not yet been extensively studied, although the experiments in germanium[10] and the giant trap theory of Lax[9] lend support. Direct measurement of electron concentrations will be used to check these conclusions. In view of the interest in hydrogenic electron exchange at low energies both in the free atom and the solid, we are trying to establish the true exchange cross section. Use of more highly doped samples (about 10^{16} P/cc) with very small compensation should favor the exchange over the interchange mechanism, and perhaps make it possible to evaluate the true exchange cross section.

Next, I would like to discuss the spin-lattice relaxation mechanisms of the conduction electrons. We recall that the bound electrons came to Boltzmann equilibrium solely by exchange or interchange with the conduction electrons, so that by monitoring the approach to equilibrium of the bound spins, we can measure T^C_{S-L}, i.e. the conduction electron spin-lattice relaxation time. We have previously presented evidence[2] (see Fig. 2) suggesting that the T^C_{S-L} mechanism is primarily due to exchange (or

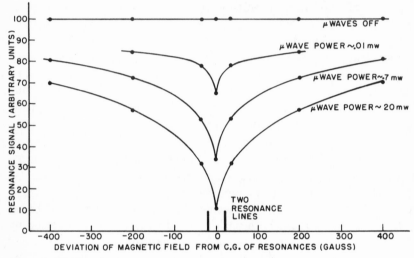

Fig. 2. Effect of microwave power, at various settings of the magnetic field, on growth of magnetization (signal size) of two main phosphorus hyperfine lines when conduction electrons are present.

Signal is corrected for Boltzmann factor dependence on magnetic field. Sample has 1.7×10^{16} P/cc, temperature is $1.3 \,^\circ$K, and microwave frequency is about 9200 ms/sec.

interchange) with fast-relaxing paramagnetic impurities, rather than due to a process involving the conduction band itself. Furthermore, we had suggested that the fast-relaxing centers are close pairs of phosphorus donors. In Fig. 2, one observes that the steady-state magnetization of the bound donors is decreased if microwave power is left on during the growth period, even though the magnetic field is set considerably off from the main resonances. In the absence of photoexcitation to the conduction band, this effect does not occur. Our interpretation was that the saturated centers contribute to the conduction electron reservoir spins of high temperature, which mix in the conduction band with electrons from non-saturated cold centers to form an intermediate spin temperature reservoir. The facts that the most effective position in this background spin distribution coincided with the g value of the donor electron,[11] and that relatively little power was needed to saturate, were taken as indications that the cold centers with which we were dealing were phosphorus pairs.[12] If interchange rather than exchange is the dominant means of electron spin transfer, as we have reason to suspect, the occurrence of this effect while irradiating with long wavelength infrared also suggests shallow trap centers.[13] Because the ratio of *pair concentration* to *donor concentration* is proportional to donor concentration, the ratio of T_{ex} to T_S of the bound electrons should decrease with decreasing concentration. This has been observed, although the decrease is not in direct proportion to the concentration decrease. For a 10^{16} P/cc sample, the donor ratio of T_{ex}/T_S is about 1/20, whereas for a 10^{15} P/cc sample, T_{ex}/T_S is about 1/50. The situation is further complicated in that the equilibrium magnetization for the latter sample corresponded to about $2.5°$K instead of to the lattice temperature of $1.3°$K. This was so whether 2-micron infrared radiation was used or $95°$K black-body radiation was used to ionize the donors. Some spin heating while the electron is at high kinetic energies is not precluded by these results, but it is also possible that conduction electron exchange (or interchange) with paired bound electrons could produce this effect. This effect is concentration dependent; for the 10^{16} P/cc sample, it does not exist.

We have discussed only a few of the results obtained on spin relaxation via conduction electron exchange processes. A more complete report is in preparation. I would like to thank Mr. R. Levitt for assistance in several of the experimental runs, and Mr. P. Bratt for his help in calibrating the gold-doped germanium photodetector. Dr. R. O. Carlson, Dr. D. C. Jillson, and Mr. A. S. Rugare of General Electric Research Laboratories at Schenectady and Syracuse kindly provided the samples used. This work was begun with the aid of a Frederick Gardner Cottrell grant from the Research Corporation.

REFERENCES

1. A. Honig, Kamerlingh Onnes Low Temperature Conference, Supplement to Physica *24* (September, 1958).
2. A. Honig, Bull. Am. Phys. Soc. II, *3*, 377 (1958).
3. Pines, Bardeen, and Slichter, Phys. Rev. *106*, 489 (1957), referred to here as PBS.
4. G. Feher and E. A. Gere, Phys. Rev. *114*, 1245 (1959).
5. We prefer to think of the exchange process in a statistical sense, rather than as a particular double exchange as in reference 4. Hence, it seems more appropriate to use T_{ex} rather than T_{ss}, reserving the latter for direct spin-spin processes.
6. Actually, the validity of such an estimate of σ_s is questionable, perhaps even as to order of magnitude. The free atom formula from which this expression came [J. R. Oppenheimer, Phys. Rev. *32*, 361 (1928)] did not include polarization effects, which certainly are important for the very low conduction electron velocities. Also, σ_s and σ_t are not necessarily different only with respect to statistical weight.
7. W. Spitzer and H. Y. Fan, Phys. Rev. *108*, 268 (1957).
8. N. Sclar and E. Burstein, Phys. Rev. *98*, 1157 (1955).
9. M. Lax, International Conference on Semiconductor Physics (August, 1958).
10. S. H. Koenig, Phys. Rev. *110*, 988 (1958).
11. Some close pairs of phosphorus atoms with a large electron exchange interaction exhibit a resonance at a magnetic field corresponding to the g value of the donor electron. See C. P. Slichter, Phys. Rev. *99*, 479 (1955).
12. Close phosphorus pairs acting as fast relaxing centers have also been proposed as the source of a concentration-dependent thermal relaxation process. See E. Strupp and A. Honig, Bull. Am. Phys. Soc. II, *4*, 261 (1959), and also A. Honig and E. Strupp, AFOSR Technical Report 59–715.
13. This effect may provide a means of measuring the ionization energy of pairs.

DISCUSSION

J. LAMBE: If the sample were illuminated over a small region, would the entire sample relax or only the illuminated portion? Would one obtain a "relaxation image" of the illumination?

A. HONIG: The electron diffusion distance is very small ($\sim 10^{-4}$ cm). Therefore, the relaxation effects are limited to the approximate location of absorption of the photons. We have used this effect to determine the infrared spectral absorption coefficient. (See reference 1 of text)

THE NEGATIVE EFFECTIVE MASS EFFECT AND QUANTUM CONSIDERATIONS IN ITS INTERPRETATION*

G. C. DOUSMANIS
RCA Laboratories, Princeton, New Jersey

A CYCLOTRON resonance spectrum showing, under input power conditions, emission rather than absorption of rf power and assigned to electrical carriers with negative effective mass has recently been observed in this laboratory.[1],[2] The purpose of the present paper is to discuss this experiment and provide an elementary quantum approach for the interpretation of this and other types of proposed negative-mass effects.[3]

Negative effective mass effects in crystals, their detection, study, and possible use has been lately the subject of considerable work,[1],[2],[3],[4],[5],[6],[7],[8],[9] mainly theoretical.[1],[3],[4],[5],[6],[7],[8],[9] In crystalline solids one is provided with a variety of energy-momentum (or wave vector) relations for the electrical carriers, electrons or holes. In certain cases, such as that of heavy holes in germanium and silicon (Fig. 1) the curvature of the energy-momentum curves, whose reciprocal is a measure of the carrier effective mass, is negative at low-energy regions. Such negative effective mass states were considered of great significance: Their experimental detection would be facilitated in these cases by their reasonable population.[1] It is of course to be understood that a particle with negative effective mass implies, under the proper experimental conditions, negative mobility and conductivity.

*Work supported in part by the U.S. Air Force, Air Research and Development Command, Cambridge Research Center.

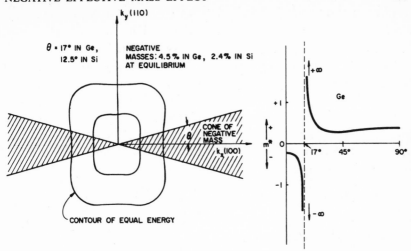

Fig. 1. Energy contours for heavy holes in Ge and Si and the two branches of effective mass for Ge

The band-structure constants used are those of Dexter, Zeiger, and Lax [Phys. Rev. *104*, 637 (1956)]. The mass is evaluated in directions perpendicular to, and radially outwards, from the (100) crystallographic axis.

It will be seen that this straight forward approach is in agreement with more sophisticated quantum schemes that one can use for these effects. It is emphasized[3] that negative-mass effects are majority carrier phenomena and are bulk effects not involving transfer of charge through p-n junctions, as is the case in usual transistor-type operation, or the corresponding electron transfer between electrodes in a vacuum tube. Thus both high frequency operation and broad-band properties are indicated for effects of this type.

The experimental technique used in the detection of the negative mass effect[1],[2] is cyclotron resonance using mainly circularly polarized microwaves. Calculations had indicated that the number of negative-mass holes in a germanium crystal was about 4 percent of the total and that the effect should be detectable[1] by this technique. Cyclotron resonance is one of the most sensitive techniques of solid-state physics and was indicated as the most promising one for initial experimental work in this new field.

The main elements of the quantum-mechanical approach to be presented here are as follows: The Landau energy levels of negative-mass carriers are reversed by comparison to those due to positive masses ($n = 0$ level near top, rather than bottom of band, then $n = 1$ etc.). This leads to a complete reversal of matrix elements and rf transition probabilities in the negative-mass regions. Thus a particle injected into the negative-mass region will emit rather than absorb rf power in contrast to the opposite behavior of positive-mass carriers. Input power must of course be provided, as is done by illumination in the experiments. This agrees with the conductivity-type approach, which suggests that a carrier will exhibit negative mobility if injected in the m^- region. Furthermore, the energy level structure changes from a discrete and equally spaced system to a broadened and closely spaced one as the energy decreases. This, as well as the increase of state density with decreasing energy in m^- systems, enhances emissive transitions and can lead to overpopulation of the central cone region and rf emission. Application of a magnetic field along the (100) axis in Ge and Si increases the population of the negative masses. These effects will be discussed in detail below.

Experimentally, circularly polarized microwaves are used to separate the small branch of negative-mass heavy holes (Fig. 1) from the more numerous positive ones. With circular waves of given polarization the positive-mass holes resonate with H oriented along one direction, whereas negative-mass holes (and also electrons) are observed when H is reversed. The carriers are generated preferably from acceptors (and partly across the band-gap) by illumination. The photons provide, in addition, input energy to the Ge samples.[2] The apparatus used,[1],[2] except for its simplicity and emphasis on circular polarization, does not differ appreciably from earlier cyclotron resonance spectrometers.[10],[11],[12] The experiments cover the range of 12.5 to 17.1 k Mc and are carried out at liquid-helium temperatures.

Typical cyclotron resonance data[2] are shown in Fig. 2. The three *absorptive* resonances, heavy holes, light holes and electrons have been extensively studied earlier.[10],[11] Under the input power conditions of the experiment, the new spectrum is

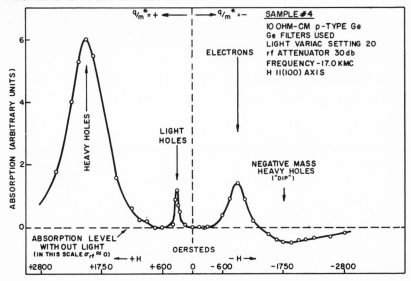

Fig. 2. Cyclotron resonance spectra of Ge taken with circularly polarized microwaves under optical excitation conditions

The new resonance on the −H side is assigned to carriers with negative effective mass (small branch in Fig. 1). The emission in the region of the "dip" overcomes rf losses in the Ge crystal.

emissive ("dip") and its position, intensity, and shape[2] are in good agreement with calculations based on the Ge band-structure constants of the Lincoln Laboratory Group.[11] The new spectrum saturates with increasing microwave power. It is not seen if H is misoriented by more than $18°$ from the (100) axis, as one would expect from the small angle of the negative-mass cone.[1] The rf reactance, as measured from the frequency shifts of the cavity resonance, is also *inverted* in the region of the "dip." This, of course, is the behavior to be expected from an emissive resonance and is considered as a substantial confirmation of the new spectrum to negative masses. It is interesting to note that the direction and magnitude of this frequency "pulling" (1 Mc in 17,000) for the positive mass spectrum (for example, the usual heavy holes) for the semiconductor case, compares well with that expected from similar effects observed with free electrons in gas discharges under cyclotron resonance conditions.[13] In the comparison, differences in m, f, τ, N and "filling factors" in the microwave cavities are taken into account. The shape of the spectrum (broad on the high-field side, Fig. 2) is in good agreement with the spread of m^* (Fig. 1) and has been discussed earlier.[2]

Basic quantum-mechanical considerations show that the energy-level structure of carriers with negative effective mass, in the presence of a magnetic field, is a system of inverted Landau levels (Fig. 3). A similar, but somewhat more complicated structure, applies[9] to the degenerate bands of heavy holes in Ge and Si. The negative-mass system, both in the simple case and

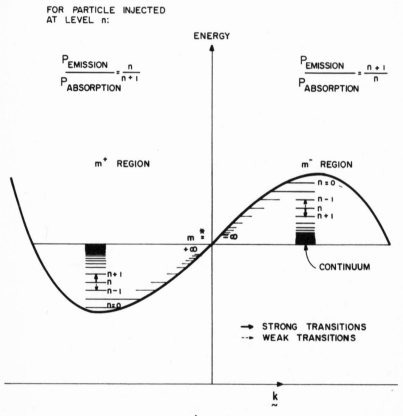

Fig. 3. Landau levels in the m^+ and m^- regions of a simple band

One obtains a closely similar structure for the energy vs k_y axis in Ge and Si for a given value of k_x which in these cases is oriented along the (100) axis. k_y is perpendicular to the (100) axis (see Fig. 1 and references 1,2,3, and 9).

those of the type of Ge and Si, is in equilibrium with the normal Landau levels of positive-mass carriers. The following may be noted:

a. The probability of transition (or the matrix element for electric dipole transitions) for a negative mass particle at a given level to one of lower energy is higher than the probability of transition to a higher one. The reverse holds for positive masses. Thus, the superiority of negative-mass systems as far as emission probability is concerned, over positive-mass systems, is conclusively demonstrated in a quantum-mechanical way. This "reversal of transition probabilities" for a particle in negative-mass regions favors emission, for a particle injected into that region, by exactly the same extent that the transition probabilities favor absorption in the positive-mass regions. This does not violate the Hermitean properties of the quantum-mechanical system. The emission-to-absorption probability (ratio of the squares of the matrix elements) in negative-mass regions is $(n + 1)/n$, ($n = 0, 1, 2$, etc.), hence it is larger than unity. By contrast, in positive-mass regions the ratio is $n/(n + 1)$, hence a particle injected in m^+ regions will absorb rf. This reversal shows the negative mobility, predicted earlier on other grounds,[3],[4],[5],[6],[7],[8] for a particle injected in m^- regions.

b. A negative-mass system has an upper energy limit to its allowed levels (near top of band), where the emission probability is a maximum.

c. The population inside the negative-mass cone is increased when a magnetic field is applied in the (100) direction. Thus, magnetic fields should be considered at least in theory, as means of enhancing negative-mass effects. For Landau level spacing hf smaller than kT, the fractional increase of negative masses is of order hf/kT, or about 20 percent in our case. This may explain, in part, the fact that the observed effect is somewhat larger (by a factor of about 1.5) than expected.[1] This effect (negative-mass paramagnetism) is quite analogous to Pauli's paramagnetism[14],[16] for electron spins, with $\pm m^*$ in our case playing the role of particles with $\pm s_z$.

d. Negligible effects are to be expected from negative masses in cyclotron resonance using circular polarization near equilibrium. The Boltzmann distribution overpopulates the region of unequally spaced levels (Fig. 3). Thus, not only utilization, but even observation of negative masses, requires power input to the crystal, and as strongly nonequilibrium conditions as possible. By contrast the same number of positive-mass carriers would yield large absorption near equilibrium (the absorptive transition probability is highest near the well-populated equally spaced levels). The very fact that a negative-mass system has an upper limit to its energies (Fig. 3) implies that no strong absorption can develop in this region even at equilibrium.

e. In this treatment a negative-mass system is simply one with strong matrix elements for rf emission. The emissive process, in addition to the favorable transition probabilities, is possibly enhanced by short relaxation (scattering, recombination) times[17] at the lower energies (edge of negative-mass cone in the case of Ge and Si). This is suggested by the Landau level broadening as one approaches the cone-edge (lower energy) regions. This broadening (lattice broadening) and its effect on other types of measurements in the m^+ case, has been shown by Harper and Peierls.[14],[16]

f. The upper-energy states in the negative-mass region are discrete and well-defined, whereas the lower final states are broad and closely spaced. In the entire region, as noted before, the matrix elements and rf transition probabilities are "reversed" i.e. favor emission, instead of absorption. The negative-mass region seems to be a unique quantum-mechanical system in that the matrix elements and transition probabilities are reversed over the entire range of the spectrum. Aside from the matrix elements, the contraction of the spectrum from a discrete system at high energies to broad and closely-spaced levels (Fig. 3) at the lowest states has an important and favorable effect in rf emission: A particle injected at the quantum-level n in the m^- region will favor the "smaller jump" rf emissive transition to the lower energy $n + 1$ level instead of the absorptive $n \rightarrow n - 1$ transition. The reverse is true in m^+ regions. This is confirmed by examination of the anharmonic oscillator wave functions in proceeding to the lower, closely-spaced levels: The probability density is concentrated mainly on the heavier m^* (lower-energy) side, which is another evidence of the tendency of m^- particles to fall towards lower and lower energies and thereby emit rf power. This again is a quantum equivalent of the negative mobility, under appropriate nonequilibrium input power conditions and relaxation processes, in directions perpendicular to the (100) crystallographic axis.

The strong emissive properties of quantum systems whose upper states are well-defined and discrete and the lower states broadened continually have been well-known in molecular spectroscopy in the optical region.[18] A spectrum analogous to the negative-mass dip is the strong ultraviolet emission from H_2 molecules in an electrical discharge. The upper states are the discrete $^3\Sigma$ states of H_2 and the final ones belong to the continuum of two hydrogen atoms with arbitrary kinetic energy.

g. It is noted that the state density Landau levels of the negative masses *increases* with *decreasing* energy. In nonequilibrium processes, where the particles are observed before they are "thermalized," this effect will enhance emissive processes, merely because of the higher availability of lower-energy states. In positive-mass regions the state density increases with increasing energy and strong absorption tendencies are indicated. These differences between positive and negative mass regions, of course, result from the reversal of energy levels in negative-mass regions that was noted earlier.

h. Contributions to the emission dip are mostly due to the central portion of the negative-mass cone. It is pointed out that in proceeding to lower energies the spectrum changes from discrete to a closely-spaced one as a result of increases in $|\,m^*\,|$ in proceeding away from the (100) axis. In proceeding away from the (100) axis ($10°$ to $15°$ in Ge), differences in m^* arise in different directions perpendicular to, but not crossing the (100) axis. This is an additional source of close-level spacing, and effectively reduces the mobility in regions far from the (100) axis. Similar effects, of course, are to be expected in the appropriate parts of m^+ regions.

These conclusions are in agreement with the earlier conductivity-type considerations used in this work,[1],[2] the basic behavior expected from negative-mass particles,[19] and the results obtained in the experiment.

The author is most grateful to her Majesty, Queen Frederika of Greece, for a detailed and helpful discussion of the negative-mass effect, and for encouragement in this work. Some aspects of this quantum approach were motivated by Her Majesty's suggestions.

I wish also to thank several of my colleagues at RCA Laboratories. In particular R. C. Duncan, Jr., J. J. Thomas, and R. C. Williams for experimental cooperation, and F. Herman, E. O. Johnson, B. Rosenblum, and M. C. Steele for several helpful discussions.

REFERENCES

1. G. C. Dousmanis, Phys. Rev. Lett. *1*, 55 (1958).
2. Dousmanis, Duncan, Thomas, and Williams, Phys. Rev. Lett. *1*, 404 (1958); Bull. Am. Phys. Soc. Ser. II, *4*, 28 (1959); the quantum approach was presented at this Am. Phys. Soc. meeting, New York (January, 1959).
3. H. Kroemer, Phys. Rev. *109*, 1856 (1958); Proc. IRE *47*, 397 (1959).
4. W. Shockley and W. P. Mason, J. Appl. Phys. *25*, 677 (1954).
5. Yu. A. Firsov, Soviet Physics, Solid State *1*, 48 (1959).
6. C. Kittel, Proc. Nat. Acad. Sci. *45*, 744 (1959).
7. D. T. Mattis and M. J. Stevenson, Phys. Rev. Lett. *3*, 18 (1959).
8. P. Kaus, Phys. Rev. Lett. *3*, 20 (1959).
9. G. C. Dousmanis, Phys. Rev. (to be published).
10. Dresselhaus, Kip, and Kittel, Phys. Rev. *98*, 368 (1955).
11. Dexter, Zeiger, and Lax, Phys. Rev. *104*, 637 (1956).
12. Fletcher, Yager, and Merritt, Phys. Rev. *100*, 747 (1955).
13. For measurements and earlier references for the free electron case in gas discharges inside microwave cavities see Fakuda, Matumoto, Uchida and Yoshimura, J. Phys. Soc. Japan *14*, 543 (1959).
14. See, for example, R. E. Peierls, *Quantum Theory of Solids,* Oxford University Press (1956).
15. A detailed quantum treatment of carriers in m regions can be carried out for specific cases by use of the methods of Luttinger and Kohn, Phys. Rev. *97*, 869 (1955) used so far in m^{+} cases; also by the methods of references 14 and 16.
16. P. G. Harper, Proc. Phys. Soc. *A 68*, 874 (1955) and 879 (1955).
17. Similar considerations have been made by Kittel, and by Mattis and Stevenson (references 6 and 7).
18. G. Herzberg, *Spectra of Diatomic Molecules*, Chapter 7, Prentice Hall (1939).
19. In maser terminology, the extent of population reversal in the negative-mass region (actually outwards flow of particles out of central cone region with rf emission) must approximate that of a

reversed Boltzmann distribution. This rough estimate is based on comparison of the experimental emissive "dip" with the positive mass spectrum, and on the present quantum scheme.

DISCUSSION

H. ZEIGER: Peierls[†] in 1933 pointed out that a region of negative mass would contribute a paramagnetic contribution to the magnetic susceptibility.

G. C. DOUSMANIS: Thank you for the reference. It should certainly be included in this paper.

M. J. STEVENSON: Do you have a more recent value of the effective mass of the negative mass holes based on your new higher frequency measurements? We have some data taken with phase-sensitive detection equipment at K-band which may be the result of a resonant reduction of absorption due to negative mass holes. However, the effective mass appears to be near the upper limit of the value given in your published data.

G. C. DOUSMANIS: The measurements at 17 kMc indicate that the observable absolute value of m^* is somewhat higher but within the limits of that we reported from the first measurements at 13.4 kMc. An increase with H is to be expected, and this was discussed at the Am. Phys. Soc. meeting in New York (reference 2). Measurements over a much wider range of frequencies are required to establish such variations.

†Peierls, Z. Physik *80* (1933).

EXPERIMENTS WITH PHONONS AT MICROWAVE FREQUENCIES

E. H. JACOBSEN

General Electric Research Laboratory, Schenectady, New York

GENERATION OF KILOMEGACYCLE ULTRASONIC WAVES

A SERIES of recent experiments[1],[2],[3],[4] has demonstrated the eminent feasibility of producing ultrasonic waves in quartz crystals at microwave frequencies by means of the piezoelectric effect. The method employed is essentially the same as that used in the more familiar ultrasonic experiments in the low radiofrequency range, but with the following exceptions:

a. The quartz crystals were prepared in the form of cylindrical rods. This arrangement eliminates the bond problem since each rod functions simultaneously as sample and transducer.

b. The dimensional tolerances of the quartz rods were held to within optical precision as the sound wavelength in this case is of the order of a few thousand angstroms.

c. The crystals were cooled to temperatures in the liquid-hydrogen range or below so as to minimize the attenuation due to scattering by the very high frequency thermal phonons.

Before discussing these experiments further, it may be well to consider briefly a matter not treated in the standard texts on piezoelectricity; namely, the manner in which a sound wave is initiated under application of an electric field. In Fig. 1 we consider the one-dimensional problem of a piezoelectric slab, with lateral dimensions large compared to thickness, placed between the plates of a parallel plate condenser; i.e., we assume the possibility of displacement and piezoelectric stress along only the x-direction. In this special case the stress-

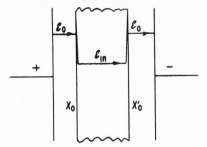

Fig. 1. Typical arrangement of piezoelectric crystal in parallel plate condenser

Source of mechanical deformation is at positions where gradient in piezoelectric stress is non-zero, in this case at x_o and x'_o.

strain equation is simply

$$T_x = c_{xx} \frac{\partial u}{\partial x} - e_{xx} E_x(t),$$

where T_x is the stress, c_{xx} the elastic constant, $\frac{\partial u}{\partial x}$ the strain, e_{xx} the piezoelectric stress constant, and $E_x(t)$ the electric field.

To derive the wave equation for ultrasound, we have simply to equate the inertial force and the divergence of the stress tensor. Thus

$$\rho \frac{\partial^2 u}{\partial^2 t} = \frac{\partial T_x}{\partial x} = c_{xx} \frac{\partial^2 u}{\partial x^2} - e_{xx} \frac{\partial E_x}{\partial x},$$

where ρ is the density. We see that in the general case this wave equation is inhomogeneous with a source term $\nabla_x E_x(t)$. In the more restrictive though typical case of Fig. 1, the above wave equation becomes homogeneous, since $\nabla_x E_x(t) = 0$ throughout the volume of the crystal. This situation implies that sound waves within the medium have their source either external to or at the boundaries of the crystal. That the boundaries act as sources follows from the boundary conditions which, in this case, require that the stress vanish at the free surfaces x_o and x_o'; i.e., $c_{xx} \nabla_x u = - e_{xx} E_x$ at x_o and x_o'. This condition leads to solutions for u of the form $\sin\{\omega t - k(x - x_o)\}$ and $\sin\{\omega t + k(x - x_o')\}$ which are really Green's function solutions to the inhomogeneous wave equation having source terms $\delta(x - x_o)$ and $\delta(x - x_o')$. The foregoing merely states that sources occur at positions where the piezoelectric stress is discontinuous. This statement is true generally as can be demonstrated by requiring continuity of the stress T_x and the displacement u across a boundary x_o joining two media of different elastic and electrical properties. Thus, for the simple case of Fig. 1, the mechanical deformation, with its coupled polarization field, starts at the two surfaces and then propagates inward rather than the other way around, as is sometimes supposed. It is, of course, possible in principle to create a gradient in the piezoelectric stress at some interior region and so initiate the deformation internally. However, such a configuration appears not generally useful nor easily achieved for ultrasonic waves in the kilomegacycle frequency range. For completeness, we remark that a more detailed account of the piezoelectric effect involving Maxwell's equations reveals the presence of an additional electroelastic wave consisting of coupled electromagnetic and mechanical components propagating through the crystal at a velocity very nearly that of light in a dielectric[6],[5]. However, this latter solution is of little importance to the problem at hand and will not be discussed further here.

The key role played by the surface of a piezoelectric crystal in initiating a sound wave was clearly demonstrated by the experiments of Bömmel and Dransfeld[1] which consisted of showing that the direction of sound propagation depends upon the angle between the surface normal and the crystallographic axes. This situation can obtain only if the sound wave is defined by and initiated at the surface.

With the foregoing in mind, the method by which microwave ultrasound is generated and detected is easily understood. Figure 2 outlines a typical pulsed microwave ultrasonic experiment which consists of two re-entrant cavities tuned to the transmitter frequency, between which is placed a crystalline

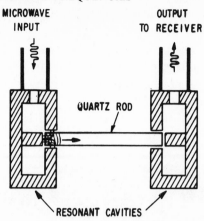

MICROWAVE
INPUT

OUTPUT
TO RECEIVER

QUARTZ ROD

RESONANT CAVITIES

Fig. 2. Microwave ultrasonic experiment: quartz crystal rod placed between re-entrant cavities tuned to transmitter frequency

Application of pulsed microwave field at one end produces sound wave pulse which arrives at opposite end after sonic delay time τ. Rod does not operate as a mechanically resonant system, as no standing waves are set up.

quartz rod. The end surfaces are polished optically flat and parallel, and located in regions of high electric field intensity as indicated. For special orientations of the rod axis and end faces relative to the crystallographic axes, a pulsed oscillating electric field impressed normal to one face will initiate a sound wave of the same frequency and duration which will propagate along the rod parallel to its axis.[7] Upon arrival of the sound wave at the opposite end, a portion[8] of its energy is converted to an electromagnetic field which is detected by a standard microwave superheterodyne receiver. The receiver output is demodulated and displayed on an oscilloscope, appearing as a series of pulses separated by a time interval characteristic of the sonic delay of the rod.

Figures 3 and 4 show the results of two such experiments performed at 9.4 kMc/sec with cavities and rod held at liquid-helium temperatures. Figure 3 gives the results for a longitudinal wave (compressional wave) produced by an X-cut rod; i.e., rod axis parallel to the X crystallographic axis of quartz. Visible in the lower portion of Fig. 3 are the first 150 of some

400 echoes. The complete echo train was observed by delayed sweep. The upper part of Fig. 3 shows the same picture on an expanded time base, where it is apparent that the first pulse arrives at the receiver cavity after a sonic delay time τ and all subsequent pulses are separated by 2 τ since these echoes have traveled twice the length of the rod. In Fig. 4 appear the results for a pure transverse wave produced by a BC-cut rod; i.e., rod axis 90° relative to the X-axis and +59° relative to the

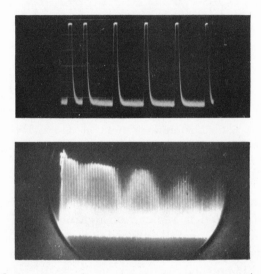

Fig. 3. Echo pattern for compressional waves (x-cut rod) at 9.4 kMc

Upper photograph identical with lower except for expanded time base. Apparent equal amplitude due to receiver saturation. "Beats" caused by propagation effects discussed in text. Measured velocity is 5.7 × 10^5 cm/sec.

Y-axis of quartz. Similar results have been achieved at 24 kMc/sec (see Fig. 5), and experiments at higher frequencies are under way. In this connection, we point out that the present frequency limit of these experiments is set by the microwave sources, which is currently in the neighborhood of 100 kMc/sec.

Aside from the apparent equal amplitude of many pulses in the two photographs (3 and 4) caused by receiver saturation, there is evident a modulation in amplitude or "beating" which

Fig. 4. Echo pattern for shear waves (BC-cut rod) at 9.4 kMc.

Apparent equal amplitude due to receiver saturation. "Beats" caused by propagation effects discussed in text. Measured velocity is 5.17×10^5 cm/sec.

turns out to be a common feature in all such pulse-echo experiments at microwave frequencies. A typical echo pattern, after correction for receiver saturation, is sketched in Fig. 6 and is due primarily to a superposition of three effects described in the next section.

Fig. 5. Echo pattern for compressional waves (x-cut) at 24 kMc.

"Beats" caused by propagation effects discussed in text. Measured velocity is 5.7×10^5 cm/sec.

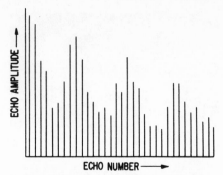

Fig. 6. Typical echo decay pattern at microwave frequencies showing the net interference effect of nonparallel end faces, off-axis propagation, and guided wave modes of differing velocities

The dominant modulation is due to nonparallel end faces, which is the usual situation in practice.

PROPAGATION EFFECTS

Assuming a typical sonic velocity of 5×10^5 cm/sec in a solid, it is immediately evident that for waves in the microwave frequency range, say 10 kMc/sec, the sonic wavelength will be of optical dimensions, in this case 5000 Å. This fact imposes a stringent requirement on the orientation, relative to the crystallographic axes, and parallelism of the end faces. Usually, the consequence of nonparallel faces is the dominant one. However, the effects of off-axis propagation, due to improper face orientation, and guided wave modes (discussed below) can easily be of comparable importance, and are manifest to some extent in almost every case.

The desirability of parallel faces is apparent from Fig. 7a. A wave of length λ is incident on an end face of diameter D. When the wave vector q makes an angle $\beta \simeq \lambda/2D$ relative to the face normal, the next half of the wave front begins to drive a portion of the face 180° out of phase with the remainder, resulting in partial cancellation of the total piezoelectric polarization. As β increases still further, which will happen after a sufficient number of reflections, the net piezoelectric polarization at the receiving end will go through a series of minima and maxima, each maximum being less than preceding one. We have neglected diffraction effects in this brief description. However, their inclusion will not be very important so long as $\frac{\lambda}{D} \ll 1$. A more complete analysis is presented by Roderick and Truell.[9] The conclusion to be drawn is that the end faces must be parallel to within an angle $\beta \sim \frac{\lambda}{2nD}$ if the first n echoes are to be free of "beats" caused by this effect. For $n = 10$, $D = 0.3$ cm, and $\lambda = 5000$ Å (10 kMc/sec), one obtains $\beta \simeq 5 \times 10^{-4}$ degrees. The upper limit on β, aside from the unwanted effect of "beats," is set by scattering from the side walls of the medium. For a 0.3 cm diameter rod of quartz operating at 10 kMc/sec, an angle $\beta \sim 0.1°$ appears to be a practical upper limit. The requirement of end face flatness, while not directly related to "beats," is as important as face parallelism if maximum signals are to be obtained. A surface that is flat to within a half sonic wavelength is desired.

The improper orientation of the end faces, relative to the crystallographic axes, is an effect often associated with the one just discussed. This phenomenon is illustrated in Fig. 7b, which shows the direction of propagation when the face normal is slightly off a pure mode axis. Such off-axis propagation will aggravate the effect of "beats," and may cause severe scattering from the walls, thereby washing out the signal entirely. An example of this latter situation is encountered for wave propa-

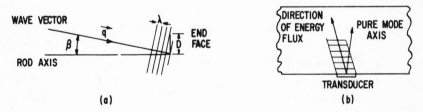

(a)   (b)

Fig. 7

(a) Wave vector incident at angle β relative to face normal. Under this condition, parts of the end face may be driven 180° out of phase, thereby reducing the net electric field at the receiver cavity. (b) Wave field propagates at skew angle unless surface is correctly oriented relative to pure mode axis.

gation along a Y-cut rod (rod axis parallel to Y-axis of quartz) because the Y-axis is not a pure mode axis for transverse or longitudinal waves. If, for example, we attempt to propagate a shear wave along a Y-cut rod, by impressing an electric field normal to an end face, the wave will propagate off the Y-axis in the Y-Z plane by an angle $\tan^{-1} \left(\dfrac{2c_{14}}{c_{11} - c_{12}} \right) = 23.2°.$[10] In this particular case no net signal can be detected at the receiving end because the wall reflection breaks up the wave front into a series of wavelets of random phase which average to zero on the receiving face. Nonetheless, sonic energy is still present in the form of a complicated wave pattern, and its presence can be detected by other than piezoelectric means; for example, light diffraction and spin resonance perturbation effects (see reference 4 in this connection). In contrast to the Y-axis, the X-axis is a pure mode axis for both compressional and shear waves, the Z-axis is pure for only compressional waves, and the BC and AC axes are pure for shear waves. Thus, if wave propagation collinear to the rod axis is desired, the proper face orientation, for a given vibration direction, is essential.

Finally, in addition to off-axis effects, there remains for discussion the fundamental problem of wave propagation in a bounded, as opposed to an infinite, medium. The phenomenon of guided waves and modes of propagation is already familiar with regard to microwave electronics. We would expect very similar ideas to hold for mechanical waves propagating in solid media when the sound field completely fills the volume, and indeed this is so. The phenomenon of guided waves in solid media was recognized long ago and has been discussed by numerous authors.[11],[12],[13],[14],[15] However, in a recent series of papers by Redwood and Lamb,[16],[17],[18] the previous ideas have been expanded and applied to the case of pulsed wave trains in bounded media. For illustration we outline below a special case discussed by Redwood.[18]

Consider the propagation of a compressional wave along a slab of isotropic material which is semi-infinite in the x-direction, infinite in the y-direction, and of finite thickness D in the z-direction. This two-dimensional problem is represented in Fig. 8. The main point of Redwood's analysis is to show that if the end at $x = 0$ is driven at frequency ω_o as a "piston" source (the entire end surface displaced uniformly at frequency ω_o), several modes are propagated, each with a slightly different phase velocity.[19] This follows from a Fourier analysis of the x-displacement as a function of z across the finite "piston" source. The first two modes, labeled 1 and 2, are shown in the diagram. Each of these modes in turn can be decomposed into a set of two or more traveling plane waves. Mode 1, for example, decomposes into a set of two plane longitudinal waves (solid lines). These components are reflected from the boundaries (guided), and at each reflection produce a transverse wave

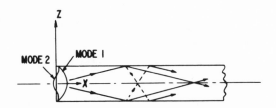

Fig. 8. Guided wave modes in a slab of thickness D*, infinite in the y-direction, and semi-infinite in the x-direction*

Each mode propagates at a slightly different velocity and is composed of a set of plane waves. See the discussion by Redwood (reference 18).

(dotted line). In the general case, the net result of the transverse waves is to drain energy from the primary longitudinal waves and to produce a set of secondary (and higher-order) longitudinal waves which arrive at a given point x after the primary waves. Fortunately, it turns out that for $\lambda/D \ll 1$, which is the case in the kilomegacycle region, the effect of transverse wave generation at the boundaries is usually entirely negligible.

In the case of compressional wave propagation along a cylindrical rod, the essential features of the above analysis remain: for a "piston" source of given frequency, a series of modes are generated. Each mode resembles qualitatively those sketched in Fig. 8 and propagates with a slightly different velocity, giving rise to interference or "beating" at the receiving end due to phase differences between the modes.

Thus, a typical experiment involves the superposition of at least three effects: nonparallel end surfaces, off-axis propagation arising from misorientation, and simultaneous propagation of two or more modes of different phase velocity. In general, these effects produce an irregular echo decay envelope and make absolute attenuation measurements via the pulse method very difficult in the kilomegacycle frequency range. Such effects will become more critical, of course, as the frequency is increased.

Although the foregoing analysis has centered mainly around the case of compressional waves, it applies equally well to the propagation of shear waves; we omit further discussion of it here.

PHONON-PHONON SCATTERING IN QUARTZ

Of the various types of phonon interactions possible in crystals, the one appropriate to quartz, and most easily studied experimentally, is the phonon-phonon scattering caused by anharmonic forces between atoms. This interaction shows up clearly in the attenuation versus temperature measurements of Figs. 9 and 10. These data[20] span a frequency range of from 1 to 24 kMc/sec and were obtained via the pulse-echo technique. Because of the great difficulty in establishing the absolute value of attenuation at high frequencies, due to interference effects described above, only the relative *change* in attenuation between a given pair of echoes is plotted for the 9.4 and 24 kMc/sec experiments. Thus all curves were normalized to zero at 4.2°K; i.e., the residual relative attenuation measured at 4.2°K was subtracted off. The *average* attenuation for a series of echoes at this temperature ranged as low as $\frac{1}{20}$ db/cm in some crystals and as high as 1 db/cm in others.

Recent theoretical work by Bömmel and Dransfeld[21] and by Ehrenreich and Woodruff[22] of this laboratory, based in part on the ideas of a calculation by Akhieser,[23] predicts an attenuation curve in rather good agreement with present experimental results.

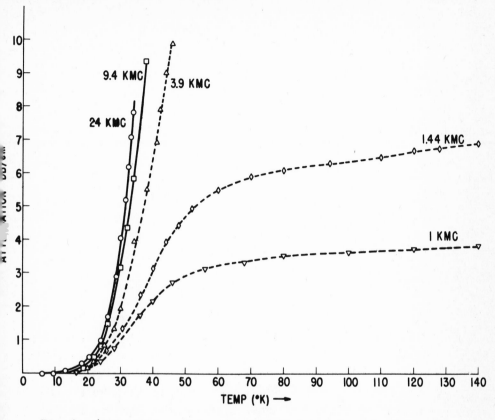

Fig. 9. Attenuation versus temperature measurements for com-
pressional waves in quartz (x-cut rods)

Data at 9.4 and 24 kMc from work of the author. Data at 1, 1.4, and
3.9 kMc taken from the work of Bömmel and Dransfeld (reference 1).

The approach is essentially phenomenological. It considers
the effect of a macroscopic perturbation, in this case the microwave ultrasound, on the distribution function of the thermal
phonons; i.e., phonons of frequencies greater than about 10^{12}
cycles per second. Akhieser solves the Boltzmann transport
equation for the phonon distribution function as affected by the
ultrasonic perturbation and uses this distribution function to
calculate the change in entropy of the thermal phonon gas.
Once the rate of entropy production is known, it is a simple

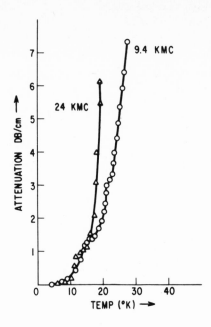

Fig. 10. Attenuation versus temperature measurements for shear waves in quarts (AC-cut rod)

matter to determine the attenuation coefficient Γ for the sound wave. Ehrenreich and Woodruff have extended Akhieser's treatment and as the lowest-order approximation they obtain the following equation for Γ:

$$\Gamma = \frac{\gamma^2 \omega^2 T}{\rho v^3} \sum_{qj} S_{qj} \frac{1}{\omega^2 \tau} \left\{ 1 - \frac{1}{2\omega\tau} \tan^{-1} 2\omega\tau \right\},$$

where γ = Grüneisen's constant
         ω = angular frequency of ultrasonic wave
         T = temperature
         v = velocity of sound (assumed constant for all modes)
         ρ = density
   S_{qj} = contribution to specific heat from mode $\vec{q}$, j
         τ = thermal phonon relaxation time, a function of $\vec{q}$, j which in the crudest approximation is replaced by an average value.

Better approximations are being developed.

From data on the specific heat and thermal conductivity of quartz at low temperatures, it is possible to calculate the sum over $S_{q,j}$ and the average relaxation time τ of the thermal phonons. With these values and a suitable choice of $\gamma(1 \leqslant \gamma \leqslant 2)$ for a given frequency, the above equations for Γ fits the curves of Figs. 9 and 10 remarkably well except for the low temperature plateaus in the data on transverse waves. These plateaus are thought to result from imperfections, although their role in the phonon-phonon scattering is not clear at this time.

Ehrenreich and Woodruff make the following assumptions in deriving the above expression for Γ: 1. The transverse and longitudinal phonon branches come to the same temperature when the crystal is strained. 2. The relaxation time τ for all thermal phonons may be set equal to an average value (this is the assumption mentioned in defining τ). 3. The condition $\omega\tau < 1$ is satisfied. The first assumption is equivalent to the statement that the perturbing sound wave produces the same effect on a thermal phonon regardless of its polarization or that of the sound wave. As these authors point out, the first two assumptions are not correct and not easily justified, but appear to give reasonable results because of the summations over phonon modes which enter into the calculation of Γ. The third approximation, $\omega\tau < 1$, is valid only at the higher temperatures, where Γ is nearly independent of temperature, as shown in the curves of Bömmel and Dransfeld in Fig. 9. (High temperature plateaus are expected in the curves of Γ for 9.4 and 24 kMc/sec. Unfortunately, such large values of Γ elude present methods of measurement.) Thus, without questioning the validity of the first two assumptions, the present theory could only be expected to work at the higher temperatures. However, the equation for Γ matches quite well both the low ($\omega\tau > 1$) and high ($\omega\tau < 1$) temperature regions, at least as regards the available data. Ehrenreich and Woodruff regard the agreement between this simple expression for Γ and experiment as somewhat fortuitous, although its derivation is undoubtedly based on the correct general picture.[24] They have carried their analysis much further than indicated here and additional theoretical and experimental work at this laboratory and elsewhere is in progress to clarify and extend the present ideas.

In conclusion it should be mentioned that, in addition to phonon-phonon interaction, there are the interesting and important phenomena of electron spin-lattice relaxation and electron-phonon interaction as pertains, for example, to semi- and superconductors. Regrettably, it is not possible to report on these topics at this writing. However, experiments aimed at exploring these areas have been planned, and it is hoped that valuable information will be forthcoming as techniques are developed.

The author gratefully acknowledges many informative and stimulating discussions with T. O. Woodruff and E. Ehrenreich concerning phonon-phonon interactions, and with M. M. Saffren relating to variational methods. It is also a pleasure to thank R. A. Dehn for his frequent and generous counsel concerning microwave techniques.

REFERENCES

1. H. C. Bömmel and K. Dransfeld, Phys. Rev. Lett. *1*, 234 (1958).
2. E. H. Jacobsen, Phys. Rev. Lett. *2,* 249 (1959).
3. H. E. Bömmel and K. Dransfeld, Phys. Rev. Lett. *2*, 298 (1959).
4. E. H. Jacobsen, N. S. Shiren, and E. B. Tucker, Phys. Rev. Lett. *3*, 81 (1959).
5. J. J. Kyame, J. Acoustical Soc. America *21,* 160 (1949).
6. K. Huang, Proc. Royal Soc. *A 208*, 352 (1951).
7. The magnitude of $\nabla_x E_x$ within the rod, though finite (see Fig. 2), is very small compared to the discontinuity of the piezoelectric stress at the end face and is therefore only a weak source of sound. Furthermore, sound originating at the interior will be difficult to detect piezoelectrically because the wave fronts so generated will be of irregular shape and therefore produce negligible total polarization across the surface at the receiving end.
8. H. E. Bömmel and K. Dransfeld (see reference 1) give a conversion ratio of ultrasonic to electromagnetic energy of between 10^{-3} and 10^{-4}. This ratio has not been checked experimentally at 9.4 and 24 kMc/sec.
9. R. L. Roderick and R. Truell, J. Appl. Phys. *23*, 267 (1952).
10. P. C. Waterman, Phys. Rev. *113*, 1240 (1959); M. J. P. Musgrave, Reports on Progress in Physics *22*, 74 (1959).
11. L. Pochammer, J. reine angew. Math. *81*, 324 (1876).
12. C. Chree, Trans. Cambridge Phil. Soc. *14*, 250 (1889).
13. D. Bancroft, Phys. Rev. *59*, 588 (1941).

14. R. M. Davies, Phil. Trans. Royal Soc. A *24*, 375 (1948).
15. H. J. McSkimin, J. Acoustical Soc. America *28*, 484 (1956).
16. M. Redwood and J. Lamb, Proc. Phys. Soc. *B 70*, 136 (1957).
17. M. Redwood, Proc. Phys. Soc. *B 70*, 721 (1957); *B 72*, 841 (1958).
18. M. Redwood, J. Acoustical Soc. America *31*, 442 (1959).

19. Typically, for $\frac{D}{\lambda} > 10$, the velocities of the lowest modes differ from one another and from the corresponding velocity in the infinite medium by less than 0.1 percent (see reference 18).
20. The data for longitudinal waves in the 1 to 3.9 kMc range are taken from the work of Bömmel and Dransfeld (see reference 3).
21. H. Bömmel and K. Dransfeld, Bull. Am. Phys. Soc. II *4*, 226 (1959).
22. private communication.
23. A. Akhieser, J. Physics (USSR) *1*, 277 (1939).
24. Conyers Herring has recently suggested that in the region $\omega\tau \geqslant 1$ it may be necessary to consider second-order three-phonon processes; i.e., two three-phonon processes in succession where the intermediate state does not conserve energy. Such a process could be very effective in determining the ultrasonic attenuation because of the large number of intermediate paths available as contrasted with a single three-phonon energy conserving transition (personal communication).

DISCUSSION

G. W. FARNELL: Have you tried to get sound waves into other materials for your paramagnetic experiments?

What bonding agents do you use between the quartz and the second material?

E. H. JACOBSEN: We have succeeded in transferring ultrasound out of the quartz into other material via bonds of indium, nonag grease, araldite cement, and General Electric Glyptal. None of these bonds appear to be very efficient.

C. F. SQUIRE: To form a good bond for low temperature work between quartz and a specimen, one can use natural gas, which liquefies at 100°K (approximately) and then put the transducer on to the sample. The bond of natural gas then goes glassy and allows a good binder between sample and quartz transducer on down to 1°K.

P. WAGNER: Is it possible to give a qualitative description of the phonon spectrum under your ultrasonic excitations?

E. H. JACOBSEN: The distribution of phonons, $N(\nu)$, in the vicinity of the ultrasonic drive frequency will approach a delta function with peak value corresponding to a mode temperature of several thousand degrees.

J. RCTHSTEIN: Have you considered the possibility of shaping the ends of the quartz rod to simplify the propagation modes, increase the efficiency of coupling, etc.?

E. H. JACOBSEN: We have considered shaping the ends so as to favor one mode, but this is a difficult task. We have not as yet attempted it. End shaping would improve the efficiency only if it resulted in a stronger electric field at the quartz surface for the same cavity Q. For physically realizable shapes, I don't believe significant gains in efficiency could be achieved by this means.

H. GERRITSEN: What was your electrical to mechanical efficiency obtained at 24 KMC/sec?

E. H. JACOBSEN: We have no reliable experimental determination of the efficiency at 24 KMC, though we hope to do so eventually be means of X-ray diffraction. Conversion of electromagnetic to sonic energy is simply a transformer problem. If the cavity and quartz losses are small (nearly lossless transformer) then nearly all the electromagnetic energy will be converted to a sound wave. In practice, high conversion efficiencies will be difficult to achieve if the electromechanical coupling coefficient k is small since this situation will require a high cavity Q (high "turns ratio"). For quartz operating as a mechanically nonresonant system at 24 KMC, we would need a $Q \simeq 10^6$ to achieve high conversion efficiency.

EFFECTS OF 9.2 KMC ULTRASONICS ON ELECTRON-SPIN RESONANCES

N. S. SHIREN and E. B. TUCKER
General Electric Research Laboratory

UTILIZING ULTRASONIC techniques which have been reported recently,[1,2] we have observed the effects of 9.2 kmc ultrasonic vibrations on electron spin resonances. The experimental technique and some preliminary results on resonances due to manganese impurities in quartz, and also on those due to radiation-induced centers[3] in quartz, have previously been reported.[4] Additional results on these systems and on iron impurities in quartz have been obtained. In particular, several experiments have been performed, or are in progress, on the radiation-induced centers in order to understand the large bandwidth (≥ 1000Mc/s) of the ultrasonic interaction with this system.

Saturation of the electron spin-nuclear spin double-flip transition in manganese, by ultrasonics, has been observed under conditions for which this transition is forbidden for oscillating magnetic fields. This result indicates that the ultrasonic technique may have important applications to nuclear polarization.

REFERENCES

1. H. E. Bommel and K. Dransfield, Phys. Rev. Lett. *1*, 234 (1958).
2. E. H. Jacobsen, Phys. Rev. Lett. *2*, 249 (1959).
3. Griffiths, Owen, and Ward, *Report of the Conference on Defects in Crystalline Solids*, The Physical Society (1955).
4. Jacobsen, Shiren, and Tucker, Phys. Rev. Lett. *3*, 81 (1959).

DISCUSSION

B. BÖLGER: [asked if the phonon absorption bandwidth for metal impurities in quartz was as large as that for radiation-induced centers]

N. S. SHIREN: The large bandwidth interaction exists only in the case of the radiation-induced resonances. For the transition metal impurity resonances the interaction bandwidth is roughly the same as the observed resonance line-width.

PULSED FIELD MILLIMETER WAVE MASER*

S. FONER, L. R. MOMO, A. MAYER** and R. A. MYERS [†]

Lincoln Laboratory, Massachusetts Institute of Technology

THE SOLID-STATE c.w. three-level maser[1] has been operated over a wide range of frequencies. Despite many advantages of this c.w. maser operation, one limitation exists — the pump frequency must always be greater than the signal frequency. This leads to limitations on the operation of such masers in the millimeter wavelength region. In particular, continuous microwave sources above 70 kMcps are severely limited in both power output and tunability, which in turn imposes limits on such maser operation. With suitable paramagnetic materials, it is expected that some modifications such as optical pumping may be useful.

Pulsed operation provides an alternate approach to very high frequency masers. In this paper, recent experiments [2],[3] with a pulsed-field ruby maser, operating at 4.2 °K, are described. The results demonstrate the feasibility of generating or amplifying very high frequencies on a pulsed basis by conversion into coherent radiation of magnetic field energy supplied to an inverted spin population. To date, operation has been observed over a wide range of frequencies extending to the 70 kMcps range; no serious limitation has been noted for higher frequency operation. One advantage of such pulsed operation is that con-

*The work reported in this paper was performed at Lincoln Laboratory, a center for research operated by Massachusetts Institute of Technology with the joint support of the U.S. Army, Navy, and Air Force.

**Now at Convair, San Diego, California.

†permanent address, Harvard University.

ventional maser materials can be employed. Probably a more important advantage of pulsed operation is that it is possible to extract more energy from the spin system as the frequency of operation is increased. Thus the use of a pulsed maser as a source in the millimeter or submillimeter range appears feasible.

PRINCIPLE OF OPERATION

The pulsed-field maser requires both an inverted spin population and a controllable pulsed field to "tune" the energy of this inverted spin population. An inverted spin population can be produced on a pulsed basis by adiabatic fast passage or a 180 degree pulse, or in a continuous manner by pumping a $\Delta M = 2$ transition as in the c.w. maser. Most of the experiments described here utilized the latter method.

Ruby[4] has been used for this pulsed maser. The pertinent transitions and the energy levels of Cr^{3+} in Al_2O_3 for applied fields perpendicular to the c-axis are shown in Fig. 1. For

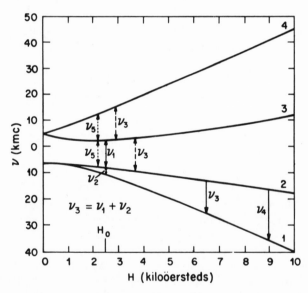

Fig. 1. Energy level diagram for Cr^{3+} in Al_2O_3 with applied field perpendicular to c-axis

Operating points for pumping at $\nu_3 = \nu_1 + \nu_2$, and emission at ν_3 and ν_4 are indicated.

simplicity, the $\Delta M = 2$ transition between levels 1 and 3 is saturated at a pump frequency $\nu_3 = \nu_1 + \nu_2$, corresponding to a fixed dc bias field, H_o, above any field where cross-relaxation effects [5] may occur, such as at ν_5. (The c.w. three-level maser would operate at $\nu_2 \ll \nu_3$, when $H = H_o$, with an inverted spin population between levels 2 and 1). If H is now increased to H_i in a time short compared to the spin-lattice relaxation time, oscillation or amplification should be obtainable at any frequency $\nu_i > \nu_2$ for which suitable maser cavity resonances occur. A gain of energy in the ratio of ν_i/ν_2 over the continuous three-level maser is obtained at the expense of energy extracted from the pulsed magnetic field. Wavelengths of about 1 mm would be generated at a field of 100 kilo-oersteds.

MASER CONSTRUCTION

A view of the pulsed-field maser assembly is shown in Fig. 2. This particular arrangement, although it makes a somewhat inefficient use of the pulsed-field energy, permits controlled maser operation.

The maser reflection cavity, a solid rectangular parallelepiped of ruby, was designed with the two lowest modes (TE_{101} and TE_{102}) occurring at $\nu_3 = 12.7$ kMc/sec and $\nu_4 = 19.2$ kMc/sec, respectively, with undercoupled loaded cavity Q's of about 2000 and 4800, respectively. The pump power and radiated energy were transmitted to and from the single cavity coupling iris by a tapered dielectric transition section attached to K_u-band waveguide. Both the dielectric transition and cavity were coated with a 0.001 in. silver plating in order to assure uniform penetration of the pulsed magnetic field throughout the cavity volume. The pulsed field, H_p, was generated in a solenoid (13 cm length, 7 cm i.d.) by discharge of a 2000-μf variable voltage capacitor bank. [6] A peak field of 9.4 kilo-oersteds was obtained at 1000 volts with a half period of about 3 msec (see Figs. 3A, 3B). The maser cavity assembly and surrounding glass Dewars were inserted in the solenoid, and the entire assembly was fixed between the pole faces of an electromagnet. The field orientations were: H_{rf} perpendicular to the c-axis, and H_o perpendicular to both the c-axis and to H_p. The mutually orthogonal orientation of H_o, H_p, and the c-axis assured that the re-

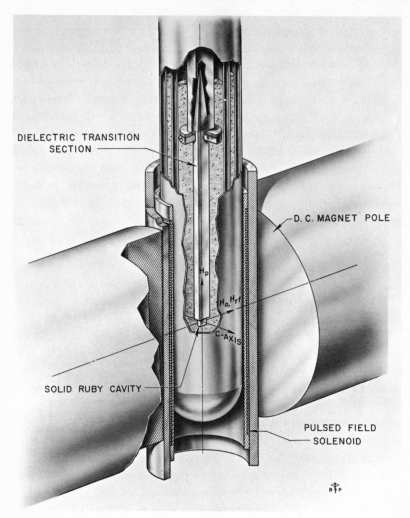

DIELECTRIC TRANSITION SECTION

D. C. MAGNET POLE

H_p

H_o, H_{rf}

C-AXIS

SOLID RUBY CAVITY

PULSED FIELD SOLENOID

Fig. 2. Pulsed-field maser assembly

sultant H was always greater than H_o, and furthermore, that H always remained perpendicular to the c-axis. The field dependence of the energy levels therefore remained as indicated in Fig. 1.

OPERATION

In order to demonstrate maser operation unambiguously, only emission from the maser cavity was analyzed. The pumping power was gated off within 10 μsec of the start of the pulsed field rise, and oscillations were observed at, e.g. ν_3 or ν_4 during the traversal of H_p through the appropriate resonance. Within the accuracy of the pulsed-field measurement, emission occurred as predicted from Fig. 1. When the pump power was not turned off, population redistribution between levels 4-3 and 3-2 was observed (see Fig. 1). Typical oscillation characteristics at 4.2 °K for the ν_4 mode are shown in Figs. 3C and 3D. The expanded scale of Fig. 3D shows the pulsating character of the oscillations, and the sensitive dependence of the emission pulses on the particular magnetic field sweep rate. The number of pulses and total energy output could be controlled by varying the pulsed-field sweep rate — the more rapid traversals resulted in lower peak output, and for a sufficiently fast rise time, no oscillations were observed. In this way it was possible to avoid emission at ν_3 completely, and yet obtain ν_4 emission at the peak of the pulsed field. When only a small portion of the inverted spin system radiated at ν_4, further emission at ν_3 was observed during the field decay. Initial results showed that the peak power output at ν_4 was greater than 300 μw, and the integrated output energy for a typical case, e.g. Fig. 3D, was greater than 0.04 erg. In both cases measurements were made of energy arriving at the crystal detector. Calculations show that a total energy of about 2 ergs would be available in the cavity if complete saturation between levels 1-3 were obtained, and if cavity losses and the spin-lattice relaxation were neglected. More recently, with increased cavity coupling and greater pump power, a peak output power of more than 2.5 mw has been obtained at 12.7 and 19.2 kMcps. The size of the single coupling iris has proven a critical variable for this maser operation, determining both which modes are observed and the power output. More than 0.025 mw has been detected with this system at about 40 kMcps. The results in the millimeter wave range are underestimated by a large unknown factor because of the non-optimum microwave system employed.

Extension of maser operation to the millimeter wave region was attained by systematically increasing the peak pulsed field. Oscillations at the two lowest TE_{10n} modes, 12.7 kMcps and 19.2 kMcps, were identified; above these frequencies, identifi-

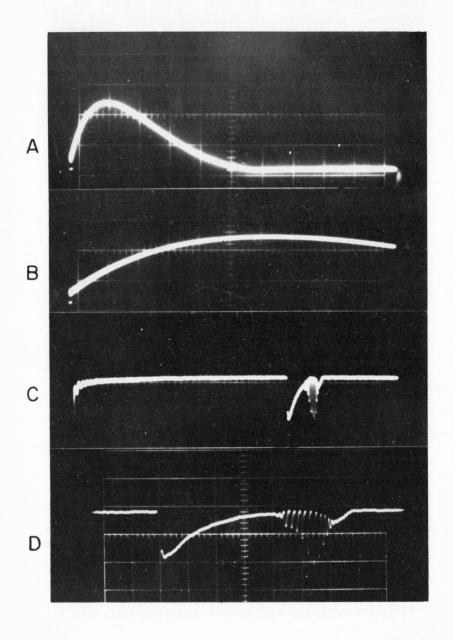

cation of cavity modes was not feasible. Lower frequency limits were ascertained by means of microwave cut-off filters introduced into the detection system, and the emission frequencies were calculated by comparing the magnitude of the applied field at emission with the energy difference ν_{12}. The highest frequency obtained thus far is 75 ± 5 kMcps; operation at higher frequencies has been limited by the available 30 köe peak magnitude of the pulsed field. More than 14 different emission frequencies have been observed in the 12 to 70 kMcps range (10 emission frequencies were above 30 kMcps) with up to six distinguishable emission frequencies during a given field traversal.

The characteristics of the pulsed-field maser are illustrated by a selected number of oscillograms shown in Figs. 4 and 5. These were obtained during a single extended experiment. All of the emissions in this series occurred above 30 kMcps, and were detected with an untuned 8 mm crystal video detector attached to a crude hybrid microwave system (see Fig. 6) composed of the K_u-band maser assembly attached to a series tee, K_u-band to K_a-band transition and a long 30 kMcps cut-off filter. Although the video response to a particular frequency was not predictable, any observed emission can be compared with itself as the peak amplitude of the pulsed field is varied. The peak pulsed field, H_{max}, and maximum observed emission frequency, f_{max}, are given for each oscillogram, and in two particular cases the frequencies of the prominent emissions are tabulated. Note that as H_{max} is increased, higher frequency emissions are observed first near H_{max}. Further increase of H_{max} leads to some

---

Fig. 3. Oscillograms of low frequency pulsed-field maser operation at 4.2°K

A. Pulsed magnetic field *versus* time — horizontal time scale 500 μsec/cm.
B. Pulsed magnetic field *versus* time — horizontal time scale 100 μsec/cm.
C. Envelope detector output showing 19.2-kMc/sec emission of pulsed-field maser — horizontal scale 100 μsec/cm. Emission is obtained during both rise and decay of field pulse.
D. 19.2-kMc/sec emission — horizontal time scale expanded to 20 μsec/cm. An intense burst of radiation occurs at the onset of emission, accounting for the short blank portion of the oscillogram.

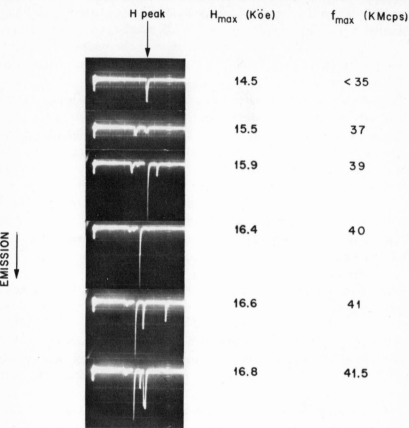

	H peak	H_{max} (Köe)	f_{max} (KMcps)
		14.5	< 35
		15.5	37
		15.9	39
		16.4	40
		16.6	41
		16.8	41.5

EMISSION

Fig. 4. Oscillograms showing relative emission versus time for pulsed-field maser operation in the millimeter wavelength region

The time at which the field reaches its peak value corresponds to H peak. The maximum field attained for a given oscillogram is indicated as H_{max}, and the maximum observed emission frequency is indicated as f_{max}. The horizontal time scale is 200 μsec/cm from left to right.

loss in resolution of the emission pulse, but the peak amplitude of the emission increases to a maximum for a characteristic field sweep rate (approximately 20 öe/μsec). Finally, for a sufficiently rapid rise of H_p, the given emission disappears. Meanwhile, several higher frequency emissions develop at still higher peak fields. Observable emissions were obtained at

30 Köe, which was the maximum field available with the present arrangement.

During preliminary attempts to obtain inversions of successive levels by adiabatic rapid passage, the biasing dc magnetic field was reduced from H_o before the pulsed magnetic field was applied. To permit such operation it was, of course, necessary to delay gating off the klystron until the pump transition was traversed. Under these conditions, saturation (or, perhaps,

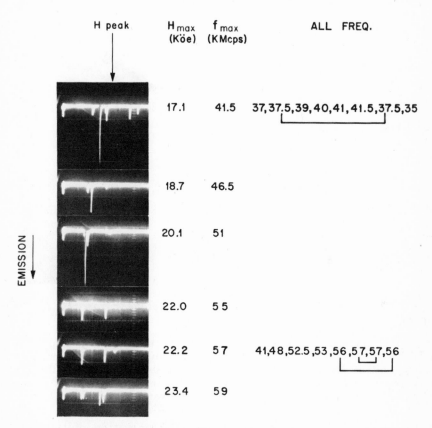

H peak	H_{max} (Köe)	f_{max} (KMcps)	ALL FREQ.
	17.1	41.5	37,37.5,39,40,41,41.5,37.5,35
	18.7	46.5	
	20.1	51	
	22.0	55	
	22.2	57	41,48,52.5,53,56,57,57,56
	23.4	59	

EMISSION

Fig. 5. Oscillograms of millimeter emission versus time for pulsed fields above those used for Fig. 4

The time scale and notation are the same as that in Fig. 4. The prominent emissions of two particular oscillograms are indicated in the column marked "all frequencies." Emissions identified on both the rise and decay of the pulsed field are joined by horizontal brackets.

partial inversion) of the normal pump transition at H_o was obtained on a transient basis, and the millimeter wavelength output remained substantially unaffected. In this experiment, millimeter wave maser operation was observed when the biasing dc field was reduced by as much as 700 öe. The limitations of this mode of operation include pumping power, traversal time of

Fig. 6. Hybrid microwave assembly employed from 12 to 70 kMcps

The components are from left to right: the maser cavity held by a polystyrene clamp attached to the tapered dielectric transition, K_u-band silvered stainless-steel waveguide, K_u-band series tee (through which pumping power is fed), tapered section, long 30 kMcps waveguide cut-off filter, and finally a K_a-band crystal detector.

the pulsed field through the $\Delta M = 2$ pump transition, initial spin populations, and the direction of the resultant magnetic field at the pump transition. Normally, one pumps most efficiently with H_o parallel to H_{rf}. However, when H_o is reduced by 700 oe, the resultant field is almost at 45° to H_{rf} when the pump transition is traversed.

SPIN-LATTICE RELAXATION

Operation of pulsed or c.w. masers would be limited to low magnetic field if the spin-lattice relaxation time varied inversely as some large power of the magnetic field. To some extent this problem can be circumvented with the pulsed maser by simply reducing the pulsed-field rise time. Some limited results have been deduced from the present maser operation.

Maser oscillations were detected at the peak of pulsed fields as high as 29.2 köe, for which the field rise-time was 600 μsec. This observation requires that any field dependence of the spin-lattice relaxation time in ruby be small, if not entirely negligible, for pulsed fields up to 29.2 köe. Such field dependence has not been extensively studied, either experimentally or theoretically,[7] but it has been suggested that it is of the form

$$1/T_1 = (1 + bH^n)/T_o.$$

If this is true, either $bH^n \ll 1$, or n is small. In the latter case, it is possible to show that $n \leqslant 1.1$ for $bH^n \gg 1$ by using our result in conjunction with a value of $T_1 = 25$ msec at 4.2°K and 4 köe obtained by Kikuchi *et al.*[8] In order to investigate the field dependence, more detailed measurements of $T_1(H)$ are being made at high dc magnetic fields.

CONCLUSIONS

With a pulsed-field maser it is possible to convert magnetic field energy into coherent radiation; one can extract more energy from a spin system as its emission frequency is increased. This suggests that such devices may be most useful for generation and amplification of energy in the millimeter and submillimeter wavelength region. For instance, 10^{19} spins radiating at 300 kMcps with a repetition rate of only 10 per second would yield an average power of 20 milliwatts — a power somewhat above that presently available.

A number of alternate schemes for pulsed field masers are feasible. One method, utilizing adiabatic fast passage, has recently been demonstrated by Hoskins.[9] Probably materials with very large zero-field splittings will be most useful. Unfortunately many of these materials have not been investigated because the required high fields and frequencies have not been available. Pulsed-field techniques are currently being applied to such systems to study the energy levels and spin interaction phenomena.

We are indebted to B. Feldman, J. J. Kelley, and B. Howland for valuable assistance, and to R. H. Kingston, H. J. Zeiger, and S. H. Autler, of this laboratory, and to S. Shapiro of the Arthur D. Little Co., Cambridge, Mass. for informative discussions.

REFERENCES

1. N. Bloembergen, Phys. Rev. *104*, 324 (1956).
2. Foner, Momo, and Mayer, Phys. Rev. Lett. *3*, 36 (1959).
3. Momo, Myers, and Foner (to be published).
4. Pink ruby (nominally 0.1 percent Cr^{3+}) supplied by Linde Air Products Company.
5. Bloembergen, Shapiro, Pershan, and Artman, Phys. Rev. *114*, 445 (1959).
6. S. Foner and H. H. Kolm, Rev. Sci. Instr. *28*, 799 (1957).
7. See for instance, J. H. Van Vleck, Phys. Rev. *57*, 426 (1940).
8. Kikuchi, Lambe, Makhov, and Terhune, Project Michigan Report No. 2144-377-T, unpublished (March, 1959).
9. See R. H. Hoskins, Phys. Rev. Lett. *3*, 174 (1959); J. Appl. Phys. *30*, 797 (1959); and R. H. Hoskins and G. Birnbaum, paper in this volume.

PULSED SOLID-STATE MASERS FOR MILLIMETER-WAVE GENERATION*

R. H. HOSKINS and G. BIRNBAUM

Research Laboratories, Hughes Aircraft Company, Culver City, California

IT WAS evident from the first that solid-state masers could be employed to generate electromagnetic radiation in the millimeter- and shorter-wave-length regions. The extensively investigated c-w microwave three-level maser is obviously limited in its application to shorter wavelengths because it requires a radiation source for spin pumping at a wavelength shorter than that at which oscillation or amplification is to be obtained. The pumping source, however, need not be coherent, and although optical or infrared radiation could be used, no breakthrough in this direction has yet been reported. In contrast with the three-level maser, the two-level device does not require a higher-frequency pumping source. The spins may be put into an emissive state by applying a pulse of r-f radiation in the method of adiabatic fast passage or the 180-degree pulse and then obtaining oscillations or amplification at the same frequency as that of the r-f pulse. Oscillations at higher, or for that matter, lower frequencies may be obtained after the inversion of the spins by pulsing the magnetic field to the appropriate value in a time much less than T_1.

It is the purpose of this paper to discuss methods for generating millimeter waves by the method of adiabatic inversion followed by a pulsed magnetic field, and to describe experiments bearing on this problem. Although the method in its simplest form would use a two-level (spin $\frac{1}{2}$) paramagnetic material, we

*This work was supported in part by the U. S. Army Signal Corps.

have found it convenient to work with substances which have more than two Zeeman levels, in particular Cr^{+3} in Al_2O_3. In materials of this type, the energy levels vary with the magnitude of the external field in a way that provides interesting possibilities for millimeter-wave generation. On the other hand, these methods are found to be limited by the circumstance that when three energy levels become equidistant, Boltzmann equilibrium is attained in a time much less than T_1, quite likely of the order of T_{12}, the cross-relaxation time,[5] or perhaps as short as T_1, the spin-spin relaxation time.

EXPERIMENTAL SETUP

In view of the fact that multilevel spin systems possess many interesting features for the possibility of millimeter-wave generation, experimental work was undertaken with Cr^{+3}-doped Al_2O_3 (ruby). The favorable dielectric properties of Al_2O_3 allow the use of a solid Al_2O_3 cavity coated with silver paint; thus, problems of pulsed-magnetic-field penetration into the cavity and of movement of cavity walls are eliminated. Early work had shown that inversion of spin-level populations of Cr^{+3} in several host crystals could be readily effected by the technique of adiabatic fast passage,[1] in which a pulse of microwave power of approximately 0.5-watt amplitude is applied as the magnetic field sweeps through the resonance in a few tens of microseconds. The microwave inverting pulse was obtained from an X-band klystron. Because of the loading of the cavity by the absorption, only a 25 percent filling factor could be used; the remainder of the cavity was pure Al_2O_3. The apparatus is sketched in Fig. 1.

The magnetic-field pulse was obtained by discharging a capacitor bank into a Helmholz pair, 3 cm in diameter, located inside the helium dewar. The switching circuit using 5C22 hydrogen thyratrons is also shown in Fig. 1. The coil and capacitors form a resonant circuit of period 1.6 msec; thus, the field pulse is in the shape of a single sinusoid. Since most of the stored energy in the capacitor bank goes into the magnetic field of the coil and is returned to the capacitor at the end of the cycle, a rather modest capacitor bank of $30\mu f$ at 2kv gives a peak field

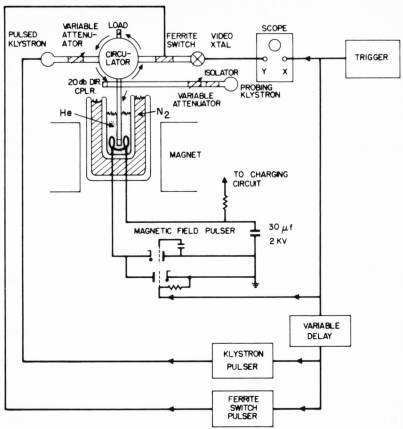

Fig. 1. Apparatus for adiabatic fast passage and pulsed magnetic-field experiments

of 18,000 oersteds. A one-second repetition rate could be maintained without excessive boiling of the liquid helium. The full sinusoid shape of the field pulse was useful in some experiments; if the second half-cycle was not needed, the second thyratron was disconnected.

GENERATION TECHNIQUES

Although inversion by fast passage had been demonstrated in ruby and two-level maser operation had been obtained at X-band,[1] the multilevel energy scheme of Cr^{+3} in ruby offers several other interesting possibilities. Pulsed saturation of the transition between the outermost of three energy levels may result in population inversion of one of the inner transitions as in the three-level c-w maser. This method, used by Foner *et al.*[2] has the advantage of requiring less pump power for inversion than adiabatic fast passage, but results in less efficient inversion.

The most efficient inversion is obtained by consecutive fast passage of successive transitions. Application of this method has resulted in oscillations at frequencies up to 28kMc.[3] For purposes of illustration, only three of the four energy levels of

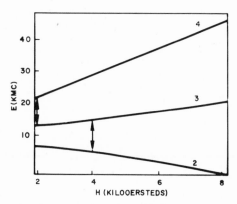

Fig. 2. Energy-level scheme for Cr^{+3} *in ruby near 60-degree orientation*

For simplicity, only the upper three of the four energy levels are shown.

Cr^{+3} need be considered as in Fig. 2; the transitions indicated are 9kMc. The spin system is allowed to come to thermal equilibrium in a fixed magnetic field of about 6000 oersteds. By using a sinusoidal field pulse of amplitude 4000 oersteds, the field is swept down through the 2-3 and 3-4 X-band transitions. Application of about 0.5 watt of X-band power during the traversal results in inversion of the spin population of levels 2 and 3 followed by inversion of levels 3 and 4. Thus, if the equilibrium value of spin populations in levels 2, 3, and 4 is $n_{02} > n_{03} > n_{04}$, after inversion we have n_{03}, n_{04}, n_{02}. The net excess of spins in level 4 over level 3 is therefore $(n_{02} - n_{04})$. The pulsed field reverses direction, and emission of radiation occurs as the field passes through values where the resonant frequencies of the cavity are equal to the Larmor frequency of the 3-4 transition. Depending upon the coupling to the particular cavity mode, either oscillation or amplification of a small probing signal at the appropriate frequency is observed. Amplification has been obtained at frequencies near 14 and 24 kMc, and oscillation pulses have been obtained at 14, 18, 24, and 28 kMc. The peak power emitted at 14 kMc was several milliwatts when a crystal having a Cr_2O_3/Al_2O_3 ratio of 0.06 percent by weight was used. In general, the shape of the output pulse was observed to be oscillatory and may be qualitatively understood from the considerations given below.

In the above methods for generating millimeter waves, it may be necessary to adjust the pulsed magnetic field so that the spin frequency corresponds to the cavity frequency when the field has its maximum value (and is therefore stationary with time) if the maximum energy is to be extracted from the spin system. For large pulsed fields it will be difficult to fix the amplitude with the necessary precision. Even when sweeping through the cavity resonance as in the present experiments, magnetic pulse jitter varies the duration and even the shape of the emitted pulse of radiation. An attractive possibility for avoiding these difficulties would be to use zero-field splitting in the following way. Consider the energy-level diagram in Fig. 3. Such levels may be obtained, for example, with a paramagnetic ion with an effective spin equal to one in a crystalline field of sufficiently low symmetry [for example, $Ni(NH_4)_2(SO_4)_2 \cdot 6H_2O$ with the magnetic field applied parallel to the z-axis].[4] The magnetic field is pulsed to point H* where the spins are tuned to a convenient source of microwave power and inverted. As the value of the applied field reduces to zero, the Larmor frequency increases to the zero-field-splitting value. Thus after each inversion the spins always radiate at the frequency determined by the crystalline field splitting. This method of pulsing down in frequency to invert has another very important advantage over those discussed previously where the spins

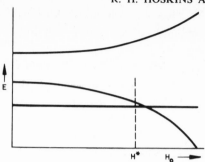

Fig. 3. Energy-level scheme for a paramagnetic ion having spin 1 in a crystalline field of low symmetry

The energy and magnetic-field scales are arbitrary.

were inverted and the field was pulsed upward; namely, the spins come to thermal equilibrium at the high frequency and the magnetization is correspondingly greater.

A serious difficulty may arise in inversion schemes involving systems of spin greater than one-half. Consider the energy-level diagram in Fig. 4. If the above method is applied to a system such as this, in returning to zero after the inversion the pulsed magnetic field must pass through a region (Point A) where the three energy levels become equidistant. In this region, spin-spin flips which conserve energy can take place in a time of order T_{12}, and a new Boltzmann population distribution may be set up which will result in a loss of the inverted spin popula-

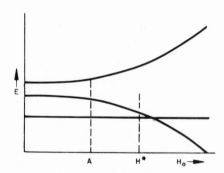

Fig. 4. Energy-level scheme for a paramagnetic ion having spin 1 in a crystalline field of low symmetry

The energy and magnetic-field scales are arbitrary.

tion.[5] This effect has been directly observed in ruby and thus far limits the successive inversion scheme described to two steps.[3] This difficulty may be sidestepped in the successive inversion scheme by using a pump frequency that is somewhat larger than the zero-field splitting. In ruby, for example, 15 kMc would suffice. For other schemes, if the field is to pass through such regions after inversion, one must ensure that these regions are traversed in a time less than T_{12}. It may be noted that if complete inversion of the populations of all the energy levels concerned can be obtained (i.e., if the new population distribution may be described by the usual Boltzmann factor with a negative T), then spin-spin flips which must conserve energy cannot destroy the negative temperature. In this case, then, regions of equidistant energy levels may be traversed with no difficulty.

SPIN DYNAMICS AND PULSE SHAPE

Let us consider a two-level spin system, or two levels of a multilevel spin system separated energetically from the other levels, interacting with the field of a resonant circuit. It is well known that when the Boltzmann populations of the two spin states are inverted, the system undergoes coherent, spontaneous emission because of the enhancement of the radiation field by the high Q cavity provided that

$$\tau_R < T_2, \tag{1}$$

where T_2 is the spin-spin relaxation time, and τ_R, the radiation damping time constant due to the reaction of the field induced in the cavity on the magnetization, is defined as

$$\tau_R = (2\pi \xi M_o Q_L \gamma)^{-1}. \tag{2}$$

Here ξ is the sample filling factor, M_o is the macroscopic magnetization per unit volume, Q_L is the loaded cavity Q (exclusive of sample), and γ is the gyromagnetic ratio. Relation (1) is easily seen to be the Townes condition for maser oscillation.

Equations describing the transient behavior of a two-level spin system initially in an emissive state[6],[7] have been derived for a homogeneously broadened line, $T_1 = \infty$, the cavity ringing time constant $\tau_c \ll \tau_R$, and $\tau_R < T_2$. It is found that the system radiates away most of its energy in a time of the order of τ_R in the form of a pulse whose maximum power P is given by

$$P = 2M_0 V H_o / \tau_R.\tag{3}$$

where V is the sample volume. The method of inversion by sweeping the magnetic field (rather than sweeping the frequency of the r-f field) has the advantage of not requiring any means for limiting the loss of inverted spin energy by radiation damping immediately after inversion. The Larmor frequency of the spin system is removed far from the resonance of the cavity frequency, and under these conditions the amount of energy radiated from the spin system should be very small. When the pulsed magnetic field tunes the Larmor frequency to some cavity resonance, the spontaneous radiation process gets started either by the rotating magnetization resulting from incomplete inversion which has not yet died away or by the noise field in the cavity.

In the present experiments the condition $\tau_c \ll \tau_R$ does not hold and comparison with the above theory is further complicated by the fact that the magnetic field is being swept through an inhomogeneously broadened line during the emission pulse. When $\tau_R < \tau_c$ the cavity-spin system may be expected to behave as two coupled oscillators where the energy is passed back and forth from one oscillator to the other. The resulting modulation of the oscillation pulse has been treated by Bloembergen and Pound,[8] and by Senitzsky.[9] Such oscillations have been observed in this and other experiments.[10] We have also noted that the structure of this modulation varies with the rate at which the Larmor frequency is swept through the cavity resonance. At larger sweep rates, no modulation of the output pulse is observed, a result which may indicate that the spins do not remain in resonance with the cavity long enough to allow the interchange between spin energy and cavity energy.

CONCLUSION

It seems possible to generate pulsed fields as high as a megagauss.[11] This value of the field corresponds to a frequency of 3×10^6 megacycles or a wavelength of 0.1 mm. Neglecting problems of microwave circuitry, and assuming an energy level scheme as in Fig. 3 with an initial splitting of 0.1 mm, we make use of expression 3 to estimate the peak power output. We may expect τ_R to be of the order of 10^{-8} sec for filling factor of 0.25 and a loaded Q of 500 if we reduce the spin concentration to, say, 10^{17} cm^{-3}. This will ensure $\tau_c < \tau_R$ and still satisfy the oscillation condition. Our previous considerations then predict an output pulse, without modulation, of amplitude of the order of 100 kilowatts and duration 10^{-8} sec under ideal conditions and assuming that the spin-lattice relaxation time is not excessively field dependent. It may be noted that a spin concentration of only 10^{17} cm^{-3} leads to $T_2 > 10^{-5}$ sec; thus, regions of equidistant energy levels may be traversed in a time shorter than T_2 and the problem of spin temperature mixing may not be serious.

The authors would like to acknowledge the helpful assistance of D. P. Devor and the technical assistance of C. R. Duncan.

REFERENCES

1. R. H. Hoskins, J. Appl. Phys. *30*, 797 (1959).
2. S. Foner, L. R. Momo, and A. Mayer, Phys. Rev. Lett. *3*, 36 (1959); and paper in this symposium.
3. R. H. Hoskins, Phys. Rev. Lett. *3*, 174 (1959).
4. J. H. E. Griffiths and J. Owen, Proc. Roy. Soc. A *213*, 459 (1952). This type of approach has also been considered by S. Foner.
5. A. Abraham and W. G. Proctor, Phys. Rev. *109*, 1441 (1958); Bloembergen, Shapiro, Pershan, and Artman, Phys. Rev. *113*, 445 (1959).
6. C. Greifinger and G. Birnbaum, IRE Trans. (to be published).
7. S. Bloom, J. Appl. Phys. *28*, 800 (1957).
8. N. Bloembergen and R. V. Pound, Phys. Rev. *95*, 8 (1954).
9. I. Senitzky, Phys. Rev. Lett. *1*, 167 (1958).
10. Feher, Gordon, Buehler, Gere, and Thurmond, Phys. Rev. *109*, 221 (1958).
11. S. Foner and H. H. Kolm, Rev. Sci. Instr. *28*, 799 (1957).

DISCUSSION

J. H. VAN VLECK: I would like to ask Mr. Bölger whether at Leiden aperiodic relaxation measurements have been made on

this same ruby material, and if so how their extrapolation compares with the measurements of Foner and collaborators as regards the dependence of T_1 on field strength?

B. BÖLGER: For diluted substances as used in masers, the
nonresonant relaxation method is not sensitive enough to be
able to study the relaxation behavior. As for the nonresonant
method of determining τ, one has the difficulty that when
changing the frequency of the transition to be studied one also
changes the matrix elements between the levels.

SOME OBSERVATIONS ON "STAIRCASE" INVERSION*

P. E. WAGNER, J. G. CASTLE, JR., and P. F. CHESTER

Westinghouse Research Laboratories, Pittsburgh, Pennsylvania

THIS NOTE discusses some problems associated with the "staircase" maser proposal of Siegman and Morris,[1] indicates an alternative scheme that avoids these problems, and gives supporting experimental evidence.

Consider the three-level spin system of Fig. 1, having the 1-2 and 2-3 transitions just resolved. The populations are initially at equilibrium, with $n_3 = 1 - \Delta$, $n_2 = 1$, and $n_1 = 1 + \Delta$, where $\Delta = n\omega_{12}/kT$, and $\Delta \ll 1$ is assumed. The applied magnetic field is now swept successively through the 1-2 and 2-3 lines under fast-passage conditions, as suggested by Siegman and Morris. We introduce a "turnover efficiency,"

$$\alpha_{ij} = \frac{(n_i - n_j) \text{ after passage}}{(n_j - n_i) \text{ before passage}},$$

and assume for simplicity that $\alpha_{21} = \alpha_{32}$. The populations can easily be shown to take on the final values of Fig. 1, giving

$$n_3 - n_1 = \Delta \left(\frac{\alpha^2 + 6\alpha - 3}{4} \right).$$

For $n_3 \geq n_1$, it is necessary that $\alpha \geq 0.46$, a value larger than we have usually obtained in practice. For the case of four nearly equally spaced levels, the condition required for $n_4 \geq n_1$ is $\alpha \geq 0.69$.

*The research reported in this paper has been sponsored in part by Electronics Research Directorate of the Air Force Cambridge Research Center, Air Research and Development Command, under Contract AF 19(604) 5589.

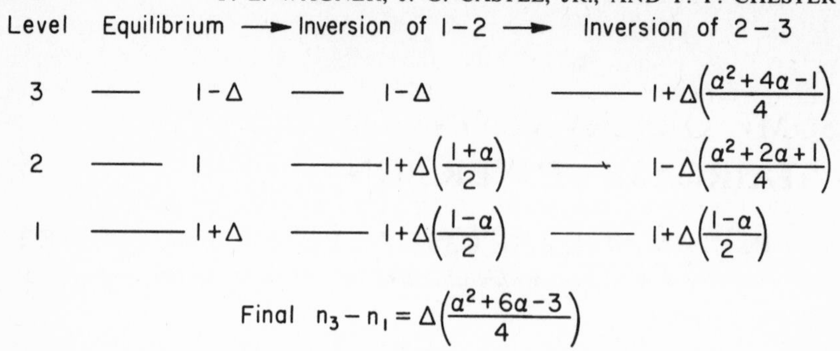

Level   Equilibrium ——▶ Inversion of 1−2 ——▶   Inversion of 2−3

3 —— $1-\Delta$ —— $1-\Delta$ —— $1+\Delta\left(\dfrac{a^2+4a-1}{4}\right)$

2 —— 1 —— $1+\Delta\left(\dfrac{1+a}{2}\right)$ —→ $1-\Delta\left(\dfrac{a^2+2a+1}{4}\right)$

1 —— $1+\Delta$ —— $1+\Delta\left(\dfrac{1-a}{2}\right)$ —— $1+\Delta\left(\dfrac{1-a}{2}\right)$

$$\text{Final}\quad n_3-n_1=\Delta\left(\frac{a^2+6a-3}{4}\right)$$

Fig. 1. *Behavior of populations under successive fast passage through 1-2 and 2-3 lines, with a turnover efficiency* α

Now consider passage through the 1-2 and 2-3 lines when they are exactly coincident. The passage is depicted in Fig. 2, in which it is assumed, following Redfield,[2] that a spin temperature can be defined for either line in the *rotating* reference frame, even in the presence of the large rf field needed for fast passage. It is also assumed that spin-spin coupling between the superposed lines holds them at the same spin temperature throughout passage. These assumptions lead to a final value of $n_3 - n_1 = 2\alpha\Delta$, implying that any turnover efficiency greater than zero results in $n_3 > n_1$. These considerations predict that for the turnover efficiencies less than 46 percent, inversion of the 1-3 line is possible when the 1-2 and 2-3 lines are coincident

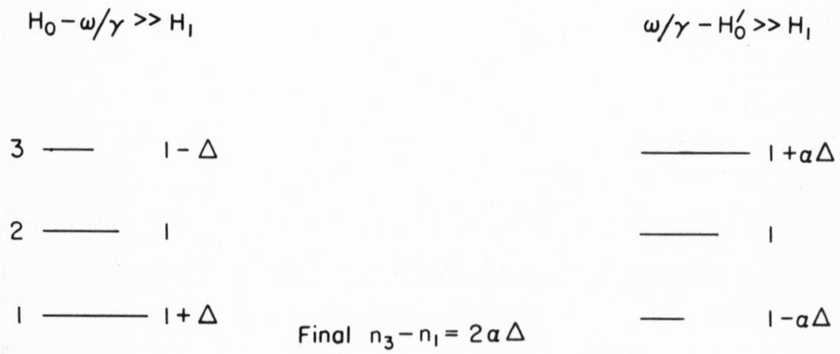

$H_0 - \omega/\gamma \gg H_1$ $\qquad\qquad\qquad\qquad$ $\omega/\gamma - H_0' \gg H_1$

3 —— $1-\Delta$ $\qquad\qquad\qquad\qquad$ —— $1+a\Delta$

2 —— 1 $\qquad\qquad\qquad\qquad\qquad$ —— 1

1 —— $1+\Delta$ $\qquad\qquad\qquad\qquad$ —— $1-a\Delta$

$$\text{Final}\quad n_3-n_1=2a\Delta$$

Fig. 2. *Behavior of populations under simultaneous fast passage through the coincident 1-2 and 2-3 lines, with a turnover efficiency* α

and is not possible when they are distinct and are inverted sequentially. Even with unity efficiency, simultaneous passage yields twice the degree of inversion obtained by sequential passage.

The role of cross relaxation[3] is also markedly different for the two types of passage. With simultaneous inversion, strong spin-spin interaction between the 1-2 and 2-3 lines has already been assumed and, presumably, has no effects other than those discussed above.

With sequential inversion, on the other hand, cross relaxation occurring during the time interval between inversion of the 1-2 and 2-3 lines can seriously reduce the final value of $n_3 - n_1$. This effect is illustrated in Fig. 3, where ε represents the

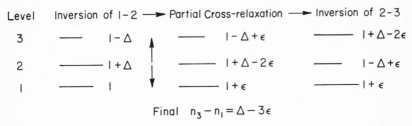

Level   Inversion of 1-2 ⟶ Partial Cross-relaxation ⟶ Inversion of 2-3

3   ——— $1-\Delta$ ——— $1-\Delta+\epsilon$ ——— $1+\Delta-2\epsilon$

2   ——— $1+\Delta$ ——— $1+\Delta-2\epsilon$ ——— $1-\Delta+\epsilon$

1   ——— 1 ——— $1+\epsilon$ ——— $1+\epsilon$

Final $n_3 - n_1 = \Delta - 3\epsilon$

Fig. 3. Effect of cross relaxation between successive fast passages of 1-2 and 2-3 lines

For complete cross relaxation, $\varepsilon = \Delta/2$ and final $n_3 - n_1 = -\Delta/2$.

change in population due to cross relaxation. If the cross relaxation were in fact complete, the 1-3 transition would not be inverted at all.

Cross relaxation occurring after the completion of both passages has no effect on $n_3 - n_1$, since a spin flip in the 2-3 line accompanied by an opposite spin flip in the 1-2 line alters n_3 and n_1 identically.

Experimentally, we have observed the $(-\frac{1}{2}, \frac{3}{2})$ line in pink ruby after field-sweep fast passage through the $(-\frac{1}{2}, \frac{1}{2})$ and $(\frac{1}{2}, \frac{3}{2})$ lines. The experiments were carried out at 9.05 KMc/sec and at 2.16°K. Approximately 12 watts of inverting power were used, and the monitoring power was roughly 0.1 μwatt. The field sweep was obtained by discharging a capacitor through coils mounted on the sample cavity. All observations were made in times short compared to the spin-lattice times.

A polar plot of the observed spectrum is given in Fig. 4 for the region of interest. The pulsed field used for simultaneous passage is shown as H_{sweep}. Starting from point B, the field was swept down to A and back to B. A slight rotation of the magnet separated the $(-\frac{1}{2},\frac{1}{2})$ and $(\frac{1}{2},\frac{3}{2})$ lines to permit sequential inversion. Experimental results are shown in Fig. 5, with absorption upward and emission downward. The time base is 50 μsec per major division.

In Fig. 5a, the $(-\frac{1}{2},\frac{1}{2})$ and $(\frac{1}{2},\frac{3}{2})$ lines are coincident. The lines appear in the order: $(-\frac{1}{2},\frac{1}{2}$ and $\frac{1}{2},\frac{3}{2})$; $(-\frac{1}{2},\frac{3}{2})$; $(-\frac{1}{2},\frac{3}{2})$; $(-\frac{1}{2},\frac{1}{2}$ and $\frac{1}{2},\frac{3}{2})$. The inverting pulse is attenuated ~ 80 db, and is seen as a perturbation of the base line during the first passage through the $(-\frac{1}{2},\frac{1}{2}$ and $\frac{1}{2},\frac{3}{2})$ line. For Fig. 5b, full inverting power was used; and inversion of both the $(-\frac{1}{2},\frac{3}{2})$ line and the coincident $(-\frac{1}{2},\frac{1}{2}$ and $\frac{1}{2},\frac{3}{2})$ line is seen.

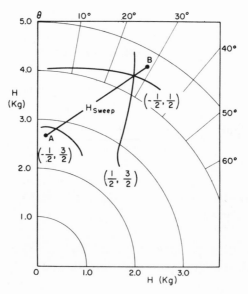

Fig. 4. Polar graph of spectrum observed in pink ruby at 9.05 KMc/sec.

Field pulsed either A → B → A or B → A → B.

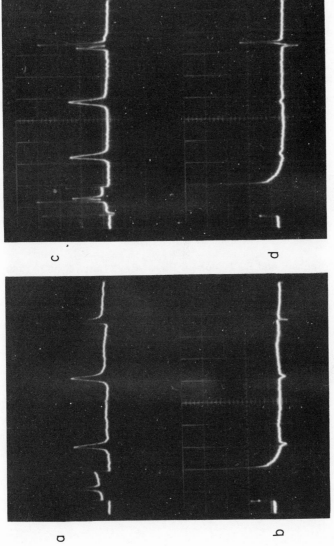

Fig. 5. Experimental Observations

Absorption is upward, emission downward.

In Figs. 5c and 5d, the magnet was rotated so that the $(-\frac{1}{2}, \frac{1}{2})$ and $(\frac{1}{2}, \frac{3}{2})$ lines were distinct. The order of passage was: $(-\frac{1}{2}, \frac{1}{2})$; $(\frac{1}{2}, \frac{3}{2})$; $(-\frac{1}{2}, \frac{3}{2})$; $(-\frac{1}{2}, \frac{3}{2})$; $(\frac{1}{2}, \frac{3}{2})$; $(-\frac{1}{2}, \frac{1}{2})$. In Fig. 5c, the pulse is again attenuated 80 db; Fig. 5d shows the results of full inverting power. It is seen that the $(-\frac{1}{2}, \frac{3}{2})$ line does not invert; in fact, we were never able to invert it when the fast passage was sequential rather than simultaneous. The $(\frac{1}{2}, \frac{3}{2})$ line inverts and the $(-\frac{1}{2}, \frac{1}{2})$ line becomes less absorptive.

All these findings are qualitatively consistent with expectation (see Figs. 1 and 2). We find the results of Fig. 5d can be explained quantitatively if $\alpha_{-\frac{1}{2}, \frac{1}{2}} = 0.64$ and $\alpha_{\frac{1}{2}, \frac{3}{2}} = 0.25$. Additional measurements of each of these two α's independently gave $\alpha_{-\frac{1}{2}, \frac{1}{2}} = 0.68$ and $\alpha_{\frac{1}{2}, \frac{3}{2}} = 0.27$, in good agreement.

REFERENCES

1. A. E. Siegman and R. J. Morris, Phys. Rev. Lett. *2*, 302 (1959).
2. A. G. Redfield, Phys. Rev. *98*, 1787 (1955).
3. Bloembergen, Shapiro, Pershan, and Artman, Phys. Rev. *114*, 455 (1959).

ANALYTICAL DESIGN OF PARAMAGNETIC AMPLIFIERS*

M. W. P. STRANDBERG

*Department of Physics and Research Laboratory of Electronics,
Massachusetts Institute of Technology*

I WOULD LIKE to talk about some things that you know all about. This makes my talk more pleasant—for people like to hear about things that they understand, and they understand the things they know about. I can only talk about a very few things today, so in a way the title is quite pretentious. It is impossible to be both brief and logical.

We are interested in the properties of amplifiers to be designed. They are as defined diagrammatically in Fig. 1. (It is hoped that amplifier builders will measure these parameters to characterize their device.) With large gain-bandwidth devices we must compute the circuit properties, taking into account not only the frequency sensitivity of the rf structure but also the frequency dependence of the paramagnetic susceptibility. This means that for a cavity with the usual notation for its parameters and a paramagnetic crystal, the circuit gain will be as follows:

$$Q_x \longrightarrow Q_x \left[\left(1 + i\,\frac{2(f - f_o)}{B_x} \right) \right]$$

Since

$$\frac{G}{Y_o} = \frac{Q_e}{Q_x} + \frac{Q_e}{Q_o}$$

*This work was supported in part by the U.S. Army (Signal Corps), the U.S. Air Force (Office of Scientific Research, Air Research and Development Command), and the U.S. Navy (Office of Naval Research).

GAIN

$$P_i \longrightarrow \boxed{} \longrightarrow G\,P_i = g^2\,P_i$$

RECIPROCITY

$$G'P_o \longleftarrow \boxed{} \longleftarrow P_i$$

BANDWIDTH

$$G(\nu)$$

$\nu \longrightarrow$

GAIN STABILITY

NOISE FIGURE

$$KT_s B \longrightarrow \boxed{} \longrightarrow \begin{array}{l} GK(T_s + T_{amp})B \\ = GK\ T_s\ B\ F \end{array}$$

TUNABILITY

DYNAMIC LINEAR RANGE

G

KTB

$P_i \longrightarrow$

SATURATION POWER $\begin{cases} \text{PULSE} \\ \text{CW} \end{cases}$

GP_i

$P_i \longrightarrow$

GAIN RECOVERY TIME

G

P_i

$t \longrightarrow$

Fig. 1. Description of useful amplifier parameters

$$\frac{B}{Y_o} = 2Q_e\,\frac{(f - f_o)}{f_o} = \frac{2\Delta f}{B_e Y_o}$$

then

$$r = \frac{Y_o - Y}{Y_o + Y} = \frac{\left(1 - \dfrac{Q_e}{Q_o} - i\,\dfrac{2\Delta f}{B_e}\right)\left(1 + i\,\dfrac{2\Delta f}{B_x}\right) - \dfrac{Q_e}{Q_x}}{\left(1 + \dfrac{Q_e}{Q_o} + i\,\dfrac{2\Delta f}{B_e}\right)\left(1 + i\,\dfrac{2\Delta f}{B_x}\right) + \dfrac{Q_e}{Q_x}}\,.$$

The bandwidth, B, of a single-tuned stage is defined as the frequency width between the points at which the magnitude of the reflection coefficient squared is reduced to half of its value at resonance.

$$|r|^2 = G = \left\{ 16\overline{\Delta f^4} + 4\overline{\Delta f^2} \left[B_e^2 \left(1 - \frac{Q_e}{Q_o} \right)^2 + B_x^2 - 2 \frac{Q_e}{Q_x} B_e B_x \right] + \right.$$

$$\left. B_e^2 B_x^2 \left(1 - \frac{Q_e}{Q_x} - \frac{Q_e}{Q_x} \right) \right\} \Big/ \left\{ 16\overline{\Delta f^4} + 4\overline{\Delta f^2} \times \right.$$

$$\left. \left[B_e^2 \left(1 + \frac{Q_e}{Q_o} \right)^2 + B_x^2 - 2 \frac{Q_e}{Q_x} B_e B_x \right] + B_e^2 B_x^2 \left(1 + \frac{Q_e}{Q_o} + \frac{Q_e}{Q_x} \right) \right\}.$$

Therefore

$$B^2 = \frac{1}{2} \left[\left\{ \left[1 + \left(\frac{Q_e}{Q_o} \right)^2 \right] B_e^2 + B_x^2 - 2 \frac{Q_e}{Q_x} B_e B_x - \right. \right.$$

$$4 \frac{Q_e}{Q_o} B_e^2 \frac{3 + 2 \left(\frac{Q_e}{Q_o} + \frac{Q_e}{Q_x} \right) + 3 \left(\frac{Q_e}{Q_o} + \frac{Q_e}{Q_x} \right)^2}{1 + 6 \left(\frac{Q_e}{Q_o} + \frac{Q_e}{Q_x} \right) + \left(\frac{Q_e}{Q_o} + \frac{Q_e}{Q_x} \right)^2} \right\}^2 -$$

$$\left. \frac{4 B_e B_x \left(1 - \left(\frac{Q_e}{Q_o} + \frac{Q_e}{Q_x} \right)^2 \right)^2}{1 + 6 \left(\frac{Q_e}{Q_o} + \frac{Q_e}{Q_x} \right) + \left(\frac{Q_e}{Q_o} + \frac{Q_e}{Q_x} \right)^2} \right]^{\frac{1}{2}} - \frac{1}{2} \left\{ \left[1 + \left(\frac{Q_e}{Q_o} \right)^2 \right] B_e^2 + \right.$$

$$\left. B_x^2 - 2 \frac{Q_e}{Q_x} B_e B_x - 4 \frac{Q_e}{Q_o} B_e^2 \frac{3 + 2 \left(\frac{Q_e}{Q_o} + \frac{Q_e}{Q_x} \right) + 3 \left(\frac{Q_e}{Q_o} + \frac{Q_e}{Q_x} \right)^2}{1 + 6 \left(\frac{Q_e}{Q_o} + \frac{Q_e}{Q_x} \right) + \left(\frac{Q_e}{Q_o} + \frac{Q_o}{Q_x} \right)^2} \right\}.$$

For large gain, the gain-bandwidth product can be reduced to

$$\sqrt{G}\ B \approx \frac{2}{\dfrac{1}{B_x} + \dfrac{Q_x}{f_o}}.$$

Care must be exercised in using the general expression for B; for gains less than 3 db, a 3-db point does not exist.

We shall first use a cavity structure and then generalize the results for a traveling-wave structure. The analysis shows that the gain-bandwidth product is logically the weighted mean of the rf bandwidth and the paramagnetic crystal resonant bandwidth. With a cascade of several unidirectional cavities, the bandwidth as a function of gain is computed as shown in Fig. 2. B_1 is the gain-bandwidth of a single stage, and B is the bandwidth of the cascade, with the over-all gain as indicated. We are also interested in the gain-stability. In a straightforward fashion the fractional change of gain with a fractional change in susceptibility for one and several cascaded unidirectional cavities is as indicated in Fig. 3.

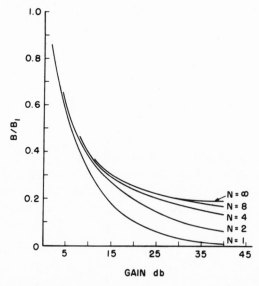

Fig. 2. *Gain versus bandwidth curves as a function of the number of cascaded unidirectional elements*

Such a cascade of cavities can be made with many so-called slow-wave structures. For single-cavity unidirectional devices, the usual circularly polarized cavity may be used in conjunction with the paramagnetic Faraday effect. A typical cavity capable of producing circularly polarized fields is one possessing geometric degeneracy as shown in Fig. 4. Such a cavity may be driven by the rf structure as shown in Fig. 5. A unidirectional amplifier for a 3-cm wavelength is shown in Fig. 6. A structure

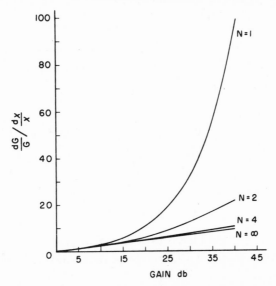

Fig. 3. Sensitivity of gain to variation of susceptibility as a function of the gain, for varying numbers of cascaded unidirectional elements

suitable for L-band use is shown in Fig. 7. Finally, a cascade of circularly polarized cavity amplifiers is shown in Fig. 8.

I will only say now that such an intrinsically unidirectional amplifier has been operated. —What can we expect from this device?

We look at the gain-bandwidth relationship

$$\sqrt{\bar{G}}\, B = \frac{2}{\dfrac{1}{B_x} + \dfrac{Q_x}{f_o}} \cdot$$

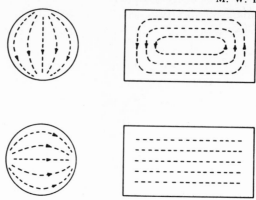

Fig. 4. Radiofrequency magnetic field configurations for the degenerate TE$_{111}$ *modes*

For pink ruby, $B_x \approx 43$ mc. The magnetic Q_x that we can obtain is computed for ruby with Al : Cr = 1 : 10^{-4} as about 200, at $T = 4.2\,^\circ$K, at 3 cm. The gain bandwidth will be

$$\frac{2}{\dfrac{1}{43} + \dfrac{200}{9000}} \approx 45 \text{ mc.}$$

Note that if the temperature is reduced to $1.5\,^\circ$K the magnetic Q will be reduced to about 70, but the gain-bandwidth will only go to

$$\frac{2}{\dfrac{1}{43} + \dfrac{70}{9000}} \approx 63 \text{ mc.}$$

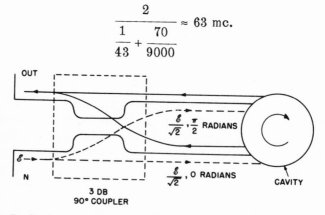

Fig. 5. Radiofrequency transmission line configuration for the 3-db coupler, circular-polarization excitor

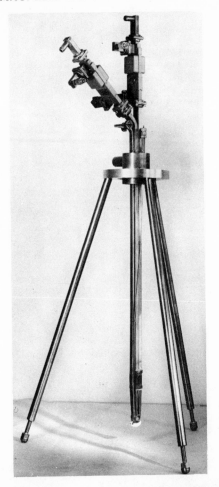

Fig. 6. An X-band circularly polarized unidirectional amplifier

This exact situation has been measured and reported by Morris, Kyhl, and Strandberg.[1] A cascade of 4 such cavities will give a gain of 20 db with about 20-mc bandwidth. Greater gain-bandwidth would require stagger-tuning of a similar cascade. These 4 cascades, stagger-tuned, would yield a gain-bandwidth product of 800 mc.

Note that since this is independent of frequency we can say that the maximum gain-bandwidth product for a single pink ruby

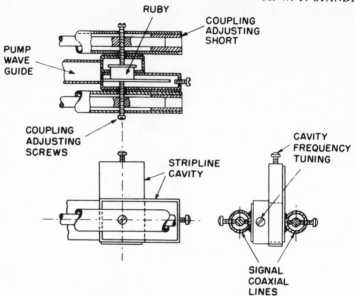

*Fig. 7. Stripline, orthogonal-cavity, circularly polarized ampli-
fier for L-band*

amplifier at any frequency should be less than 100 mc unless
very cleverly executed steps are taken to artificially widen the
paramagnetic linewidth.   Many people have reported the operation of paramagnetic amplifiers with $\sqrt{G}\,B$ products of 300 mc[2]

Fig. 8. A cascade of circularly polarized cavity amplifiers

and 800 mc[3] for single-cavity structures. On the basis of the preceding analysis it must be concluded that these amplifying structures are more complicated than their creators realized, and certainly more complicated than the simply-coupled structure that is calculated here. On the other hand, other results[1],[4] indicate that simple structures have been realized, and a limiting $\sqrt{G}\,B$ product for pink ruby of less than 80 mc is observed and understood.

REFERENCES

1. R. J. Morris, R. L. Kyhl, and M. W. P. Strandberg, Proc. IRE *47*, 80 (1959).
2. C. H. Townes, private communication.
3. W. H. From, Microwave J. *2*, 9 (1959).
4. A. M. Prokhorov, private communication.

DISCUSSION

B. BÖLGER: The nonreciprocal cavity maser as mentioned and so skillfully made by you has been proposed by Robinson and myself about one and a half years ago.[a]

E. O. SCHULZ-DuBOIS: The formula for gain-bandwidth product is well known. It has been derived by Pound and DeGrasse, to name just two. It has been obvious to many that this implies a dependence of gain-bandwidth on temperature less acute than T^{-1}.

In our experience it has been necessary to employ nonreciprocal attenuation in addition to nonreciprocal gain. This can be obtained in cavity masers too, if a degenerate mode having regions of counter-rotating magnetic fields is selected. To exaggerate the point, the use of nonreciprocal attenuation makes the difference between a practical amplifier and a laboratory instrument.

[a]B. Bölger and B. J. Robinson, Archiv Sci. Genève *11*, 187 (1958); also Commun. Kam. Onnes Lab., Leiden, Suppl. No. 114.

A. E. SIEGMAN: These nonreciprocal paramagnetic devices have the gyrotropic devices (usually placed externally) already built in. The traveling-wave maser has a built-in resonance attenuator (as well as a resonance amplifier); Professor Strandberg's nonreciprocal cavity maser essentially has two built-in circulators.

In response to Dr. Schulz-DuBois: I believe one can show that the r-f magnetic field in a resonant cavity must be everywhere in phase at resonance. Therefore, circular polarization can only be obtained in a degenerate cavity, having two distinct modes driven 90° out of phase.

S. OKWIT: I would like to add the factor of tunability to Dr. Schulz-DuBois's comment on the practicality of Dr. Strandberg's multi-cavity maser, as compared to the traveling-wave maser.

In a single cavity maser tuning is usually accomplished by[b]
1. adjusting the cavity resonance at the pump frequency
2. adjusting the cavity resonance at the signal frequency
3. adjusting the D.C. magnetic field
4. adjusting the r-f pumping frequency
5. adjusting the signal coupling loop (gain adjustment).

In a multiple cavity maser this tuning procedure is quite obviously more complicated. Complicated, perhaps, to the point of impracticality.

However, in a traveling-wave maser, tuning is easily accomplished[c] by simply adjusting the D.C. magnetic field and the pumping frequency. This procedure readily lends itself to electronic tuning.

[b]F. Arams and S. Okwit, "A Packaged Tunable L-Band Maser System," Proc. IRE (to be published).
[c]R. W. DeGrasse et al., "A Three Level Solid State Traveling Wave Maser", BSTJ (March, 1959).

MASER OSCILLATOR LINE SHAPES*

J. R. SINGER
University of Californis, Berkeley

EXPERIMENTAL MASER oscillators were built by Combrisson, Honig, and Townes,[1] Feher *et al.*,[2] Chester, Wagner, and Castle,[3] and many others since. Both two-level and three-level maser oscillators have been operated. In each case the oscillation appears with a periodic or almost periodic amplitude modulation (superimposed upon an exponential decay for the two-level type). The explanation for the amplitude modulation may be found by solving the equations of motion for the magnetization vector or, alternatively, by critically examining the equations for the transition probabilities. We have previously shown that earlier explanations for the oscillator line shape are not valid.[4]

In the discussion below, we shall treat the simple case of a set of spins acting as a permanent magnet. This concept was first used by Bloch and then by Bloembergen and Pound in a fundamental paper on radiation damping.[5]

OSCILLATOR WITH VERY NARROW LINE WIDTH

The energy equation for the narrow line spin collection and its radiation in a cavity maser oscillator starting from a negative temperature state, and neglecting the spin relaxation terms, is

$$\frac{1}{4\pi} \int_V \mu H_1^2 \, dV + \frac{1}{4\pi} \int_0^t \int_V \frac{\mu H_1^2 \omega}{Q} \, dV \, dt = \int_V \mu H_o M_o (1 + \cos \theta) \, dV \quad (1)$$

*This research was supported by the U. S. Air Force through the AFOSR of the Air Research and Development Command, under Contract No. AF 49(638)-102.

where H_1 is the r-f magnetic field

H is the permeability of the medium and the space

V is the volume of the cavity including the crystal

Q is the loaded cavity Q

ω is the radial frequency of oscillation

H_o is the static magnetic field

M_o is the volume magnetization of the maser crystal

θ is the angle between the spin vector and H_o.

Spin relaxation processes are not important because T_1 is much longer than the phenomena of interest, and T_2 is longer than a modulation period. After one period, the spins of an inhomogeneously broadened line are rephased. By using the concept of a filling factor, and differentiating with respect to time, one obtains

$$2 H_1 \dot{H}_1 + H_1^2 \omega/Q = -4\pi\eta H_o M_o \omega_1 \sin \theta. \tag{2}$$

We next make use of the Larmor precession relationship for the spin vector about H_1, which is

$$\omega_1 = \left| \frac{d\theta}{dt} \right| = |\gamma| H_1 \tag{3}$$

where ω_1 is the radial precession frequency about H_1, and γ is the gyromagnetic ratio. Using Equations (2) and (3) one obtains

$$\ddot{\theta} + \frac{\omega\dot{\theta}}{2Q} = -2\pi \gamma^2 \eta H_o M_o \sin \theta \tag{4}$$

which is the nonlinear differential equation describing the angle θ of the spin vector measured from the direction of H_o. The equation is also descriptive of a physical pendulum with a damping term. If the damping term is ignored, the equation may be obtained in the form of an elliptic integral which is then solved readily. It will be convenient to first define two parameters:

$$\tau = Q/\omega$$

$$\tau_r = (2\pi\eta M_o Q \gamma)^{-1} \tag{5}$$

where τ_r is the same as the reaction time constant introduced by Bloembergen and Pound and τ is one half the cavity ringing time. Using these relationships, Equation (4) becomes

$$\ddot{\theta} + \frac{\theta}{2\tau} + \frac{1}{\tau \tau_r} \sin \theta = 0. \tag{6}$$

If the damping term is ignored, then the period may be readily determined using the classical solution as discussed by Page.[6] Without the damping term, the frequency of oscillation f is approximately

$$f \cong \frac{1}{\pi \sqrt{\tau \tau_r}}. \tag{7}$$

The damping term causes a slowing in the nutation of the spin vector. The solution of Equation (6) with the damping term as a perturbation has been carried out by J. Kemp and will be published. The frequency given by Equation (7) is sufficiently precise to invite comparison with experimental data.

In the limit of small variations for θ, Equation (6) should agree with Bloembergen and Pound.[5] This agreement occurs for long T_2 when we make the assumption of small angles, that is, we let $\sin \theta \approx \theta$. For this case, Equation (6) is linear, with solution,

$$\theta = \theta_o \exp \left[-\frac{1}{4\tau} \pm \left(\frac{1}{16\tau^2} - \frac{1}{\tau \tau_r} \right)^{\frac{1}{2}} \right] t. \tag{8}$$

In comparing the solution (7) to previously published experimental results, we must be careful to note the conditions for validity. Equation (6) is derived for a set of spins initially at a negative temperature (i.e. the spins are inverted), with negligible line width, and having H_o set to resonance. These conditions are difficult to satisfy experimentally. Perhaps the most serious deviation consists of the practice of sweeping the magnetic field while observing the oscillation. Such a procedure introduces a resultant field which starts the oscillation before the resonance condition is reached. In effect, an adiabatic fast-passage transition of the spin vector occurs. Consequently, the initial amplitude modulation of the field swept maser oscillator is not directly comparable with Equation (7) which predicts a frequency the order of one megacycle. If we ignore the first few cycles of the oscillation, however, then previous results[2],[3] agree with Equation (7). We are presently operating an adiabatic fast passage maser using neutron-irradiated calcite. The resonance line width is only a tenth of an oersted, and we are planning to carefully compare theory and experiment.

THE THREE-LEVEL MASER OSCILLATOR

One might expect that no amplitude modulation of the three-level maser oscillator would occur, but such a deduction would not be in accord with experimental observations. The energy of a three-level maser oscillator may be described by Equation (1) if a term to describe the augmentation of the spin vector by the pumping mechanism is added. We have not yet derived the requisite formulation nor the solution. However, one observation may be pertinent. To eliminate amplitude modulation effects, the pumping must be many orders of magnitude greater than that needed to overcome thermal relaxation processes since the nutation occurs in the order of a microsecond compared with fractional second T_1's.

It is a pleasure to thank Shyh Wang and James Kemp for several interesting discussions of this problem.

REFERENCES

1. Combrisson, Honig, and C. H. Townes, C. R. Acad. Sci. 242, 2451 (1956).
2. G. Feher, J. P. Gordon, E. Buehler, E. A. Gere, and C. D. Thurmond, Phys. Rev. 109, 221 (1958).
3. P. F. Chester, P. E. Wagner, and J. G. Castle, Jr., Phys. Rev. 110, 281 (1958).
4. A. Yariv, J. R. Singer, and J. Kemp, J. Appl. Phys. 30, 265 (1959),
5. N. Bloembergen and R. V. Pound, Phys. Rev. 95, 8 (1954).
6. L. Page, Introduction to Theoretical Physics, p. 87, Van Nostrand (1935).

DISCUSSION

A. YARIV: The problem of the observed modulation in the emitted power of an inverted two-level spin system was programmed and solved with the aid of an IBM 704 computer at the Bell Telephone Laboratories. The model assumed was that of a homogenous line whose center frequency is equal to that of the cavity. The numerical details are the same as those prevailing in the experiments of Chester, Wagner, and Bolef of Westinghouse. The plotted curve of the emitted power agrees closely, in shape and detail, with the pattern observed by Chester *et al.*, with one important exception; the time scale is contracted by a factor of ~ 10. One possible and highly speculative explanation for the discrepancy is the possibility of a time bottleneck due to the necessity for spins outside the central region in inhomogenous lines to diffuse to the central region before their energy can be coupled out in the manner described above.

P. WAGNER: Is the modulation frequency $f = \dfrac{1}{\pi\sqrt{\tau\,\tau_R}}$ truly independent of the cavity Q?

R. SINGER: [No.]

P. WAGNER: An emission pulse that is not distorted by any field sweep is shown in: Chester, Wagner, and Castle, Proceedings of Fort Monmouth Maser Symposium, P. 42 (June, 1958).

TRANSIENTS AND OSCILLATION PULSES IN MASERS

H. STATZ and G. deMARS

Research Division, Raytheon Company, Waltham, Massachusetts

IT HAS been observed by Kikuchi *et al.*[1] that a maser under certain pump conditions, instead of oscillating continuously may either show a "ripple" in the oscillation output or even show discrete pulses of oscillation output with periods in between the pulses where no sign of oscillation can be detected. Similarly, Foner *et al.*[2] detected in their pulsed-field maser that the oscillations may also be discontinuous. Observations of pulsed oscillations have also been made in this laboratory by the authors and also certain transients have been observed which belong to the same class of phenomena. For example, Fig. 1 shows the power output when the maser starts to oscillate after applying the pump or after having saturated the pair of levels between which amplification or oscillation is to take place. The oscillation power output does not increase smoothly in time but rather the oscillation goes off and on and finally approaches a steady-state power output. The power output as a function of time in this initial period resembles a damped vibration. The present measurements were made on a three-level ruby maser operating at 1.3 kmc.

We shall give, in the following, an explanation of the above-described phenomena. The explanation differs from that given by Senitzky.[3] Since we do not require a coherent motion of the spin system, the present treatment applies also to cases in which the time between oscillation pulses is much larger than T_2, the spin-spin relaxation time. However, we require in general three levels and our model is not suitable for a spin $\frac{1}{2}$.

The phenomenon follows qualitatively from accepted equations describing maser action, retaining, however, certain nonlinear terms. If we denote the quality factor of the cavity by Q_L including the external coupling and the energy emitting or absorbing properties of the active material, then

$$\frac{dP}{dt} = -\frac{1}{Q_L} \omega P \tag{1}$$

where P is the energy stored in the cavity and ω is the frequency at which maser action takes place.

$$\frac{1}{Q_L} = \frac{1}{Q_o} + \frac{1}{Q_e} - Cn = \frac{1}{Q} - Cn. \tag{2}$$

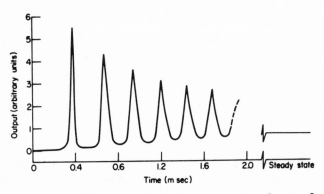

Fig. 1. Experimentally observed energy output from ruby maser

Equation (2) states that the total quality factor depends upon the inverted population $n = n_3 - n_2$. Q_o is the quality factor including wall losses and dielectric absorption in the active material. Q_e describes the energy taken out of the cavity through external coupling. We define $Q^{-1} = Q_o^{-1} + Q_e^{-1}$. C is a constant.

The time rate of change of n is given by

$$\frac{dn}{dt} = -\frac{n - n_1}{\tau} - Dn P. \tag{3}$$

In Equation (3) n_1 is the equilibrium value for $n_3 - n_2$ with pump on when there is no electromagnetic energy in the cavity at the signal frequency. τ is the time constant with which a disturbance in n decays. It is normally equal to the spin lattice relaxation time. D is a proportionality constant which determines the rate at which spins flip in an applied rf field. We obtain a set of dimensionless equations from Equations (1), (2), and (3).

$$\frac{d\pi}{dT} = \frac{1}{Q} \pi (\eta - 1) \tag{4}$$

$$\frac{d\eta}{dT} = -\frac{\eta - \alpha}{T_o} + \frac{1 - \alpha}{T_o} \eta \pi. \tag{5}$$

in which $\pi = P/P_o$, where P_o = the steady-state energy stored in the cavity under normal oscillation conditions; $\eta = n/n_o$, where n_o is the amount of level inversion required to overcome the losses characterized by Q^{-1}; $\tau = n_1/n_o$; $T = \omega t$; and $T_o = \omega \tau$. The value of α is expected to depend upon the extent to which the pump power saturates the pump transition.

Solutions to Equations (4) and (5) have been obtained using an analog computer. In Fig. 2 we show three choices of the parameters Q, α, and T_o. These cases are characteristic of the types of behavior observed experimentally.

These types of solutions can be easily understood by considering, for example, Fig. 2a. η starts to build up from some value smaller than one with the time constant T_o. As η crosses the value 1 the maser is basically unstable and oscillations start to build up. $\eta = 1$ corresponds to the case where the losses due to the cavity and the external coupling are just balanced by the emission from the spin system. As the oscillation amplitude becomes rather large it tends to saturate levels 2 and 3, i.e., η tends to decrease. However, the oscillation level π continues to increase until no more net energy is fed into the cavity, i.e., until η has decreased to 1. The electromagnetic energy in the cavity now has its maximum value and continues to flip spins so that η decreases below 1. π now also decreases. At some particular value of $\eta < 1$, the rate at which inverted spins are generated equals that at which spins are flipped. While π further decreases η starts to build up again. At the point where $\eta = 1$, π stops decreasing and for $\eta > 1$ π also increases again.

Qualitatively we can distinguish between two cases. If π has decreased essentially to the noise level in the cavity, before η

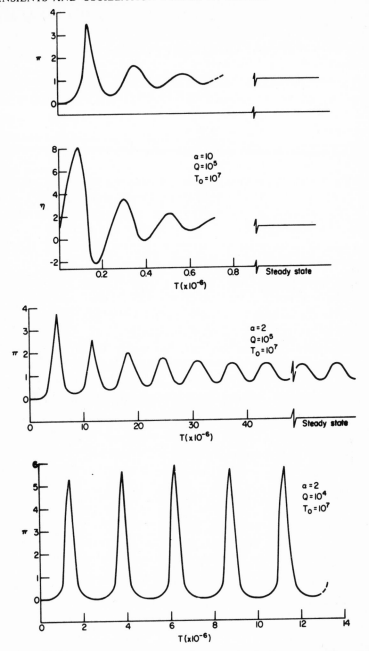

Fig. 2. Theoretical time dependence of electromagnetic energy in maser cavity

on its way up crosses the value 1, then the original cycle repeats exactly. π has lost its memory from the previous cycle. This corresponds to continuous oscillation pulses as reported by Kikuchi et al.[1] If π has decreased only a little below 1 when η again crosses 1, then the next oscillation pulse is already considerably damped. After a few such cycles the steady-state oscillation condition is reached. What happens in between these two extremes can only be decided with the help of the exact solution of Equations (4) and (5). The nature of the solution is thus determined by Q on the one side and T_o and α on the other. The smaller the Q, the faster the electromagnetic energy decay; the smaller the T_o and the larger the α, the faster the η recovers to values larger than one.

In considering Fig. 2a for example, let us evaluate the time between two oscillation peaks. We notice $\Delta T = \omega \Delta t = 2 \times 10^6$. For the observations in Fig. 1 ω corresponds to 1.3 kmc. In approximate agreement with the experimental results we thus obtain $\Delta t = 2.5 \times 10^{-4}$ sec. The particular parameters chosen in Fig. 2c give a pulse repetition rate which is higher by about a factor of 20 than that observed by Kikuchi et al.[1] A different choice of parameters, however, can duplicate their results.

At first glance, the large values of Q which are necessary to obtain steady-state oscillations appear disturbing. In Fig. 2a, for example, $Q = 10^5$. The experimental results (Fig. 1) were obtained with a Q_e of approximately 1000. Let us consider the other parameters. In the calculations, T_o is 10^7 which corresponds to a τ of 1.2×10^{-3} sec. According to Kikuchi et al.,[7] we should have used a value for τ of 2.5×10^{-2} sec which would have required even higher values for Q. Also the value of $\alpha = 10$, we believe, is too large to correspond to the experimental conditions. The answer to this question can be found by considering the effects of cross relaxation[4] or by considering spectral diffusion within one line.[5],[6] In pink ruby which has been used in the present experiments the lines can be shown to be mainly inhomogeneously broadened by dipolar magnetic fields resulting from the Al nuclei. As an oscillation pulse tends to "eat a hole" into the resonance line, cross relaxation supplies inverted spins at the oscillation frequency at a rate much faster than the spin-lattice relaxation mechanism.

At first glance one might think that it would be sufficient to reduce the spin-lattice relaxation time T_o. It is indeed possible
to obtain the correct type of solution, i.e. steady-state oscillations are possible with rather small values of Q. When the
oscillation approaches its steady-state value, however, the
times between the oscillation pulses are too short.

In order to prove that cross relaxation or spin diffusion indeed corrects this deficiency we have constructed a simplified
model shown in Fig. 3. We have divided up the line into spins
which are resonant more or less exactly at the maser oscillation
frequency and spins which are further removed from the oscil-

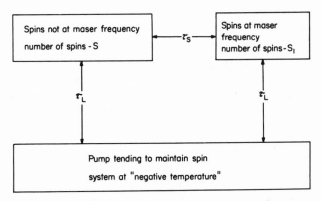

*Fig. 3. Block diagram illustrating the equations which include
cross relaxation or spectral diffusion*

lation frequency. The two spin systems are coupled together
by a time constant τ_s which is assumed to be much shorter than
the spin-lattice relaxation time. Both systems tend to be maintained at an inverted population characterized by a time constant τ_L which, essentially, will be equal to the spin-lattice
relaxation time. The spin system at the maser frequency will
be assumed to contain a substantially smaller number of spins
than the other system. The appropriate equations describing
this system may be written as follows:

$$\frac{dP}{dt} = -\frac{1}{Q_L}\,\omega\,P \qquad (6)$$

$$\frac{1}{Q_L} = \frac{1}{Q} - Cn \tag{7}$$

$$\frac{dn}{dt} = -\frac{n - \frac{S_1}{S} N}{\tau_s} - Dn\,P \tag{8}$$

$$\frac{dN}{dt} = -\frac{N - N_2}{\tau_L} + \frac{n - \frac{S_1}{S} N}{\tau_s}. \tag{9}$$

Equations (6) and (7) are identical to Equations (1) and (2). However n refers now to the number of the inverted spins in the small system. Equation (8) is very similar to Equation (3), however, n tends now to approach a value determined by the spin temperature of the large system with a time constant τ_s. If we denote the total number of spins in the large system by S and those in the small system by S_1, then equal spin temperature means $n/S_1 = N/S$, where N is the number of inverted spins in the large system. We have neglected in Equation (8) the inverted spins which are supplied by the pump. We are justified in doing so, if $\tau_s \ll T_L$ and $S_1 \ll S$. Equation (9) describes the behavior of the inverted spins in the large system. In the absence of microwave power at the signal frequency N would approach N_2 with a time constant τ_L. The second term contains the transfer of inverted spins to the small system.

Equations (6–9) have been integrated on an analog computer assuming the following values: $Q = 10^3 - 5 \times 10^3$; $\tau_s = 2 \times 10^{-5}$ sec; $\tau_L = 2.5 \times 10^{-2}$ sec; $S/S_1 = 20$; and $\omega = 2\pi \times 1.3 \times 10^9$ cycles/sec. In reducing the equations again into a dimensionless form analogous to Equations (4) and (5) we have to specify in addition to the above quoted values the quantity N_2/n_o, where n_o is the amount of inversion in the small system required to overcome the losses characterized by Q. We have assumed $N_2/n_o = 40$, which corresponds approximately to a value of $\alpha = 2$ in Equation (5). In the above range of Q values we cover again the type of solutions as in Fig. 2, however, with spacings between the oscillation pulses of a few msec. We have thus indeed shown that cross relaxation or spectral diffusion changes the results in the desired direction.

In the derivation of the equations, it has been assumed that the pump power is being applied at some time and then left on continuously. However similar types of solutions may be obtained under pulsed operating conditions. For example, in the experiments by Foner et al.[2] the pump levels have been saturated before the dc magnetic field was pulsed. This saturation of levels is expected to be maintained for some time during the pulse and thus even at the high magnetic field, inverted spins may be supplied at the signal frequency. It is thus possible that the present model may even apply to certain types of pulsed masers.

We wish to thank Dr. L. Rimai for stimulating discussions. We also wish to thank Dr. Foner for an interesting conversation regarding his experiments.

REFERENCES

1. C. Kikuchi, J. Lambe, G. Makhov, and R. W. Terhune, J. Appl. Phys. *30*, 1061 (1959).
2. S. Foner, L. R. Momo, and A. Mayer, Phys. Rev. Lett. *3*, 36 (1959).
3. I. R. Senitzky, Phys. Rev. Lett. *1*, 167 (1958).
4. N. Bloembergen, S. Shapiro, P. S. Pershan, and J. O. Artman, Phys. Rev. *114*, 445 (1959).
5. A. M. Portis, Phys. Rev. *104*, 584 (1956).
6. P. W. Anderson, Phys. Rev. *109*, 1492 (1958).

QUANTUM THEORY OF COUPLED SYSTEMS HAVING APPLICATION TO MASERS

W. H. WELLS

California Institute of Technology

IN THIS paper we discuss the theory of maser-like devices in cases where the signal is so weak that we must consider the radiation field as a set of quantum oscillators; i.e. we treat the quantum electrodynamics of masers. Results will be given only for an idealized beam-type maser, but the method can be applied to many more problems. The main emphasis is on a formalism of quantum mechanics that makes this subject simpler and more intuitive.

To fix our ideas, let us consider as an example a linear maser amplifier being used in a communications application. A distant antenna is driving the field classically. The output of the amplifier is classical radiation, but the weak input and perhaps first stages of the amplifier must be treated quantum-mechanically.

Of the many coupled quantum systems, we focus our attention on the field oscillators, because they carry the signal from the antenna. No measurements are performed on the active amplifying elements nor on the lossy elements such as cavity and wave guide walls. We want somehow to integrate out of the problem those variables which describe the state of the unmeasured systems. We want to do this in a formalism such that the remaining problem of coupled driven oscillators is as simple as possible.

The clue for formulating the theory of the driven oscillators in the simplest way was first noted by Wigner.[1] He invented a joint probability density of position and momentum defined by

$$P(x_j, P_j) = \left(\frac{1}{\pi\hbar}\right)^n \int \cdots \int_{-\infty}^{\infty} \exp\left(2i \sum_{j=1}^{n} p_j y_j / \hbar\right) \cdot$$

$$\cdot \psi^*(x_j + y_j)\, \psi(x_j - y_j) \prod_{k=1}^{n} dy_k.$$

Here the coordinates $x_1 \ldots \ldots x_n$ describe the system of n degrees of freedom. Nothing is lost in integration, since ψ may be recovered by the inverse Fourier transformation. When the system is not in a pure state ψ, but is described by a density matrix ρ, then the generalization is given by the substitution

$$\psi^* \psi \longrightarrow \rho\,(x_j + y_j,\; x_j - y_j).$$

Wigner's function is not a true probability density in the usual sense, because it can have negative values. But it can be used like a true one in certain formulas for expected value, where it gives the true quantum-mechanical expected value. Furthermore, in the classical limit, this function becomes the classical probability density. This is an extra convenience in our amplifier example, because somewhere in the stages of amplification we take a classical limit. Wigner showed that for coupled driven oscillators P obeys

$$\frac{\partial P}{\partial t} = \sum_j \frac{p_j}{m_j} \frac{\partial P}{\partial x_j} - \sum_j \frac{\partial V}{\partial x_j} \frac{\partial P}{\partial p_j}.$$

But this is just the equation for a classical probability density of position and momentum when the forces are known, but the initial conditions are in doubt. So when we talk in terms of the Wigner density, we can say that harmonic oscillators follow only classical paths in space-time. The quantum theory just puts uncertainty into the initial conditions.

Figure 1 illustrates this. There contour maps of $P(x,p)$ are drawn at times O and T. Along the time axis, we see how one increment of probability propagates along its classical path in space-time. Now the whole idea of the work reported here is to translate the quantum theory into the language of these clas-

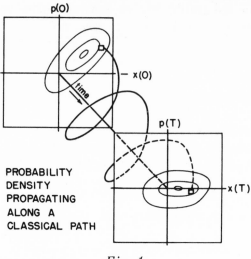

Fig. 1

sical paths that propagate the Wigner density in time. By talking about these paths we can keep all the familiar classical
concepts for describing them: driving force, impedance, equivalent circuits, noise autocorrelation, and higher order correla-
tions. We never have to mention concepts like photons which
put more strain on one's intuition.

Now consider one mode in a cavity or waveguide—no active
amplifying element yet. The oscillation is weakly coupled to a
resistance, that is a vast number of quantum systems in the
metal walls, electrons, lattice modes, etc. Now the wall systems are in general not harmonic oscillators and their Wigner
densities propagate via paths other than the classical ones.
Nevertheless we can think of these systems as having certain
probabilities (in the Wigner sense) of following each of a variety of paths obeying differential equations of motions. The
Wigner density is still the distribution of the initial conditions
of these paths. So as time passes, the uncertain initial conditions of the wall systems give rise to all sorts of uncertain
motions which perturb the oscillator with a noisy force. This
noise is qualitatively like thermal noise, but now there is a
piece dependent on $\hbar$ that does not vanish as the temperature
of the walls goes to zero. This piece is due to the ground state

uncertainty in the initial Wigner density of the wall systems. Now the field oscillator loses to the wall all memory of its initial conditions. But the initial conditions were the only non-classical feature of the oscillator, since it follows only classical paths in space-time. So we can now think of the signal carrying oscillators in the maser as exactly classical, but we find added to the noise power spectrum perturbing these oscillators a piece dependent on $\hbar$. It can be shown that the oscillator feels, as a result of its couplings, a resistance $R(\omega)$ and a noise power spectrum $W(\omega)$ which are related by

$$W(\omega) = R(\omega)\ \alpha(\theta,\omega)/\pi \qquad (1)$$

where θ is the wall temperature, and

$$\alpha(\theta,\omega) = \hbar\omega\ \left(\tfrac{1}{2} + \frac{1}{e^{\hbar\omega/k\theta}-1}\right), \qquad (2)$$

$$\alpha \longrightarrow k\theta \text{ as } \theta \longrightarrow \infty,\ \alpha \longrightarrow \frac{\hbar\omega}{2} \text{ as } \theta \longrightarrow 0.$$

Now the main theoretical problem is to keep this convenient near-classical description when amplifying quantum systems are coupled to the field oscillators. This problem has been solved, but here space permits only partial results and a few remarks about the method of solution. Wigner's density was propagated for a long time interval by the methods of Feynman's space-time approach to non-relativistic quantum mechanics.[2] A certain quantity which appears in the propagation rule for the Wigner density of a system may (in the Wigner sense) be interpreted as the probability of a path of the system in space-time. Some paths have negative probability and give rise to the familiar interference effects of quantum mechanics by canceling positive probabilities. When the variables of the active systems of the maser are integrated out, there results a quantity which can be interpreted as the probability density of force on the field oscillators, again probability in the Wigner sense. The force probability density is just like the probability density of Gaussian force from a noisy impedance, except now, since we're doing quantum mechanics, there are noise contributions dependent on $\hbar$. For an active element, the resistive part of the impedance is negative, and the noise includes spontaneous emission.

Consider an idealized NH_3 maser with a beam of equally-spaced molecules arriving at the rate n. We need a coupling function that describes the strength with which each molecule couples to the field oscillator as is passed through the cavity. For simplicity we choose the Gaussian coupling

$$\gamma(t) = \frac{\gamma_o}{\sqrt{\pi}} e^{-(t/\tau)^2}.$$

Now the effect on the field oscillator of coupling to this beam is described by the impedance

$$Z(\omega) = -\frac{n(\mu\gamma_o\tau)^2}{2\pi\hbar\omega} \exp\left[-\frac{\tau^2}{2}(\omega - \omega_o)^2\right] \times$$

$$\left\{1 + i \text{ erf }\left[-\frac{\tau}{\sqrt{2}}(\omega - \omega_o)\right]\right\}, \quad (3)$$

and the noise power spectrum

$$W(\omega) = \frac{\hbar\omega}{2\pi}\left|\text{Re } Z(\omega)\right|. \quad (4)$$

Here μ is the dipole moment of a molecule and $\omega_o/2\pi$ the molecular resonant frequency. The resistance $\text{Re } Z(\omega)$ is negative. The reactance $\text{Im } Z(\omega)$ describes the way the molecules pull the oscillation toward the molecular frequency $\omega_o/2\pi$. The noise from the beam is related to the absolute value of the resistance the same way the noise of a lossy element at $\theta = 0$ is related to its resistance. This makes sense since the idealized beam may be thought of as having a temperature of $-0\,^\circ K$.

Consider the lower limit of maser amplifier noise at zero temperature. The positive and negative resistances nearly cancel. Let us call their magnitude R. Then from Equations (1), (2), and (4), we have for the total power spectrum

$$W = 2\left(\frac{\hbar\omega}{2\pi} R\right) = \frac{\hbar\omega}{\pi} R.$$

We can relate this to the classical thermal noise of a resistor by putting the classical $\alpha = k\theta$ in Equation (1) obtaining

$$W = Rk\theta/\pi.$$

Comparing these two equations shows that spontaneous emission is equivalent to a temperature of $\hbar\omega/k$. This is a well known result, but in Equations (1) through (4) we have considerably more detailed results.

The method has also been applied to a rather idealized solid-state maser. However, the equations require lengthy explanation, and so will not be given here. The author expects to publish details of the method and the results of several maser problems soon.

Recall that through all our discussion of classical paths in space-time (or for a field oscillator we should say a path on a graph of amplitude of the mode vs. time) we are really doing quantum mechanics, since these paths are to be interpreted as propagating the Wigner density. But we never have to calculate any Wigner densities because all we ask in an amplifier problem is the classical signal coming out of the last stage of amplification. We obtain this just by imagining that the world is classical, treating the coupled modes in terms of equivalent LC circuits, and putting in equivalent impedances and Gaussian noise generators such as those described by Equations (1) through (4).

Note that we have completely avoided talking about photons. After all the word photon refers to a description of the field in terms of energy eigenstates. These states are a convenient description if the energy of the quantized field is being measured, but in normal maser operation no one is measuring energy, one only looks at the classical amplified signal. So it is an inconvenience to talk in terms of energy states, because it obscures questions of coherence and incoherence of the signal. The photon description is prepared to describe the jumpy character of the field if someone disturbs it by making repeated energy measurements which force it into eigenstates. But as long as these measurements are not being made it seems more practical to talk in terms of the Wigner density and classical paths. These paths are smooth and do not contain any feature that one could describe as shot noise of randomly arriving photons.

The author is grateful to Dr. R. P. Feynman for his assistance in setting up the problem in terms of his space-time methods.

REFERENCES

1. E. Wigner, Phys. Rev. *40*, 749 (1932).
2. R. P. Feynman, Rev. Mod. Phys. *20*, 367 (1948).

SPIN SYSTEMS AND CAVITY MODES

K. W. H. STEVENS
Nottingham University, England

AS PART of the maser program which is being carried out at the University of Nottingham, under the sponsorship of C.V.D., we have been making a theoretical investigation of the way in which spin systems couple to the modes of oscillation of a cavity. In this report I would like to give a survey of the progress we have made and also try and give an indication of further developments which seem possible.

THE DAMPED HARMONIC OSCILLATOR

The methods we are using depend very substantially on a quantum-mechanical description of a damped harmonic oscillator.[1] I was very much struck by the fact that in all maser problems one only obtains amplification by using a tuned circuit which has enough damping in it to prevent oscillation, and no simple quantum-mechanical treatment of the damped oscillator existed. There seems to be a feeling that some reason exists why no such treatment can be given and it was therefore with some surprise that I found that a reasonably simple discussion is possible. In writing it up for publication I took the view that this was interesting, rather than important, but since then I have been trying to see whether there is more in it, and I now believe that it can be justified. I would like to outline the argument for this.

The Hamiltonian used is

$$H \equiv e^{-Rt/L} \cdot \frac{P^2}{2AL} + e^{Rt/L} \cdot \frac{AR^2}{2C} - Ae^{Rt/L} \cdot VQ$$

where, for a simple lumped circuit, L, C, and R have their usual meanings, V is a driving voltage and A is a constant. Q is the charge and P is its conjugate variable. If one works classically the motion is obtained from Hamilton's equations

$$\dot{Q} = \frac{\partial H}{\partial P}, \qquad \dot{P} = \frac{-\partial H}{\partial Q}.$$

If one works quantum-mechanically, taking $QP - PQ = i\hbar$, the rate of change of the expectation value of an operator X is

$$\frac{d}{dt} < t \,|\, X \,|\, t > \, = \, < t \,|\, [X, H] \,|\, t >.$$

A direct comparison between the two problems then shows that the differential equations for the changes, classically in the actual variables, quantum-mechanically in the expectation values, are identical. Thus on integration the solutions only differ because of possible differences in constants of integration. However, we are dealing with a nonconservative system so that we shall most likely always be prepared to specify our variable at some particular time. From then on it does not matter whether one uses a classical or a quantum-mechanical formulation.

Suppose now that one considers a different problem, that of an undamped tuned circuit coupled to an infinitely long artificial line, the elements of which can be varied as necessary to turn it into a transmission line. Actually the line need not be infinitely long, but just so long that within the time intervals in which we are interested no reflections ever return from the far end. There can, however, be waves traveling along the line towards the tuned circuit. All the condensers and inductances are regarded as perfect, so that no loss mechanisms are included and the system is conservative. However, as far as the tuned circuit is concerned, the line looks like a voltage source and provides a loss mechanism. One can discuss this problem in a Hamiltonian formalism and prove a result similar to that above, namely that if at some instant the actual values of all the dynamical variables (expectation values in the quantum-mechanical case) are specified then it does not matter whether the subsequent development is treated classically or quantum-mechanically, for the results will be identical. The final step is to bridge the gap, classically, by showing that the behavior of the undamped tuned circuit when coupled to the line is the same as that of a suitably damped tuned circuit with a driving voltage in it. This driving voltage is precisely equal to the voltage, in the line problem, which is arriving at the undamped circuit from the waves on the line which are traveling towards the circuit. Provided then that the voltage term in the damped harmonic oscillator is suitably chosen there seems every reason to believe that it gives an adequate description. In most of our work so far we have, for convenience, taken this voltage to be zero, which means, in the line problem, that nothing is coming along the line towards the circuit. An obvious development is to suppose that there is a noise voltage being sent along, such as might arise from a resistive termination placed in a thermal bath, and we have done a certain amount using this idea. There is a logical difficulty because the line is now terminated with a lossy element and the problem is no longer conservative. Apart from this, the mathematical treatment is not easy.

SPINS IN A CAVITY

In order to feel our way we have considered the following simple problem. A rectangular cavity contains a single spin of $\frac{1}{2}$ which is in an external magnetic field. One mode of the cavity, which is supposed to contain a lossy dielectric but to have perfectly conducting walls (a dodge to obtain losses with simple boundary conditions), has the same frequency as the spin resonance and sets up a magnetic field, at the spin, which is perpendicular to the external field. No other modes are considered, and our particular mode is supposed to have a known energy at t_o and is not driven in any way. Thus its energy decays through the resistive losses (or, if it is preferred, by sending energy down the transmission line) and also there can be an exchange of energy with the spin. With the single approximation that the spin only responds to that component of the transverse field which is rotating in the same direction as it is precessing we have solved the time dependent Schrödinger equation completely. This should shortly be published[2] and as the problem is highly academic I shall not discuss it further.

The next problem we tried was that in which there are N spins of $\frac{1}{2}$ in the cavity, under the same conditions as the single spin, above. In particular we assume that each spin is subject to the same cavity field. The problem now becomes too complicated for exact solution and we have had to approximate. The most important result is that obtained for the case in which one starts off, at t_o, with all the spins in their highest energy state. Then we find that the expectation value of s_z is given, approximately, by

$$< s_z > = \tfrac{1}{2}N + \tfrac{1}{2}(n + 1) \left[1 - \cosh \left\{ \frac{2K(x - 1)\sqrt{N}}{\hbar} \right\} \right]$$

where $x = \exp\{-\omega(t - t_o)/Q_o\}$, the energy in the mode at t_o is approximately $n\hbar\omega$ and K is a complicated term, which for a mode having vector potential

$$A = A_1\{i h_2 \cos h_1 x \sin h_2 y - j h_1 \sin h_1 x \cos h_2 y\} \sin h_3 z$$

and with the spins at $x = \pi/2k_1$, $y = 0$, $z = 0$ equals

$$-4 h_1 h_3 g p Q_o \left[\frac{\pi \mu \hbar}{(h_1^2 + h_2^2 + h_3^2)(h_1^2 + h_2^2)} \right]^{\frac{1}{2}}.$$

In this, g is the spectroscopic splitting factor, Q_o is the Q of the mode, μ is the permeability of the material filling the cavity ($= 1$, usually), V is the volume of the cavity and ω is the frequency of the mode. We estimate that with $Q_o \sim 5000$ and for a reasonable cavity, working at

$$\omega = 2\pi \cdot 10^{10} \text{ sec}^{-1}, \quad \frac{2K}{\hbar} \sim -10^{-8}.$$

To see what this expression means, we note that x is related to t by an exponential, so that at $t = t_o$, $x = 1$ and that it falls to zero in a time of the order of the decay time of the cavity. Thus, at t_o $< s_2 >$ equals $\frac{1}{2}N$, but in a few microseconds it has changed to

$$\tfrac{1}{2}N + \tfrac{1}{2}(n + 1) \left[1 - \cosh \frac{2K}{\hbar} \sqrt{N} \right]$$

and from then on is effectively constant (note that there is no thermal noise in this treatment). Now the approximation is only valid provided that $< s_z >$ does not change too much, which requires that $\cosh \left\{ \dfrac{2K}{\hbar} \sqrt{N} \right\}$ be less than $\frac{1}{2}N$ (assuming $n = 0$). This is so for N less than about 10^{18}, but for $N \sim 10^{20}$ we see that the formula predicts a very rapid change in $< s_z >$ with time, for

$$\cosh \left\{ \frac{2K}{\hbar} \sqrt{N} \right\} = \cosh 100 \sim 10^{43}.$$

We interpret this change in behavior as the threshold for a two-level maser. With such a concentration of spins the energy in the spins is very rapidly given to the cavity. With a smaller concentration nothing very exciting happens. It is unfortunate that our approximation breaks down when $< s_z >$ begins to change rapidly, but there are indications that it actually undergoes an oscillatory motion, corresponding to an interchange of energy between the spins and the cavity. This gradually disappears, because at all times the energy in the cavity is being dissipated. A full account of this work is also given in the paper[2] previously quoted.

THE DIPOLE-DIPOLE INTERACTION

With many spins in the cavity a further step might be to include the dipole-dipole coupling, although we should also then have to space the spins in the cavity.

Thinking about this we began to wonder where the usual formula

$$g^2 p^2 \left\{ \frac{\vec{s}_1 \cdot \vec{s}_2}{r^3} - \frac{3 (\vec{s}_1 \cdot \vec{r})(\vec{s}_2 \cdot \vec{r})}{r^5} \right\}$$

comes from. The commonest derivation is from magnetostatics! We therefore decided not to use it but to suppose, instead, that each spin in the cavity can only interact with the electromagnetic fields in the cavity. If these are set up by the presence of other spins, then it is only in this way that the spins are aware of one another. For convenience we have assumed that the cavity is undamped and that there are just two spins in our rectangular cavity, each interacting with all the cavity modes. Then, by using what is really a spin-Hamiltonian method and by not being too careful about degeneracies we have, in second-order perturbation theory, shown that the total energy of the system can be regarded as made up of the cavity energy alone together with self-energies of the spins and a mutual energy of coupling. This mutual energy is most interesting, for we find that it consists of an infinite number of terms, the largest of which is the standard energy, given above. The other terms occur because each spin has an infinity of geometrical images in the walls of the cavity and the first spin has a standard dipole-dipole interaction with all the images of the second spin and vice versa.

One may ask whether such a change in the dipolar interaction is detectable. As far as we can see the answer is no, in paramagnetic resonance, but in ferrimagnetic resonance the effect (though here it is altered because of wall losses) is responsible for the so-called wall effect,[3] for the images then have macroscopic moments. A problem in which we are much interested is to discover what happens if the cavity modes are damped, but this is proving rather difficult. If now we survey our results we find that in one of our problems we have tried to treat the interaction with a single mode as fully as possible, and this leads to a threshold condition. In another we have worked with all the modes but to a low order in perturbation theory and this produces a type of dipole-dipole interaction. The first result is of considerable interest and only arises because we have, effectively, taken the treatment of one mode to high orders in perturbation theory. There seems little virtue in assuming that the spins are coupled by dipolar forces if thereby one neglects terms which may be important, and we suggest that it is better to take the more fundamental approach, which regards each spin as interacting with all the cavity modes and use this as the Hamiltonian for the many spin case. The usual dipolar interaction terms must then be omitted.

INTERACTION WITH THE LATTICE

So far we have been discussing the treatment of the interactions of a spin with an electromagnetic field in a cavity. For spin-lattice relaxation problems we need to study how the spin interacts with a lattice vibration. There may clearly be a close resemblance between the two problems. To see this we must study the interactions. In the electromagnetic case the interaction between a mode and the spin has the form

$$Q \, \vec{\alpha} \cdot \vec{S}$$

where Q is an electromagnetic field variable and $\vec{\alpha}$ is a vector which describes the way in which the direction and amplitude of the magnetic field of the mode varies with position in the cavity. In the interaction with the lattice one effect of a lattice vibration is to change the electric field at an ion and thereby modulate the g-value. Thus the interaction of a spin with an external magnetic field will have the form $\vec{S} \cdot g \cdot \vec{H}$ where g has the form

$$g = 2 - \frac{\lambda}{\Delta} + Q \left[\frac{\partial}{\partial Q} \left(\frac{-\lambda}{\Delta} \right) \right]_{Q=0}$$

and where Q is now a variable describing a lattice mode. There is thus again a linear coupling between Q and S. It will also be noticed that the coupling to the lattice is dependent on H. In a detailed discussion there will be a number of differences, of course; there are many more lattice than cavity waves which coincide in frequency with the spin resonance frequency, and their wavelength is much shorter than the electromagnetic wavelengths. Further I know very little about their damping. Nevertheless it seems that the techniques which we have been developing to describe the interactions of a spin with the damped electromagnetic modes in a cavity may have a direct application to spin-lattice relaxation problems. If this proves to be so, we may find that the direct process in spin-lattice relaxation can alternatively be regarded as the response of the spin to the charges (or currents) in a set of damped tuned circuits, each of which is being driven by a noise voltage arising from the thermal contact of its resistance with a temperature bath.

A good deal of the work described above has been done in collaboration with **Dr. B. Josephson, Jr.**

REFERENCES

1. Stevens, K. W. H., Proc. Phys. Soc. *72*, 1027 (1958).
2. Josephson, B., Jr., and Stevens, K. W. H., Proc. Phys. Soc. (to be published).
3. Spencer, E. G. and LeCraw, R. L., J. Appl. Phys. *26*, 250 (1955).

INFRARED AND
OPTICAL MASERS

A. L. SCHAWLOW

Bell Telephone Laboratories, Murray Hill, New Jersey

AS YET, nobody knows for sure what form a practical source of coherent infrared or optical radiation will take. Still, the maser principle gives us at least one very promising direction in which to work, and several groups are following it.

It has long been realized that atomic and molecular systems provide us with copious supplies of natural resonators, tuned to almost any desired frequency in the infrared or optical region. Many ways are known of exciting these resonators, so that they will emit radiation. However, it is only with the addition of the maser principle that we have a way to make the individual resonators emit in phase, or at least with a fixed relative phase. By using a high Q resonator, we can match the radiation resistance of the individual oscillator to that of space, and so make it radiate much faster than it would do if left alone. This is particularly important in the microwave region. Moreover, we can make the radiation come out in a single mode, such as a plane wave with a desired direction.

For the infrared and optical regions, it is convenient, and probably necessary, to use a resonant cavity with dimensions much greater than the wavelength.[1] Figure 1 shows such a system, with an active medium between two small reflecting plates. The active medium has, for at least one frequency, a negative temperature. Then light emitted by one atom in the general direction of the axis of the system, will be amplified, and grow as it bounces back and forth between the plates. Light traveling in any other direction will leave the system before making many passes and so will not interact strongly with the

MIRROR   ACTIVE MEDIUM   MIRROR

Fig. 1. A simple optical maser

active medium. As the number of excited atoms is increased,
the threshold of maser oscillation will be reached first for a
wave whose direction is very close to the axis of the system.
Then the output will be a wave which is not only very monochromatic and coherent, but is nearly all propagated in a single
direction. The output will thus correspond to a single one of
the many modes which could be supported by a cavity resonator
of comparable dimensions.

The general principles of optical masers have been discussed,
with special reference to potassium vapor as the active medium.[1]
It was shown the number of atoms which must be supplied to
the excited state per second (assuming that the lower state of
the transition is empty) is

$$\frac{n}{\tau} = \frac{8\pi^2}{(\pi \ln 2)^{\frac{1}{2}}} \frac{V}{\lambda^3} \cdot \frac{1}{t} \cdot \frac{1}{\Phi} \frac{\Delta\nu}{\nu} \tag{1}$$

where V is the volume between the reflecting plates,

   λ is the wavelength of the emitted light, and

   t is the time during which emitted light remains between
   the plates. $t = L/(1 - \alpha) C$ where L is the distance between the plates, α is the reflectivity, and C is the velocity
   of light.

   $\Delta\nu/\nu$ is the fractional width of the spectral line.

   Φ is the fraction of excited atoms which decay spontaneously
   in the desired transition.

This number does not depend explicitly on the transition
probability or on the lifetime of the excited state. If the lifetime is long because of a small transition matrix element, more
atoms are needed in the excited state, but there is more time to
accumulate them.

As a specific example, let us again consider potassium. Fig.
2 shows the energy levels of atomic potassium. The $5P_{\frac{3}{2}}$ level

can be populated directly from the 4S ground state by radiation of 4044 Å wavelength, which is available from potassium discharge lamps. For mirrors with 1 cm² area, separated by 10 cm of potassium vapor at 435°K a power input of 1.2×10^{-3} watt is needed. These requirements can be met, but not easily. At Columbia University, C. H. Townes, H. Cummins, I. Abella, and O. S. Heavens are exploring the problems of this particular system. Following some suggestions of D. A. Jackson, they have made temperature-controlled potassium lamps with output several times larger than for a simple air-cooled lamp. They have also found that a moderate pressure serves to shift the mercury 4046 Å line to the right wavelength to pump the potassium, while retaining a high intensity per wavelength interval.

The postulated reflectivity of 0.98 at the output wavelength of 3.14 microns is quite conservative. Several metals will do that well, particularly since only one plate needs to have a coating thin enough to transmit some light. Multilayer dielectric coatings have even less loss for a given reflectivity. In the infrared region, rather thick layers are needed, and these have a

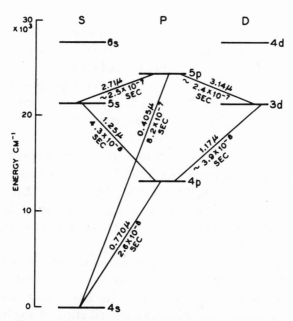

Fig. 2. Energy levels of atomic potassium

microcrystalline structure, which may cause appreciable scattering. Even so, reflectivities as high as 99 percent can probably
be attained.

If much more powerful methods of selectively populating
excited states could be achieved, correspondingly lower reflectivity could be tolerated. Gould[2] has described an ingenious
arrangement in which one mirror is replaced by a hollow cylindrical cup having on its inside a fine coating of magnesium
oxide. By repeated scattering, light entering along the axis
returns in predominantly the same direction. The effective reflectivity of such an arrangement is not as high as with a mirror.
If sufficiently efficient pumping methods are available, the
broader resonance could be an advantage.

PUMPING METHODS

The optical excitation scheme proposed for potassium vapor
depends for its working on two points. First, atoms are supplied directly to the desired excited state and only to that
state. Second, atoms leave the lower state by radiation faster
than they are supplied by decay of the upper state. The second
factor alone might be sufficient, even if atoms were supplied
randomly into a large number of excited states. It is very probable that this kind of population inversion can be made to occur
in a gas discharge under suitable conditions. This possibility
has occurred in various forms to several people quite independently, among them W. S. Boyle, J. H. Sanders, A. Javan,
and G. Gould. J. H. Sanders has considered the effect of an
electrical discharge in, for example, helium gas.[3] There, the
6678 Å line of helium I is due to a transition between the 3^1D_2
upper state with a mean life of 1.5×10^{-8} sec and the 2^1P_1
lower state with a mean life of 4.3×10^{-10} sec. Even if atoms
were supplied to these states in equal numbers, the average
population of the upper state would be considerably greater
than that of the lower state.

As Sanders points out, many complicated processes occur in
gas discharges. Javan[4] has made a careful analysis of excitation processes in a discharge. He has shown that most of
them tend to restore a Boltzmann distribution of excited states

in thermal equilibrium with the hot electrons. However, there are also further possibilities, such as the use of mixed gases with transfer of energy from one to the other by collisions. Some of these more sophisticated excitation methods have been discussed by Javan. It seems possible that very large excess populations might be obtained in a suitable gas discharge system.

It is also possible to construct solid optical masers. Solids do exist which, when suitably excited, emit strong sharp lines. Moreover, it is not unusual for the same material to have also a broad absorption which can be used to populate the upper level of the sharp transition. Transfer between the band and line levels takes place rapidly, and often efficiently, through non-radiative processes involving the crystal lattice.

For example, consider the optical spectrum of ruby, i.e. Cr^{3+} in Al_2O_3. There is a broad absorption band in the green and others in the ultraviolet. When excited through these bands, the crystal emits a moderate number of sharp lines in the deep red (near 7000 Å). The two strongest lines (at 6919 Å and 6934 Å) go to the ground state, so that they will always have more atoms in their lower state, and are not suitable for maser action. However, the strongest satellite line (at 7009 Å), which in "normal" ruby ($\frac{1}{2}$ percent Cr) is nearly as strong as the main lines, goes to a lower state which is normally empty at liquid-helium temperatures, and might be usable.

To be sure, there are a number of competing lines in ruby, and most atoms lose their excitation entirely without radiation. Moreover, the line width of the main lines in "normal" ruby is about 1 cm^{-1}, while the desired 7009 Å line is two or three times broader.

There is not very much information about how sharp lines can be in solids. The main ruby lines are much sharper at low concentrations, and have been observed[5] to be as narrow as 0.2 cm^{-1} so that $\Delta\nu/\nu = 1.4 \times 10^{-5}$. Further narrowing might result if the samples were annealed, as strain is surely one source of line width. In dilute rare earth crystals, lines as narrow as 0.1 cm^{-1} have been observed (private communication from G. H. Dieke).

Unfortunately, we cannot narrow the 7009 Å line in ruby by diluting, because its relative intensity decreases rapidly at low concentrations. This fact, and others, show that it originates in transitions, not of a single chromium ion, but of an exchange-coupled pair of ions.[6] This line might be narrowed by annealing, but taking it as it is, a pumping power of several hundred watts would be needed for maser action. Since this pumping power is broadband, this much might be achieved, but cooling problems would probably enforce pulsed operation. It may well be that more suitable solid materials can be found, and we are looking for them.

The structure of a solid-state optical maser could be especially simple. In essence, it would be just a rod with one end totally reflecting and the other end nearly so. The sides would be left clear to admit pumping radiation.

MASERS FOR THE FAR INFRARED

One of the things we expect to do in an optical maser is to increase the total rate of emission of radiation from a given number of excited atoms. This property might be expected to be especially useful in the far infrared or submillimeter region. According to Equation (1), the number of excited atoms needed per second is

$$\frac{n}{\tau} = \frac{8\pi^2}{(\pi \ln 2)^{\frac{1}{2}}} \frac{V}{\lambda^3} \cdot \frac{1}{\tau} \cdot \frac{1}{\Phi} \frac{\Delta\nu}{\nu}.$$

Thus if all other factors remained constant, $\dfrac{n}{\tau}$ should decrease rapidly as λ increases. But other factors will not remain constant. The radiative lifetime of an excited state is proportional to μ^2/λ^3, where μ is the dipole moment matrix element of the transition, and becomes very long as λ increases. This is shown in Table 1, for two dipole moments chosen to be roughly representative of electric and magnetic dipole transitions. With such long radiative lifetimes, competing processes are usually dominant, and many more excited atoms must be supplied. In particular, in solids, lattice vibrations usually produce rapid relaxation, particularly in the neighborhood of the Debye frequency.

Table 1. Natural (radiative) lifetimes of excited states

$$\tau_{sec} = \frac{3h\lambda^3}{64\pi^4\mu^2}$$

λcm	$\mu = 1 \times 10^{-18}$ e.s.u.	$\mu = .01 \times 10^{-18}$ e.s.u.
1	3×10^6	3×10^{10}
10^{-2}	3	3×10^4
10^{-4}	3×10^{-6}	3×10^{-2}

For the submillimeter range, it would be desirable to have a system with the largest possible dipole moment. Beam-type masers using molecules have been proposed by Dicke[7] and by Prokhorov.[8] A very large dipole moment matrix element can be obtained in a cyclotron resonance. At least in the case of negative mass holes in germanium[9] there exists a method of preferentially populating the upper level. If the relaxation time is suitable, cyclotron resonance might be usable for generation of submillimeter waves.

APPLICATIONS

The output of an infrared or optical maser should be powerful (at least by infrared standards), monochromatic, coherent, and unidirectional. These properties form the basis of those applications which have been suggested so far. Sanders[10] has suggested that Zeeman components radiated together by a maser would be narrow enough to give good beats. Simultaneous measurement of the frequency and wavelength of the beats would give a precise value of the velocity of light.

The narrowness expected for the line would make it attractive for a wavelength standard. As in microwave masers, the line can be pulled somewhat by the cavity resonance if the latter is not much broader, or does not coincide with the peak of the natural line shape. However, one may follow the procedures developed for microwave masers to tune the cavity to the line center. For example, some lines should show a symmetrical splitting when a magnetic field is applied. If it is not symmetrical, adjustment of the cavity is required.

The high directionality is equivalent to propagating all the output in a single, accurately plane, wave mode. Such a wave can, as pointed out by Townes, be focused in a very small spot, probably not much larger than a wavelength. If a plane wave output of, say, 1 milliwatt can be concentrated into a spot of 10^{-8} cm^2, the power density achieved will be 10^5 watts per cm^2 at the focus. This corresponds to an optical frequency electric field of several hundred e.s.u. per cm. Such a large field, even though very localized, might be sufficient to show nonlinear effects either in its interaction with matter or with other light waves.

If maser oscillators can be developed to give powerful sources of infrared of the right frequency, they might be used to excite a particular vibrational mode of a molecule. By doing so vigorously enough, it may be possible eventually to influence the course of chemical reactions.

Other applications will surely be suggested, but we already see enough to feel that the effort to construct an optical maser is worth while.

REFERENCES

1. A. L. Schawlow and C. H. Townes, Phys. Rev. *112*, 1940 (1958).
2. G. Gould, Summer Symposium on Optical Pumping, University of Michigan, Ann Arbor, Michigan (unpublished).
3. J. H. Sanders, Phys. Rev. Lett. *3*, 86 (1959).
4. A. Javan, Phys. Rev. Lett. *3*, 87 (1959); also, paper in this symposium.
5. F. Varsanyi, D. L. Wood, and A. L. Schawlow (to be published).
6. A. L. Schawlow, D. L. Wood, and A. M. Clogston, Phys. Rev. Lett. (September 15, 1959).
7. R. H. Dicke, U. S. Patent 2,851,652 (September 5, 1958).
8. A. M. Prokhorov, JETP (USSR) *34*, 1658 (1958).
9. Dousmanis, Duncan, Thomas, and Williams, Phys. Rev. Lett. 1, 404 (1958).
10. J. H. Sanders, Nature *183*, 312 (1959).

J. C. GILL: I was interested to hear of the "nearest-neighbor" satellites in the optical spectrum of ruby, as I have observed similar satellites in the X-band paramagnetic absorption spectrum. The satellite system is complex, since there are several inequivalent ion pairs even with the direct magnetic field parallel to the crystalline axis. An attempt at analysis is being made—it may be possible to obtain information on the exchange fields between adjacent Cr^{3+} ions.

R. H. DICKE: It is interesting than an optical oscillation, a short burst, highly directional can in principle be obtained by arranging many atoms in a pencil array, all in an excited state. The diameter of the pencil is preferably the geometric mean of the length of the pencil and the wave length. The principle of operation is discussed in my Physical Review paper on "Coherence and Spontaneous Radiation." Briefly speaking, each photon which is emitted by the gas makes that direction of emission more probable for the next photon, but the two directions along the pencil are strongly favored because of the large solid angle defined by the array in those directions. This can be thought of qualitatively as an optical fuse with previously emitted light passing along the pencil.

G. GOULD: Professor Dicke has remarked that a tube terminated by windows rather than mirrors, and containing a medium which is capable of amplifying an "optical" electromagnetic wave, may generate a spatially incoherent light burst. Planer coherent light pulses may be obtained by pulsing a resonant light oscillator of the type described by Dr. Schawlow. If such a pulse is passed through the amplifying tube envisaged by Professor Dicke, nonlinear amplification should build up an extremely short and powerful pulse which is still flat. Calculations indicate possible peak pulse powers as high as 1 megawatt from long-lived states which we are studying experimentally.

J. WEBER: First a historical comment. I believe that Professor Willis E. Lamb pointed out the possibility of getting a negative temperature in a discharge in 1950 (in his Physical Review articles on the Lamb shift).

Since we have only recently been shown how to get high Q and separate modes, it may be worthwhile to review the ancient methods using free electrons. Noise is not an issue and an absolute standard is not required, at least initially, so most of the motivation for use of molecules, or bound states disappears. I am suggesting then the study of essentially the methods of klystron and traveling-wave tubes together with the kinds of cavity suggested by Dicke, by Townes and Schawlow, and by Prokhorov.

M. STITCH: Dr. Levitt of Hughes has proposed a scheme which might increase the mode resolution and directionality of your Fabry-Perot mirrors. This ties in with Jacobsen's interesting work mentioned this morning. The idea is to replace the metallic film mirrors with a suitable dielectric in which ultrasonic standing waves are set up as shown:

The Brillouin periodic transmission pattern can be made by proper excitation to have a narrow reflection zone and transmission zone. One then has the effect of Lippmann fringes with very narrow mode selection.

A. L. SCHAWLOW: Isn't this somewhat like multiple dielectric films?

M. L. STITCH: Yes.

W. LOW: While measuring attenuation of microwaves of 3 cms behind shockwaves we observed the emission of radiation from the excited state of the fine structure level at 0.365 cm^{-1} in atomic hydrogen. This experiment was made on a shock wave in argon which was slightly contaminated with hydrogen. Apparently in shock waves and at temperatures of a few thousand degrees before the gas has established thermodynamic equilibrium one can achieve negative temperatures. This has indeed been anticipated by Professor W. E. Lamb in the appendix of the first paper in 1950, by Lamb and Rutherford, in which they discussed the possibility of obtaining negative temperatures in a Woods discharge.

POSSIBILITY OF OBTAINING NEGATIVE TEMPERATURE IN ATOMS BY ELECTRON IMPACT

A. JAVAN

Bell telephone Laboratories, Murray Hill, New Jersey

CONSIDER A pure gas consisting of atoms subjected to electron bombardment. The population distribution of the excited atoms will depend on the energy distribution of the electrons, the lifetimes of the excited-state atoms and their modes of excitations by electron impacts. Such a system, in general, is a nonthermodynamical system. Under favorable conditions, a state of negative temperature between two of the excited atomic levels may be expected.

Let us label the two excited states by indices 1 and 2 with the level 1 as the lower of the two levels. If the rates of excitations of these two levels are R_1 and R_2 and their lifetimes τ_1 and τ_2, the populations of these levels will be given by $R_1 \tau_1$ and $R_2 \tau_2$. This consideration leads to a simple suggestion that if τ_1 is sufficiently smaller than τ_2, $R_1 \tau_1$ may be smaller than $R_2 \tau_2$ leading to a negative temperature. However, complications appear as soon as one examines the modes of excitations of these levels and their corresponding values of R_1 and R_2. In many instances one finds that a short-lived level which may appear suitable for the lower of the two levels may have such a large excitation cross section by electron impact as to yield this level unsuitable for production of negative temperature.

Once in a given atom two levels are selected on the basis of their lifetimes, it is not hard to investigate theoretically the major sources of excitation of these levels and establish reasonably well the chances for obtaining a negative temperature. Even in the absence of exact knowledge of the excitation cross sections and lifetimes of the levels involved, such an investigation is important at this stage of the game. In this way many cases which at the first sight may appear suitable for this purpose can be ruled out, certain borderline cases may be found, and indeed one or two promising cases are encountered.

In this paper, our method of analysis will be described briefly for a few specific cases without going into details of the numerical calculations. Only some of the results will be stated.

On the basis of the symmetry properties of the electric dipole matrix elements, it can be shown easily that if two levels are connected by an electric dipole matrix element and if one of these levels is allowed for an optical transition to a third level, the other level will be forbidden for a transition to the same third level. On the basis of this assertion, most of the interesting cases which one encounters can be classified into two groups. The first group contains those cases in which the level 1, i.e., the lower of the two levels is optically allowed for a transition into the ground state. The second group are those in which the level 2 is allowed for a transition into the ground state. Obviously, there exist cases which do not fit into either of these groups, namely, those in which neither of the two levels are optically connected to the ground state. This latter possibility will be mentioned briefly at the end and its relation to some of the aspects of the first two classes of systems will be described.

Consider the first group of systems. In most cases of this type, the level 1 is short lived by virtue of its transition to the ground state. In these cases, the gas pressure should be below a few microns. At a larger pressure, the effective lifetime of this level will be increased due to the trapping of the photons arising from the transition of this level to the ground state. In these cases, however, the cross section of excitation of these levels by electron impact should be examined carefully. A level which is optically allowed for a transition to the ground state, as a rule, has particularly large excitation cross section by electron impact. This fact may lead to a large value of R_1 as compared to R_2, which in turn, may give rise to a positive temperature in spite of short life of the state 1.

Allowing for the above-mentioned factors, the transition $2^1P \leftarrow 3^1D$ of He appears at first sight to be a possible candidate for production of the negative temperature. The author has recently given a brief analysis of this case.[1] However, other difficulties appear to exist which may render these levels useless for a practical maser. Notice that at a low pressure the cascade transitions from the higher excited levels into the 3^1D is not an important factor. The few important levels which may decay into the 3^1D are also allowed for a transition to the ground state with a higher rate of decay. Only a small fraction of the population of these levels will decay into the 3^1D level. Thus, the main source of population of the 3^1D level will be by direct electron impact. If the electron density is low and a very small fraction of atoms are found in the excited states of the He atoms, the main source of excitation of the 3^1D will be direct collision of electrons with the He atoms in their ground state. Under this condition negative temperature may be expected. However, as soon as densities of the order of 10^9 atoms/cc for the population of 3^1D are required, one can easily show that the densities of the metastable He, namely, the 2^1S and 2^3S, become such a large fraction of the total density of the atoms that the collision of electrons with the metastables becomes the predominant source of excitation of the 3^1D state. It can be shown that this process will then lead to a positive temperature for the population of 3^1D and 2^1P levels. Notice that the main difficulty is the low pressure requirement of the total gas pressure. Under this condition, the populations of the long-lived excited state atoms become a very large fraction of the total atoms, which upsets the favorable collision processes arising from electron impacts with the atoms in the ground state.

In spite of these difficulties, it is quite worthwhile to study this particular case both in a gas discharge and also by means of electron bombardment using an electron gun. The lifetimes of these levels are extremely attractive and the possibility of an unexpected and pleasant surprise may not be ruled out!

Incidentally, a discharge at a gas pressure of a few microns can be maintained by microwave excitation in a magnetic field with the value of the field at the electron cyclotron resonance.[3]

In this way it is possible to obtain a very large electron temperature at a low gas pressure.

In a recent publication,[2] J. H. Sanders has also mentioned the case of He and has proposed this as a maser material.

The second group of systems are those in which the higher level (level 2) is optically allowed for a transition to the ground state. In cases of this type, normally the radiative lifetime of this level is short by virtue of its transition to the ground state. By itself this lifetime may be even shorter than that of the level 1. At low pressure such a system may not be suitable for production of negative temperature. However, at larger gas pressure, say one millimeter of mercury or more, where the resonant photons arising from the decay of the level 2 into the ground state are completely trapped, the effective lifetime of this level will be increased and determined by its radiative decay into the other available low-lying levels. Under this condition, there exist many instances where the effective lifetime of the level 2 becomes larger than that of the level 1. Furthermore, since the level 2 is optically allowed for a transition to the ground state, the rates of excitation of these two levels, R_1 and R_2, by electron impacts with the atoms in the ground state is much more favorable as compared to the first groups of atoms mentioned above.

As an example, the level $2s_3$ and $2p_{10}$ of Ne (in Paschen designation) have the properties described above and the author has already given a brief analysis of this case.[1] It should be noted that in this case also the main difficulty is to prevent appreciable excitation of these levels by electron impact with the metastable Ne. However, this is now a matter of the ingenuity of the experimenter and not a basic difficulty. Unlike the case of He, the larger gas pressure implies a smaller fraction of total atoms in the excited states. Simple estimates show that by introducing a small amount of a quenching gas such as argon and keeping the electrons in the discharge at a moderate density, this difficulty may be prevented.

The inert gases have a very colorful and rich spectrum. They present many interesting possibilities. Unfortunately, experimental information on the lifetimes and electron excitation cross sections of most of these levels is not available. However, very rough estimates of these quantities in some of these cases appear to suggest some further possibilities. For instance, some of the higher excited levels of Ne, such as those belonging to the $2p^5(^2P_{\frac{1}{2}})3d$ electron configurations appear to have suffi-

ciently long lifetimes. Under favorable conditions, the excitations of these levels by electron impact with the Ne metastables may lead to a state of negative temperature.

A further scheme for preferentially populating a given energy level is the use of transfer of excitation between excited states of two different atoms in a gas mixture. This technique may be far more powerful than the cases described above for pure gases.

Consider a long-lived excited state of a given atom (such as a metastable state). This state can be populated appreciably at moderate electron densities. If an excited state of a second atom happens to lie very close in energy to that of the level of the first atom, a large cross section is expected to exist for an inelastic collision resulting in a transfer of excitation from the metastable state level to the excited state of the other atom and vice versa. Due to the non-adiabatic nature of the process of collision, the levels of the second atom which differ in energy considerably from that of the metastable level of the first atom do not show appreciable cross sections for transfer of excitation.

The transfer of excitation has been studied in the past in connection with the so-called "sensitized fluorescent effect."[4] The author has already given a brief account of this process in connection with its use for production of negative temperature.[1] A mixture of He and Ne or Hg and Na and several other cases present quite advantageous levels for producing negative temperature. A lengthy analysis of these cases is planned for a future publication.

It should be noted that this effect is analogous to that used by Feher and Scovil[5] in operating a three-level maser. These authors have made use of the short relaxation time of the cerium impurity in gadolinium-lanthanum ethylsulfate to increase the contact of one of the paramagnetic levels of gadolinium with the lattice which is at low temperature. This takes place as soon as the energy separation of two levels of cerium becomes near resonance of separation of two levels of gadolinium. In our case the presence of a long-lived state of one atom increases the contact of a short-lived nearby state of a second atom with the electrons which are hot and at high temperature.

A project is underway by the author for further work on some of the proposals described above, in connection with the development of an optical maser. For the purpose of electron bombardment, a gas discharge and also an electron gun of special design is being used.

In Fig. 1, a block diagram is given of one of our electronic detection schemes for detecting the presence of negative temperature and optimizing it. The "lamp" provides the spectral line to be amplified. The light emitted from the lamp is transmitted through a "cell" which consists of either an electron gun or a

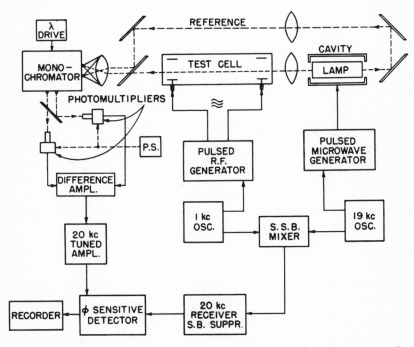

Fig. 1. Block diagram of electronic circuit for detecting the presence of negative temperature

discharge cell containing the amplifying gas. The transmitted light is focused on the input slit of a monochromator. The particular spectral line is selected by the monochromator and is then detected by a photomultiplier. In order to distinguish the amplified signal from the background signal arising from the spontaneous emission in the cell, the lamp and the cell are modulated at two different frequencies in the audio range. For instance, suppose the lamp is modulated at 19 kc/sec and the cell at 1 kc/sec. If the cell amplifies or attenuates the particular spectral component of the transmitted light, the photomultiplier output will have a 19 kc signal which is amplitude moduated at the rate of 1 kc/sec. The output of the photomultiplier is fed to a receiver which is tuned to one of the side bands, resulting from such an amplitude modulation, for instance at 20 kc/sec. Thus, the amplifier will respond only to either attenuation or amplification of the light transmitted through the cell. In order to provide a narrow band detection and, at the same time, to tell amplification from attenuation, the following feature is added. The 19 kc/sec and the 1 kc/sec signals used for the purpose of modulating the lamp and the cell are mixed in a diode. The 20 kc/sec component of their beat note is selected and amplified in a second receiver. Notice that this signal should have a constant phase compared to the output of the first receiver which is fed by the photomultiplier. In this way a phase-sensitive detector is used after the first receiver. The reference signal for the phase detector is the large output of the second receiver. Some further features have been added to this detection scheme to improve sensitivity and eliminate some of the noise sources orginating from fluctuations of the light outputs of the lamp and the cell. For instance, a part of the light output of the lamp is transmitted outside of the cell and focused at a slightly different spot of the input slit of the monochromator. By a simple arrangement at the output slit, the light transmitted through the cell and that transmitted outside of the cell are fed into two different photomultimpliers. The difference of these two signals are then fed to the receiver at the 20 kc/sec.

REFERENCES

1. A. Javan, Phys. Rev. Lett. *3*, 87 (1959).
2. J. H. Sanders, Phys. Rev. Lett. *3*, 86 (1959)
3. See for instance H. Beutler and B. Josephy, Z. Physik *53*, 747 (1929).
4. D. O. Akhurst, S. J. Buchsbaum, and E. I. Gordon, "Low Pressure Microwave Plasma in a Magnetic Field," Proceedings of the 10th Annual Gaseous Electronics Conference (October 2, 1957).
5. G. Feher and H. E. D. Scovil, Phys. Rev. *105,* 760 (1957).

DISCUSSION

W. V. SMITH: Is it correct that trapping of resonance radiation of the pumped upper state can result in a longer lifetime than that of the lower state whose radiation to the ground state is partially forbidden? Would not this lower state transition also be partly trapped?

A. JAVAN: The lower transition decays by allowed transitions to other states which are above the ground state, hence there is no trapping of radiation here.

G. GOULD: Dr. Javan has mentioned the possibility of selective excitation of a neon level by collisions of the second kind with metastable Helium atoms.

A similar effect has been observed in Na-Hg gas mixtures under discharge conditions by Bentler and Josephy in the early 1930's. Hg $[6^2P_o]$ metastables excite Na atoms to the 7S state. Their rough data indicate higher 7S populations than those of lower states, with inverted population ratios as high as 4 : 1.

NEW POSSIBILITIES FOR FUNDAMENTAL EXPERIMENTS AND TECHNIQUES

R. H. DICKE

Palmer Physical Laboratory, Princeton University

THE RESPONSIBILITY (possibly irresponsibility) of introducing a discussion on experiments and techniques of the future is a heavy one that is carried lightly. Everyone is so familiar with the hazards of practicing the art of reading the crystal ball that great accuracy is not expected.

What are the new techniques of tomorrow? If yesterday is any guide, they will be at least in part generalizations of what is already known and familiar today. The extension to infrared, visible, and even γ radiation of techniques familiar in the microwave frequency region is to be expected. The enormous bandwidth available in the optical frequency region suggests that here is virgin territory for the communication engineer. It may be noted in this connection that the bandwidth of 10^{15}cycles/sec available in the optical frequency band permits in principle the transmission of a 10 character word in one second with but one photon.

Twenty years ago such words as "oscillator," "mixer," "phase detector," "modulator," and "amplifier," suggested only low frequencies. To those of us active in the microwave development during the war, it was fascinating to see how, by generalization, these same basic devices could be produced in the microwave frequency region. The corresponding extension to still shorter waves has yet to appear, but it is very likely not far off. Just as the microwave devices looked not at all like their radio frequency counterparts, the optical devices will not necessarily resemble their microwave counterparts.

It is interesting to note that the extension of the concepts of the radio engineer into the optical frequency region where quantum effects are important has yet to be carried out. In this connection there has been considerable misunderstanding of the coherence concepts in the past. Thus when Forrester *et al.*, commenced their experiment on the beating of two light waves in a photocell, there were some who expected a null result on the grounds that the photons from two independent sources would be uncorrelated and could not show interference effects. More recently the discussion in the literature following the photon experiment of Hanbury-Brown and Twiss has shown how confusing are coherence concepts when quantum effects are important.

A trend has been apparent in recent years which will very likely continue in the future. Whereas length determinations were the most accurate laboratory measurements 30 years ago, this honor is now given to the determinations of times and frequencies. Precision time and frequency measurements can often be used in lieu of length measurements. An interesting example of this is provided by the suggestion of M. Golay that microwave radiation be used continuously to determine the distance to an artificial planet for the purpose of determining an accurate orbit for both the earth and the satellite. By obtaining continuous range information accurate to a fraction of a wave length, an astounding accuracy is possible. Expressed in meters the radius of the earth's orbit is 1.5×10^{11}. An accuracy of a part in 10^{12} for the basic range data should eventually be possible. In similar fashion artificial satellites orbiting the various planets of the solar system could give very accurate values for many of the parameters of the solar system.

A possible extension of precision measurements to short waves is already apparent. It is interesting that the narrowest spectroscopic lines ever observed have been obtained, not with the use of atomic beams or collision narrowing at microwave frequencies, but with gamma rays. These lines with a relative width at half maximum of only 10^{-10} are narrower by a factor of 100 than the best of microwave resonances.

The techniques used to obtain these narrow resonances and to study their line shapes are not unfamiliar to the physicists in-

terested in high resolution work. It has long been known that a
radiating atom confined to a small box radiates among other frequencies a non-Doppler shifted sharp line. This collision narrowing technique is now under investigation at several laboratories. In similar fashion a nucleus occupying a box at a lattice
site in a solid may radiate such a sharp non-shifted line. The
use of a frequency modulation of the signal to observe the line
shape of the sharp resonance is well known. However, the use
of a moving source and the resulting Doppler shift to obtain the
frequency modulation is probably new. Professor Lamb, one of
the scheduled speakers for this section, will discuss possibilities for hyperfine structure measurements making use of this
type of narrow resonance.

An old adage, appearing frequently in textbooks discussing
spectroscopic line breadth, states that although collision and
Doppler contributions to line breadth can be reduced, nothing
can be done about the natural breadth due to radiation damping.
The truth of the matter is that it is possible in at least two different ways to reduce this contribution to line broadening. The
first way is to put the atom in a resonator or cavity which is
tuned off resonance. The second way, to be discussed by Professor Hughes, is to select for consideration out of a group of
radiating atoms, those which happen to live longer than normal.
Professor Hughes will discuss the possibilities of making precision hyperfine structure measurements on hydrogen using this
technique for reducing the natural line breadth.

It is interesting that the increased accuracy of modern atomic
clocks makes possible, for the first time, an experimental investigation of a number of very fundamental cosmological questions. While many of these ideas are not new, they are sufficiently obscure that a brief discussion is warranted.

Since the 17th century, there have been variations of but two
basic concepts of the nature of space. Physical space is thought
of as a structure in its own right or it is considered to have a
structure only to the extent that it represents the relations of
physical bodies to each other. Closely akin to this problem is
the nature of inertial forces. From the one point of view, that of
Newton, inertial forces appear whenever a laboratory is accelerated relative to an absolute space. From the other point of view,

that of Mach or more properly Bishop Berkeley, inertial forces appear in a laboratory whenever the rest of the matter in the universe accelerates relative to the laboratory. Thus, in terms of a modernized version of the ideas of Berkeley, inertial forces may be considered to be due to retarded gravitational interaction with distant matter. The accelerated distant matter may be thought of as generating a gravitational wave that interacts with the laboratory.

From the point of view of Mach, the locally observed inertial interaction is actually global in origin. For this reason the results of experiments carried out in the laboratory may be affected by the matter distribution of the universe. The laws of physics would not change qualitatively from one epoch or place to another, for a qualitative change would imply a discontinuity. However, the numerical constant of the laws of physics expressed by the values of all the dimensionless physical constants might be expected to change in a continuous way with time, position, and velocity relative to the rest of the universe.

This general conclusion runs counter to one of the most cherished of beliefs of the physicist. He has long contended that he was not subject to the ills of the astronomer, geologist, or biologist who must consider the whole universe, earth, or organism. He has in fact habitually ignored everything but the miniscule problem of the moment and with amazing success. It should be noted that both of the above views of the nature of space are in conflict with this belief. For if space is absolute, it would be reasonable to expect that motion relative to the space would lead to observable effects. On the other hand, if the geometry of space and inertial forces have their origin in all the matter of the universe, it would be expected that the distribution of matter and the relation of the laboratory to the matter in the universe would have effects upon phenomena in the laboratory.

In considering the possibility of a variability of physical "constants," it is well to consider first the dimensionless gravitational coupling constant

$$\frac{GM^2}{\hbar c} \sim 10^{-40}.$$

Here M is a typical particle mass such as the electronic mass. The gravitational constant expressed in this form has long been suspect. There is little hope of a theoretical account of such a dimensionless number if it must be generated as a simple function of such numbers as π or e. It is also peculiar that dimensionless numbers of this order of magnitude occur also in the structure of the universe. Thus, for example, the time required for light to cross the radius of a classical electron is roughly 10^{-40} times the age of the universe. Also the number of protons in the universe out to the Hubble radius is roughly $(10^{40})^2$. Eddington first pointed out these relations. Dirac suggested that the gravitational coupling constant might change with time to preserve these relations.

From the point of view of Mach the gravitational acceleration of a body relative to distant matter in the universe should depend upon matter distribution in the universe. From Mach's point of view the inertial force experienced in an accelerated laboratory may be considered to be the gravitational force generated as a retarded interaction by distant matter in the universe. It should be noted that with the assumption that distant matter is distributed isotropically such a gravitational force would appear only with the acceleration of distant matter relative to the laboratory. Thus the inertial interaction may, if desired, be considered to be due to a gravitational wave generated by distant accelerated matter. From this point of view the acceleration of the earth toward the sun is independent of any imagined gravitational coupling strength, for the exact balance of gravitational and "inertial" force in the coordinate frame in which the earth is stationary would not be upset by doubling all gravitational forces including "inertial." The acceleration is dependent upon the mass distributions only.

It is easy to obtain an approximate expression for the acceleration of the earth toward the sun for a simplified model of the universe. Consider a universe consisting of a large spherical shell having mass M and radius R. Assume that the mass of the sun is $m \ll M$ and its distance from the earth is $r \ll R$. Because of the teaching of Newton it would be expected that the earth's acceleration toward the sun would be proportional to m/r^2. The acceleration should also depend upon M, R, and c, this being the propagation velocity of gravitational waves.

With these assumptions, the only expression for the earth's acceleration compatible with dimensions is

$$a = \gamma \, \frac{m}{r^2} \, \frac{RC^2}{M}$$

where γ is a dimensionless constant, presumably of the order of unity. It would be expected that this expression would be valid only in lowest order in m/M and r/R. It should be noted that this expression implies that the gravitational constant satisfies the equation

$$\frac{GM}{RC^2} \equiv \gamma.$$

This in turn seems to imply either that G depends upon the structure of the universe or that the only possible universe structures are those compatible with this equation. This latter alternative ignores the fact that it is possible to change the structure of the universe as seen from the laboratory simply by changing the laboratory's position, waiting for the universe to expand or causing the laboratory to move rapidly relative to the universe. As an example consider a laboratory in the center of a white dwarf star. The contribution of the mass of the star to the generation of an inertial field would be expected to be appreciable. In similar fashion it would be expected that the presence of the sun would contribute in the next higher approximation in m/M to the value of G. In order of magnitude the effect of the presence of the sun on the value of G^{-1} would be expected to be

$$\delta\,(G^{-1}) \sim \frac{m}{rc^2}.$$

At the earth's orbit this is roughly a part in 10^8.

It is interesting to note that if, as implied by the above, the gravitational constant is a function of some field variable generated by the universe as a whole, it will probably be necessary to revise gravitational theory by including with the metric tensor some other field variable to represent gravitation. This can be seen by noting that there is no way of forming a nontrivial invariant from the metric tensor alone, or in combination with a four velocity. While an invariant, such as the scalar curvature, can be formed by introducing gradients, this would not be satisfactory as then nearby matter would be more important than distant matter in the generation of inertial forces.

The purpose of this fragmentary introduction has been to point out that precision atomic clocks can be used to help answer questions of constancy of physical constants. As a first example it should be noted that in agreement with Dirac's conjecture, the magnitude of variation of G which would be expected to result from the expansion of the universe is

$$\frac{\delta G}{G} \sim 10^{-10}/\text{year}.$$

This might be observed by using an artificial earth satellite as a gravitational time keeper and comparing this with an atomic clock over a period of a few years.

In similar fashion, because of the eccentricity of the earth's orbit and the consequent annual change in the sun's distance it would be expected that, if the above conjecture is correct, there would be an annual variation in the rate of an earthbound gravitational clock implying a change in the gravitational constant of about

$$\frac{\delta G}{G} \sim 10^{-10}.$$

A velocity dependence of G is also possible within the frame of Lorentz invariant theories. If a vector field is generated by the universe as a whole, an invariant can be formed by combining this vector field with a four velocity. It is paradoxical that, although historically the absence of the effect of laboratory motion on physical phenomena leads to the formulation of Special Relativity and Lorentz invariance, Lorentz invariance is compatible with such motional effects. A velocity dependence of the order of

$$\frac{\delta G}{G} = \beta \left(\frac{v}{c}\right)^2 \qquad .1 < |\beta| < 10$$

would be reasonable. Here v is the velocity of the laboratory relative to the coordinate system in which the universe appears isotropic. The change in velocity of the earth resulting from the orbital velocity of the earth would result in an annual variation in G. An annual amplitude of

$$\frac{\delta G}{G} \sim 10^{-8} - 10^{-9}$$

would be reasonable if such a velocity dependence existed.

These two effects leading to an annual variation of $10^{-8}-10^{-10}$ could be sought after by using a time-keeping satellite which could be compared with an atomic clock. This experiment should be somewhat easier to perform than the first one mentioned.

Another class of experiments concerns the possibility of variations of other dimensionless physical constants such as the fine structure constant of the ratios of particle masses. It may be argued that these numbers, which do not differ greatly from unity, if they do vary with the structure of universe, could not vary in a sensitive way. The argument is not completely convincing but is elementary. If $\alpha = \frac{e^2}{\hbar C}$ were to vary proportional to some simple power of the time, it would be remarkable for it to differ so little from unity at the present time for the present must be regarded as largely random.

It has been suggested occasionally that some of the difficulties with renormalized field theories could be alleviated if the gravitational interaction between the constituent parts of an elementary particle served to introduce a cutoff into field theories at the gravitation length

$$\lambda_g = \left(\frac{G\hbar}{C^3}\right)^{\frac{1}{2}} \sim 10^{-33} \; cms.$$

Along this line Landau has suggested that it would be reasonable to assume that the expression

$$\alpha \log \frac{\lambda_c}{\lambda_g}$$

should be of the order of unity if such a cutoff were effective. Here λ_c is the Compton wave length of the electron. The numerical values are such that the above expression is very nearly $\frac{3}{8}$.

It is clear that if these considerations have any validity and the gravitational interaction is dependent upon the structure of the universe, there would be a variability of α also. The variation would be minor, however; in fact, the connection is such that

$$\frac{\delta\alpha}{\alpha} \sim 10^{-2}\, \frac{\delta G}{G}\,.$$

Such a slow, weak variation in α would lead to a number of interesting consequences which cannot be discussed here. It should be noted, however, that in general the secular variation and annual variation in the local value of G discussed above should have counterparts in a variation of α, assuming the existence of the effects. The numbers quoted previously need only be reduced by a factor of 100 to be applicable to a variation in α.

A convenient way to expose such variations in α would be to compare two atomic clocks of different types, such as ammonia and cesium. The frequencies in question involve α to different powers in the two cases in question. Bononomi has made the comparison, and his accuracy is such as to be on the threshold of being significant for cosmological purposes. Another interesting experiment which throws light on the question of a possible velocity dependence is that of Townes[1] group which compared the frequencies of two oppositely directed ammonia beams. While this experiment does not have enough sensitivity to exclude a velocity dependence in α, it sets limits on the possible magnitude of the effect.

REFERENCE

1. Cedarholm, Bland, Havens, and Townes, Phys. Rev. Lett. *1*, 342 (1958).

C. H. TOWNES: The beam-maser experiment of Cedarholm *et al.* at Watson Laboratories has now been repeated at four times during the year with intervals of three months, in order to obviate any null in the ether drift caused by accidental cancelation of the earth's orbital velocity and a uniform velocity of the solar system. The result is negative in each case, showing no effect of ether drift greater than $\frac{1}{1000}$ that expected on a simple ether theory. Combination of all data probably sets this limit at least as low as $\frac{1}{2000}$ This makes less likely, but does not rule out, Dicke's proposed term proportional to α which might be expected to be comparable with $\frac{1}{200}$ of the effect due to a simple ether.

An experiment which will check the existence of small ether-drift terms of the form $\left(\frac{v}{c}\right)^2$ to even more precision than does the beam-maser experiment at Watson Laboratories appears possible with the use of optical maser oscillators. Such an oscillator should produce a frequency defined to somewhat better than one part in 10^{12} which depends primarily on the distance between etalon plates if the width of the Fabry-Perot resonance is somewhat narrower than the width of the atomic resonance used. Two such oscillators may be arranged to beat together in a photon detector and their frequencies thus compared to an accuracy near 10^{-12}. If now one oscillator is rotated back and forth 90° about a vertical which is parallel to the plane of one of the etalons, shifts in frequency due to ether drift should be observed as in the Michelson-Morley experiment. Since $\left(\frac{v}{c}\right)^2$ is about one part in 10^8, any shift as large as about 10^{-4} of this should be detectable. This will give an order of magnitude improvement over present results and perhaps allow a more definitive search for the small term $\alpha \left(\frac{v}{c}\right)^2$ suggested by Dicke, or other residual anisotropies of space.

NARROW LINEWIDTHS FOR DECAYING STATES BY THE METHOD OF SEPARATED OSCILLATING FIELDS*

V. W. HUGHES

Gibbs Laboratory, Yale University

THE REMARKS I should like to make were stimulated by the recent experiment of Madansky and Owen[1] in which an intense beam of fast hydrogen atoms in the metastable $2^2 S_{\frac{1}{2}}$ state was produced. The beam was produced by passing protons from an rf ion source having an energy of some 10 kev through low-pressure hydrogen gas ($\sim 10^{-4}$ mm of Hg). A proton has a sufficiently high probability for capturing an electron from a H_2 gas molecule to form the metastable state of atomic H so that about 1 percent of the initial proton beam from the ion source forms the metastable state of H. The resultant beam intensity of metastable H atoms is many orders of magnitude greater than the metastable beams used by Lamb and his colleagues in their experiments[2] on the fine structure of hydrogen. Furthermore, the present beam can be highly directional and hence is not subject to the inverse square law loss. The beam energy of 10 kev can be controlled to about 0.1 percent without difficulty, so that a highly monochromatic rather than a Maxwellian beam is available.

I should like to discuss one possible application of such a beam to the measurement of the fine structure of hydrogen by use of the method of separated oscillating fields. Since the velocity of an atom in the beam is about 10^8 cm/sec, the atom will travel an appreciable distance in the 10^{-8} sec to 10^{-7} sec spent in the transition region, so separated oscillating fields

*This work has been supported by the National Science Foundation.

can be realized physically. In the experiments done thus far on the fine structure of hydrogen, the linewidth is the natural one determined by the optical decay rate of the $2p$ state and amounts to 100 Mc/sec. In principle, linewidths narrower than this natural width can be obtained by use of the method of separated oscillating fields.

In Fig. 1, a schematic diagram illustrating the method of separated oscillating fields[3] is shown. The radiofrequency field is applied over two short regions of length l separated by a relatively long region of length L in which no rf field is present.

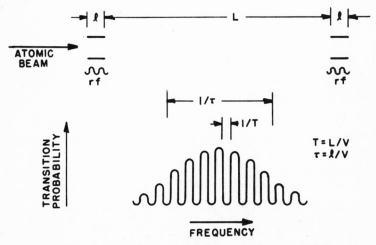

Fig. 1. Method of separated oscillating fields

The principal features of the line shape are indicated for a transition between two stable energy levels for a monoenergetic atomic beam. The overall width corresponds to the transit time τ through the short regions l. The narrower interference peaks correspond to the transit time T through the long region L.

The problem under consideration is the extension of the theory of transitions by the method of separated oscillating fields to include a decay rate for one of the two states. Figure 2 indicates two energy levels p and q; the level q has a decay rate γ_q. This diagram would apply to the $2\,^2S_{\frac{1}{2}}$ and $2\,^2P_{\frac{1}{2}}$ levels in hydrogen, in which only the decay rate of the $2p$ level need be considered.

$$p \ \underline{\hspace{6cm}} \quad \gamma_p = 0$$

$$q \ \underline{\hspace{6cm}} \quad \gamma_q$$

$$H = H_o + v(t)$$

$$H_o \phi_n = w_n \phi_n$$

$$V_{pq} = \hbar\, b e^{+i\omega t}; \quad V_{qp} = \hbar\, b^* e^{-i\omega t}; \quad V_{pp} = V_{qq} = 0$$

$$\psi = \sum_n c_n(t)\, \phi_n$$

$$c_n(t) = a_n(t)\, e^{-\frac{i w_n}{\hbar} t}$$

$$\dot{a}_p = a_q(-i\, b)\, e^{+i(\omega_{pq} + \omega)t}$$

$$\dot{a}_q = a_p(-i\, b^*)\, e^{+i(\omega_{qp} - \omega)t} - \underline{\gamma}_q\, a_q$$

Fig. 2. Equations of motion

The usual formulation[4] of the transition process is given in which $V(t)$ is the time-dependent interaction with the rf field. The time-dependent Schrödinger equation for the state amplitudes a_p and a_q are given. The a's are so defined that a_p is constant if $V(t)$ is zero. The optical decay rate of state q is treated in the usual phenomenological manner[5] through the term $-(\gamma_q/2)\, a_q$.

$$a_p = A_1 e^{-\delta_1 t} + A_2 e^{-\delta_2 t}$$

$$a_q = -\frac{i}{b}\left[\delta_1 \Delta_1 e^{-\delta_1 t + i\lambda t} - \delta_2 A_2 e^{-\delta_2 t + i\lambda t}\right]$$

$$\delta_{1,2} = \left(+\frac{i\lambda}{2} + \frac{\gamma_q}{4}\right) \pm \frac{i}{2}\left[\lambda + \frac{\gamma_q}{2}^2 + 4\, bb^*\right]^{\frac{1}{2}}$$

$$\lambda = \omega_{qp} = \omega$$

Fig. 3. General solution

Figure 3 gives the general solution of these coupled differential equations. The quantities A_1 and A_2 are determined by the initial conditions. The quantities δ_1 and δ_2 depend on the energy separation ω_{qp}, on the decay rate γ_q, on the transition matrix element b, and on the applied frequency ω.

Figure 4 gives the solution for a_p for the case of separated oscillating fields. The atom is assumed to be in the state p at

$$(a_p = 1, \quad a_q = 0 \text{ at } t = 0)$$

$$a_p(2\tau + T) = \left(\frac{\delta_2}{\delta_2 - \delta_1} e^{-\delta_1 \tau} - \frac{\delta_1}{\delta_2 - \delta_1} e^{-\delta_2 \tau}\right)^2$$

$$+ \frac{\delta_1 \delta_2}{\delta_2 - \delta_1} (e^{-\delta_1 \tau} - e^{-\delta_2 \tau}) e^{-i\lambda T}$$

$$- \frac{\gamma_q}{2} T \left[\frac{1}{\delta_2 - \delta_1} (e^{-\delta_2 \tau} - e^{-\delta_1 \tau})\right]$$

$$a_p(2\tau + T) = A_{pp}^2(\tau) + A_{pq}(\tau) A_{qq}(T) A_{qp}(\tau)$$

$$P_{pp}(2\tau + T) = a_p(2\tau + T) a_p^*(2\tau + T)$$

$$P_{pp}(2\tau + T) = |A_{pp}^2(\tau)|^2 + e^{-\frac{\gamma_q}{2}} \{A_{pp}^2(\tau) A_{pq}^*(\tau) A_{qp}^*(\tau) e^{+i\lambda T}$$

$$+ A_{pp}^2(\tau)^* A_{pq}(\tau) A_{qp}(\tau) e^{-i\lambda T}\}$$

$$+ e^{-\gamma_q T} |A_{pq}(\tau) A_{qp}(\tau)|^2$$

Fig. 4. Solution for separated oscillating fields case

time $t = 0$ as it enters the first oscillating field region and the probability amplitude $a_p(2\tau + T)$ that it is in the state p at the end of the second oscillating field region is given. This probability amplitude is expressible as the sum of two terms. The first term, $A_{pp}^2(\tau)$ is the product of the probability amplitude, $A_{pp}(\tau)$, that the atom be in the state p at the end of its traversal of the first oscillating field region (at time τ) times the probability amplitude that the atom remain in state p during the time T

(which is 1) times the probability amplitude that the atom remain in state p during its traversal of the second oscillating field, which is again $A_{pp}(\tau)$. The second term is the product of the probability amplitude $A_{pq}(\tau)$ that the atom is in the state of q at the time τ times the probability amplitude $A_{qq}(\tau)$ that the atom remain in the state q during the time T, which is the exponential optical decay factor $e^{-\gamma_q T/2}$, times the probability amplitude for returning to the state p in the traversal of the second oscillating field region.

The observable probability, $P_{pp}(2\tau + T)$, that the atom be in the state p at the time $2\tau + T$ is $|a_p(2\tau + T)|^2$, which is expressed as the sum of three terms in the last equation. The first term is simply the absolute square of the first term in the expression for $a_p(2\tau + T)$, and the third term is the absolute square of the second term for $a_p(2\tau + T)$. The middle term is an interference term which arises from a cross product of the first and second terms for $a_p(2\tau + T)$. In the limiting case of $\gamma_q = 0$, which applies for two stable energy levels, the expression for $P_{pp}(2\tau + T)$ reduces to the usual expression for the transition probability in the separated oscillating field method, and the middle term is responsible for the sharp interference peaks of frequency width approximately $1/T$. In the case under consideration with $\gamma_q \neq 0$, the middle term also gives rise to interference peaks of width $1/T$, but their amplitude is reduced by the exponential factor $e^{-\gamma_q T/2}$. Hence the achievement of a narrow interference line is severely limited by the attendant reduction in intensity of the interference peak.

I estimate that in an experiment which seeks to study the $2s \rightarrow 2p$ transition in hydrogen it may be possible to obtain an interference peak $\frac{1}{3}$ of the usual natural width of 100 Mc/sec with reasonable signal to noise. In order to achieve this it will be necessary to utilize the facts that the transition probability for all atoms is closely the same because of the monoenergetic character of the beam and that the interference term of interest depends on the relative phases of the radiofrequency in the two oscillating field regions whereas the other terms for the transition probability do not.

I should like to suggest that apart from this possibility of achieving lines narrower than the natural width with a fast beam of hydrogen metastable atoms, the high intensity, unidirectionality, and monoenergetic character of the beam may by themselves prove useful in fine structure measurements. Also with a fast atomic beam time dilation experiments may be possible. Finally it may be possible to form high-beam intensities of He^+ and of Li^{++} in the $2^2 S_{\frac{1}{2}}$ state and hence to do fine structure measurements on these ions. At Yale we are undertaking some experiments to investigate these possibilities.

In conclusion, I might say that the principal motivations at present for higher precision fine-structure experiments seem to be the determination of the fine-structure constant α to a higher precision (a more precise value of α would be most valuable in correction with the interpretation of the hyperfine structure of hydrogen for information on the structure of the proton[6]) and the further study of the substantial discrepancy between the experimental and theoretical values of the Lamb shift in singly ionized helium.[7]

REFERENCES

1. L. Madansky and G. E. Owen, Phys. Rev. Lett. *2*, 209 (1959).
2. W. E. Lamb, Jr., and R. C. Rutherford, Phys. Rev. *79*, 549 (1950).
3. N. F. Ramsey, Phys. Rev. 78, 698 (1950).
4. N. F. Ramsey, *Molecular Beams*, Oxford University Press (1956).
5. W. E. Lamb, Jr., Phys. Rev. *85*, 259 (1952).
6. A. C. Zemach, Phys. Rev. *104*, 1771 (1956).
7. E. Lipworth and R. Novick, Phys. Rev. *108*, 1434 (1957).

DISCUSSION

C. O. ALLEY: I should like to point out the similarity between the method using spatially separated oscillatory fields described by Professor Hughes and the method using a single coherently pulsed oscillatory field discussed in my paper presented at this Symposium.

POSSIBLE USE OF HIGHLY MONOCHROMATIC GAMMA RAYS FOR MICROWAVE SPECTROSCOPY

W. E. LAMB, Jr.

University of Oxford, England

MÖSSBAUER[1] HAS shown that some of the gamma radiation (~ 100 kev) emitted by long-lived (~ 10^{-10} sec) isomeric states of nuclei bound in solids has no Doppler shift. The recoil momentum is taken up by the solid as a whole.[2] The linewidth of such a gamma ray is 1.6×10^3 Mc/sec, i.e., only about 5×10^{-11} its frequency. The amount of resonance absorption of such gamma radiation can be changed by a relative motion of source and absorber of a few centimeters per second. When isomers of somewhat longer life and suitable crystalline environment are studied, it should be possible to resolve the hyperfine structure corresponding to the orientation energies of the nuclear states involved.

REFERENCES

1. R. L. Mössbauer, Z. Natur. *14*, 211 (1959).
2. W. E. Lamb, Jr., Phys. Rev. *55*, 190 (1939).

GASEOUS QUANTUM COUNTER (GQC)

A. LUBIN

Naval Supersonic Labs, Massachusetts Institute of Technology

IT IS the intent of this paper to describe an approach towards developing a gaseous quantum counter utilizing the singlet metastable level of helium. The metastable level is excited by electron bombardment. This level is then raised to a normal excited level by external radiation, and the emission of the downward transition is observed in order to measure the width and intensity of the transition caused by the external radiation.

Previous investigators[1],[2],[3],[4] have examined the excitation of metastable levels in helium by electron impact phenomena. The majority have reported, rather extensively, on the lower lying triplet metastable level at 19.82 ev, while relatively few have detailed calculations and experimental results for the slightly higher singlet metastable level at 20.62 ev. In some of the experiments[5] the singlet and triplet levels could not be separated, making an evaluation of the cross section quite difficult. See Fig. 1.

It was decided, therefore, to attempt the construction of an electron gun and energy selector having an energy spread of ±0.1 ev, and centered at the optical excitation value for the $2\,^1S$ state of 20.62 ev. It was also decided that it would be of major interest to examine the width of an allowed absorption line from the $2\,^1S$ metastable level to the first singlet P level ($2\,^1P$) where the wavelength of the absorption line is about 20,582Å. See Fig. 2.

The concommitant emission from the $2\,^1P$ state to the ground state (584.4Å) is detected by means of a scintillator crystal and the intensity of the $2\,^1S$-$2\,^1P$ transition is related by standard pulse height techniques.

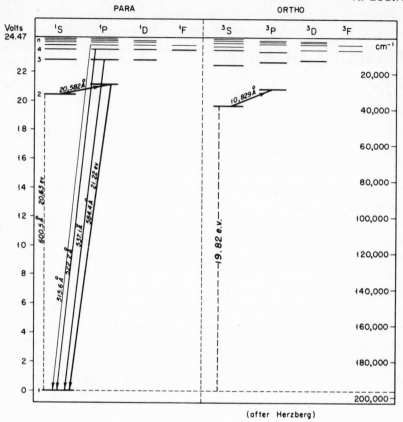

Fig. 1. Energy level of helium diagram

The width and structure of the line is obtained by slowly sweeping a grating monochromator through the range of interest.

THEORY

A study was made of previous techniques to calculate the cross section for excitation of the metastable level and of the correspondence to experimental results. In particular, reference is made to a paper by Baranger and Gerjouy on helium excitation cross sections near threshold.

Some work was done to determine the number of metastable helium atoms created by bombardment with nearly monoenergetic electrons. The physical picture assumed was that of a normal

He wave in and out with a perturbing electron entering in the middle. The scattering cross section was calculated for a range of energies that covered the expected energy spread of the electron beam.

The wave function for the system of a helium atom and an electron is found by solving the Schrödinger equation:

$$\left[-\frac{\hbar^2}{2m} \sum_{i=1}^{3} \nabla_e^2 - 2e^2 \sum_{i=1}^{3} \frac{1}{\vec{r}_i} + e^2 \sum_{i=1}^{3} \sum_{j=1}^{3} \frac{1}{\vec{r}_{ij}} - E \right] \times$$

$$\psi_E(1,2,3) = 0 \quad (1)$$

where

$\psi_E(1,2,3)$ is completely antisymmetric in 1,2,3, the coordinates (including spin) of the three electrons.

$\vec{r}_i$ is the position vector of the ith electron, $\vec{r}_{ij} = |\vec{r}_i - \vec{r}_j|$.

Writing

$$\psi_E(1,2,3) = \frac{1}{\sqrt{3}} [\psi(1,2/3) + \psi(2,3/1) + \psi(3,1/2)] \quad (2)$$

where

$\psi_E(i,j/k)$ is antisymmetric in the coordinates of i and j.

Equation (1) can be rewritten to form

$$\Sigma_{Pc} \, P_c \, [H_o(i,j/k) + V(i,j/k) - E] \, \psi_E(i,j/k) = 0 \quad (3)$$

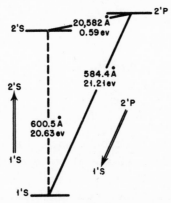

Fig. 2. Energy states of interest

where

$$H_o(i,j/k) = -\frac{\hbar^2}{2m} \sum_{i=1}^{3} \nabla_e^2 - \frac{2e^2}{\vec{r}_i} - \frac{2e^2}{\vec{r}_j} + \frac{e^2}{\vec{r}_{ij}}$$

$$V(i,j/k) = -\frac{2e^2}{\vec{r}_k} + \frac{e^2}{\vec{r}_{ik}} + \frac{e^2}{\vec{r}_{jk}}.$$

$\Sigma_{P_c} P_c$ means the sum over cyclic permutations of i, j, and k. A particular solution may be written as

$$[H_o(i,j/k) + V(i,j/k) - E] \, \psi_E(i,j/k) = 0 \qquad (4)$$

by assuming that each term in the sum vanishes.

Now, prescribing the boundary conditions of $\psi_E(i,j/k)$ from physical arguments following the method of Schiff,[5]

$$\psi_E(i,j/k) \xrightarrow[\vec{r}_k \to \infty]{} \Phi_E^-(i,j/k) + f_E(k)\Phi_E^+(i,j/k)$$

$$\psi_E(i,j/k) \xrightarrow[\vec{r}_{i,j} \to \infty]{} G_E(i,j)\Phi_E^+(i,j/k)$$

where $f_E(k)$ is the scattering amplitude of the kth particle

G_E is the exchange scattering amplitude
$\Phi_E^-(i,j/k)[\Phi_E^+(i,j/k)]$ is the wave function for an incident electron, f and G depend only on the angular coordination of the scattered particles.

Incorporating these boundary conditions, we have

$$\psi_E(i,j/k) = \Phi_E^-(i,j/k) -$$

$$\int G(i,j/k/i\,'j\,'/k\,') \, V(i,j/k) \, \psi_E(i\,'j\,'/k\,') \, d\tau_i{}'d\tau_j{}'d\tau_k{}' \quad (5)$$

where

$G(i,j/k/i\,'j\,'/k\,')$ is Green's function.

This particular form of Green's function is chosen so that the asymptotic expressions of the above equation agree with the physical picture.

In general, the incoming beam of electrons is not perfectly monochromatic, but has some distribution—also, the energy level of the atom may not be perfectly well defined and hence the total energy of the system may not be exactly E, but some distribution around E. Therefore it is necessary to write the wave function of the system as a superposition of the solutions of the Schrödinger equation. If $A(E)$ is the distribution function of the initial noninteracting system,

$$\psi(1,2,3) = \int A(E)\, \psi_E(1,2,3)\, dE. \tag{6}$$

Thus, since the total cross section for the process which leaves the system in a state specified by the set of quantum numbers denoted by E is determined by f_E and G_E, the problem is solved for f_E and G_E.

However, at best, only approximations are available since an exact knowledge of all the functions are not in general available. What has been done is to expand the functions for f_E and G_E and to program the entire expression for the computer. It is hoped that maximizing the approximations will lead to substantially better agreement with experimental values than has heretofore been noted.

EXPERIMENTAL

In brief, the experimental model for the $G\,Q\,C$ consists of an electron gun and energy selector fashioned after a prototype at Laval University built under the direction of Professor Larkin Kerwin and Paul Momonet, an impact chamber with associated electronics, vacuum systems and readout devices, designed by MIT personnel and under fabrication by the Microwave Electron Tube Company. See Fig. 3.

I must apologize for not describing the energy selector in detail, but it is to be the subject of a paper soon forthcoming from Laval University. However, I can say that on a recent visit to the Canadian facility, the energy selector was demonstrated and produced a beam 0.05 ev wide centered at about 2.5 ev. By slightly modifying the potentials it should be possible to have an energy spread of ± 0.1 ev at 20 ev. See Fig. 4.

The entire system is evacuated down to 10^{-9} mm of Hg by means of a titanium ion pump described in an article by J. G. King and J. R. Zacharias in *Advances in Electronics and Elec-*

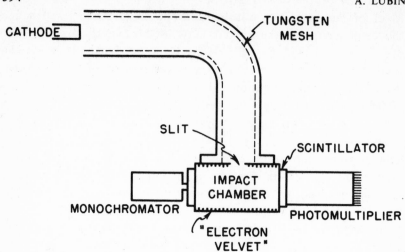

Fig. 3. Experimental arrangement

tron Physics, Vol. VIII. It is important that as few as possible of the metastable atoms be lost through collision.

The helium gas will be evolved from liquid helium and introduced into the impact chamber to a pressure of about 0.3 mm Hg. The external radiation to cause the 2^1S-2^1P transition will be introduced through an appropriate window into the chamber. The Q or acceptance width of the line will be determined by sweeping a monochromator through a given range of interest and plotting pulse heights observed on a scope.

The emission actually observed is, however, the 584.4Å line from the 2^1P-1^1S transition. According to reports from Avivi and Cohen of the Hebrew University, sodium salicylate will be used as the scintillator. A photomultiplier and associated electronics completes the experimental setup.

CONCLUSIONS

It is expected that the experiments described will lead to a measurement of the absorption coefficient of the upward transition 2^1S-2^1P. The technique employed should also be applicable to other gases showing metastable states and near normal excited states. It is also expected that the calculations of cross section will lead to a more accurate estimate and agreement with physical experimental results.

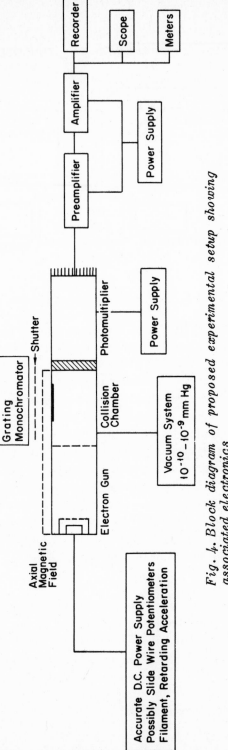

Fig. 4. Block diagram of proposed experimental setup showing associated electronics

REFERENCES

1. H. Maier-Leibnitz, Z. Physik *95*, 499 (1935).
2. R. Dorrenstein, Physica *9*, 447 (1942).
3. J. P. M. Woudenberg and J. M. W. Milatz, Physica *8*, 871 (1941).
4. G. J. Schultz and R. E. Fox, Phys. Rev. *106*, 1179 (1957).
5. L. I. Schiff, p. 100, *Quantum Mechanics*, McGraw-Hill (1949).

TRAVELING-WAVE TECHNIQUES FOR MICROWAVE RESONANCE MEASUREMENTS*

A. E. SIEGMAN

Stanford Electronics Laboratory, Stanford University

THE MAIN thesis of this paper can be very briefly stated: transmission-line circuits which propagate slowly-traveling waves offer many useful features for magnetic resonance measurements at microwave frequencies, in comparison with the commonly used resonant cavity. Slow-wave circuits have found little use in the past, probably because of their comparative unfamiliarity. However, the recent successful development of traveling-wave versions of the solid-state maser should stimulate greater interest in traveling-wave techniques. Some of the properties and advantages of slow-wave circuits are briefly discussed in the following.

The physical arrangement envisioned here is a slow-wave circuit with the magnetic resonance sample distributed along its length, as shown in Fig. 1. The r-f signal is fed into one end of the circuit and abstracted from the other. The magnetic resonance permeability $\chi = \chi' + j\chi''$ is detected by the additional insertion loss and/or phase shift which it gives to the signal passing down the circuit.

SENSITIVITY

Slow-wave circuits in general are inferior to cavities in sensitivity, but the difference is not as large as might be supposed. The measure of sensitivity for a conventional cavity-type mag-

*The research related to this paper was supported by the U. S. Army Signal Engineering Laboratory and the Wright Air Development Center of the U. S. Air Force.

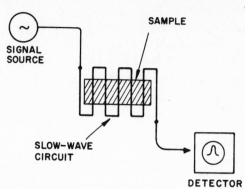

Fig. 1. Schematic of a traveling-wave apparatus for magnetic resonance measurements

netic resonance spectrometer is the cavity Q. For a power input P, filling factor η, and permeability χ'', the change dP in power to the detector from a cavity at magnetic resonance is

$$dP \approx \eta\chi''P \cdot \tfrac{1}{2}Q \qquad (1)$$

where small absorption is assumed. For a traveling-wave spectrometer, the analogous expression is

$$dP \approx \eta\chi''P \cdot 2\pi \left(\frac{c}{v_g}\right)\left(\frac{L}{\lambda_o}\right)$$

$$= \eta\chi''P \cdot 2\pi\,SN \qquad (2)$$

where $N \equiv L/\lambda_o$ is the number of free-space wavelengths λ_o in the length L of the slow-wave circuit, and the slowing factor $S \equiv c/v_g$ is the velocity of light c divided by the group velocity v_g of the circuit. The quantity η is now a filling factor per unit length. The quantity $2\pi\,SN$ is analogous to $Q/2$; and low group velocity v_g is obviously the key to high sensitivity.

In practical narrow-band circuits, the $2\pi\,SN$ product can nearly equal typical cavity Q's; while for large bandwidths the sensitivity has roughly an inverse dependence on bandwidth. At, say, 10 cm wavelength, a circuit length of 2.5 cm $\equiv$ 1 inch gives $N = \frac{1}{4}$, while at shorter wavelengths N is correspondingly larger. A slowing factor $S = 1000$ or greater is practical for a circuit bandwidth of a few percent; while in broadband circuits, uniform slowing factors of $S = 20$ over a five-to-one frequency range, $S = 50$ over a two-to-one frequency range, or $S = 100$ over a 25 percent bandwidth are readily obtained. Therefore, a 1-inch long circuit with a 25 percent bandwidth at 3000 Mc/s could have an equivalent Q of $4\pi SN = 1200$.

In short, the loss of sensitivity in low-group-velocity circuits is not enormous, and in many instances can be readily tolerated.

FREQUENCY RANGE

The most apparent advantage of the traveling-wave technique is the wide frequency range possible in a single apparatus without adjustments. A very simple and useful structure, for example, is the helix, consisting of a tightly wound helical coil of copper wire or tape, connected directly to the center conductor of a coaxial line at each end. A sample can be placed close to the wire, either just inside or just outside the helix, without doing violence to the wave propagation along the helix. Five-to-one bandwidths with reasonable sensitivity are readily obtained with this arrangement, permitting examination of resonance spectra over a wide frequency range, study of special phenomena as a function of frequency, exact measurement of zero-field splittings, and similar measurements. The very-wide-range backward-wave oscillator forms a convenient signal source for such an apparatus.

Narrower-band but more sensitive circuits, such as the comb and meander-line structures used for traveling-wave masers, can be very conveniently used for such purposes as line-shape studies; adiabatic fast passage by frequency sweep (with only a high-impedance frequency-controlling electrode needing to be swept); studies of spin diffusion; and cross-relaxation studies, where two or more signals at different frequencies are applied simultaneously and then separated into different receivers. Two signals at exactly or very nearly the same frequency can also be applied to a sample and then separated to different receivers with small cross coupling by using the scheme shown in Fig. 2.

SIMPLIFIED MEASUREMENT PROCEDURES

Measurement procedures in the traveling-wave spectrometer are simpler than in the cavity case. Cavity measurements bas-

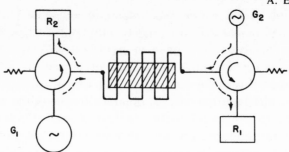

Fig. 2. A scheme using two circulators to apply signals from generators G_1 *and* G_2 *simultaneously and separate them to receivers* R_1 *and* R_2

ically involve the measurement of either cavity Q or cavity resonant frequency, or at least of small changes in these quantities, while the traveling-wave measurements involve measuring only the added loss or phase shift along the slow-wave circuit. The background loss and phase shift need not be known and do not affect the measurement accuracy or sensitivity. The signal source need not be stabilized or locked to the cavity resonance, and residual f-m noise on the signal source does not introduce noise into the detector. By simply measuring the output power from the circuit, one measures χ'' only, without necessity for balancing a bridge to eliminate χ'. Absolute measurements are perhaps not as easy on a slow-wave circuit as in a cavity, but the electromagnetic field solutions for some slow-wave circuits are known exactly and would permit accurate calculation of filling factor and hence of χ'' from Equation (2).

CIRCULARLY POLARIZED FIELDS

Slow-wave circuits are ideally suited to the production of uniform circularly polarized r-f fields over large volumes. This property has already been used to great advantage in obtaining nonreciprocal forward gain and reverse loss in traveling-wave masers. Without going into details, we will merely assert that in circuits such as the comb or meander line, which are derived from a planar array of parallel tapes or wires running transversely to the circuit axis, the r-f fields are circularly polarized about an axis parallel to the wires, with opposite sense of polarization above and below the circuit. Reversing the direction of signal propagation reverses the sense of polarization. The utility of this fact in Faraday rotation measurements and similar experiments is apparent. The helix also has nearly circularly polarized fields, although the axis of polarization is in the azimuthal direction roughly parallel to the helical wires. Flattening the helix can straighten out the axis of polarization while retaining the general broadband characteristics of the cylindrical helix.

STRONG R-F FIELDS

Certain experiments, such as saturation or fast-passage experiments, require a strong r-f magnetic field H_1. It is generally accepted that a resonant cavity, by concentrating the fields, gives maximum r-f field strength for given r-f power. However, the slow-wave circuit can be competitive in this regard. If we assume for simplicity a resonant cavity one-half wavelength in each dimension, an approximate relationship between r-f field strength, power and cavity Q is

$$H_1 \sim \left(\frac{16P}{\omega \mu_0 \; \lambda_0^3} \right)^{\frac{1}{2}} \cdot Q^{\frac{1}{2}} \tag{3}$$

The significant point about the slow-wave circuit, in comparison, is that the r-f fields on typical slow-wave circuits hug the circuit closely, extending out from the circuit's surface with a "skin depth" of the order of one pitch p of a periodic circuit. Assuming a flat planar circuit one-half wavelength wide, the expression analogous to Equation (3) is then

$$H_1 \sim \left(\frac{8\pi P}{\omega \mu_0 \; \lambda_0^3} \right)^{\frac{1}{2}} \left(\frac{\lambda_0}{p} \; \frac{c}{v_g} \right)^{\frac{1}{2}}. \tag{4}$$

The slowing factor $S = c/v_g$ has already been discussed; for the transverse-wire circuits mentioned above, the wavelength-to-pitch ratio λ_0/p can easily be 50 or 100 to 1. The r-f field strength on the traveling-wave circuit then compares very well with the cavity case.

UNSHIELDED CIRCUITS

All of the slow-wave circuits mentioned—helix, comb, meander line—are open circuits, requiring neither ground plane nor shielding enclosure. They do not radiate, and are unaffected by objects placed more than a few "skin depths" away. They are, therefore, well suited for experiments involving optical irradiation of a sample, or the application of some other type of external effect. Of course, the traveling-wave maser, in which the slow-wave circuit is placed inside the waveguide or cavity which carries the pump power, is a prominent example of this possibility.

CONCLUSION

Some properties of slow-traveling-wave circuits which may prove extremely useful for various fundamental magnetic resonance experiments have been mentioned. Specific circuits have been only briefly mentioned, since more detailed discussions are available in the references. The properties of slow-wave circuits have been intensively used in the past by workers in the field of microwave electronics. Perhaps these circuits will now find similarly wide applications in magnetic resonance applications.

REFERENCES

1. R. W. DeGrasse, "Slow-wave structures for unilateral solid-state maser amplifiers," 1958 IRE WESCON Conv. Rec., Part 3, 29 (1959). R. W. DeGrasse, E. O. Schulz-DuBois, and H. E. D. Scovil, "The three-level solid-state traveling-wave maser," Bell System Technical Journal *38*, 305 (1959).
2. W. S. C. Chang, J. Cromack, and A. E. Siegman, "Cavity and traveling-wave masers using ruby at S-band," 1959 IRE WESCON Conv. Rec., Part 1, 142 (1959).
3. H. D. Tenney, R. W. Roberts, and P. H. Vartanian, "An S-band traveling-wave maser," 1959 IRE WESCON Conv. Rec., Part 1, 151 (1959).
4. J. E. Geusic, E. O. Schulz-DuBois, R. W. DeGrasse, and H. E. D. Scovil, "Three level spin refrigeration and maser action at 1500 Mc/s," J. Appl. Phys. *30*, 1113 (1959).
5. W. S. C. Chang, paper in this symposium.

QUANTUM ELECTRONICS
CONFERENCE PARTICIPANTS

Alley, C. O., Princeton University
Arditi, M., International Telephone and Telegraph Company
Arp, H. C., Jet Propulsion Laboratory, California Institute of Technology
Artman, J. O., Applied Physics Laboratory, Johns Hopkins University
Auer, M., U. S. Army Signal Research and Development Laboratory
Barchukov, A. I., Lebedev Institute, Moscow
Barker, W. A., University of St. Louis
Barnes, F. S., University of Colorado
Barrett, A., University of Michigan
Basov, N. G., Lebedev Institute, Moscow
Beaty, E. C., National Bureau of Standards, Washington
Beers, Y., New York University
Bender, P. L., National Bureau of Standards, Washington
Bergmann, S. M., Laboratory for Electronics
Berman, A., Philco Corporation
Birnbaum, G., Hughes Research Laboratories
Birnbaum, M., Polytechnic Institute of Brooklyn
Bloembergen, N., Harvard University
Bölger, B., Kamerlingh Onnes Laboratory, Leiden
Bonanomi, J., Laboratoire Suisse de Recherches Horlogères
Bowers, K. D., Bell Telephone Laboratories
Boyle, W. S., Bell Telephone Laboratories
Brossel, J., Ecole Normale Superieure, Paris
Brown, C., Ohio State University
Burstein, E., University of Pennsylvania
Butcher, P. N., Royal Radar Establishment, Malvern
Byrne, F. T., Office of Naval Research
Castle, J. G., Jr., Westinghouse Electric Corporation
Chang, W. S. C., Ohio State University
Chester, P. F., Westinghouse Electric Corporation
Clogston, A. M., Bell Telephone Laboratories
Collins, S., Sperry Gyroscope Company
Combrisson, J., Centre d'Études Nucléaires de Saclay
Cooper, B., Harvard University
Costain, C. C., National Research Council of Canada
Cromack, J., Stanford University
Davis, C. F., Jr., Texas Instruments, Inc.
Dicke, R. H., Princeton University
Dousmanis, G., Radio Corporation of America Laboratories

Dransfield, K., Bell Telephone Laboratories
Farmer, D. J., Space Technology Laboratories
Farnell, G. W., McGill University
Feher, G., Bell Telephone Laboratories
Fletcher, R. C., Bell Telephone Laboratories
Foner, S., Lincoln Laboratories, Massachusetts Institute of Technology
Forrester, P. A., Royal Radar Establishment, Malvern
Fox, A. G., Bell Telephone Laboratories
Franzen, W., Arthur D. Little, Inc.
Friedburg, H., Technische Hochschule Karlsruhe
Gallagher, J. J., The Martin Company
Gamo, H., International Business Machines Corporation, Lamb Estate
Garstens, M. A., Office of Naval Research
Gerritsen, H., Radio Corporation of America Laboratories
Gill, J. C., Royal Radar Establishment, Malvern
Glaser, H., Office of Naval Research
Gordon, J. P., Bell Telephone Laboratories
Gould, G., Technical Research group, Inc.
Hahn, E., University of California
Harrison, S., Radio Corporation of America Laboratories
Heavens, O. S., Columbia University
Heer, C. V., Ohio State University
Heffner, H., Stanford University
Heller, G. S., Lincoln Laboratories, Massachusetts Institute of Technology
Helmer, J. C., Varian Associates
Hempstead, C. F., Bell Telephone Laboratories
Higa, W., Jet Propulsion Laboratory, California Institute of Technology
Hirsh, M. N., International Telephone and Telegraph Laboratories
Holloway, J. H., National Company
Honig, A., Syracuse University
Hopfer, S., Polytechnic Research and Development Company
Hughes, W. V., Yale University
Inui, T., University of Tokyo
Jacobsen, E. H., General Electric Company
Javan, A., Bell Telephone Laboratories
Jaynes, E. T., Stanford University
Jen, C. K., Applied Physics Laboratory, Johns Hopkins University
Johnson, P. S., Air Force Office of Scientific Research
Kalra, S. N., National Research Council of Canada
Katzman, M., U. S. Army Signal Research and Development Laboratory
Kiel, A., Radiation Laboratory, Johns Hopkins University
Kittel, C., University of California
Kleppner, D., Harvard University
Kompfner, R., Bell Telephone Laboratories
Kornienko, L. S., Lebedev Institute, Moscow
Krisher, L., Columbia University
Kyhl, R. L., Massachusetts Institute of Technology

Lamb, W. E., Jr., The Clarendon Laboratory, Oxford
Lambe, J., University of Michigan
Lax, B., Lincoln Laboratories, Massachusetts Institute of Technology
Lessin, I., Air Force Cambridge Research Center
Loubser, J., Columbia University
Low, W., Hebrew University of Jerusalem
Lubin, A., Naval Supersonic Laboratory, Massachusetts Institute of Technology
Maiman, T., Hughes Research Laboratories
Marcuvitz, N., Polytechnic Institute of Brooklyn
Matthews, T., California Institute of Technology
McWhorter, A. L., Lincoln Laboratories, Massachusetts Institute of Technology
Miles, P. A., Massachusetts Institute of Technology
Minkowski, J., Radiation Laboratory, Johns Hopkins University
Mockler, R., National Bureau of Standards, Boulder
Newstein, M. C., Technical Research Group, Inc.
Nierenberg, W., University of California
Novick, R., University of Illinois
Okaya, A., Columbia University
Okwit, S., Airborne Instruments Company
Peter, M., Bell Telephone Laboratories
Pierce, J. R., Bell Telephone Laboratories
Prokhorov, A. M., Lebedev Institute, Moscow
Reder, F. H., U. S. Army Signal Research and Development Laboratory
Roberts, R. W., Microwave Engineering Laboratories
Rorschach, H. E., The Rice Institute
Rosenbloom, J. H., Office of Naval Research
Rosenblum, B., Radio Corporation of America Laboratories
Rothstein, J., Edgerton, Germeshausen and Grier, Inc.
Rowe, I., Office of Naval Research
Rydbeck, O., Chalmers Institute of Technology, Gothenberg
Sagalyn, P. L., Ordnance Materials Laboratory
Sanders, J. H., Oxford University
Sarles, L. R., Varian Associates
Schawlow, A. L., Bell Telephone Laboratories
Schechter, D., Sylvania Research Laboratories
Schlier, C., University of Bonn
Schulz-DuBois, E. O., Bell Telephone Laboratories
Scovil, H. E. D., Bell Telephone Laboratories
Senitzky, I. R., U. S. Army Research and Development Laboratory
Shapiro, S., Arthur D. Little, Inc.
Shimoda, K., University of Tokyo
Shiren, N. S., General Electric Company
Shostak, A., Office of Naval Research
Siegman, A. E., Stanford University
Simpson, J. H., General Precision Laboratory, Inc.
Singer, J. R., University of California
Smaller, B., Argonne National Laboratories
Smith, W. V., International Business Machines Corporation

Sorokin, P. P., International Business Machines Corporation
Squire, C. F., The Rice Institute
Statz, H., Raytheon Company
Stevenson, M. J., International Business Machines Corporation
Stitch, M. L., Hughes Research Laboratories
Strain, R. J., University of Illinois
Strandberg, M. W. P., Massachusetts Institute of Technology
Sugano, S., University of Tokyo
Terhune, R., University of Michigan
Theissing, H. H., U. S. Army Signal Research and Development Laboratory
Title, R. S., International Business Machines Corporation
Townes, C. H., Columbia University
Tucker, E. B., General Electric Company
Van Vleck, J. H., Harvard University
Vessot, R. F. C., Massachusetts Institute of Technology
Vuylsteke, A. A., General Motors Corporation
Wagner, P. E., Westinghouse Electric Corporation
Weber, J., University of Maryland
Weiss, M., Hughes Research Laboratories
Wells, W. H., Jet Propulsion Laboratory, California Institute of Technology
Wessel, G. K., General Electric Company
White, L. D., Bell Telephone Laboratories
Wieder, I., Westinghouse Electric Corporation
Wilcox, L., Harvard University
Winter, J. M., Centre d'Études Nucléaires de Saclay
Yariv, A., Bell Telephone Laboratories
Yost, C. F., Air Force Office of Scientific Research
Zeiger, H. J., Lincoln Laboratories, Massachusetts Institute of Technology
Zwerdling, S., Lincoln Laboratories, Massachusetts Institute of Technology

CONFERENCE STAFF:

I. Abella	A. Penzias
D. Carter	W. Rose
H. Cummins	E. Rosenwasser
J. Giordmaine	M. Schlereth
H. Lecar	P. Thaddeus
J. Lyle	B. Turlington
M. Morrow	R. W. Siegel
F. Nash	